Don Irvine
School of Geology
Univ. of Oklahoma
January, 1948

MINERALOGY

AN INTRODUCTION TO THE STUDY OF MINERALS AND CRYSTALS

The quality of the materials used in the manufacture of this book is governed by continued postwar shortages.

Books by

EDWARD H. KRAUS

---

with CHESTER B. SLAWSON

KRAUS AND SLAWSON—
GEMS AND GEM MATERIALS (*Fourth Edition*)
287 pages, 6×9, 344 Illustrations

---

with WALTER F. HUNT

KRAUS AND HUNT—
TABLES FOR THE DETERMINATION OF
MINERALS (*Second Edition*)
266 pages, 6×9

---

with WALTER F. HUNT
and
LEWIS S. RAMSDELL

KRAUS, HUNT, AND RAMSDELL—
MINERALOGY (*Third Edition*)
638 pages, 6×9, 812 Illustrations

MINERALOGY

AN INTRODUCTION TO THE STUDY

OF

MINERALS AND CRYSTALS

BY

EDWARD HENRY KRAUS, Ph. D., Sc. D.

*Professor of Crystallography and Mineralogy and Dean of the College
of Literature, Science, and the Arts, University of Michigan*

WALTER FRED HUNT, Ph. D.

*Professor of Petrology and Director of the Mineralogical
Laboratory, University of Michigan*

AND

LEWIS STEPHEN RAMSDELL, Ph. D.

*Associate Professor of Mineralogy
University of Michigan*

Third Edition
Tenth Impression

McGRAW-HILL BOOK COMPANY, Inc.

NEW YORK AND LONDON

1936

THE MAPLE PRESS COMPANY, YORK, PA.

PREFACE TO THE THIRD EDITION

Numerous changes have been introduced in this edition. They were necessitated by the advances which have been made in the various fields of mineralogy during the eight years since the second edition appeared. The entire book, in fact, has been reset, with the exception of the tables for the determination of minerals.

The most notable changes have been made in the chapters on Physical Properties, the Polarizing Microscope, Crystal Structure and X-ray Analysis, and the Formation and Occurrence of Minerals. Simple, understandable interpretations of the internal structure of minerals are given in the light of recent X-ray data. In the chapter on the Classification of Minerals According to Elements, the practical applications of minerals in industry have again been stressed and the statistics brought up to date. Forty-six illustrations have been added, and the number of pages has been increased by thirty-four.

E. H. K.
W. F. H.
L. S. R.

MINERALOGICAL LABORATORY,
UNIVERSITY OF MICHIGAN,
April, 1936

PREFACE TO THE SECOND EDITION

Although it is only eight years since the first edition was issued, it has seemed advisable to revise and enlarge the text. The authors have been encouraged in this because of the very favorable reception of the book, which has passed through four impressions.

Changes and corrections have been made in all chapters, some of which were set up entirely new. A chapter on Crystal Structure and X-ray Analysis has been added. In the chapters on Crystallography and Descriptive Mineralogy many of the illustrations of crystal models and of minerals have been replaced by new ones. Views of important mining and mineral localities have been introduced in the chapter on the Classification of Minerals According to Elements. Throughout the book 70 cuts have been added and the total number of illustrations increased to 766.

Our thanks are due to all who from time to time have offered suggestions or have assisted us in securing suitable illustrations.

E. H. K.
W. F. H.

MINERALOGICAL LABORATORY,
UNIVERSITY OF MICHIGAN,
June, 1928.

PREFACE TO THE FIRST EDITION

This text is the result of long experience in teaching large classes of beginning students, and the subject is accordingly presented in a direct and simple manner. The essentials of the various phases of the science have been treated so that a single book may serve the needs of the average student. The conventional line drawings of crystals, which students commonly have difficulty in properly visualizing, have been superseded to a very large extent by excellent photographs of crystal models, natural crystals, and minerals, such as are actually handled in the laboratory. These are all original photographs of material contained in the various collections of the University of Michigan.

Furthermore, an attempt has been made to vitalize the subject as much as possible, and accordingly there are chapters on the importance of mineralogy in modern civilization, on gems and precious stones, and on the production and uses of the important economic minerals. Numerous photographs and short sketches of distinguished mineralogists have also been introduced in the hope that they will add a human touch.

The chapters on crystallography are based very largely upon the senior author's "Essentials of Crystallography," while much of the material in the descriptions of the 150 minerals given in this text has been taken from his "Descriptive Mineralogy." The determinative tables are an abridgment of the authors' "Mineral Tables."

We are greatly indebted to Mr. George R. Swain, technical expert in photography in the University of Michigan, whose varied experience and unusual skill made the excellent photographs of models and minerals possible; also to Dr. George F. Kunz for valuable assistance in securing a considerable number of very desirable photographs.

Edward H. Kraus.
Walter F. Hunt.

Mineralogical Laboratory,
University of Michigan,
    August, 1920.

CONTENTS

MINERALOGY

AN INTRODUCTION TO THE STUDY OF MINERALS AND CRYSTALS

CHAPTER I

INTRODUCTION

Mineralogy and Civilization.—In the older classifications of natural history all substances occurring in nature were commonly referred to three kingdoms—*animal, vegetable, mineral.* In the *animal* kingdom the early scientists placed the animal forms observed on the land, in the sea, and in the air. From the study of the various types of animals, zoology, anatomy, surgery, animal breeding, and related subjects have been developed. The *vegetable* kingdom included the plants and trees, and the study of these has given us the science of botany and the closely allied subjects of forestry and agriculture. In the opinion of the ancients, the *mineral* kingdom included the whole inanimate world, that is, the minerals, rocks, soil, and the "waters of the earth." Since bright colors, regularity of form, transparency, and other prominent properties have always attracted attention, there is little wonder that minerals with their great diversity of color and form should have been among the first objects studied by primitive man.

Although mineralogy as a science is comparatively young, minerals and crystals were nevertheless used very early in the development of civilization. In fact, the earliest stage in the development of civilization is commonly referred to as the *stone* age. In this age, rocks or stones were hewn into numerous shapes and used for utensils of various kinds. They were also made into crude weapons. At first, the stones were for the most part rough, but subsequently methods were devised so that they could be rendered smooth and polished to some extent. This period, therefore, is frequently divided into the rough and smooth *stone* ages, the *paleolithic* and *neolithic* ages, respectively.

As his knowledge of rocks and minerals increased and he was able to recover metals from them, man emerged successively into the *copper, bronze, iron,* and *coal* ages. The present day is commonly called the *machine* age, a machine being an assemblage of metals. Indeed, as our

1

civilization becomes more advanced and complex, the demand for metals of all sorts and, hence, for minerals ever increases.[1]

Sources of Raw Materials.—The principal sources of raw materials are the mines and quarries, the farms, the forests, the sea, and the atmosphere. Of these, the farms, forests, and the mines and quarries are the greatest contributors.

Divisions of Human Activity.—Upon the exploitation of these natural resources rest the greatest and most important divisions of human activity, namely, agriculture, mining, and commerce and industry. As is well known, agriculture furnishes us with many of the products so necessary to our sustenance; that is, with the cereals and other crops. Indirectly, it gives us much of our meat products, wearing apparel, and the like. In order to carry on agriculture with marked success, a knowledge of the composition and nature of soils is absolutely essential. Soils consist to a very large extent of minerals and mineral products. Indeed, all balanced soils suited to general cropping contain a preponderance of mineral matter.

It is obvious that in mining a most comprehensive knowledge of mineralogy is necessary. In many localities mining is the chief occupation. Indeed, as Del Mar says:

Desire for the precious metals, rather than geographical researches or military conquest, is the principal motive which has led to the dominion of the earth by civilized races. Gold has invariably invited commerce, invasion has followed commerce, and permanent occupation has completed the process.

Several instances may be cited. Thus, it is well known that the discovery of gold in California in 1849 gave a great stimulus to world-wide migration and trade. About 1850, in further search for gold Englishmen began to populate antipodal Australia. Moreover, the discovery of diamonds near Kimberley in 1867 and of gold in the Rand district in 1885 led to the subsequent settlement of large sections of Africa. Alaska came into prominence only after the discovery of gold and other valuable minerals toward the close of the last century. The value of the minerals produced in Alaska, since those discoveries were made, exceeds $700,-000,000. It is of interest to know that this sum is many times larger than the purchase price, $7,200,000, which the United States paid to Russia in 1867 for the entire territory.

Mining has often been the forerunner of agriculture. It is also to a large extent the basis of commerce and industry. In fact, commerce and industry may be said to rest, in general, upon agriculture and mining. In the exploitation of valuable mineral deposits important lines of transportation and communication have invariably been developed.

[1] See T. T. Read, "Our Mineral Civilization," The Century Company, New York, 1932.

Thus, the principal commerce of the Great Lakes consists of carrying enormous quantities of iron ore from the Lake Superior region to various points on the lower lakes and of transporting coal from these ports on the return trip. Likewise, many of the industries in the vicinity of the Great Lakes are directly dependent upon mining in that they utilize the products of the mines and quarries. Furthermore, conservative estimates show that the carrying of minerals and mineral products constitutes nearly two-thirds of the total traffic of our railroads and about one-fourth of the ocean trade.

The Nation and Its Mineral Resources.—Today, as never before, the mineral resources of a nation are recognized as one of its foundations of power.[1] They are also considered among its most valuable assets. In this respect the United States has been unusually fortunate, for we possess very large deposits of the important economic rocks and minerals and vast areas of very fertile soil. Dr. George O. Smith, formerly director of the U. S. Geological Survey, has well said:

Independence through possession of the material resources essential to modern life is itself a promise of a nation's integrity, and the nation that makes the whole world its debtor through shipments of the mineral fuels and the metals and the mineral fertilizers occupies a strategic position in the construction of international policy.

In no small measure the successful exploitation of these natural resources has contributed to the present commanding position of the United States among the nations. For a period of years this country produced annually about 50 per cent. of the world's copper, 50 per cent. of the iron, 35 per cent. of the lead, 40 per cent. of the zinc, 25 per cent. of the silver, 30 per cent. of the aluminum, 60 per cent. of the petroleum, 35 per cent. of the coal, 70 per cent. of the corn, 20 per cent. of the wheat, and 60 per cent. of the cotton. During recent years, however, owing to the disturbed economic conditions the world over, there have been marked fluctuations in these percentages.

Relation of Mineralogy to Other Sciences.—Mineralogy, then, must be considered as a science which is fundamental in our present civilization. It is a subject of vital importance to many types of students, namely to students of geology, chemistry, pharmacy, physics, forestry, soils, and engineering, not to include those looking forward to mineralogy as a profession.

The geologist whose task it is to observe and interpret the processes which are and have been at work upon the earth should be well grounded in mineralogy, for the earth consists largely of rocks which, in turn, are made up of minerals. The chemist and the pharmacist are deal-

[1] See C. K. Leith, "World Minerals and World Politics," Whittlesey House, McGraw-Hill Book Company, Inc., New York, 1931.

ing, to a large extent, with raw materials which consist of minerals. Many of the important chemical processes are dependent wholly or in part upon the use of minerals. This is especially true of inorganic chemistry. Thus, the well-known Solvay process for the manufacture of the alkalies uses as raw materials—limestone, halite or common salt, and coal—products of the mines or quarries. Moreover, many scientific advances have been made possible by the use, in research and industry, of the optical methods devised by the mineralogist. These methods have many applications in the rapid and accurate determination of substances even when they are available only in very small amounts.

Many of the important laws in physics, especially those relating to the properties of light, have been studied principally on crystallized minerals. The Nobel prizes in physics for 1914 and 1915 were awarded to Laue and the Braggs (father and son) for epoch-making investigations

upon the structure of crystallized minerals by means of X rays.

In this country, the forester and the student of soils are very frequently at work in undeveloped sections. In their field surveys they should recognize at a glance the character of the soil and of the rock exposures. They should also be able to pass fairly accurate judgment upon the possible value of any minerals or ore deposits they may find. In order to do this, some knowledge of mineralogy is required.

In railroad, highway, and waterway construction, the engineer is constantly encountering problems which involve a knowledge of

FIG. 1.—Abraham G. Werner (1750–1817). Pioneer mineralogist.

mineralogy. As in the case of the forester and the student of soils, he is frequently working in undeveloped sections of the country. Some of our most valuable ore deposits were discovered as the direct result of railroad building. The great mineral deposits at Sudbury, Ontario, which now furnish such enormous quantities of nickel, and the valuable silver mines at Cobalt, Ontario, to mention only two examples, were discovered in this way.

History of Mineralogy.—Mineralogy is a comparatively young science, having been developed more recently than astronomy, chemistry, mathematics, or physics. Although minerals and metals were frequently used by the ancients, the first extensive work on mineralogy did not appear until 1546, when Georg Agricola published his *De Natura Fossilium*. It is commonly conceded that Werner (1750–1817), for many years a professor in the famous school of mines at Freiberg, Saxony, was the first to place mineralogy upon a scientific basis. At first, mineralogy and geology were not differentiated, and only in comparatively recent times have they been recognized as distinct sciences.

Minerals and Rocks.—The exterior of the earth is made up of solids, liquids, and occluded gases. The solids are commonly called *rocks*. It is with the rocks that we are concerned. Some of the general characteristics of several of the most common rocks may now be discussed. Thus, if we examine granite (Fig. 2), it is at once seen that it is hetero-

  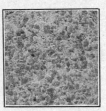

FIG. 2.—Granite.   FIG. 3.—Syenite.   FIG. 4.—Sandstone.   FIG. 5.—Marble.

geneous in character; that is, it is made up of several components. In general, one can easily recognize in a hand specimen three components: first, a colorless, granular, and glassy material which is called quartz; second, a substance with rather even surfaces, known as feldspar; and third, a dark-colored and scaly material, which is commonly designated as mica. If these three crystalline components are analyzed, it will be noted that characteristic chemical compositions can be assigned to them: thus to quartz, SiO_2, to feldspar, $KAlSi_3O_8$, and to mica, $K(Mg,Fe)_3(OH)_2AlSi_3O_{10}$. In examining another common rock, such as syenite (Fig. 3), it will be found that it is quite frequently composed of two components—mica and feldspar. On the other hand, such rocks as sandstone (Fig. 4) and marble (Fig. 5) consist of one component only—quartz and calcite, $CaCO_3$, respectively. When these substances are studied, it is generally observed that they

FIG. 6.—Anhydrite. Oakwood Salt Shaft, Detroit, Michigan.

occur in regular forms; that is, they are bounded by natural plane surfaces. These rock constituents are called *minerals*.

Definition of a Mineral.—A mineral, then, may be defined as a *substance occurring in nature with a characteristic chemical composition and usually possessing a definite crystalline structure, which is sometimes expressed in external geometrical forms or outlines.* Characteristic of a mineral is its occurrence in nature. A chemical substance, for example $CaSO_4$, may be found in nature, or it may be prepared in the chemical laboratory. When found in nature, it is designated as a mineral and has a special mineralogical name assigned to it, anhydrite (Fig. 6). When prepared in the laboratory, it is not interpreted as a mineral but is usually referred to by its chemical name, calcium sulphate. In order to be classified as a mineral, therefore, a substance must be the product of nature and not the result of processes carried on in the laboratory.

Most minerals are inorganic in character and are either chemical elements or combinations of such elements; that is, chemical compounds. Some substances of an organic nature, such as coal, amber, petroleum, and asphalt, are frequently classified as minerals. As indicated, a few minerals are very simple in composition, such as sulphur, silver, copper, and gold. These are elements.

Crystals.—When minerals occur with definite geometrical outlines they are called *crystals* (Figs. 7 and 8). Unlike minerals, crystals may be the result of processes carried on either in nature or in the laboratory.

Fig. 7.—Calcite. Joplin, Missouri.

Fig. 8.—Quartz. Dauphiné, France.

They are solids bounded by natural plane surfaces called *crystal faces*. Many minerals are found as excellent crystals. Accurate and rapid determination of minerals can, in many cases, be most successfully made by recognizing the crystal form. Crystallography is the science which deals with the form and various properties of crystals. A knowledge of the essentials of geometrical crystallography is absolutely indispensable in the rapid determination of minerals.

Divisions of Mineralogy.—An elementary course in mineralogy may be conveniently divided into (1) crystallography, (2) physical mineralogy, (3) chemical mineralogy, (4) descriptive mineralogy, (5) determinative mineralogy.

Crystallography.—This subject aims to make the student familiar with the common crystal forms exhibited by minerals, first by the study of crystal models and later by the recognition of the various forms exhibited by natural crystals.

Physical Mineralogy.—This includes the consideration of the various physical properties such as hardness, cleavage, color, luster, streak, specific gravity, as well as the optical properties and the internal structure of crystallized minerals. The study of the optical properties involves the use of the mineralogical or polarizing microscope.

Chemical Mineralogy.—In this portion of the science, the various chemical properties of minerals, and also their origin and formation, are considered. The determination of their chemical constituents, especially by blowpipe methods, is treated in detail.

Descriptive Mineralogy.—In Chap. XVI, 150 of the most common minerals are described as to their crystallography, chemical and physical properties, occurrences and associates, and uses. The use of minerals as precious stones is discussed in Chap. XVII, while statistics of mineral production and the application of minerals in industry, as well as the classification of minerals according to their important chemical constituents, are given in Chap. XVIII.

Determinative Mineralogy.—For the purpose of acquiring facility in the rapid recognition of minerals by means of their physical properties, pages 453 to 621 contain determinative tables for the 150 minerals described in this text.

CHAPTER II

CRYSTALLOGRAPHY

Subdivisions of Crystallography.—This science treats of the various properties of crystals and crystallized bodies. It may be subdivided as follows:

1. Geometrical crystallography.
2. Physical crystallography.
3. Chemical crystallography.

Geometrical crystallography, as the term implies, describes the various forms occurring upon crystals. The relationships existing between the crystal form and the physical and chemical properties of crystals are the subjects of discussion of the second and third subdivisions of this science, respectively. In order to be able to determine minerals rapidly, at least the essentials of geometrical crystallography must have been mastered.

Constancy of Interfacial Angles.—In general, crystals may result from solidification from a solution, state of fusion, or vapor. Let us suppose

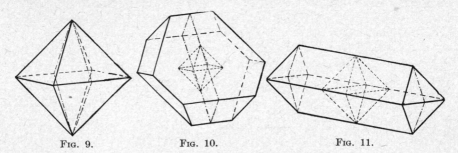

Fig. 9.   Fig. 10.   Fig. 11.

that some ammonium alum, $(NH_4)_2Al_2(SO_4)_4.24H_2O$, has been dissolved in water and the solution allowed to evaporate slowly. As the alum begins to crystallize, it will be noticed that the crystals are, for the most part, bounded by eight plane surfaces. If these surfaces are all of the same size, that is, equally developed, the crystals will possess an outline as represented by Fig. 9. Such a form is termed an *octahedron*. The octahedron is bounded by eight equilateral triangles. The angles between any two adjoining surfaces or *faces*, as they are often called, is the same, namely, 109° 28¼'. On most of the crystals, however, it will be seen that the various faces have been developed unequally, giving rise to the forms illustrated by Figs. 10 and 11. Similar cross sections

8

through these forms are shown in Figs. 12, 13, and 14, and it is readily seen that, although the size of the faces and hence the resulting shapes

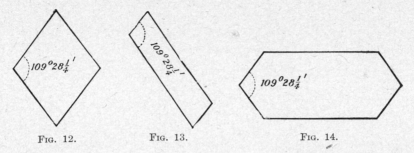

FIG. 12.   FIG. 13.   FIG. 14.

have been materially changed, the angle between the adjoining faces has remained the same, namely, 109° 28¼′. Such forms of the octahedron are said to be *misshapen* or *distorted*. *Distortion* is quite common on all crystals regardless of their chemical composition.

It was the Danish physician and natural scientist Nicolaus Steno (Fig. 15) who in 1669 first showed that the angles between similar faces on crystals of quartz remain constant regardless of their development. Figures 16 and 17 represent two crystals of quartz, and Figs. 18 and 19 show similar cross sections through them. This constancy of angles between similar faces applies not only to quartz but to all crystallized substances. This is a fundamental law, and it may be stated as follows: *Measured at the same temperature, similar angles on crystals of the same substance remain constant regardless of the size or shape of the crystal.*

FIG. 15.—Nicolaus Steno (1638–1687). Discoverer of the law of the constancy of interfacial angles.

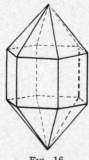 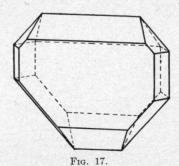

FIG. 16.   FIG. 17.

Crystal Habit.—During the process of crystallization crystals may assume various shapes. Figures 9, 10, and 11 show some of the shapes observed on alum crystals. These shapes are called their *habits*. Thus, in Fig. 9, the eight faces are about equally developed and this may be termed the *octahedral* habit. The *tabular* habit (Fig. 10) is due to the predominance of two parallel faces. Figure 11 shows four parallel-edged faces predominating, and the resulting form is the *prismatic* habit.

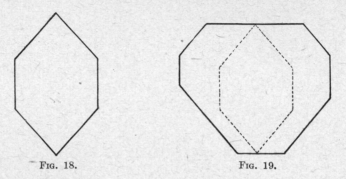

Fig. 18.　　　　　　　　　　　　Fig. 19.

Crystallographic Axes.—Inasmuch as the crystal form of any substance is dependent upon its physical and chemical properties, it necessarily follows that an almost infinite variety of forms is possible. In order, however, to study these forms and define the position of the faces occurring on them advantageously, straight lines are assumed to pass through the ideal center of each crystal. These lines are the *crystallographic axes*. Their intersection forms the *axial cross*. Figure 20 shows

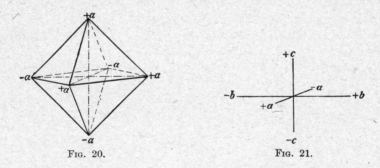

Fig. 20.　　　　　　　　　　　　Fig. 21.

the octahedron referred to its three crystal axes. In this case the axes are of equal length and are termed *a* axes. The extremities of the axes are differentiated by the use of the plus and minus signs, as shown in Fig. 20.

If the axes are of unequal lengths, the one extending from front to rear is termed the *a* axis, the one from right to left the *b*, while the vertical axis is called the *c* axis. This is illustrated by Fig. 21. The axes are always referred to in the following order, namely, *a*, *b*, *c*.

Crystal Systems.—Although a great variety of crystal forms is possible, it has been shown in many ways that all forms may be classified into six large groups, called *crystal systems*. In the grouping of crystal forms into systems, we are aided by the crystallographic axes. The systems may be differentiated by means of the axes as follows:

1. *Cubic System.*—Three axes, all of equal lengths, intersect at right angles. The axes are designated by the letters *a, a, a*.

2. *Hexagonal System.*—Four axes—three of which are equal, lie in a horizontal plane, and intersect at angles of 60°. These three axes are often termed the *lateral* axes and are designated by *a, a, a*. Perpendicular to the plane of the lateral axes is the vertical axis, which may be longer or shorter than the *a* axes. This fourth axis is called the *principal* or *c* axis.

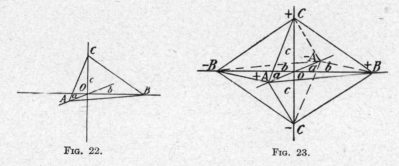

FIG. 22.   FIG. 23.

3. *Tetragonal System.*—Three axes—two of which are equal, horizontal, and perpendicular to each other. The vertical *c* axis is at right angles to and either longer or shorter than the horizontal or *lateral a* axes. The vertical axis is often called the *principal* axis.

4. *Orthorhombic System.*—Three axes of unequal lengths intersect at right angles. These axes are designated by *a, b, c*, as shown in Fig. 21.

5. *Monoclinic System.*—Three axes—all unequal, two of which (*a, c*) intersect at an oblique angle, the third axis (*b*) being perpendicular to these two.

6. *Triclinic System.*—Three axes (*a, b, c,*) are all unequal and intersect at three different angles.

Parameters and Parametral Ratio.—In order to determine the position of a face on a crystal, it must be referred to the crystallographic axes. Figure 22 shows an axial cross of the orthorhombic system. The axes *a, b, c* are, therefore, unequal and perpendicular to each other. The plane *ABC* cuts the three axes at the points *A, B*, and *C*, hence, at the distance $OA = a$, $OB = b$, $OC = c$, from the center *O*. These distances *OA, OB*, and *OC* are known as the *parameters* and the ratio $OA : OB : OC$ as the *parametral ratio* of the plane *ABC*. This ratio may be abbreviated to $a : b : c$.

There are, however, seven other planes possible about this axial cross which possess parameters of the same lengths as those of the plane ABC (Fig. 23). The simplified ratios of these planes are

$$a \;:\; -b \;:\; c$$
$$a \;:\; b \;:\; -c$$
$$a \;:\; -b \;:\; -c$$
$$-a \;:\; b \;:\; c$$
$$-a \;:\; -b \;:\; c$$
$$-a \;:\; b \;:\; -c$$
$$-a \;:\; -b \;:\; -c.$$

These eight planes are all similarly located with respect to the crystallographic axes. These planes constitute a *crystal form* and may be represented by the general ratio $(a : b : c)$. The number of faces in a crystal form depends, moreover, not only upon the intercepts or parameters but also upon the elements of symmetry possessed by the crystal (see page 17). Those forms which enclose space are called *closed*

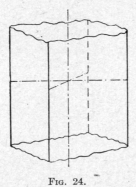

Fig. 24.

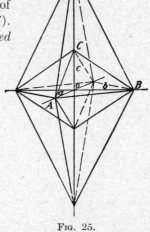

Fig. 25.

forms. Figure 23 is such a form. Those, however, which do not enclose space on all sides, as shown in Fig. 24, are termed *open* forms.

Fundamental and Modified Forms.—In Fig. 25 the enclosed form possesses the general ratio $a : b : c$. The face ABM of the outer form, however, has the parametral ratio $oA : oB : oM$, where $oA = a$, $oB = b$, and $oM = 3oC = 3c$. Hence, this ratio may be written $a : b : 3c$. But, as in the previous case, this ratio represents a form consisting of eight faces as shown in the figure. That form, the parameters of which are selected as the unit lengths of the crystallographic axes, is known as the *unit* or *fundamental* form. In Fig. 25 the inner bipyramid, or double pyramid, is a *unit*, whereas the outer bipyramid is a *modified* form.

Combinations.—Several different forms may occur simultaneously upon a crystal, giving rise to a *combination*. Figures 26 and 27 show a combination of two bipyramids observed on sulphur; $p = a : b : c$ (unit) and $s = a : b : \frac{1}{3}c$ (modified). Figures 28 and 29 show the two forms $o = a : a : a$, and $h = a : \infty a : \infty a$ (see page 23).

Axial Ratio.—If the intercepts of a unit form cutting all three axes be expressed in figures, the intercept along the b axis being considered

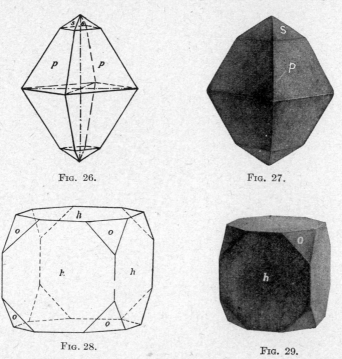

Fig. 26.   Fig. 27.

Fig. 28.   Fig. 29.

as unity, we obtain the *axial ratio*. In Figs. 26 and 27, which represent a crystal of sulphur, the axial ratio is

$$a : b : c = 0.8131 : 1 : 1.9034.$$

Every crystallized substance has its own axial ratio. This is illustrated by the ratios of three minerals crystallizing in the orthorhombic system:

Aragonite, $CaCO_3$, $a : b : c = 0.6228 : 1 : 0.7204$
Anglesite, $PbSO_4$, $a : b : c = 0.7852 : 1 : 1.2894$
Topaz, $Al_2(F,OH)_2SiO_4$, $a : b : c = 0.5281 : 1 : 0.9442$

In the hexagonal and tegragonal systems, since the horizontal axes are equal, that is, $a = b$ (see page 11), the axial ratio is reduced to $a : c$, a now being unity. Thus, the axial ratio of zircon ($ZrSiO_4$), which is tetragonal, may be expressed as follows: $a : c = 1 : 0.6404$; that of quartz (SiO_2), hexagonal, by $a : c = 1 : 1.0999$. Obviously, in the cubic system (page 11), since all three axes are equal, there is no axial ratio.

However, in the monoclinic and triclinic systems, where either one or more axes intersect obliquely, it is not only necessary to give the axial ratio but also to indicate the values of the angles between the crystallographic axes. For example, gypsum ($CaSO_4.2H_2O$) crystallizes in the monoclinic system and has the following axial ratio:

$$a : b : c = 0.6896 : 1 : 0.4133,$$

and the inclination of the a to the c axis is $98° 58'$. This angle is known as β (Fig. 30).

In the triclinic system, since all axes are inclined at unequal angles, it is also necessary to know the value of these angles, which are located as shown in Fig. 31, namely, $b \wedge c = \alpha$, $a \wedge c = \beta$, $a \wedge b = \gamma$.

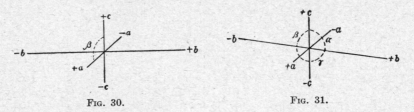

FIG. 30.　　　　　　　　　　FIG. 31.

Elements of Crystallization.—The axial ratio and the angles showing the inclination of the axes are termed the *elements of crystallization*. Thus, the triclinic mineral albite ($NaAlSi_3O_8$) possesses the following elements of crystallization:

$$a : b : c = 0.6330 : 1 : 0.5573$$
$$\alpha = 94° 5'$$
$$\beta = 116° 27'$$
$$\gamma = 88° 7'.$$

If the angles between the crystallographic axes equal $90°$, they are not indicated. Therefore, in the tetragonal, hexagonal, and orthorhombic systems, the axial ratios alone constitute the elements of crystallization, while in the cubic system there are no unknown elements.

Rationality of Coefficients.—The parametral ratio of any face may be expressed in general by $na : pb : mc$, where the coefficients n, p, m are, according to observation, always rational. In Fig. 32, the inner bipyramid is assumed to be the fundamental form (page 12), with the following value of the intercepts: $oa = 1.256$, $ob = 1$, $oc = 0.739$. Being a fundamental or unit form, the coefficients n, p, m are obviously all equal to unity. The ratio is, hence, $a : b : c$.

The outer bipyramid, however, possesses the intercepts $oa = 1.256$, $oB = 2$, $oC = 2.217$. These lengths, divided by the unit lengths of

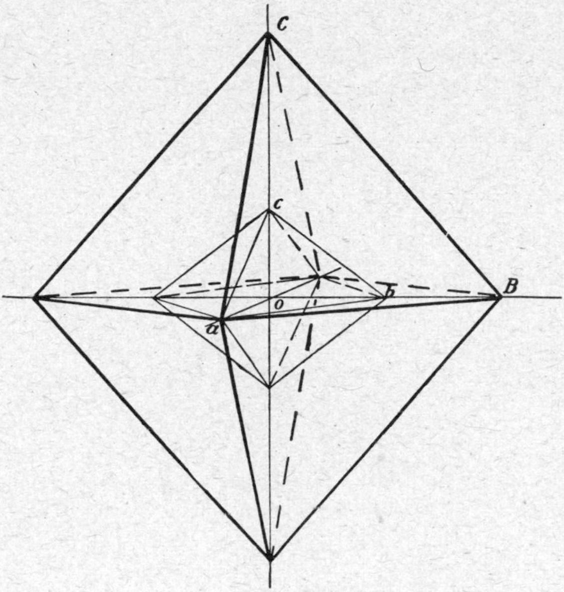

FIG. 32.

each axis, as indicated above, determine the values of n, p, and m for the outer bipyramid, namely:

$$n = \frac{1.256}{1.256} = 1; \quad p = \frac{2}{1} = 2;$$

$$m = \frac{2.217}{0.739} = 3.$$

These values of n, p, and m are therefore rational. Such values as $\frac{1}{2}$, $\frac{1}{3}$, $\frac{1}{6}$, $\frac{5}{3}$, or $\frac{2}{5}$ are also possible, but never 3.1416+, 2.6578+, $\sqrt{3}$, and so forth.

Symbols.—The parametral ratio of the plane *ABM* (Fig. 25) may be written as follows:

$$na : pb : mc.$$

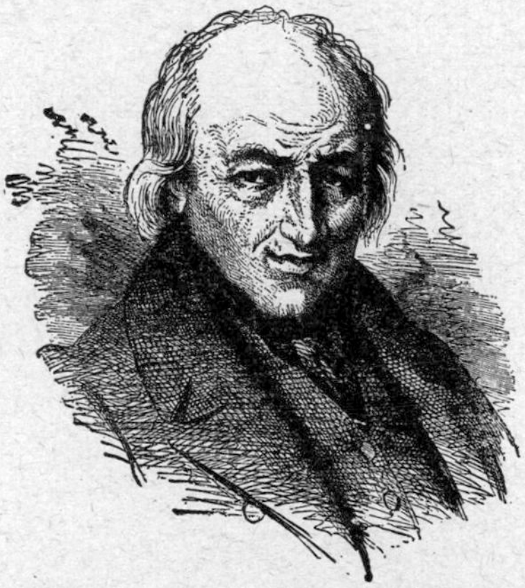

FIG. 33.—René Haüy (1743–1822). Curator of mineralogy in the Museum of Natural History of Paris (1802–1822). Pioneer crystallographer.

But since, in this case, $n = 1$, $p = 1$, $m = 3$, the ratio becomes

$$a : b : 3c.$$

If, however, the coefficients had the values $\frac{1}{2}$, $\frac{2}{3}$, and $\frac{4}{3}$, respectively the ratio would then read

$$\tfrac{1}{2}a : \tfrac{2}{3}b : \tfrac{4}{3}c.$$

This, when expressed in terms of b, becomes

$$\tfrac{3}{4}a : b : 2c.$$

Hence, the ratio

$$na : b : mc$$

expresses the most general ratio or symbol for forms belonging to the orthorhombic, monoclinic, and triclinic systems. In the hexagonal

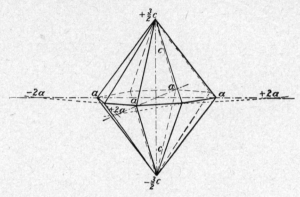

FIG. 34.

and tetragonal systems, since the a and b axes are equal, this general symbol becomes

$$a : na : mc.$$

Figure 34 shows a form, the ditetragonal bipyramid, with the symbol $a : 2a : \tfrac{3}{2}c$. In the cubic system, all three axes are equal and the general symbol reads

$$a : na : ma.$$

The ratio $a : \infty a : \infty a$, for example, symbolizes a form in the cubic system consisting of six faces, which cut one axis and extend parallel to

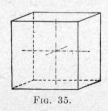

FIG. 35.

FIG. 36.

the other two. Such a form is the cube (Figs. 35 and 36). The ratio $a : 2a : \infty a$ represents a form with 24 faces; each face cuts one axis at a unit's distance, the second at twice the distance, and extends parallel to the third axis. Figures 37 and 38 show such a form, the tetrahexahedron. This system of crystallographic notation is known as the *Weiss system*. These symbols are very readily understood and well adapted for beginners.

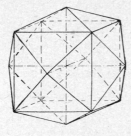

FIG. 37.   FIG. 38.

Miller's Indices.—In this system of notation the letters referring to the various crystallographic axes are not indicated, the values given being understood as referring to the a, b, and c axes, respectively (page 10). The reciprocals of the Weiss parameters are reduced to the lowest common denominator. The numerators then constitute the Miller symbols, called *indices*. For example, the reciprocals of the Weiss parameters $2a : b : 3c$ would be $\frac{1}{2}$, $\frac{1}{1}$, $\frac{1}{3}$. These, reduced to the lowest common denominator, are $\frac{3}{6}$, $\frac{6}{6}$, $\frac{2}{6}$. Hence, 3 6 2 constitute the corresponding Miller indices. These are read *three, six, two.*

A number of examples will make this system of notation clear. Thus, $a : \infty b : \infty c$ becomes 100; $2a : b : 5c$, 5.10.2; $a : a : 3c$, 331; $a : \infty a : 2c$, 201; and so forth. The Miller indices corresponding to the general ratios $a : na : ma$ and $na : b : mc$ are written hkl. The Miller indices are important because of their almost universal application in mathematical crystallography.

FIG. 39.—William H. Miller (1801–1880). Professor of mineralogy in the University of Cambridge (1832–1880):

Elements of Symmetry.—The laws of symmetry find expression upon a crystal in the distribution of similar angles and faces. The presence, therefore, of planes, axes, or a center of symmetry—these are the *elements of symmetry*—is of great importance for the correct classification of a crystal. Only those elements of symmetry most useful in the recognition of the geometrical development of crystals are here considered.

Planes of Symmetry.—Any plane which passes through the center of a crystal and divides it into two symmetrical parts, the one-half being the *mirror image* of the other, is a *plane of symmetry*. Figure 40 shows a crystal of gypsum $(CaSO_4.2H_2O)$ with its one plane of symmetry.

Every plane of symmetry is parallel to some face, which is either *present* or *possible* upon the crystal.

It is sometimes convenient to designate planes of symmetry as *axial*, *diagonal*, *principal*, or *intermediate* planes. Figure 41 illustrates a

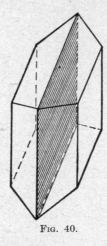

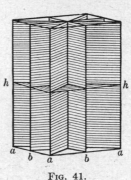

| FIG. 40. | FIG. 41. |

crystal of the tetragonal system with five planes of symmetry. Plane *h* is the *horizontal axial* or *principal* plane. The vertical planes are the *vertical axial* (*a*) and *intermediate* (*b*) planes of symmetry.

FIG. 42.—Victor Goldschmidt (1853–1933). Eminent mineralogist and crystallographer. For many years professor in the University of Heidelberg.

Axes of Symmetry.—The line about which a crystal may be revolved as an axis so that after a definite angular revolution the crystal assumes exactly the same position in space which it originally had is termed an *axis of symmetry*. Depending upon the rotation necessary, four types of axes of symmetry are possible from the standpoint of crystallography:

a. Those axes about which the original position is reassumed after a revolution of 60° are said to be axes of *sixfold, six-count,* or *hexagonal*[1] symmetry. Such axes may be indicated by the symbol ◆. Figure 43 shows such an axis.

b. If the original position is regained after the crystal is revolved through 90°, the axis possesses *fourfold, four-count,* or *tetragonal* symmetry. These axes are represented by ■, as illustrated in Fig. 44.

c. Axes requiring an angular revolution of 120° are *threefold, three-count, trigonal* axes of symmetry and may be symbolized by ▲. Figure 45 illustrates this type of axis.

[1] Because in a complete revolution of 360° the position is reassumed six times.

d. An axis of *twofold, two-count, or binary* symmetry necessitates a revolution through 180°. These are indicated by ● in Fig. 44.

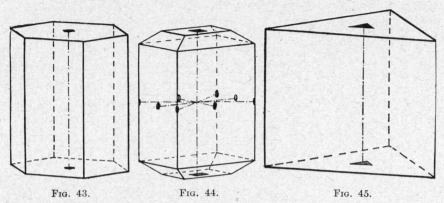

FIG. 43.   FIG. 44.   FIG. 45.

In addition to these four types of axes, there is a type of axis in which rotation is combined with reflection. Such axes are called *rotary-reflection* axes.

Center of Symmetry.—That point within a crystal through which straight lines may be drawn, so that on either side of and at the same distance from it similar portions of the crystal (faces, edges, angles, and so forth) are encountered, is a *center of symmetry.* Figure 46 has a center of symmetry—the other elements of symmetry are lacking.

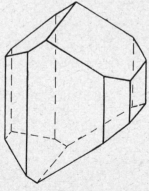

FIG. 46.

Angular Position of Faces.—Since crystals are oftentimes *misshapen* or *distorted* (page 9), it follows that the elements of symmetry are not always readily recognized. The *angular position* of the faces in respect to these elements is the essential feature

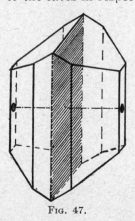

FIG. 47.   FIG. 48.

and not their distances from one another or their relative sizes. Figure 47 shows a crystal with a plane of symmetry, a twofold axis, and a center of symmetry.   Figure 48 shows a distorted crystal of the same substance, which possesses these elements of symmetry, because the angular position of the faces is the same as in Fig. 47.

Classes of Symmetry.—Depending upon the elements of symmetry present, crystals may be divided into 32 distinct groups, called *classes of symmetry*.[1] Only forms which belong to the same class can occur in combination with each other. *A crystal system,* however, includes all those classes of symmetry which can be referred to the same type of crystallographic axes (page 11). The various elements of symmetry and an important representative are given for each of the 32 classes in the tabular classification on page 445. Only 13 classes will be discussed in detail.

[1] Also termed *classes of crystals.*

CHAPTER III

CUBIC SYSTEM[1]

Crystallographic Axes.—All crystals which can be referred to three equal and perpendicular axes belong to cubic system. Figure 49 shows the axial cross. One axis is held vertically, a second extends from front to rear, and a third from right to left. These axes are all interchangeable, each being designated by *a*. Since there are no unknown elements of crystallization in this system (page 14), all substances, regardless of their chemical composition, crystallizing in this system with forms having the same parametral ratios must of necessity possess the same interfacial angles.

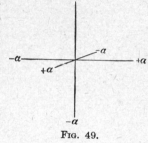

FIG. 49.

Classes of Symmetry.—The cubic system includes five groups or classes of symmetry. Beginning with the class of highest symmetry, they are:

1. Hexoctahedral class.
2. Hextetrahedral class.
3. Dyakisdodecahedral class.
4. Pentagonal icositetrahedral class.
5. Tetrahedral pentagonal dodecahedral class.

Of these classes, the first three are the most important and will be considered in detail.

HEXOCTAHEDRAL CLASS

Elements of Symmetry. *a. Planes.*—Forms of this class are characterized by nine planes of symmetry. Three of these are parallel to the planes of the crystallographic axes and, hence, perpendicular to each other. They are the *axial* planes of symmetry. They divide space into eight equal parts called *octants*. The six other planes are each parallel to one of the crystallographic axes and bisect the angles between the other two. These are termed the *diagonal* planes of symmetry. By them space is divided into 24 equal parts. The nine planes together divide space into 48 equal sections. Figures 50 and 51 illustrate the location of the axial and diagonal planes, respectively.

[1] Also termed the *isometric, regular, tesseral,* or *tessular* system.

b. Axes.—The intersection lines of the three axial planes of symmetry give rise to the three axes of *fourfold* symmetry. These are the

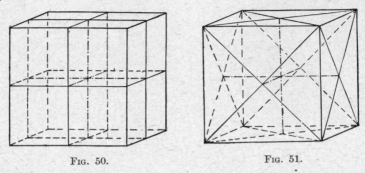

FIG. 50.   FIG. 51.

crystallographic axes, as illustrated by Fig. 52. The four axes equally inclined to the crystallographic axes are of *threefold* symmetry, as shown by

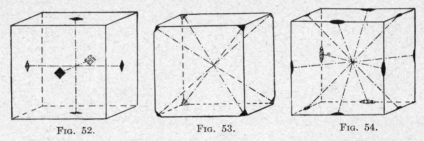

FIG. 52.   FIG. 53.   FIG. 54.

Fig. 53. There are also six axes of *twofold* symmetry. These lie in the axial planes of symmetry and bisect the angles between the crystallographic axes. Their location is indicated in Fig. 54. These 13 axes of symmetry may be indicated as follows:

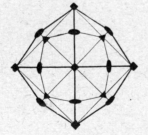

FIG. 55.

$$3 \blacksquare + 4 \blacktriangle + 6 \bullet = 13.$$

c. Center.—The forms of this class also possess this element of symmetry. Hence, all planes have parallel counterplanes.

The projection of the most general form of this class upon a plane perpendicular to the vertical axis, that is, in this case an axial plane of symmetry, shows the symmetry relations[1] (Fig. 55).

Octahedron.—As the name implies, this form consists of eight faces. Each face is equally inclined to the crystallographic axes. Hence, the parametral ratio may be written $(a : a : a)$, which according to Miller

---

[1] The heavy lines indicate edges through which axial planes of symmetry pass. The light, full lines show the location of the diagonal planes, while dashed lines indicate the absence of planes (see Fig. 86, p. 29).

would be {111}. The faces intersect at an angle of 109° 28′ 16″ and in the ideal form (Figs. 56 and 57) are equal, equilateral triangles.

The crystallographic axes and, hence, the axes of fourfold symmetry pass through the tetrahedral angles. The four threefold axes join the centers of opposite faces, while the six twofold axes bisect the 12 edges.

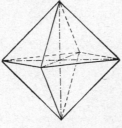

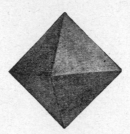

FIG. 56.   FIG. 57.

Dodecahedron.—This form consists of 12 faces, each cutting two of the crystallographic axes at the same distances but extending parallel to the third. The symbols are, therefore, $(a : a : \infty a)$ or {110}. In the

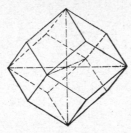

FIG. 58.   FIG. 59.

ideal form (Figs. 58 and 59) each face is a rhombus, and, hence, the form is often termed the *rhombic dodecahedron*.

The crystallographic axes pass through the tetrahedral angles, the threefold axes join opposite trihedral angles, and the twofold axes the

FIG. 60.   FIG. 61.

centers of opposite faces. It follows, therefore, that the faces are parallel to the diagonal planes of symmetry.

Hexahedron or Cube.—The faces of this form cut one axis and are parallel to the other two. This is expressed by $(a : \infty a : \infty a)$. {100}.

Six such faces are possible and when the development is ideal (Figs. 60 and 61) each is a square.

The crystallographic axes pass through the centers of the faces. The axes of threefold symmetry join opposite trihedral angles, while the twofold axes bisect the 12 edges (compare Figs. 52, 53, and 54).

Trigonal Trisoctahedron.[1]—The faces of this form cut two crystallographic axes at equal distances and the third at a greater distance, *ma*.

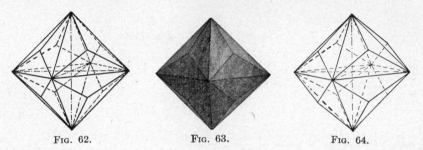

FIG. 62.   FIG. 63.   FIG. 64.

The coefficient *m* is some rational value greater than one but less than infinity. The ratio is $(a : a : ma)$ and it requires 24 similar faces to enclose space. The Miller symbols are $\{hhl\}$, where *h* is greater than *l*. Because the general outline of this form is similar to that of the octahedron, each face of which in the ideal form is replaced by three equal isosceles triangles, it is termed the *trigonal trisoctahedron*, Figs. 62 and 63, $(a : a : 2a)$, $\{221\}$, and Fig. 64, $(a : a : 3a)$, $\{331\}$.

The crystallographic axes join opposite octahedral angles. The threefold axes pass through the trihedral angles and the six twofold axes bisect the 12 long edges.

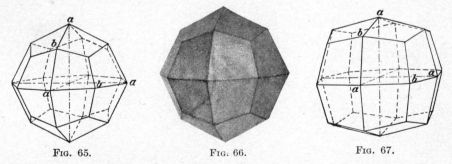

FIG. 65.   FIG. 66.   FIG. 67.

Tetragonal Trisoctahedron.[2]—This form consists of 24 faces, each cutting one axis at a unit's distance and the other two at greater but equal distances *ma*. The value of *m* is, as above, $1 < m < \infty$. The symbols are, therefore, $(a : ma : ma)$, or $\{hll\}$, $h > l$. The ideal forms,

[1] Also known as the *trisoctahedron*.

[2] Also termed the *trapezohedron*, *icositetrahedron*, and *leucitohedron*.

Figs. 65 and 66, $(a : 2a : 2a)$, $\{211\}$ and Fig. 67, $(a : 4a : 4a)$, $\{411\}$, bear some resemblance to the octahedron, each face of which has been replaced by three four-sided faces (trapeziums) of equal size. The form is, therefore, termed the *tetragonal trisoctahedron*. The six tetrahedral angles[1] a indicate the position of the crystallographic axes. The axes of threefold symmetry join opposite trihedral angles, while those of twofold symmetry connect the tetrahedral angles[2] b.

Tetrahexahedron.—In this form the faces cut one axis at a unit's distance, the second at the distance ma, where $1 < m < \infty$, and extend

parallel to the third axis. The symbols are, therefore, $(a : ma : \infty a)$ or $\{hk0\}$. The 24 faces in the ideal forms, Figs. 68 and 69, $(a : 2a : \infty a)$, $\{210\}$ and Fig. 70, $(a : 4a : \infty a)$, $\{410\}$, are equal isosceles triangles. Since this form may be considered as a cube, whose faces have been replaced by tetragonal pyramids, it is often called the *pyramid cube* or *tetrahexahedron*.

The crystallographic axes are located by the six tetrahedral angles. The axes of threefold symmetry pass through opposite hexahedral angles, while the twofold axes bisect the long edges.

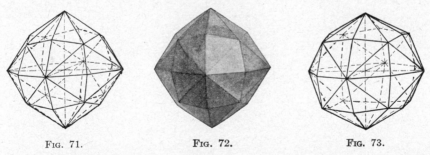

Hexoctahedron.—As is indicated by the name, this form is bounded by 48 faces. Each cuts one crystallographic axis at a unit's distance, and the other two at greater but unequal distances na and ma, respectively; n is less than m, the value of m being, as heretofore, $1 < m < \infty$.

[1] With four equal edges.

[2] These have two pairs of equal edges.

Hence, the symbols may be written ($a : na : ma$) or $\{hkl\}$. Figures 71 and 72, ($a : 3/2a : 3a$), $\{321\}$ and Fig. 73, ($a : 5/3a : 5a$), $\{531\}$, show ideal forms, the faces being scalene triangles of the same size.

The crystallographic axes pass through the octahedral angles, while the hexahedral angles locate those of threefold symmetry. The twofold axes pass through opposite tetrahedral angles.

The seven forms just described are the only ones possible in this class.

Summary.—The following table gives a summary of the most important features of the hexoctahedral class.

Symmetry	Planes		Axes			Center
	Axial	Diagonal	■	▲	●	
	3	6	3	4	6	1

Forms	Symbols		Faces	Solid angles			
	Weiss	Miller		Trihedral	Tetrahedral	Hexahedral	Octahedral
Octahedron	$a : a : a$	$\{111\}$	8	–	6	–	–
Dodecahedron	$a : a : \infty a$	$\{110\}$	12	8	6	–	–
Hexahedron	$a : \infty a : \infty a$	$\{100\}$	6	8	–	–	–
Trigonal Trisoctahedron	$a : a : ma$	$\{hhl\}$	24	8	–	–	6
Tetragonal Trisoctahedron	$a : ma : ma$	$\{hll\}$	24	8	$6^1 + 12^2$	–	–
Tetrahexahedron	$a : ma : \infty a$	$\{hk0\}$	24	–	6	8	–
Hexoctahedron	$a : na : ma$	$\{hkl\}$	48	–	12	8	6

[1] These have four equal edges.

[2] Two pairs of two equal edges each.

From this tabulation we see that the ratios of the octahedron, dodecahedron, and hexahedron contain no variables and, hence, each is represented by but one form. These are often called *singular* or *fixed* forms. The other ratios, however, contain either one or two variables and, therefore, each represents a series of forms (compare Figs. 62 to 73).

Relationship of Forms.—The relationship existing between the above forms is well expressed by the diagram on page 27.

The three fixed forms are placed at the corners of the triangle and, as is obvious, must be considered as the limiting forms of the others. For example, the value of m in the trigonal trisoctahedron $(a : a : ma)$ varies between unity and infinity (page 24). Hence, it follows that the octahedron and dodecahedron are its limiting forms. The tetragonal trisoctahedron $(a : ma : ma)$ similarly passes over into the octahedron or cube, depending upon the value of m. The limiting forms are, therefore, in every case readily recognized. Faces of those forms, which are on

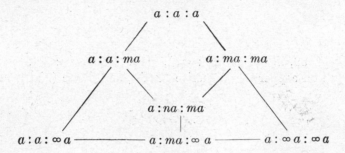

the sides of the triangle,[1] lie in the same zone, that is, their intersection lines are parallel.

Combinations.—The following figures illustrate some of the combinations of the forms of this class, which are observed most frequently.

Figures 74, 75, and 76, $o = (a : a : a)$, $\{111\}$; $h = (a : \infty a : \infty a)$, $\{100\}$. This combination is frequently observed on galena (PbS). In Fig. 74 the octahedron predominates, in Fig. 75 both forms are equally developed, while in Fig. 76 the cube is the predominant form.

FIG. 74.   FIG. 75.   FIG. 76.

Figure 77, $o = (a : a : a)$, $\{111\}$; $d = (a : a : \infty a)$, $\{110\}$. Observed on spinel, $Mg(AlO_2)_2$; magnetite, $Fe(FeO_2)_2$; and franklinite, $(Fe,Zn,Mn)(FeO_2)_2$.

Figure 78, $h = (a : \infty a : \infty a)$, $\{100\}$; $d = (a : a : \infty a)$, $\{110\}$. Frequently observed on galena (PbS) and fluorite (CaF_2).

Figure 79, $d = (a : a : \infty a)$, $\{110\}$; $i = (a : 2a : 2a)$, $\{211\}$. This is a frequent combination on garnet ($M_3''M_2'''Si_4O_{12}$).

[1] For example, the octahedron, trigonal trisoctahedron, and dodecahedron.

Figures 80, 81, and 82, $h = (a : \infty a : \infty a)$, $\{100\}$; $o = (a : a : a)$, $\{111\}$; $d = (a : a : \infty a)$ $\{110\}$. Also observed on galena (PbS).

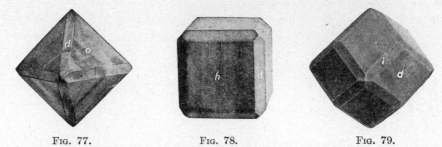

| FIG. 77. | FIG. 78. | FIG. 79. |

Figure 83, $h = (a : \infty a : \infty a)$, $\{100\}$; $e = (a : 2a : \infty a)$, $\{210\}$. Observed on copper (Cu), fluorite (CaF_2), and halite (NaCl).

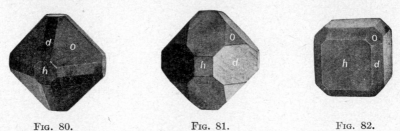

| FIG. 80. | FIG. 81. | FIG. 82. |

Figure 84, $h = (a : \infty a : \infty a)$, $\{100\}$; $i = (a : 2a : 2a)$, $\{211\}$. Observed on analcite ($NaAlSi_2O_6.H_2O$) and argentite (Ag_2S).

| FIG. 83. | FIG. 84. | FIG. 85. |

Figure 85, $d = (a : a : \infty a)$, $\{110\}$; $s = (a : 3/2a : 3a)$, $\{321\}$. Sometimes observed on garnet ($M_3''M_2'''Si_4O_{12}$).

HEXTETRAHEDRAL CLASS

Elements of Symmetry.—The elements of symmetry of this class consist of six diagonal planes and four trigonal and three binary axes. The trigonal axes are polar in character. The crystallographic axes possess binary symmetry. The diagonal planes of symmetry are easily located since they pass through the edges of the various forms of this class. The symmetry relations are shown in Fig. 86. The absence of the axial planes of symmetry is emphasized by the shading of opposite octants. The faces of the positive forms of this class are located in the unshaded octants, those of the negative forms in the shaded ones. In this class, there are four new forms which differ morphologically from those having the same ratios in the hexoctahedral class, namely, tetrahedrons, tetragonal tristetrahedrons, trigonal tristetrahedrons, and hextetrahedrons. Of these forms the tetrahedrons are the most important.

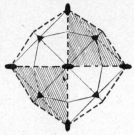

Fig. 86.

Tetrahedrons.—These are bounded by four equilateral triangles intersecting at equal angles of 70° 32'. Each face is equally inclined to the crystallographic axes, and consequently the symbols are the same as for the octahedron (page 23), namely, $\pm (a : a : a)$ or $\{111\}$ and $\{1\bar{1}1\}$. There are two tetrahedrons possible, which differ only with respect to the positions they occupy in space, as illustrated in Figs. 87 to 90. If the upper face to the front lies in the positive octant,

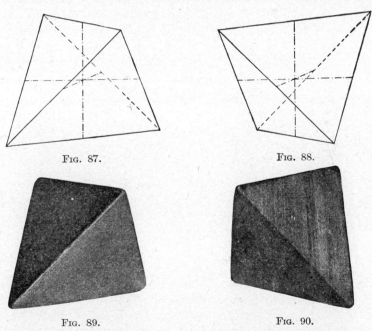

Fig. 87.   Fig. 88.

Fig. 89.   Fig. 90.

the form is designated as *positive* (Figs. 88 and 90), if not, it is *negative* (Figs. 87 and 89). The forms are said to be *congruent*, for a positive form may be brought into the position of a negative form by rotating through an angle of 90°, and *vice versa*.

The crystallographic axes pass through the centers of the edges and possess twofold symmetry. The threefold axes pass from the trihedral angles to the centers of opposite faces and are *polar* in character.

Tetragonal Tristetrahedrons.—These forms possess a tetrahedral habit and are bounded by 12 faces, which in the ideal development are similar trapeziums. Each face has four angles. Plus and minus forms are possible. The symbols are the same as for the trigonal tris-octahedron (page 24), namely, $\pm(a : a : ma)$ or $\{hhl\}$ and $\{h\bar{h}l\}$. The

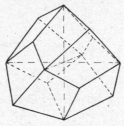

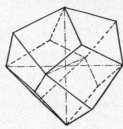

Fig. 91.   Fig. 92.

differentiation between positive and negative forms is analogous to that referred to under tetrahedrons. Figure 92 represents a *positive* and Fig. 91 a *negative* form. The forms are sometimes called *deltoids* or *deltoid dodecahedrons*.

The crystallographic axes pass through opposite tetrahedral angles, while the axes of threefold symmetry join opposite trihedral angles, one of which is acute, the other obtuse.

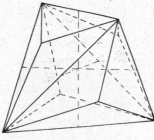

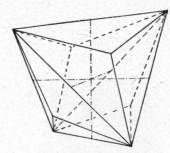

Fig. 93.   Fig. 94.

Trigonal Tristetrahedrons.—These are two congruent forms bounded by 12 similar isosceles triangles (Figs. 93 and 94). The habit is tetra-hedral, and the forms might be considered as tetrahedrons whose faces have been replaced by trigonal pyramids. They are sometimes called *pyramid tetrahedrons* or *trigonal dodecahedrons*. The symbols are analo-gous to those of the tetragonal trisoctahedron (page 24), namely, $\pm(a : ma : ma)$ or $\{hll\}$ and $\{h\bar{l}l\}$. Figure 94 illustrates the *positive* and Fig. 93 the *negative* position.

The crystallographic axes bisect the long edges. The threefold axes pass from the trihedral to the opposite hexahedral angles.

Hextetrahedrons.—When these forms are ideally developed, they possess a tetrahedral habit and are bounded by 24 similar scalene triangles. They are congruent and hence designated as *positive* (Fig. 96) and *negative* (Fig. 95). The symbols are of the same character as those of the hexoctahedron (page 25), namely, $\pm(a : na : ma)$ or $\{hkl\}$ and $\{h\bar{k}l\}$.

The crystallographic axes connect opposite tetrahedral angles. The axes of threefold symmetry pass through opposite hexahedral angles, one of which is obtuse, the other acute.

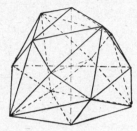

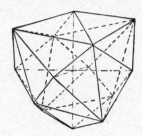

FIG. 95.   FIG. 96.

Other Forms.—The hexahedron, dodecahedron, and tetrahexahedron are morphologically exactly similar to those of the hexoctahedral class. Their symmetry is, however, of a lower grade. This is not recognized on models. On crystals, however, the luster, surface striations, and shape and orientation of *etch figures* will generally reveal the lower grade of symmetry.[1]

Naturally when these forms occur in combination with those which are morphologically new, the lower grade of symmetry of this class is at once apparent.

[1] When crystals are subjected to the action of some solvent for a short time, small depressions or elevations, the so-called *etch figures*, appear. Being dependent upon the internal structure, their form and position indicate the symmetry of the crystal. For instance, Fig. 97 shows the etch figures on a crystal (cube) of halite (NaCl). Here,

FIG. 97.   FIG. 98.

it is evident, that the symmetry of the figures with respect to that of the cube is such as to place the crystal in the hexoctahedral class. Figure 98 represents a cube of sodium bromate ($NaBrO_3$), which geometrically does not differ from the crystal of halite. A lower grade of symmetry is, however, revealed by the shape and orientation of the etch figures. This crystal belongs to the tetrahedral pentagonal dodecahedral class (p. 21) for no planes of symmetry can be passed through these figures, which at the same time are planes of symmetry of the cube, as is the case with the crystal of halite. (See also p. 110.)

Summary.—The table below shows the important features of the forms of this class of symmetry.

Symmetry	Planes		Axes			Center
	Axial	Diagonal	■	▲	●	
	0	6	0	4 (Polar)	3	0

Forms	Symbols		Faces	Solid angles		
	Weiss	Miller		Trihedral	Tetrahedral	Hexahedral
Tetrahedrons	$\pm\ a:a:a$	$\{111\}$ $\{1\bar{1}1\}$	$\}4$	4	—	—
Tetragonal Tristetrahedrons	$\pm\ a:a:ma$	$\{hhl\}$ $\{h\bar{h}l\}$	$\}12$	4+4	6	—
Trigonal Tristetrahedrons	$\pm\ a:ma:ma$	$\{hll\}$ $\{h\bar{l}l\}$	$\}12$	4	—	4
Hextetrahedrons	$\pm\ a:na:ma$	$\{hkl\}$ $\{h\bar{k}l\}$	$\}24$	—	6	4 + 4
Dodecahedron	$a:a:\infty a$	$\{110\}$				
Tetrahexahedron	$a:ma:\infty a$	$\{hk0\}$	Morphologically the same as in the hexoctahedral class.			
Hexahedron	$a:\infty a:\infty a$	$\{100\}$				

Figures 99, 100, and 101 show three cubes representing crystals of fluorite (CaF_2) (Fig. 99), sphalerite (ZnS) (Fig. 100), and pyrite (FeS_2) (Fig. 101). From the character and position of the striations on the faces of these cubes, it is at once recognized that through Fig. 99, nine planes of symmetry may be passed, through Fig. 100

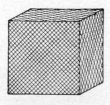

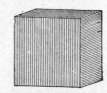

FIG. 99.   FIG. 100.   FIG. 101.

six, and through Fig. 101 only three. That is, the striations indicate clearly that fluorite has the symmetry of the hexoctahedral class, sphalerite of the hextetrahedral class, and pyrite of the dyakisdodecahedral class.

Combinations.—Some of the more common combinations are illustrated by the following figures:

Fig. 102.   Fig. 103.   Fig. 104.

Figure 102, $o = (a : a : a)$, $\{111\}$; $o' = -(a : a : a)$, $\{1\bar{1}1\}$. This combination is common on sphalerite (ZnS).

Figure 103, $h = (a : \infty a : \infty a)$, $\{100\}$; $o = (a : a : a)$, $\{111\}$. Observed on sphalerite (ZnS) and tetrahedrite (Cu_3SbS_3).

Figure 104, $o = (a : a : a)$, $\{111\}$; $h = (a : \infty a : \infty a)$, $\{100\}$. Observed on boracite ($Mg_7Cl_2B_{16}O_{30}$) and tetrahedrite (Cu_3SbS_3).

Fig. 105.   Fig. 106.   Fig. 107.

Figures 105, 106, and 107, $o = (a : a : a)$, $\{111\}$; $i = (a : 2a : 2a)$, $\{211\}$; $d = (a : a : \infty a)$, $\{110\}$. Frequently on tetrahedrite (Cu_3SbS_3).

DYAKISDODECAHEDRAL CLASS

Elements of Symmetry.—The elements of symmetry of this class consist of three axial planes, three twofold and four threefold axes, and the center of symmetry. The crystallographic axes possess twofold symmetry. Figure 108 shows the symmetry relations. The faces of the *positive* forms of this class are located in the unshaded sections, those of the *negative* forms in the shaded ones.

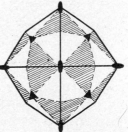

Fig. 108.

There are two new forms in this class which differ morphologically from those thus far considered, namely, the pyritohedrons and dyakisdodecahedrons.

Pyritohedrons.—The symbols of these forms are analogous to those of the tetrahexahedron (page 25), namely, $\pm(a : ma : \infty a)$, or $\{hk0\}$ and

$\{kh0\}$, two axes being cut at unequal distances. There are two congruent forms possible, Fig. 110, *positive*, and Fig. 109, *negative*.

Each form is bounded by 12 similar faces. The faces are unequilateral pentagons, four sides of which are equal. The crystallographic axes possess twofold symmetry and bisect the six long edges. The threefold axes pass through the trihedral angles, the edges of which are of

Fig. 109.　　　　　　　　　　Fig. 110.

equal lengths. The three planes of symmetry pass through the long edges. These forms are termed *pyritohedrons* because they are very frequently observed upon the very common mineral pyrite (FeS_2). They are also designated as *pentagonal dodecahedrons*.[1]

Dyakisdodecahedrons.—These are congruent forms bounded by 24 similar trapeziums. They possess symbols corresponding to the hexoctahedron, namely, $\pm(a : na : ma)$ or $\{hkl\}$ and $\{hlk\}$, and they

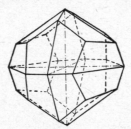

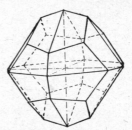

Fig. 111.　　　　　　　　　　Fig. 112.

are sometimes termed *didodecahedrons* or *diploids*. Figure 112 shows a *positive* and Fig. 111 a *negative* form. The crystallographic axes pass through the six tetrahedral angles possessing two pairs of equal edges. The threefold axes join opposite trihedral angles. The three planes of symmetry pass through the continuous edges.

Other Forms.—The hexahedron, octahedron, dodecahedron, trigonal trisoctahedron, and tetragonal trisoctahedron occur in this class, each

---

[1] The regular pentagonal dodecahedron of geometry, bounded by equilateral pentagons intersecting in equal edges and angles, is crystallographically an impossible form, the value of m being $\dfrac{1 + \sqrt{5}}{2}$, which is irrational.

with the same morphological development as in the hexoctahedral class. They, however, possess a lower grade of symmetry. If they occur independently, the lower grade of symmetry may be recognized by etch figures or peculiar physical characteristics of the faces (see page 31).

Summary.—In the following table, the important features of the various forms of this class are given.

Symmetry	Planes		Axes			Center
	Axial	Diagonal	■	▲	●	
	3	0	0	4	3	1

Forms	Symbols		Faces	Solid angles			
				Trihedral		Tetrahedral	
	Weiss	Miller		3 Equal Edges	2 + 1 Edges	2 + 2 Edges	2 + 1 + 1 Edges
Pyritohedrons	$\pm a : ma : \infty a$	$\{hk0\}$ $\{kh0\}$	} 12	8	12	—	—
Dyakisdodecahedrons	$\pm a : na : ma$	$\{hkl\}$ $\{hlk\}$	} 24	8	–	6	12
Octahedron	$a : a : a$	$\{111\}$					
Dodecahedron	$a : a : \infty a$	$\{110\}$					
Hexahedron	$a : \infty a : \infty a$	$\{100\}$	Morphologically the same as in the hexoctahedral class.				
Trigonal Trisoctahedron	$a : a : ma$	$\{hhl\}$					
Tetragonal Trisoctahedron	$a : ma : ma$	$\{hll\}$					

Combinations.—The accompanying figures show some combinations of the forms of this class.

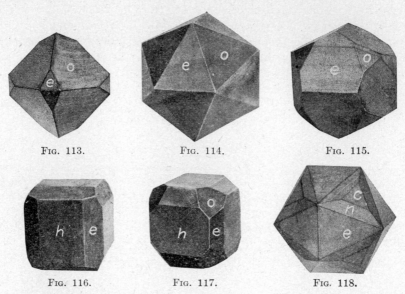

FIG. 113.   FIG. 114.   FIG. 115.

FIG. 116.   FIG. 117.   FIG. 118.

Figures 113 to 118, $o = (a : a : a)$, $\{111\}$; $e = (a : 2a : \infty a)$, $\{210\}$; $h = (a : \infty a : \infty a)$, $\{100\}$; $n = (a : \frac{3}{2}a : 3a)$, $\{321\}$. These combinations are frequently observed on pyrite (FeS_2).

CHAPTER IV

HEXAGONAL SYSTEM

Crystallographic Axes.—This system includes all crystals which can be referred to four axes, three of which are equal and lie in a horizontal plane, and intersect each other at an angle of 60°. These are termed the *lateral* axes, being designated by the letter a. These axes are interchangeable. The fourth or *principal* axis is perpendicular to the plane of the lateral axes and is called the c axis. It may be longer or shorter than the lateral axes. The three equal axes, which bisect the angles between the lateral axes, are the *intermediate* axes. These may be designated by b. Figure 119 shows an axial cross of this system.

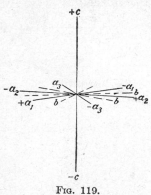

Fig. 119.

In reading crystals of the hexagonal system, it is customary to hold the c axis vertically, letting one of the lateral or a axes extend from right to left. The extremities of the lateral axes are alternately designated as plus and minus, see Fig. 119. In referring a form to the crystallographic axes, it is common practice to consider them in the following order: a_1 first, then a_2, thirdly a_3, and lastly the c axis. The symbols always refer to them in this order. It is also to be noted that in following this order at least one of the lateral axes will always be preceded by a minus sign.

Since the lengths of the a and c axes differ, it is necessary to assume for each substance crystallizing in this system a fundamental form, whose intercepts are taken as representing the unit lengths of the lateral and principal axes, respectively. The ratio which exists between the lengths of these axes is called the *axial* ratio and is always an irrational value, the a axis being assumed as unity (page 13).

Classes of Symmetry.—The hexagonal system includes a larger number of classes of symmetry than any other system, namely, 12. Beginning with the class of highest symmetry, they are
  * 1. Dihexagonal bipyramidal class.
  * 2. Dihexagonal pyramidal class.
  † 3. Ditrigonal bipyramidal class.
  †* 4. Ditrigonal scalenohedral class.
  * 5. Hexagonal bipyramidal class.

37

    6. Hexagonal trapezohedral class.

†* 7. Ditrigonal pyramidal class.

    8. Hexagonal pyramidal class.

†   9. Trigonal bipyramidal class.

†*10. Trigonal trapezohedral class.

†*11. Trigonal rhombohedral class.

† 12. Trigonal pyramidal class.

Those classes marked with an * are the most important, for nearly all of the crystals of this system belong to some one of them. Those marked † are often grouped together and form the *trigonal* system. Only classes 1, 4, 5, 7, and 10 will be discussed in detail. A fairly comprehensive idea of the hexagonal system, amply sufficient for beginning students, may be obtained from a consideration of classes 1 and 4.

DIHEXAGONAL BIPYRAMIDAL CLASS

Symmetry.—This class possesses the highest grade of symmetry of any in the hexagonal system.

    a. Planes.—In all there are seven planes of symmetry. One of these, the *horizontal axial* or *principal* (h) plane, is the plane of the horizontal

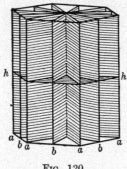

Fig. 120.

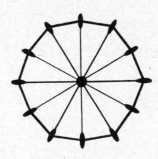

Fig. 121.

axes. The other planes are vertical and are divided into two series of three each, which are termed the *vertical axial* (a) and the *intermediate* (b), respectively. They intersect at angles of 60°. The intermediate planes bisect the angles between the vertical axial planes.

    The four axial planes divide space into 12 equal parts, called *dodecants;* the seven planes, however, into 24 parts (Fig. 120).

    These planes are often designated as follows:

1 horizontal axial + 3 vertical axial + 3 vertical intermediate =
                                     7 planes.

    b. Axes.—The c axis is an axis of sixfold symmetry, while the lateral and intermediate axes possess twofold symmetry. These axes are often indicated, thus,

$$1 \; \bullet \; + 3 \; \bullet \; + 3 \; \bullet \; = 7 \text{ axes.}$$

c. Center.—This element of symmetry is also present, requiring every face to have a parallel counterface. Figure 121, the projection of the most complicated form upon a plane perpendicular to the vertical axis, shows the elements of symmetry of this class.

Hexagonal Bipyramid of the First Order.—From Fig. 122, it is obvious that any plane which cuts any two adjacent lateral axes at the unit distance from the center must extend parallel to the third. If such a plane be assumed to cut the *c* axis at its unit length from the center, the parametral ratio would then be

$$a_1 : \infty a_2 : a_3 : c.$$

According to the above elements of symmetry, 12 planes possessing this ratio are possible. They enclose space and give rise to the form termed the *hexagonal bipyramid*[1] *of the first order* (Figs. 122 and 123). In

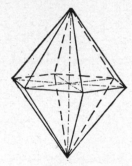

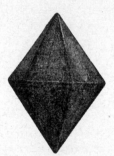

FIG. 122.   FIG. 123.

the ideal form, the faces are all equal isosceles triangles. The symbols are $(a : \infty a : a : c)$, $\{10\bar{1}1\}$.[2] Because the intercepts along the *c* and two lateral axes are taken as units, such bipyramids are also known as *fundamental* or *unit* bipyramids (page 12).

Planes are possible, however, which cut the two lateral axes at the unit distances but intercept the *c* axis at the distance *mc*, the coefficient *m* being some rational value smaller or greater than one (page 14). Such bipyramids, according as *m* is greater or less than unity, are more acute or obtuse than the fundamental form. They are termed *modified* hexagonal bipyramids of the first order. Their symbols are

$$(a : \infty a : a : mc) \text{ or } \{h0\bar{h}l\}, \text{ where } m = \frac{h}{l}, \text{ also } 0 < m < \infty.$$

The principal axis passes through the hexahedral angles, the lateral axes join tetrahedral angles, while the intermediate axes bisect the hori-

[1] Since these are really double pyramids, the term *bipyramid* is employed.

[2] In this system it is advantageous to employ the indices as modified by Bravais ($hk\bar{\imath}l$) rather than those of Miller, who uses but three.

zontal edges. Hence, when such bipyramids are held correctly, a face is directed toward the observer. The various elements of symmetry are located by means of these axes.

Hexagonal Bipyramid of the Second Order.—In form this bipyramid is similar to the preceding. It is, however, to be distinguished by its

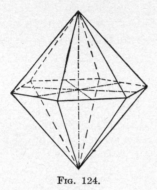

Fig. 124.

Fig. 125.

position with respect to the lateral axes. The bipyramid of the second order is so held that an edge, and not a face, is directed toward the observer. This means that the lateral axes are perpendicular to and bisect the horizontal edges as shown in Figs. 124 and 125. Figure 126 shows the cross section including the lateral and intermediate axes. From these figures it is obvious that each face cuts one of the lateral axes at a

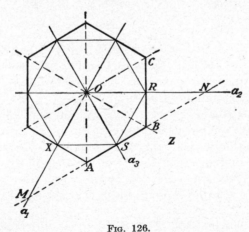

Fig. 126.

unit distance, the other two at greater but equal distances. For example, AB cuts a_3 at the unit distance OS, and a_1 and a_2 at greater but equal distances, OM and ON, respectively.

The following considerations will determine the length of OM and ON, the intercepts on a_1 and a_2, in terms of $OS = 1$.

As already indicated, the lateral axes are perpendicular to the horizontal edges, hence OS and ON are perpendicular to AB and BC, respectively. Therefore, in the right triangles ORB and NRB, the side RB is common and the angles OBR and NBR are equal.[1]

Therefore, $OR = RN$. But $OR = OS = 1$.

Hence, $ON = OR + RN = 2$.

In the same manner it can be shown that the intercept on a_1 is equal to that along a_2, that is, twice the unit length. The parametral ratio of the hexagonal bipyramid of the second order, therefore, is $(2a : 2a : a : mc)$ or $\{hh\overline{2h}l\}$, where $\dfrac{2h}{l} = m$. Figure 126 shows the positions of the bipyramids of both orders with respect to the lateral axes,

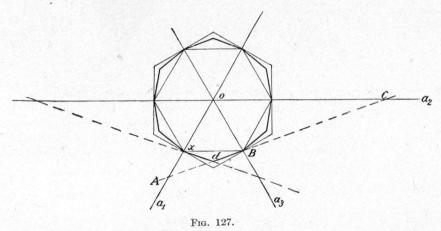

Fig. 127.

the inner hexagonal outline representing that of the first, the outer outline the one of the second order.

Dihexagonal Bipyramid.—The faces of this form cut the three lateral axes at unequal distances. For example, in Fig. 127 the face represented by dB cuts the a_1 axis at A, a_2 at C, and a_3 at B. Assuming the shortest of these intercepts as unity, $OB = a = 1$, we at once see that one of these axes is cut at a unit's distance from O, the other two, however, at greater distances. If we let the intercepts OA and OC be represented by $n(OB) = na$, and $p(OB) = pa$, respectively, the ratio will read

$$(na : pa : a : mc), \{hk\overline{\imath}l\}.$$

In this ratio $p = \dfrac{n}{n-1}$. Twenty-four planes having this ratio are possible and give rise to the form called the *dihexagonal bipyramid* (Figs. 128 and 129). In the ideal form the faces are equal scalene tri-

---

[1] Since angle ABC equals 120°, angle NBR is 60°, being the supplement of ABC. But the intermediate axis OZ bisects the angle ABC, hence angle OBR is also 60°.

angles cutting in 24 polar edges,[1] a and b, and in 12 equal basal[2] edges. The polar edges and angles are alternately equal. This is shown by Fig. 130, where the heavy inner outline represents the form of the first order, the outer the one of the second, and the intermediate outlines the dihexagonal type, with respect to the lateral axes.

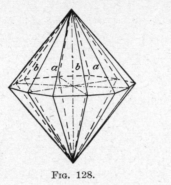

FIG. 128.

FIG. 129.

These three hexagonal bipyramids are closely related, for, if we suppose the plane represented by AB (Fig. 130) to be rotated about the point B so that the intercept along a_2 increases in length, the one along a_1 decreases until it equals $oB' = oB = 1$. Then the plane is parallel to a_2, and the ratio for the bipyramid of the first order results.

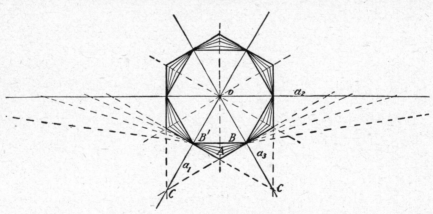

FIG. 130.

If, however, AB is rotated so that the intercept along a_2 is decreased in length, the one along a_1 increases until it equals $oC = 2oB' = 2a$. When this is the case, the intercept on a_2 is also equal to $2a$, for then the plane is perpendicular to a_3. This gives rise to the ratio of the bipyramid of the second order.

[1] Those joining the horizontal and principal axes.
[2] These lie in the horizontal plane of symmetry.

That the bipyramids of the first and second orders are the limiting forms of the dihexagonal bipyramid is also shown by the fact that $p = \dfrac{n}{n-1}$. For, if $n = 1$, it follows that $p = \infty$, which gives the ratio of the form of the first order. But, when $n = 2$, $p = 2$ also, therefore the ratio for the second order results. With dihexagonal bipyramids the following holds good:

$$1 < n < 2 \text{ and } 2 < p < \infty.$$

The dihexagonal bipyramid whose polar edges and angles are all equal is crystallographically not a possible form, because the value of n would then be $\frac{1}{2}(1 + \sqrt{3}) = \sqrt{2} \sin 75° = 1.36603+$, which of course is irrational. It also follows that in those dihexagonal bipyramids, where the value of n is less than $1.36603+$, for instance, $\frac{6}{5} = 1.20$, the more acute pole angles indicate the location of the lateral axes, the more obtuse that of the intermediate, and *vice versa*, when n is greater than $1.36603+$, for example, $\frac{8}{5} = 1.60$. This is clearly shown by Fig. 130.

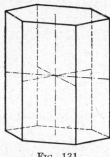 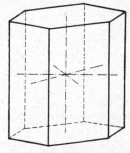

Fig. 131.   Fig. 132.

Hexagonal Prism of the First Order.—This form is easily derived from the bipyramid of the same order by allowing the intercepts along the c axis to assume their maximum value, infinity. Then the 12 planes of the bipyramid are reduced to six, each plane cutting two lateral axes at the unit distance and extending parallel to the c axis. The symbols are $(a : \infty a : a : \infty c)$ or $\{10\bar{1}0\}$. This form cannot enclose space and, hence, may be termed an *open form* (page 12). It cannot occur independently and is always to be observed in combination (Fig. 131). The lateral axes join opposite edges, that is, a face is directed towards the observer when properly held.

Hexagonal Prism of the Second Order.—This prism bears the same relation to the preceding form that the bipyramid of the second order does to the one of the first (page 40). The symbols are $(2a : 2a : a : \infty c)$ or $\{11\bar{2}0\}$. It is, hence, an open form consisting of six faces. The lateral axes join the centers of opposite faces, hence an edge is directed towards the observer (Fig. 132).

Dihexagonal Prism.—This form may be obtained from the corresponding bipyramid by increasing the value of m to infinity, which gives $(na : pa : a : \infty c)$ or $\{hk\bar{\imath}0\}$. This prism consists of 12 faces whose alternate edges and angles are equal. This form (Fig. 133) is closely related to the corresponding bipyramid, and, hence, all that has been said concerning the dihexagonal bipyramid (page 41) with respect to the location of the lateral axes and its limiting forms might be repeated here, substituting, of course, for the bipyramids of the first and second orders the corresponding prisms.

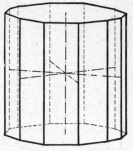

Fig. 133.

Hexagonal Basal Pinacoid.—The faces of this form are parallel to the horizontal plane of symmetry and possess the following symbols ($\infty a : \infty a : \infty a : c$), $\{0001\}$. It is evident from the presence of a center and a horizontal axial plane of symmetry that two such planes are possible. This, like the prisms, is an open form and must always occur in combination. Figure 131 shows this form in combination with the prism of the first order.

Summary.—The seven forms of this class and their principal features may be summarized as follows:

Symmetry	Planes			Axes			Center
	Horizontal	Vertical		Vertical	Horizontal		
	Axial	Axial	Intermediate	Axial	Axial	Intermediate	
	1	3	3	1	3	3	1

Forms	Symbols		Number of angles	Solid angles		
	Weiss	Miller-Bravais		Tetrahedral	Hexahedral	Dodecahedral
Unit Bipyramid—First order	$a: \infty a: a: c$	$\{10\bar{1}1\}$	12	6	2	—
Modified Bipyramids—First order	$a: \infty a: a: mc$	$\{h0\bar{h}l\}$	12	6	2	—
Bipyramids—Second order	$2a: 2a: a: mc$	$\{hh\overline{2h}l\}$	12	6	2	—
Dihexagonal Bipyramids	$na: pa: a: mc$	$\{hk\bar{\imath}l\}$	24	6+6	—	2
Prism—First order	$a: \infty a: a: \infty c$	$\{10\bar{1}0\}$	6	—	—	—
Prism—Second order	$2a: 2a: a: \infty c$	$\{11\bar{2}0\}$	6	—	—	—
Dihexagonal Prisms	$na: pa: a: \infty c$	$\{hk\bar{\imath}0\}$	12	—	—	—
Basal Pinacoid	$\infty a: \infty a: \infty a: c$	$\{0001\}$	2	—	—	—

Relationship of Forms.—The following diagram, similar to the one for the cubic system (page 27) expresses very clearly the relationship existing between the various forms:

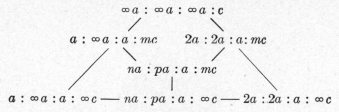

Combinations.—The following figures illustrate some of the combinations of forms of this class:

Figure 134, $p = (a : \infty a : a : c)$, $\{10\bar{1}1\}$; $n = (2a : 2a : a : c)$, $\{11\bar{2}2\}$.
Figure 135, $m = (a : \infty a : a : \infty c)$, $\{10\bar{1}0\}$; $p = (a : \infty a : a : c)$, $\{10\bar{1}1\}$.

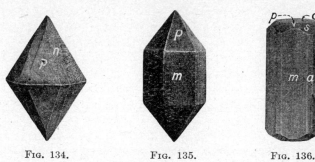

| Fig. 134. | Fig. 135. | Fig. 136. |

Figure 136, $m = (a : \infty a : a : \infty c)$, $\{10\bar{1}0\}$; $a = (2a : 2a : a : \infty c)$, $\{11\bar{2}0\}$; $p = (a : \infty a : a : c)$, $\{10\bar{1}1\}$; $s = (2a : 2a : a : 2c)$, $\{11\bar{2}1\}$; $c = (\infty a : \infty a : \infty a : c)$, $\{0001\}$. This combination is observed on beryl ($Be_3Al_2Si_6O_{18}$).

DITRIGONAL SCALENOHEDRAL CLASS

Symmetry.—The symmetry consists of three intermediate planes, three axes of twofold and one of threefold symmetry, and the center of symmetry. The twofold axes are the lateral crystallographic axes. The principal crystallographic, or c, axis possesses threefold symmetry. Figure 137 shows the distribution of these elements of symmetry. This class contains two forms which are morphologically new, rhombohedrons and scalenohedrons. The faces of the positive forms of this class are located in the unshaded sections (Fig. 137), those of the negative forms in the shaded ones.

Fig. 137.

Rhombohedrons.—These are bounded by six rhombic faces intersecting in eight trihedral angles. The c axis passes through the two equal trihedral angles which may be either larger or smaller than the other six, which among themselves are equal. This is illustrated by Figs. 138, 139, and 140. The size of these angles depends upon the value of the ratio $a : c$.[1] Positive (Figs. 139 and 140) and negative (Fig. 138) rhombo-

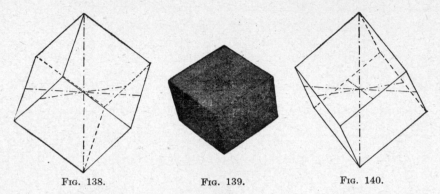

FIG. 138.　　　　　　　FIG. 139.　　　　　　　FIG. 140.

hedrons are possible. In the positive form, the upper dodecant to the front possesses a face; the negative dodecant an edge. The symbols are: $\pm(a : \infty a : a : mc)$, or $\{h0\bar{h}l\}$ and $\{0h\bar{h}l\}$. These ratios correspond to those of the hexagonal bipyramids of the first order (page 39).

The principal crystallographic axis passes through the two equal trihedral angles. The lateral axes bisect opposite lateral edges which form a zigzag line about the form. These axes possess threefold and

[1] The cube, when held so that one of its axes of threefold symmetry (p. 24) is vertical, may be considered as a rhombohedron whose edges and angles are equal. The ratio $a : c$ in this case would be $1 : \sqrt{1.5} = 1 : 1.2247+$. Those rhombohedrons,

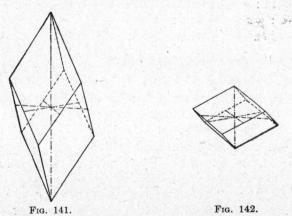

FIG. 141.　　　　　　　FIG. 142.

therefore, whose c axes have a greater value than $1.2247+$, have pole angles less than 90°. When, however, the value is less than $1.2247+$, the pole angles are then greater than 90°. Such rhombohedrons may, hence, be spoken of as *acute* and *obtuse*, respectively (Figs. 141 and 142).

twofold symmetry, respectively. The intermediate planes of symmetry bisect the various faces vertically.

Scalenohedrons.—These forms are bounded by 12 similar scalene triangles intersecting in six obtuse and six more acute polar edges, and in six zigzag lateral edges. The forms are congruent and hence may be positive (Figs. 144 and 145) or negative (Fig. 143) in character. As is the case with the rhombohedrons, obtuse and acute scalenohedrons are also possible, depending upon the value of $a : c$.

The symbols are $\pm (na : pa : a : mc)$, or $\{hk\bar{\imath}l\}$ and $\{kh\bar{\imath}l\}$. These symbols correspond to those of the dihexagonal bipyramids (page 41).

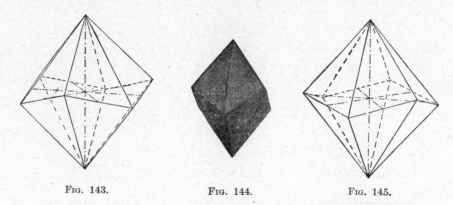

FIG. 143.   FIG. 144.   FIG. 145.

Scalenohedrons with 12 equal polar edges are crystallographically impossible as such forms would possess irrational coefficients.

The axis of threefold symmetry passes through the two hexahedral angles, while those of twofold symmetry bisect opposite zigzag lateral edges. The intermediate planes of symmetry pass through the polar edges.

Other Forms.—The other forms of this class are the hexagonal bipyramids of the second order, the hexagonal prisms of the first and second orders, the dihexagonal prism, and the basal pinacoid, all of which are exactly similar to those of the dihexagonal bipyramidal class.

Sym-metry	Planes			Axes			Center
	Horizontal	Vertical		Vertical	Horizontal		
	Axial	Axial	Intermediate	▲ Axial	● Axial	● Intermediate	
	0	0	3	1	3	0	1

Forms	Symbols		Faces	Solid angles		
	Weiss	Miller-Bravais		Trihedral	Tetrahedral	Hexahedral
Rhombohedrons	$\pm a : \infty a : a : mc$	$\{h0\bar{h}l\}$ $\{0h\bar{h}l\}$ $\}$ 6		$2 + 6$	—	—
Hexagonal Bipyramids Second order	$2a : 2a : a : mc$	$\{hh\overline{2h}l\}$	Morphologically the same as in the dihexagonal bipyramidal class.			
Scalenohedrons	$\pm na : pa : a : mc$	$\{hk\bar{\imath}l\}$ $\{kh\bar{\imath}l\}$ $\}$ 12		—	6	2
Hexagonal Prism First order	$a : \infty a : a : \infty c$	$\{h0\bar{h}0\}$	Morphologically the same as in the dihexagonal bipyramidal class.			
Hexagonal Prism Second order	$2a : 2a : a : \infty c$	$\{11\bar{2}0\}$				
Dihexagonal Prisms	$na : pa : a : \infty c$	$\{hk\bar{\imath}0\}$				
Basal Pinacoid	$\infty a : \infty a : \infty a : c$	$\{0001\}$				

Combinations.—Many important minerals crystallize in this class, for example—calcite, hematite, corundum, and chabazite.

Fɪɢ. 146.   Fɪɢ. 147.   Fɪɢ. 148.

Figures 146 to 149, $m = (a : \infty a : a : \infty c)$, $\{10\bar{1}0\}$; $e = -(a : \infty a : a : \frac{1}{2}c)$, $\{01\bar{1}2\}$; $v = (\frac{3}{2}a : 3a : a : 3c)$, $\{21\bar{3}1\}$; $r = (a : \infty a : a : c)$, $\{10\bar{1}1\}$; $f = -(a : \infty a : a : 2c)$, $\{02\bar{2}1\}$. These combinations are frequently observed on calcite ($CaCO_3$).

Figures 150 and 151, $r = (a : \infty a : a : c)$, $\{10\bar{1}1\}$; $n = (2a : 2a : a : \frac{4}{3}c)$, $\{22\bar{4}3\}$; $u = (a : \infty a : a : \frac{1}{4}c)$, $\{10\bar{1}4\}$; $c = (\infty a : \infty a : \infty a : c)$, $\{0001\}$. Hematite (Fe_2O_3).

Figures 152 and 153, $a = (2a : 2a : a : \infty c)$, $\{11\overline{2}0\}$; $n = (2a : 2a : a : \frac{4}{3}c)$, $\{22\overline{4}3\}$; $r = (a : \infty a : a : c)$, $\{10\overline{1}1\}$; $c = (\infty a : \infty a : \infty a : c)$, $\{0001\}$.   Corundum (Al_2O_3).

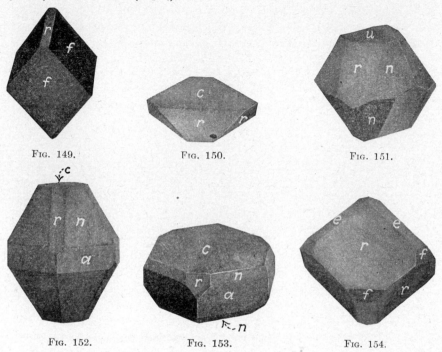

Fig. 149.   Fig. 150.   Fig. 151.

Fig. 152.   Fig. 153.   Fig. 154.

Figure 154, $r = (a : \infty a : a : c)$, $\{10\overline{1}1\}$; $e = -(a : \infty a : a : \frac{1}{2}c)$, $\{01\overline{1}2\}$; $f = -(a : \infty a : a : 2c)$, $\{02\overline{2}1\}$.   Chabazite $(CaAl_2Si_6O_{16}.8H_2O)$.

HEXAGONAL BIPYRAMIDAL CLASS

Symmetry.—Crystals of this class possess the horizontal axial or principal plane, the sixfold axis, and the center of symmetry.   The

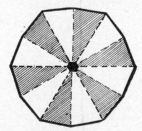

Fig. 155.

sixfold axis is obviously the vertical or c axis.   Figure 155 shows the relation of these elements of symmetry.   The faces of the positive forms of this class are located in the unshaded sections, those of the negative forms in shaded ones. This class contains two forms which are new, namely, the hexagonal bipyramids and prisms of the third order.

Hexagonal Bipyramids of the Third Order.—These bipyramids are analogous to those of the first and second orders but differ from them with respect to their orientation. Their symbols correspond to those of the dihexagonal bipyramids (page 41), namely: $\pm(na : pa : a : mc)$

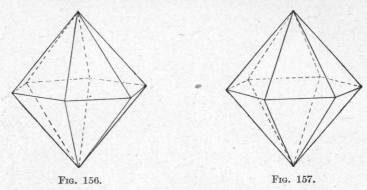

FIG. 156.   FIG. 157.

or $\{hk\bar{\imath}l\}$ and $\{kh\bar{\imath}l\}$ (Figs. 156 and 157). They are bounded by 12 equal isosceles triangles.

The axis of sixfold symmetry passes through the hexahedral angles. The positions of the lateral crystallographic axes are shown in Figs. 158 and 159. These axes do not pass through the tetrahedral angles or the centers of the basal edges, as is the case with the forms of the first and

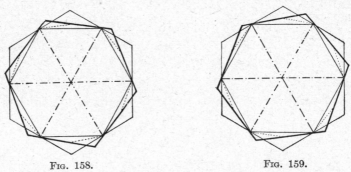

FIG. 158.   FIG. 159.

second orders, respectively, but through some point between them depending upon the value of n (compare Figs. 122 and 124).

Hexagonal Prisms of the Third Order.—These forms bear the same relation to those of the first and second orders as do the hexagonal bipyramids of the third order to the bipyramids of the other two orders. These prisms consist of two forms of six planes each, designated as positive (Fig. 161) and negative (Fig. 160). Figures 158 and 159 show the relation of these forms to the other hexagonal prisms. Their symbols correspond to those of the dihexagonal prisms (page 44) and are $\pm(na : pa : a : \infty c)$ or $\{hk\bar{\imath}0\}$ and $\{kh\bar{\imath}0\}$.

The axis of sixfold symmetry is parallel to the vertical edges.

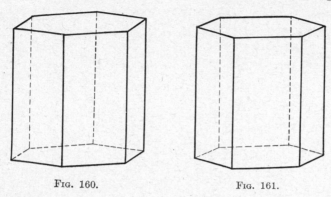

FIG. 160.   FIG. 161.

Other Forms.—The other forms of this class are the hexagonal bipyramids and prisms of the first and second orders and the basal pinacoid. They correspond to the analogous forms of the dihexagonal bipyramidal class.

Summary.—The principal features of this class have been summarized in the following table:

Symmetry	Planes			Axes			Center
	Horizontal	Vertical		Vertical	Horizontal		
	Axial	Axial	Intermediate	Axial	Axial	Intermediate	
	1	0	0	1	0	0	1

Forms	Symbols		Faces	Angles	
	Weiss	Miller-Bravais		Tetrahedral	Hexahedral
Hexagonal Bipyramids First order	$a : \infty a : a : mc$	$\{h0\bar{h}l\}$	Morphologically like those in di-hexagonal bipyramidal class.		
Hexagonal Bipyramids Second order	$2a : 2a : a : mc$	$\{hh\overline{2h}l\}$			
Hexagonal Bipyramids Third order	$\pm na : pa : a : mc$	$\{hk\bar{\imath}l\}$ $\{kh\bar{\imath}l\}$	12	6	2
Hexagonal Prism First order	$a : \infty a : a : \infty c$	$\{h0\bar{h}0\}$	Morphologically like those in di-hexagonal bipyramidal class.		
Hexagonal Prism Second order	$2a : 2a : a : \infty c$	$\{11\bar{2}0\}$			
Hexagonal Prisms Third order	$\pm na : pa : a : \infty c$	$\{hk\bar{\imath}0\}$ $\{kh\bar{\imath}0\}$	6	—	—
Basal Pinacoid	$\infty a : \infty a : \infty a : c$	$\{0001\}$	Morphologically like those in di-hexagonal bipyramidal class.		

Combinations.—Figures 162 and 163, $m = (a : \infty a : a : \infty c)$, $\{10\bar{1}0\}$; $a = (2a : 2a : a : \infty c)$, $\{11\bar{2}0\}$; $p = (a : \infty a : a : c)$, $\{10\bar{1}1\}$;

FIG. 162.

FIG. 163.

$y = (a : \infty a : a : 2c)$, $\{20\bar{2}1\}$; $r = (a : \infty a : a : 1/2c)$ $\{10\bar{1}2\}$; $s = (2a : 2a : a : 2c)$, $\{11\bar{2}1\}$; $\mu = (3/2a : 3a : a : 3c)$, $\{21\bar{3}1\}$; $c = (\infty a : \infty a : \infty a : c)$, $\{0001\}$. These combinations have been observed on apatite $(Ca_5F(PO_4)_3)$.

DITRIGONAL PYRAMIDAL CLASS

Symmetry.—There are three intermediate planes and one axis of threefold symmetry in this class. The axis of symmetry is the c axis and has a polar development. The forms of this class, therefore, show a *hemimorphic* development, that is, the upper and lower ends of the c axis do not have the same type of faces. The symmetry relations are shown in Fig. 164. The faces of the positive forms of this class are located in the unshaded sections, those of the negative forms in shaded ones. The following forms are morphologically different from those previously described, namely, the trigonal pyramids and prisms of the first order, and the ditrigonal pyramids and prisms.

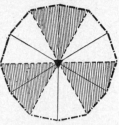

Fig. 164.

Since the c axis has a polar development, all forms cutting it will occur as upper and lower forms. Thus, instead of having bipyramids, as discussed thus far, we now have upper and lower pyramids.

Trigonal Pyramids of the First Order.—These are bounded by three equal isosceles triangles. They are open forms and may occur in four distinct positions designated as

Positive upper, $+u(a : \infty a : a : mc)$, $\{h0\bar{h}l\}$ (Fig. 167)
Positive lower, $+l(a : \infty a : a : mc)$, $\{h0\bar{h}\bar{l}\}$ (Fig. 168)
Negative upper, $-u(a : \infty a : a : mc)$, $\{0h\bar{h}l\}$ (Fig. 165)
Negative lower, $-l(a : \infty a : a : mc)$, $\{0h\bar{h}\bar{l}\}$ (Fig. 166)

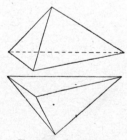

Figs. 165 and 166.

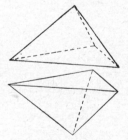

Figs. 167 and 168.

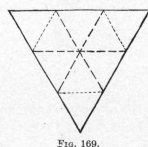

Fig. 169.

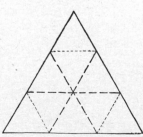

Fig. 170.

These symbols correspond to those of the hexagonal bipyramids of the first order (page 39). The axis of threefold symmetry passes through the trihedral angle with equal edges, and the intermediate planes of symmetry bisect the faces.

Trigonal Prisms of the First Order.—These prisms possess three faces and occur in positive (Fig. 172) and negative (Fig. 171) forms.

The symbols are

$$\pm(a : \infty a : a : \infty c), \text{ or } \{h0\bar{h}0\} \text{ and } \{0h\bar{h}0\}.$$

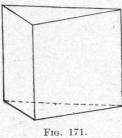

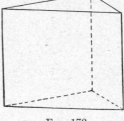

Fig. 171.   Fig. 172.

The threefold axis is parallel to the intersection lines of the prism faces, and the intermediate planes of symmetry pass through the vertical edges and bisect the opposite faces. Figures 169 and 170 show the positions of the various trigonal pyramids and prisms with respect to the crystallographic a axes.

Ditrigonal Pyramids.—These pyramids are also open forms and are bounded by six scalene triangles. Four distinct positions are possible.

Their symbols are

Positive upper, $+u(na : pa : a : mc)$, $\{hk\bar{\imath}l\}$ (Fig. 175)
Positive lower, $+ l(na : pa : a : mc)$, $\{hk\bar{\imath}\bar{l}\}$ (Fig. 176)
Negative upper, $-u(na : pa : a : mc)$, $\{kh\bar{\imath}l\}$ (Fig. 173)
Negative lower, $- l(na : pa : a : mc)$, $\{kh\bar{\imath}\bar{l}\}$ (Fig. 174)

The threefold axis passes through the hexahedral angles, and the intermediate planes of symmetry include an obtuse and an acute edge.

Ditrigonal Prisms.—These prisms are bounded by six faces intersecting in edges which are alternately alike. Positive (Fig. 180) and negative (Fig. 179) forms are possible.

The symbols are

$$\pm(na : pa : a : \infty c), \text{ or } \{hk\bar{\imath}0\} \text{ and } \{kh\bar{\imath}0\}.$$

The threefold axis is parallel to the intersection lines of the prism faces, and the intermediate planes of symmetry join opposite edges of unequal character. Figures 177 and 178 indicate the position of the ditrigonal pyramids and prisms with respect to the a axes.

Basal Pinacoids.—On account of the fact that the c axis has a polar development, the basal pinacoids occur with but one face (Figs. 165 to

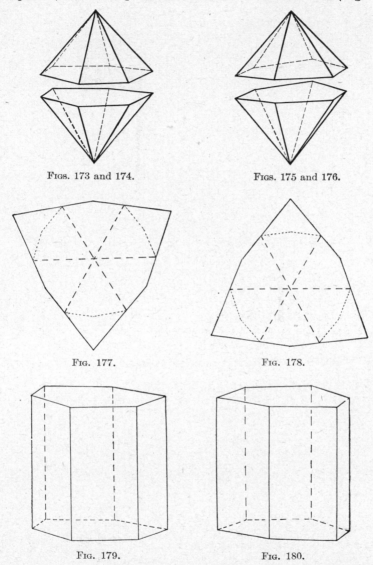

FIGS. 173 and 174.   FIGS. 175 and 176.

FIG. 177.   FIG. 178.

FIG. 179.   FIG. 180.

168). We may therefore speak of an upper and a lower basal pinacoid. The symbols are

$$u, l \ (\infty a : \ \infty a : \ \infty a : c), \text{ or } \{0001\} \text{ and } \{000\overline{1}\}.$$

Hexagonal Pyramids of the Second Order.—These forms are the upper and lower portions, respectively, of the hexagonal bipyramid of the second order described on page 40.

The symbols are

$$u, l\ (2a : 2a : a : mc),\ \text{or}\ \{hh\overline{2hl}\}\ \text{and}\ \{hh\overline{2h}\overline{l}\}.$$

Hexagonal Prisms of the Second Order.—This form is identical morphologically with that described on page 43.

Summary.—The following table shows the principal features of the forms of this class:

Symmetry	Planes			Axes			Center
	Horizontal	Vertical		Vertical	Horizontal		
	Axial	Axial	Intermediate	▲ Axial	● Axial	● Intermediate	
	0	0	3	1 (Polar)	0	0	0

Forms	Symbols		Number of faces	Solid angles	
	Weiss	Miller-Bravais		Trihedral	Hexahedral
Trigonal Pyramids First order	$\pm u, \pm l, a : \infty a : a : mc$	$\{h0\bar{h}l\}$ $\{h0\bar{h}\bar{l}\}$ $\{0h\bar{h}l\}$ $\{0h\bar{h}\bar{l}\}$	3	1	—
Hexagonal Pyramids Second order	$u, l, 2a : 2a : a : mc$	$\{hh\overline{2hl}\}$ $\{hh\overline{2h}\bar{l}\}$	6	—	1
Ditrigonal Pyramids	$\pm u, \pm l, na : pa : a : mc$	$\{hk\bar{\imath}l\}$ $\{hk\bar{\imath}\bar{l}\}$ $\{kh\bar{\imath}l\}$ $\{kh\bar{\imath}\bar{l}\}$	6	—	1
Trigonal Prisms	$\pm a : \infty a : a : \infty c$	$\{h0\bar{h}0\}$ $\{0h\bar{h}0\}$	8	—	—
Ditrigonal Prisms	$\pm na : pa : a : mc$	$\{hk\bar{\imath}0\}$ $\{kh\bar{\imath}0\}$	6	—	—
Hexagonal Prism Second order	$2a : 2a : a : \infty c$	$\{hh\overline{2h}0\}$	Morphologically like those in dihexagonal bipyramidal class.		
Basal Pinacoids	$u, l, \infty a : \infty a : \infty a : c$	$\{0001\}$ $\{000\bar{1}\}$	1	—	—

Combinations.—The mineral tourmaline furnishes excellent combinations of the above forms.

Fig. 181.　　　　　　　　Fig. 182.

In the accompanying Figs. 181 and 182, $m = +(a : \infty a : a : \infty c)$, $\{10\overline{1}0\}$;　$a = (2a : 2a : a : \infty c)$,　$\{11\overline{2}0\}$;　$u = +u(\tfrac{5}{3}a : \tfrac{5}{2}a : a : 5c)$, $\{32\overline{5}1\}$;　$o = -u(a : \infty a : a : 2c)$,　$\{02\overline{2}1\}$;　$o' = +l(a : \infty a : a : 2c)$, $\{20\overline{2}1\}$; $r = -l(a : \infty a : a : c)$, $\{01\overline{11}\}$; $c = l(\infty a : \infty a : \infty a : c)$, $\{000\overline{1}\}$.

TRIGONAL TRAPEZOHEDRAL CLASS

Symmetry.　The c axis possesses threefold symmetry, while the lateral or a axes have twofold symmetry with a polar development.　The symmetry relations are given in Fig. 183.

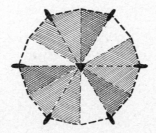

Fig. 183.

The trigonal trapezohedrons are the characterizing forms of this class.

Rhombohedrons of the First Order.—These are identical morphologically with those of the ditrigonal scalenohedral class.

Their symbols are

$$\pm(a : \infty a : a : mc), \text{ or } \{h0\overline{h}l\} \text{ and } \{0h\overline{h}l\}.$$

Trigonal Bipyramids of the Second Order.—These forms are bounded by six equal isosceles triangles and possess the following symbols:

$$\pm(2a : 2a : a : mc), \text{ or } \{hh\overline{2h}l\} \text{ and } \{2h\overline{h}\overline{h}l\}.$$

The crystallographic *a* axes pass from a tetrahedral angle to the center of the opposite horizontal edge.

Trigonal Trapezehedrons.—There are four forms of this type possible. Each is bounded by six faces, which when the development is

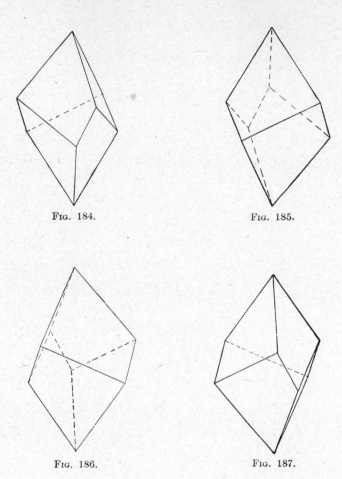

FIG. 184.   FIG. 185.

FIG. 186.   FIG. 187.

ideal are equal trapeziums. The symbols are analogous to those of the dihexagonal bipyramids, namely,

1. Positive right, $+r(na : pa : a : mc)$, $\{hk\bar{\imath}l\}$ (Fig. 185)
2. Positive left, $+l(na : pa : a : mc)$, $\{i\bar{k}\bar{h}l\}$ (Fig. 184)
3. Negative right, $-r(na : pa : a : mc)$, $\{kh\bar{\imath}l\}$ (Fig. 187)
4. Negative left, $-l(na : pa : a : mc)$, $\{i\bar{h}\bar{k}l\}$ (Fig. 186)

Forms 1 and 2, 3 and 4 are among themselves enantiomorphous, while 1 and 3, 2 and 4 are congruent.

The polar axes of twofold symmetry bisect opposite zigzag edges.

Trigonal Prisms of the Second Order.—These possess three vertical planes and have the following symbols:

$$\pm(2a : 2a : a : \infty c), \text{ or } \{hh\overline{2h}0\} \text{ and } \{2h\bar{h}\bar{h}0\}.$$

The axes of twofold symmetry pass through a vertical edge and bisect the opposite face.

Ditrigonal Prisms.—Two forms of this type are possible and are designated as positive (Fig. 189) and negative (Fig. 188) ditrigonal prisms. The vertical edges are alternately alike.

The symbols are

$$\pm(na : pa : a : \infty c), \text{ or } \{hk\bar{i}0\} \text{ and } \{i\bar{k}\bar{h}0\}$$

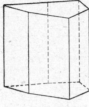
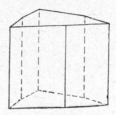

Fig. 188.   Fig. 189.

Other Forms.—The hexagonal prism of the first order and the basal pinacoid are analogous to those described on pages 43 and 44.

Summary.—The important features of this class are given in the table on page 60.

Fig. 190.   Fig. 191.

Combinations.—Quartz (SiO_2), (the *alpha* or *low-temperature* modification, see page 268) and cinnabar (HgS) furnish excellent examples of minerals crystallizing in this class.

Figures 190 and 191. $m = (a : \infty a : a : \infty c)$, $\{10\bar{1}0\}$; $r = +(a : \infty a : a : c)$, $\{10\bar{1}1\}$; $z = -(a : \infty a : a : c)$, $\{01\bar{1}1\}$;

Symmetry	Planes			Axes			Center
	Horizontal	Vertical		Vertical	Horizontal		
	Axial	Axial	Intermediate	▲ Axial	● Axial	● Intermediate	
	0	0	0	1	3 (Polar)	0	0

Forms	Symbols		Faces	Solid angles	
	Weiss	Miller-Bravais		Trihedral	Tetra-hedral
Rhombohedrons First order	$\pm a: \infty a: a: mc$	$\{h0\bar{h}l\}$ $\{0h\bar{h}l\}$ ⎫⎬⎭ 6		Morphologically like those in the ditrigonal scalenohedral class.	
Trigonal Bipyramids Second order	$\pm 2a: 2a: a : mc$	$\{hh\overline{2h}l\}$ $\{2h\bar{h}\bar{h}l\}$ ⎫⎬ 6		2	3
Trigonal Trapezohedrons	$\pm r,\ \pm l,\ na: pa: a: mc$	$\{hk\bar{\imath}l\}$ $\{i\bar{k}\bar{h}l\}$ $\{kh\bar{\imath}l\}$ $\{i\bar{h}\bar{k}l\}$ ⎫⎬⎭ 6		2 + 6	
Hexagonal Prism First order	$a: \infty a: a: \infty c$	$\{h0\bar{h}0\}$ 6		Morphologically like those in the dihexagonal bipyramidal class.	
Trigonal Prisms Second order	$\pm 2a: 2a: a: \infty c$	$\{hh\overline{2h}0\}$ $\{2h\bar{h}\bar{h}0\}$ ⎫⎬ 3			
Ditrigonal Prisms	$\pm na: pa: a: \infty c$	$\{hk\bar{\imath}0\}$ $\{i\bar{k}\bar{h}0\}$ ⎫⎬ 6			
Basal Pinacoid	$\infty a: \infty a: \infty a: c$	$\{0001\}$ 2		Morphologically like those in the dihexagonal bipyramidal class.	

s(Fig. 191) $= +(2a:2a:a:2c)$, $\{11\bar{2}1\}$; s(Fig. 190) $= -(2a:2a:a:2c)$, $\{2\bar{1}\bar{1}1\}$; x(Fig. 191) $= +r(\frac{6}{5}a:6a:a:6c)$, $\{51\bar{6}1\}$; x(Fig. 190) $= +l(\frac{6}{5}a:6a:a:6c)$, $\{6\bar{1}\bar{5}1\}$. Quartz.

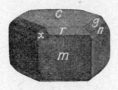

Fig. 192.   Fig. 193.

Figures 192 and 193. $c = (\infty a:\infty a:\infty a:c)$, $\{0001\}$; $m = (a:\infty a:a:\infty c)$, $\{10\bar{1}0\}$; $g = -(a:\infty a:a:\frac{1}{2}c)$, $\{01\bar{1}2\}$; $n = -(a:\infty a: a:2c)$, $\{02\bar{2}1\}$; $h = -(a:\infty a:a:\frac{2}{3}c)$, $\{02\bar{2}3\}$; $r = +(a:\infty a:a:c)$, $\{10\bar{1}1\}$; $r' = -(a:\infty a:a:c)$, $\{01\bar{1}1\}$; $y = +r(\frac{3}{2}a:3a:a:\frac{3}{7}c)$, $\{21\bar{3}7\}$; $x = +l(\frac{8}{5}a:\frac{8}{3}a:a:\frac{8}{5}c)$, $\{83\bar{5}5\}$. Cinnabar.

CHAPTER V

TETRAGONAL SYSTEM[1]

Crystallographic Axes.—The tetragonal system includes all crystals which can be referred to three perpendicular axes, two of which are equal and lie in a horizontal plane. These are termed the *lateral* axes and are designated as the *a* axes. Perpendicular to the plane of the lateral axes is the *principal* or *c* axis, which may be longer or shorter than the *a* axes. The axes, which bisect the angles between the *a* axes, are the *intermediate* axes. They are designated as the *b* axes in Fig. 194.

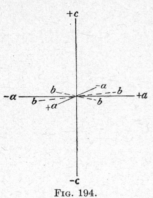

Fig. 194.

Crystals of this system are held so that the *c* axis is vertical, while one of the *a* axes is directed toward the observer.

Since the lengths of the *a* and *c* axes differ, it is necessary to know the ratio existing between these axes, that is, the axial ratio, as was the case in the hexagonal system (compare pages 13 and 37).

Classes of Symmetry.—This system embraces seven classes of symmetry, as follows:

1. Ditetragonal bipyramidal class.
2. Ditetragonal pyramidal class.
3. Tetragonal scalenohedral class.
4. Tetragonal bipyramidal class.
5. Tetragonal trapezohedral class.
6. Tetragonal pyramidal class.
7. Tetragonal bisphenoidal class.

Classes 1 and 3 are the most important and will be discussed in detail.

DITETRAGONAL BIPYRAMIDAL CLASS

Symmetry. *a. Planes.*—In this class there are five planes of symmetry. The plane of the lateral and intermediate axes is termed the *horizontal axial* or *principal* (*h*) plane. The vertical planes including the *c* axis and one of the *a* axes are called the *vertical axial* (*a*) planes, while

---

[1] Also termed *quadratic* or *pyramidal* system.

62

those which include one of the *b* axes are termed the *intermediate* (*b*) planes (Fig. 195).

The three axial planes divide space into eight equal parts, termed *octants,* while the five planes (Fig. 195) divide it into 16 equal sections. The five planes may be designated as follows:

1 horizontal axial + 2 vertical axial + 2 intermediate = 5 planes.

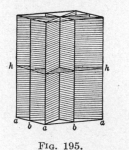

FIG. 195.

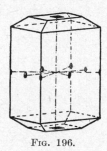

FIG. 196.

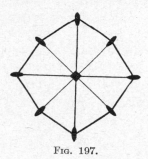

FIG. 197.

b. Axes.—The *c* axis is an axis of *fourfold* symmetry. The lateral and intermediate axes possess *twofold* symmetry (Fig. 196). These may be written: 1 ■ + 2 ● + 2 ● = 5 axes.

c. Center.—A center of symmetry is also present in this class. These elements of symmetry are shown in Fig. 197, which represents the projection of the most complex form upon the principal plane of symmetry.

Tetragonal Bipyramid of the First Order.—This form is analogous to the octahedron of the cubic system (page 23). But, since the *c* axis

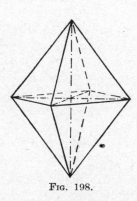

FIG. 198.

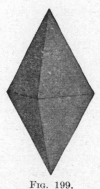

FIG. 199.

differs from the lateral axes, the ratio must be written (*a* : *a* : *c*), which would indicate the cutting of all three axes at unit distances[1] (Figs. 198 and 199). As the intercept along the *c* axis may be longer or shorter than the unit length, the general symbols would be (*a* : *a* : *mc*) or {*hhl*}, where *m* is some rational value between zero and infinity. Like the octa-

[1] Indicating a *unit* form (compare p. 12).

hedron, this form, the *tetragonal bipyramid*,[1] is bounded by eight faces which enclose space. The faces are equal isosceles triangles when the development is ideal.

The principal crystallographic axis passes through the two tetrahedral angles of the same size, the lateral axes through the other four equal tetrahedral angles, while the intermediate axes bisect the horizontal edges.

Tetragonal Bipyramid of the Second Order.—The faces of this form cut the c axis and one of the a axes but extend parallel to the other. The symbols are, therefore, $(a : \infty a : mc)$ or $\{h0l\}$. Eight faces are required to enclose space, and the form is termed the *bipyramid of the second order* (Figs. 200 and 201).

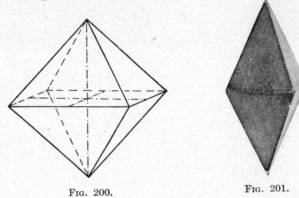

Fɪɢ. 200.　　　　　　　　Fɪɢ. 201.

This bipyramid is very similar to the preceding, but can be readily distinguished from it on account of its position with respect to the lateral axes. In this form, the lateral axes bisect the horizontal edges and the intermediate axes pass through the four equal tetrahedral angles. This is the opposite of what was noted with the bipyramid of the first order (compare Figs. 198 and 199). Hence, the bipyramid of the first order is always held so that an edge is directed toward the observer, whereas the bipyramid of the second order presents a face. In both bipyramids the principal axis passes through the two equal tetrahedral angles.

Ditetragonal Bipyramid.—The faces of this bipyramid cut the two lateral axes at different distances, while the intercept along the c axis may be unity or mc. Sixteen such faces are possible, and hence the term *ditetragonal bipyramid* is used (Figs. 202 and 203).[2]

The symbols are

$$(a : na : mc) \text{ or } \{hkl\}.$$

---

[1] The more the ratio $a : c$ approaches $1 : 1$, the more does this form simulate the octahedron. This tendency of forms to simulate those of a higher grade of symmetry is spoken of as *pseudosymmetry*.

[2] Compare Fig. 34 (p. 16).

Since the polar edges[1] are alternately similar, it follows that the faces are equal, similar scalene triangles. The ditetragonal bipyramid possessing equal polar edges is crystallographically an impossible form, for then the ratio $a : na : mc$ would necessitate a value for n equal to the tangent of 67° 30′, namely, the irrational value 2.4142+.[2]

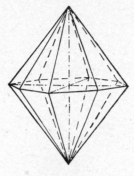

FIG. 202.   FIG. 203.

From the above it follows that, when n is less than 2.4142+, the ditetragonal bipyramid simulates the tetragonal bipyramid of the first order, and finally, when it equals 1, it passes over into that form. On the other hand, if n is greater than 2.4142+, it approaches more the bipyramid of the second order, and when it is equal to infinity passes over into that form. Hence, $1 < n < \infty$. Figure 204 illustrates this clearly.

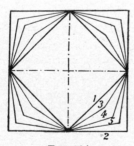

FIG. 204.   FIG. 205.

It is also to be noted that, when n is less than 2.4142+, the lateral axes pass through the more acute angles, whereas, where n is greater than 2.4142+, they join the more obtuse. Outline 1 represents the cross section of the tetragonal bipyramid of the first order, 2 that of the second order, and 3, 4, and 5 the cross sections of ditetragonal bipyramids where n equals $\frac{3}{2}$, 3, and 6, respectively.

[1] Compare footnote (p. 42).
[2] See also p. 43.

Tetragonal Prism of the First Order.—If the value of the intercept along the c axis of the tetragonal bipyramid of the first order becomes infinity, the number of the faces of the bipyramid is reduced to four, giving rise to the *tetragonal prism of the first order* (Fig. 205). This is an open form and possesses the following symbols:

$$(a : a : \infty c) \text{ or } \{110\}.$$

The lateral axes join opposite edges, hence an edge is directed toward the observer.

Tetragonal Prism of the Second Order.—The same relationship exists between this form and its corresponding bipyramid as was observed on the preceding form.

The symbols are

$$(a : \infty a : \infty c) \text{ or } \{100\}.$$

Fig. 206.   Fig. 207.

This is also an open form consisting of four faces (Fig. 206). The lateral axes join the centers of opposite faces. Hence, a face is directed toward the observer.

Ditetragonal Prism.—As is obvious, this form consists of eight faces possessing the following symbols:

$$(a : na : \infty c) \text{ or } \{hk0\}.$$

What was indicated on page 65 concerning the polar angles and the position of the lateral axes applies here also. Figure 207 represents a ditetragonal prism.

Basal Pinacoid.—This form is similar to that of the hexagonal system (page 44). It is parallel to the lateral axes but cuts the c axis. The symbols may be written

$$(\infty a : \infty a : c) \text{ or } \{001\}.$$

This form consists of but two faces. They are shown in combination with the three prisms in Figs. 205, 206, and 207.

Summary.—The seven forms in this class and the chief characteristics are given in the following table:

Symmetry	Planes			Axes			Center
	Horizontal	Vertical		Vertical	Horizontal		
	Axial	Axial	Intermediate	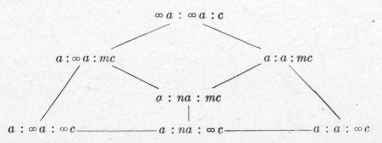 Axial	Axial	Intermediate	
	1	2	2	1	2	2	1

Forms	Symbols		Faces	Solid angles	
	Weiss	Miller		Tetrahedral	Octahedral
Unit Bipyramid First order	$a:a:c$	{111}	8	2+4	—
Modified Bipyramids First order	$a:a:mc$	{hhl}	8	2+4	—
Bipyramids Second order	$a:\infty a:mc$	{h0l}	8	2+4	—
Ditetragonal Bipyramids	$a:na:mc$	{hkl}	16	4+4	2
Prism First order	$a:a:\infty c$	{110}	4	—	—
Prism Second order	$a:\infty a:\infty c$	{100}	4	—	—
Ditetragonal Prisms	$a:na:\infty c$	{hk0}	8	—	—
Basal Pinacoid	$\infty a:\infty a:c$	{001}	2	—	—

Relationship of Forms.—This is clearly expressed by the following diagram (compare pages 27 and 45):

$$\infty a : \infty a : c$$
$$a : \infty a : mc \qquad\qquad a : a : mc$$
$$a : na : mc$$
$$a : \infty a : \infty c \qquad a : na : \infty c \qquad a : a : \infty c$$

Combinations.—Some of the more common combinations are illustrated by the following figures.

Figures 208 to 211. $m = (a : a : \infty c)$, $\{110\}$; $p = (a : a : c)$, $\{111\}$; $a = (a : \infty a : \infty c)$, $\{100\}$; $x = (a : 3a : 3c)$, $\{311\}$. These combinations have been observed on zircon ($ZrSiO_4$).

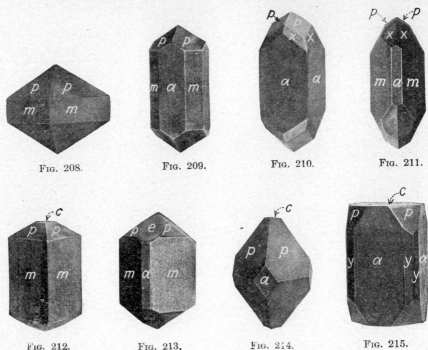

FIG. 208.   FIG. 209.   FIG. 210.   FIG. 211.

FIG. 212.   FIG. 213.   FIG. 214.   FIG. 215.

Figure 212. $m = (a : a : \infty c)$, $\{110\}$; $p = (a : a : c)$, $\{111\}$; $c = (\infty a : \infty a : c)$, $\{001\}$.   Vesuvianite ($Ca_6[Al(OH,F)]Al_2(SiO_4)_5$).

Figure 213. $m = (a : a : \infty c)$, $\{110\}$; $a = (a : \infty a : \infty c)$, $\{100\}$; $p = (a : a : c)$, $\{111\}$; $e = (a : \infty a : c)$, $\{101\}$. Observed on rutile (TiO_2).

Figures 214 and 215. $a = (a : \infty a : \infty c)$, $\{100\}$; $p = (a : a : c)$, $\{111\}$; $c = (\infty a : \infty a : c)$, $\{001\}$; $y = (a : 3a : \infty c)$, $\{310\}$.   Apophyllite ($KFCa_4(Si_2O_5)_4.8H_2O$).

FIG. 216.

TETRAGONAL SCALENOHEDRAL CLASS

Symmetry.—This class possesses two intermediate planes and three axes of twofold symmetry. One of the axes of twofold symmetry is the c axis, the other two are the a axes. This is clearly illustrated in Fig. 216. The faces of the positive forms of this class are located in the unshaded octants, those of the negative forms in the shaded ones. There are two forms in this class which are morphologically new, namely, the tetragonal bisphenoids and scalenohedrons.

Tetragonal Bisphenoids.—These forms consist of two types, *positive* (Fig. 218) and *negative* (Fig. 217), each bounded by four equal isos-

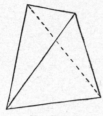

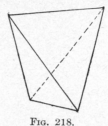

Fig. 217.   Fig. 218.

celes triangles. Their symbols are analogous to those of the tetragonal bipyramids of the first order, namely:

$$\pm(a : a : mc), \text{ or } \{hhl\} \text{ and } \{hh\bar{l}\}.$$

The *a* axes bisect the four edges of equal length, while the *c* axis passes through the centers of the other two.

Tetragonal Scalenohedrons.—These consist of eight similar scalene triangles and are termed *positive* (Fig. 220) and *negative* (Fig. 219) forms. Their symbols are

$$\pm(a : na : mc), \text{ or } \{hkl\} \text{ and } \{h\bar{k}l\}.$$

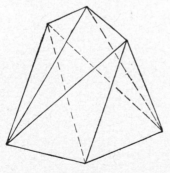

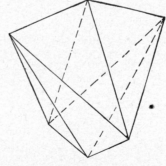

Fig. 219.   Fig. 220.

These symbols correspond to those of the ditetragonal bipyramids (page 64). The *c* axis joins those tetrahedral angles which possess two pairs of equal edges. The *a* axes bisect the four zigzag edges.

Other Forms.—The tetragonal bipyramids of the second order, the tetragonal prisms of the first and second orders, the ditetragonal prisms, and the basal pinacoid are morphologically identical with those of the ditetragonal bipyramidal class (page 62).

Summary.—The characteristics of the forms of the tetragonal scalenohedral class may be tabulated as follows:

Symmetry	Planes			Axes			Center
	Horizontal	Vertical		Vertical	Horizontal		
	Axial	Axial	Intermediate	Axial	Axial	Intermediate	
	0	0	2	1	2	0	0

Forms	Symbols			Solid angles		
	Weiss		Miller	Faces	Trihedral	Tetrahedral
Bisphenoids First order	$\pm a : a : mc$		$\{hhl\}$ $\{h\bar{h}l\}$	4	4	—
Bipyramid Second order	$a : \infty a : mc$		$\{h0l\}$	Morphologically like those in ditetragonal bipyramidal class		
Tetragonal Scalenohedrons	$\pm a : na : mc$		$\{hkl\}$ $\{h\bar{k}l\}$	8	—	2+4
Prism—First order	$a : a : \infty c$		$\{110\}$	Morphologically like those in ditetragonal bipyramidal class		
Prism—Second order	$a : \infty a : \infty c$		$\{100\}$			
Ditetragonal Prisms	$a : na : \infty c$		$\{hk0\}$			
Basal Pinacoid	$\infty a : \infty a : c$		$\{001\}$			

Combinations.—The following combinations (Figs. 221 and 222)

FIG. 221. FIG. 222.

occur on chalcopyrite ($CuFeS_2$): $p = (a : a : c)$, $\{111\}$; $p' = -(a : a : c)$, $\{1\bar{1}1\}$; $\Phi = (a : a : \frac{7}{2}c)$, $\{772\}$; $x = (a : 2a : c)$, $\{212\}$.

CHAPTER VI

ORTHORHOMBIC SYSTEM[1]

Crystallographic Axes.—This system includes all crystals which can be referred to three unequal and perpendicular axes (Fig. 223). One axis is held vertically, which is, as heretofore, the *c* axis. Another is directed toward the observer and is the *a* axis, sometimes also called the *brachyaxis*. The third axis extends from right to left and is the *b* axis or *macroaxis*. There is no principal axis in this system, hence any axis may be chosen as the vertical or *c* axis. On this account one and the same crystal may be held in different positions by various observers, which has led in some instances to considerable confusion, for, as is obvious, the nomenclature of the various forms cannot then remain con-

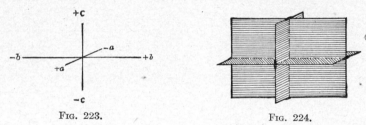

| Fig. 223. | Fig. 224. |

stant. In this system the axial ratio consists of two unknown values, for example, for sulphur, $a : b : c = 0.8130 : 1 : 1.9034$ (compare page 13).

Classes of Symmetry.—The orthorhombic system comprises three classes of symmetry, as follows:

1. Orthorhombic bipyramidal class.
2. Orthorhombic pyramidal class.
3. Orthorhombic bisphenoidal class.

Numerous representatives of all these classes have been observed among minerals and artificial salts. The first class is, however, the most important and will be considered in detail.

ORTHORHOMBIC BIPYRAMIDAL CLASS

Symmetry. *a. Planes.*—There are three axial planes of symmetry (Fig. 224). Inasmuch as these planes are all dissimilar, they may be written

$$1 + 1 + 1 = 3 \text{ planes.}$$

[1] Sometimes termed the *rhombic, trimetric,* or *prismatic* system,

b. Axes.—Three axes of twofold symmetry are to be observed (Fig. 224). They are the crystallographic axes and indicated thus:

$$1 \bullet + 1 \bullet + 1 \bullet = 3 \text{ axes.}$$

c. Center.—This element of symmetry is also present and demands parallelism of faces. Figure 225 shows the above elements of symmetry.

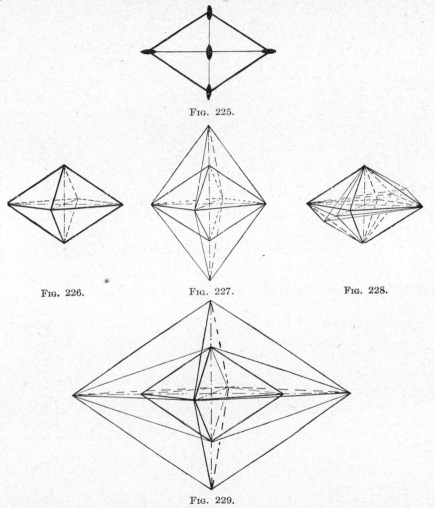

Fig. 225.

Fig. 226.   Fig. 227.   Fig. 228.

Fig. 229.

Orthorhombic Bipyramids.—The form whose faces possess the ratio $(a : b : c)$ or $\{111\}$ is known as the *unit or fundamental orthorhombic bipyramid.* It consists of eight similar scalene triangles (Fig. 226).

The outer form (Fig. 227) possesses the ratio $(a : b : mc)$ or $\{hhl\}$, $(0 < m < \infty)$. In this case $m = 2$. This is a *modified orthorhombic bipyramid.*

In Fig. 228, the heavy, inner form is the unit bipyramid. The lighter bipyramids intercept the b and c axes at unit distances but the a axis at distances greater than unity. Their ratios may, however, be indicated in general as

$$(na : b : mc), (n > 1; 0 < m < \infty) \text{ or } \{hkl\}, \text{ where } k > h.$$

These are the *brachybipyramids*, because the intercepts along the *brachyaxis* are greater than unity.

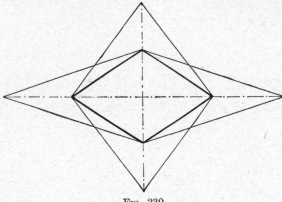

Fig. 230.

Figure 229 shows two bipyramids (outer) which cut the a axis at unity but intercept the b axis at the general distance nb, $(n > 1)$. The ratios would, therefore, be expressed by $(a : nb : mc)$. Since the intercepts along the *macroaxis* are greater than unity, these are called *macrobipyramids*.

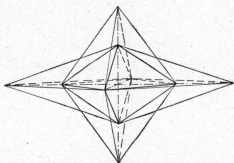

Fig. 231.

Figure 230 shows the relationship existing between the *unit, macro-,* and *brachybipyramids*, while Fig. 231 shows it for the *unit, modified,* and *macrobipyramids*.

Prisms.—Similarly there are three types of prisms, namely, the *unit, macro-,* and *brachyprisms*. Each consists of four faces, cutting the a and b axes but extending parallel to the c axis.

Figures 232 and 233 represent *unit prisms* with the following symbols.

$$(a : b : \infty c) \text{ or } \{110\}.$$

The *brachyprism* (outer form) is shown in Fig. 234. Its symbols are

$$(na : b : \infty c) \text{ or } \{hk0\}.$$

FIG. 232.   FIG. 233.

In Fig. 235, there is a unit prism surrounded by a macroprism, whose symbols may be written

$$(a : nb : \infty c) \text{ or } \{kh0\}.$$

For the relationship existing among these three prisms, compare Fig. 230.

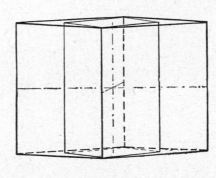

FIG. 234.   FIG. 235.

Domes.—These are *horizontal* prisms and, hence, cut the c and one of the horizontal axes. Domes which are parallel to the a or brachyaxis are called *brachy-* or *side domes.* Their general symbols are

$$(\infty a : b : mc) \text{ or } \{0hl\} \text{ (Fig. 236)}.$$

Those, which extend parallel to the macroaxis, are termed *macro-* or *front domes* (Figs. 237 and 238). Their symbols are

$$(a : \infty b : mc) \text{ or } \{h0l\}.$$

As is obvious, prisms and domes are open forms and, hence, can only occur in combination with other forms.

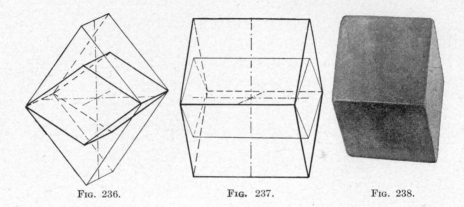

Fig. 236.   Fig. 237.   Fig. 238.

Pinacoids.—These cut one axis and extend parallel to the other two. There are three types, as follows:

Basal pinacoid, $(\infty a : \infty b : c)$ or $\{100\}$; also called the *base*.

Brachypinacoid, $(\infty a : b : \infty c)$ or $\{010\}$; often termed the *side* pinacoid.

Macropinacoid, $(a : \infty b : \infty c)$ or $\{100\}$; frequently designated as the *front* pinacoid

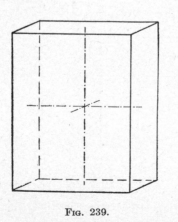

Fig. 239.   Fig. 240.

These forms consist of two faces. Figures 239 and 240 show a combination of the three types of pinacoids.

Summary.—The characteristics of the forms of this class are given in the following table:

Symmetry	Planes (axial)	Axes	Center
	$1+1+1$	$1\bullet +1\bullet +1\bullet$	1

Forms		Symbols		Faces	Tetrahedral solid angles
		Weiss	·Miller		
Orthorhombic Bipyramids	Unit	$a:b:c$	$\{111\}$	8	2+2+2
	Modified	$a:b:mc$	$\{hhl\}$		
	Brachy	$na:b:mc$	$\{hkl\}$		
	Macro	$a:nb:mc$	$\{khl\}$		
Orthorhombic Prisms	Unit	$a:b:\infty c$	$\{110\}$	4	
	Brachy	$na:\ b:\infty c$	$\{hk0\}$		
	Macro	$a:nb:\infty c$	$\{kh0\}$		
Domes	Brachy	$\infty a:b:mc$	$\{0hl\}$	4	
	Macro	$a:\infty b:mc$	$\{h0l\}$		
Pinacoids	Basal	$\infty a:\infty b:c$	$\{001\}$	2	
	Brachy	$\infty a:b:\infty c$	$\{010\}$		
	Macro	$a:\infty b:\infty c$	$\{100\}$		

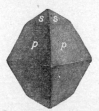

Fig. 241.

Fig. 242.

Combination.—Figures 241 and 242. $p = (a:b:c)$, $\{111\}$; $s = (a:b:\frac{1}{3}c)$, $\{113\}$; $n = (\infty a:b:c)$, $\{011\}$; $c = (\infty a:\infty b:c)$, $\{001\}$. These combinations occur on native sulphur.

Figure 243. $m = (a : b : \infty c)$, $\{110\}$; $b = (\infty a : b : \infty c)$, $\{010\}$; $k = (\infty a : b : c)$, $\{011\}$. Aragonite ($CaCO_3$).

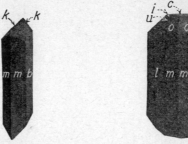

FIG. 243. FIG. 244.

Figure 244. $m = (a : b : \infty c)$, $\{110\}$; $l = (2a : b : \infty c)$, $\{120\}$; $u = (a : b : c)$, $\{111\}$; $i = (a : b : 2/3c)$, $\{223\}$; $o = (a : b : 2c)$, $\{221\}$; $y = (\infty a : b : 4c)$, $\{041\}$; $c = (\infty a : \infty b : c)$, $\{001\}$. Topaz ($Al_2(F,-OH)_2SiO_4$).

Figure 245. $m = (a : b : \infty c)$, $\{110\}$; $c = (\infty a : \infty b : c)$, $\{001\}$; $d = (a : \infty b : \frac{1}{2}c)$, $\{102\}$; $o = (\infty a : b : c)$, $\{011\}$. Barite ($BaSO_4$).

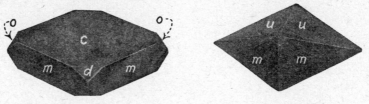

FIG. 245. FIG. 246.

Figure 246. $m = (a : b : \infty c)$, $\{110\}$; $u = (\infty a : b : \frac{1}{4}c)$, $\{014\}$. Arsenopyrite (FeAsS).

CHAPTER VII

MONOCLINIC SYSTEM[1]

Crystallographic Axes.—To this system belong those crystals which can be referred to three unequal axes, two of which (a and c) intersect at an oblique angle, while the third axis (b) is perpendicular to

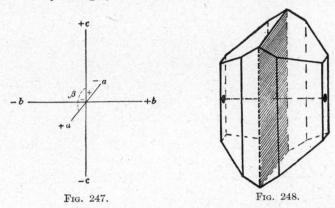

FIG. 247.

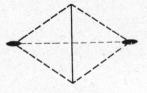

FIG. 248.

these two. The oblique angle between the a and c axes is termed β. Figure 247 shows an axial cross of this system.

It is customary to place the b axis so as to extend from right to left. The c axis is held vertically. The a axis is then directed toward the observer. Since the a axis is inclined, it is called the *clinoaxis*. The b axis is often spoken of as the *orthoaxis*. The obtuse angle between the a and c axes is the *negative* angle β, whereas the acute angle is *positive*. Obviously, they are supplementary angles. The elements of crystallization consist of the axial ratio and the angle β, which may be either the obtuse or the acute angle (compare page 14).

FIG. 249.

Classes of Symmetry.—The monoclinic system includes three classes of symmetry, as follows:

1. Prismatic class.
2. Domatic class
3. Sphenoidal class.

The first class is the most important and is the only one which will be considered.

[1] Also termed the *clinorhombic, hemiprismatic, monoclinohedral, monosymmetric,* or *oblique* system.

MONOCLINIC PRISMATIC CLASS

Symmetry.—This class possesses one axial plane of symmetry (*a* and *c* axes). It is directed toward the observer. Perpendicular to this plane is an axis of twofold symmetry (*b* axis). A center of symmetry is also present. In Fig. 248 the presence of these elements is readily recognized. These elements are represented diagrammatically in Fig. 249, which is a projection of a monoclinic form upon the plane of the *a* and *b* axes.

Hemi-bipyramids.—On account of the presence in this class of only one plane of symmetry and an axis of twofold symmetry, a form with

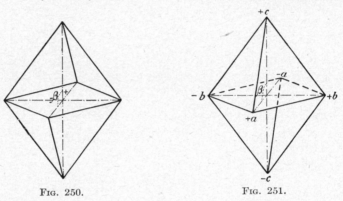

| Fig. 250. | Fig. 251. |

unit intercepts, that is, with the parametral ratio *a* : *b* : *c*, can possess but four faces. Figure 250 shows four such faces, which enclose the positive angle β and are said to constitute the *positive unit hemi-bipyramid*. Figure 251 shows four faces with the same ratio enclosing the negative angle β and comprising the *negative unit hemi-bipyramid*. It is obvious that the faces of these hemi-bipyramids are dissimilar, those over the

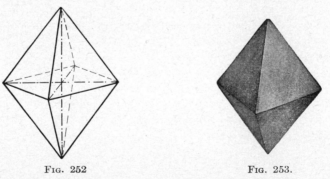

| Fig. 252 | Fig. 253. |

negative angle being the larger. The symbols are ±(*a* : *b* : *c*), or {11$\bar{1}$} and {111}. Two unit hemi-bipyramids occurring simultaneously constitute the *monoclinic unit bipyramid* (Figs. 252 and 253).

Since this system differs essentially from the orthorhombic in the obliquity of the *a* axis, it follows that *modified*, *clino*, and *ortho* hemi-bipyramids are also possible. They possess the following general symbols:

Modified hemi-bipyramids,

$$\pm(a : b : mc),\ 0 < m < \infty,\ \text{or } \{hh\bar{l}\} \text{ and } \{hhl\}.$$

Clino hemi-bipyramids,

$$\pm(na : b : mc),\ n > 1;\ \text{or } \{hk\bar{l}\} \text{ and } \{hkl\}.$$

Ortho hemi-bipyramids,

$$\pm(a : nb : mc),\ n > 1;\ \text{or } \{hk\bar{l}\} \text{ and } \{hkl\}.$$

Prisms.—As was the case in the orthorhombic system (page 74), there are also three types of prisms possible in this system, namely, *unit*, *clino-*, and *orthoprisms*. These forms cut the *a* and *b* axes and extend parallel to the vertical axis.

The general symbols are:

Unit prism, $(a : b : \infty c)$, $\{110\}$ (Figs. 254 and 255).
Clinoprism, $(na : b : \infty c)$, $\{hk0\}$; $n > 1$.
Orthoprism, $(a : nb : \infty c)$, $\{kh0\}$; $n > 1$.

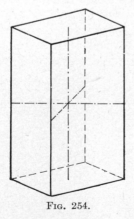 

Fig. 254.   Fig. 255.

Domes.—In this system two types of domes are also possible, namely, those which extend parallel to the *a* and *b* axes, respectively. Those which are parallel to the *a* axis, are termed *clinodomes* and consist of four faces (Fig. 256). The general symbols are

$$(\infty a : b : mc),\ \{0hl\}.$$

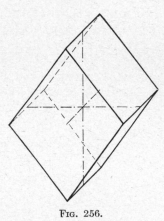

Fig. 256.

Since the *a* axis is inclined to the *c* axis, it follows that the domes which are parallel to the *b* axis consist of but two faces. Figure 257 shows such faces enclosing the positive angle and are termed the *positive hemi-ortho-dome,* whereas in Fig. 258 the *negative hemi-orthodome* is represented. It is evident that the faces of the positive form are always the smaller. Figure 259 shows these hemidomes in combination. Their general symbols are

Positive hemi-orthodome,

$$(a : \infty b : mc), \{h0\bar{l}\}.$$

Negative hemi-orthodome,

$$(a : \infty b : mc), \{h0l\}.$$

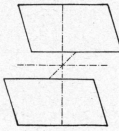

Fig. 257.

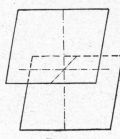

Fig. 258.

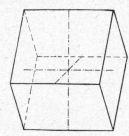

Fig. 259.

Pinacoids.—There are three types of pinacoids possible in the monoclinic system, namely,

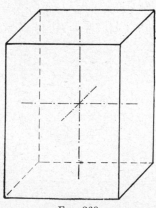

Fig. 260.

Fig. 261.

Basal pinacoid, $(\infty a : \infty b : c)$, $\{001\}$.
Clinopinacoid, $(\infty a : b : \infty c)$, $\{010\}$.
Orthopinacoid, $(a : \infty b : \infty c)$, $\{100\}$.

These forms may also be termed the *base*, and the *side* and *front* pinacoids, respectively. They consist of but two faces. Figures 260 and 261 show combinations of these pinacoids.

All forms of the monoclinic system are open forms, and, hence, every crystal of this system is a combination.

Summary.—The forms of this class may be tabulated as follows:

Symmetry	Plane	● Axis	Center
	1 (*a* and *c* axes)	1 (*b* axis)	1

Forms		Symbols		Faces
		Weiss	Miller	
Hemi-bipyramids	Unit	$\pm(a:b:c)$	$\{11\bar{1}\}$ $\{111\}$	4
	Modified	$\pm(a:b:mc)$	$\{hh\bar{l}\}$ $\{hhl\}$	
	Clino-	$\pm(na:b:mc)$	$\{hk\bar{l}\}$ $\{hkl\}$	
	Ortho-	$\pm(a:nb:mc)$	$\{kh\bar{l}\}$ $\{khl\}$	
Prisms	Unit	$a:b:\infty c$	$\{110\}$	4
	Clino-	$na:b:\infty c$	$\{hk0\}$	
	Ortho-	$a:nb:\infty c$	$\{kh0\}$	
Clinodome		$\infty a:b:mc$	$\{0hl\}$	4
Hemi-orthodomes	Positive	$a:\infty b:mc$	$\{h0\bar{l}\}$	2
	Negative	$a:\infty b:mc$	$\{h0l\}$	
Pinacoids	Basal	$\infty a:\infty b:c$	$\{001\}$	2
	Clino-	$\infty a:b:\infty c$	$\{010\}$	
	Ortho-	$a:\infty b:\infty c$	$\{100\}$	

Combinations.—The following models show some combinations of the forms of this class:

Figure 262. $m = (a : b : \infty c)$, $\{110\}$; $b = (\infty a : b : \infty c)$, $\{010\}$; $p = -(a : b : c)$, $\{111\}$. Gypsum ($CaSO_4.2H_2O$).

FIG. 262.   FIG. 263.   FIG. 264.   FIG. 265.

Figures 263, 264, and 265. $m = (a : b : \infty c)$, $\{110\}$; $b = (\infty a : b : \infty c)$, $\{010\}$; $c = (\infty a : \infty b : c)$, $\{001\}$; $y = (a : \infty b : 2c)$, $\{20\bar{1}\}$; $x = (a : \infty b : c)$, $\{10\bar{1}\}$; $o = (a : b : c)$, $\{11\bar{1}\}$; $z = (3a : b : \infty c)$, $\{130\}$. Orthoclase ($KAlSi_3O_8$).

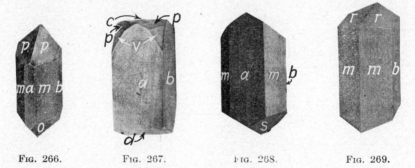

FIG. 266.   FIG. 267.   FIG. 268.   FIG. 269.

Figures 266, 267, and 268. $m = (a : b : \infty c)$, $\{110\}$; $a = (a : \infty b : \infty c)$, $\{100\}$; $b = (\infty a : b : \infty c)$, $\{010\}$; $c = (\infty a : \infty b : c)$, $\{001\}$; $p = -(a : b : c)$, $\{111\}$; $v = -(a : b : 2c)$, $\{221\}$; $o = (a : b : 2c)$, $\{22\bar{1}\}$; $d = (a : \infty b : c)$, $\{10\bar{1}\}$; $s = (a : b : c)$, $\{11\bar{1}\}$. Augite.

Figure 269. $m = (a : b : \infty c)$, $\{110\}$; $b = (\infty a : b : \infty c)$, $\{010\}$; $r = (\infty a : b : c)$, $\{011\}$. Hornblende.

CHAPTER VIII

TRICLINIC SYSTEM[1]

Crystallographic Axes.—This system includes all crystals which can be referred to three unequal axes intersecting each other at unequal angles. The axes are designated as in the orthorhombic system, namely, *a, brachyaxis, b, macroaxis,* and *c, vertical axis.* From this it follows that one axis must be held vertically, a second is directed toward the observer, and then the third is inclined from right to left or *vice versa.* Usually the brachyaxis is the shorter of the two lateral axes. Figure 270 shows an axial cross of the triclinic system. The three angles between the axes are indicated as follows: $b \wedge c = \alpha$, $a \wedge c = \beta$, and $a \wedge b = \gamma$. The elements of crystallization consist of the axial ratio and the three angles α, β, and γ (page 14).

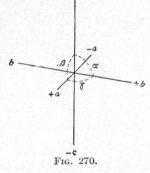

Fig. 270.

Classes of Symmetry.—There are but two classes of symmetry in the triclinic system, namely:

1. Pinacoidal class.
2. Asymmetric class.

The first is the important class.

PINACOIDAL CLASS

Symmetry.—A center of symmetry is the only element present. Hence, forms can consist of but two faces, namely, face and parallel counterface. This is represented diagrammatically by Fig. 271, which shows a triclinic combination projected upon the plane of the *a* and *b* axes.

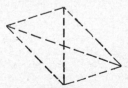

Fig. 271.

Tetarto-bipyramids.—As already shown, triclinic forms consist of but two faces. Therefore, since the planes of the crystallographic axes divide space into four pairs of dissimilar octants, it follows that four types of pyramidal forms must result. These are spoken of as *tetarto-bipyramids.* There are, hence, four tetarto-bipyramids, each cutting the axes at their unit lengths. The same is also true of the modified, brachy-, and macro-

[1] Also termed the *anorthic, asymmetric,* or *clinorhomboidal* system

85

bipyramids. That is to say, the various bipyramids of the orthorhombic system, on account of the obliquity of the three axes, now yield four tetarto-bipyramids each. They are designated as *upper right, upper left, lower right,* and *lower left* forms, depending upon which of the front octants the form encloses. The general symbols for all types are given

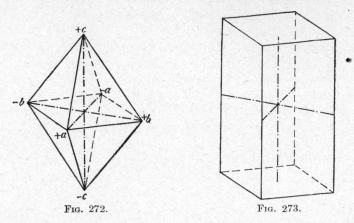

Fig. 272.

Fig. 273.

in the tabulation on page 87. Figure 272 shows the four unit tetarto-bipyramids in combination.

Hemiprisms.—Obviously the prisms are now to be designated as *right* and *left* forms. These two forms are in combination with the basal pinacoid in Fig. 273.

Hemidomes.—All domes now consist of but two faces. Hence, we may speak of *right* and *left hemi-brachydomes,* and *upper* and *lower hemi-macrodomes.* These forms are shown in combination with the macro- and brachypinacoids, respectively, in Figs. 274 and 275.

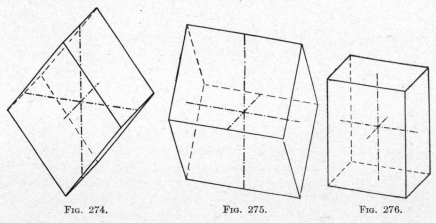

Fig. 274.

Fig. 275.

Fig. 276.

Pinacoids.—These forms occur with their usual number of faces and are designated, as heretofore, by the terms *basal, brachy-,* and *macro-pinacoids,* depending upon the fact whether they intersect the *c, b,* or *a* axes. They are called the *base*, and the *side* and *front* pinacoids, respectively. Figure 276 shows these pinacoids in combination.

Summary.—The various forms and symbols are given in the following table:

Symmetry		The only element of symmetry in this class is the *center of symmetry*	
		All forms consist of two faces	
Forms		Symbols	
		Weiss	Miller
Tetarto-bipyramids	Unit	a: b: c a: $-b$: c a: b: $-c$ a: $-b$: $-c$	$\{111\}$ $\{1\bar{1}1\}$ $\{11\bar{1}\}$ $\{1\bar{1}\bar{1}\}$
	Modified	a: b: mc a: $-b$: mc a: b: $-mc$ a: $-b$: $-mc$	$\{hhl\}$ $\{h\bar{h}l\}$ $\{hh\bar{l}\}$ $\{h\bar{h}\bar{l}\}$
	Brachy	na: b: mc na: $-b$: mc na: b: $-mc$ na: $-b$: $-mc$	$\{hkl\}$ $\{h\bar{k}l\}$ $\{hk\bar{l}\}$ $\{h\bar{k}\bar{l}\}$
	Macro	a: nb: mc a: $-nb$: mc a: nb: $-mc$ a: $-nb$: $-mc$	$\{khl\}$ $\{k\bar{h}l\}$ $\{kh\bar{l}\}$ $\{k\bar{h}\bar{l}\}$
Hemiprisms	Unit	a: b: ∞c a: $-b$: ∞c	$\{110\}$ $\{1\bar{1}0\}$
	Brachy	na: b: ∞c na: $-b$: ∞c	$\{hk0\}$ $\{h\bar{k}0\}$
	Macro	a: nb: ∞c a: $-nb$: ∞c	$\{kh0\}$ $\{k\bar{h}0\}$
Hemidomes	Brachy	∞a: b: mc ∞a: $-b$: mc	$\{0hl\}$ $\{0\bar{h}l\}$
	Macro	a: ∞b: mc a: ∞b: $-mc$	$\{h0l\}$ $\{h0\bar{l}\}$
Pinacoids	Basal	∞a: ∞b: c	$\{001\}$
	Brachy	∞a: b: ∞c	$\{010\}$
	Macro	a: ∞b: ∞c	$\{100\}$

Combinations.—Figure 277. $x = (a : b : c)$, $\{111\}$; $r = (a : -b : c)$, $\{1\bar{1}1\}$; $m = (a : b : \infty c)$, $\{110\}$; $M = (a : -b : \infty c)$, $\{1\bar{1}0\}$; $s = (a : \infty b : 2c)$, $\{201\}$; $a = (a : \infty b : \infty c)$, $\{100\}$. Axinite ($HCa_3Al_2BSi_4O_{16}$).

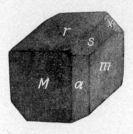

Fɪɢ. 277.   Fɪɢ. 278.   Fɪɢ. 279.

Figures 278 and 279. $m = (a : b : \infty c)$, $\{110\}$; $M = (a : -b : \infty c)$, $\{1\bar{1}0\}$; $b = (\infty a : b : \infty c)$, $\{010\}$; $c = (\infty a : \infty b : c)$, $\{001\}$; $x = (a : \infty b : -c)$, $\{10\bar{1}\}$; $o = a : b : -c$ $\{11\bar{1}\}$; $y = (a : \infty b : -2c)$, $\{20\bar{1}\}$; $n = (\infty a : -b : 2c)$, $\{0\bar{2}1\}$; $f = (3a : b : \infty c)$, $\{130\}$; $z = (3a : -b : \infty c)$, $\{1\bar{3}0\}$. Albite ($NaAlSi_3O_8$).

CHAPTER IX

COMPOUND CRYSTALS

General Statement.—The crystals considered thus far have been bounded by either a single form as in the case of an octahedron (Fig. 57, page 23), or by a combination of forms (Fig. 78, page 28). They have, however, in all cases been single individuals. In many instances,

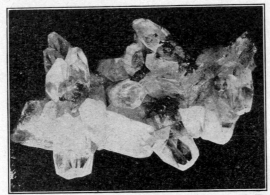

Fig. 280.—Aggregate of crystals, calcite. Cumberland, England.

crystals occur in groups and may be designated as *crystal aggregates* or *parallel groups*. A single crystal is sometimes made up of two or more individuals arranged according to some definite law. These crystals are designated as *twin crystals* or, simply, *twins*.

Crystal Aggregates.—These are groups of crystals arranged in no definite manner. They are usually singly terminated (Fig. 280, and Figs. 512 and 560, pages 250 and 269).

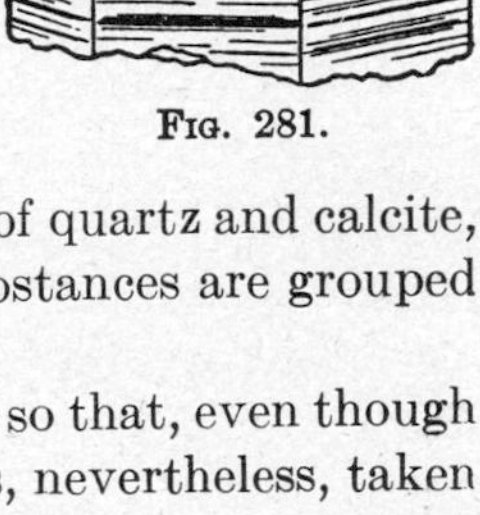

Parallel Groups.—Oftentimes two or more crystals of the same substance are observed to have so intergrown that the crystallographic axes of the one individual are parallel to those of the others. Such an arrangement of crystals is termed a *parallel group*. Figures 281, 282, and 283 show such groups of quartz and calcite, respectively. Occasionally, crystals of different substances are grouped in this way.

Fig. 281.

Twin Crystals.—Two crystals may also intergrow so that, even though parallelism of the crystals is wanting, the growth has, nevertheless, taken

89

place in some definite manner. Such crystals are spoken of as *twin crystals*, or in short, *twins*. Figure 284 illustrates a twin crystal commonly observed on staurolite. In twin crystals both individuals have at least one crystal plane or a direction in common. Figure 285 shows a twinned octahedron. The plane common to both parts is termed the *composition plane*. In general, the plane to which the twin crystal is symmetrical is the *twinning plane*. In some instances, *composition* and

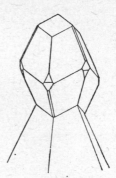

Fig. 282.—Parallel group of quartz crystals. Quindel, Switzerland.

Fig. 283.

twinning planes coincide. Both, however, are parallel to some possible face of the crystal, which is not parallel to a plane of symmetry. The line or direction perpendicular to the twinning plane is the *twinning axis*. A *twinning law* is expressed by indicating the *twinning plane* or *twinning axis*.

Twin crystals are commonly divided into two classes: (1) *Contact* or *juxtaposition* twins, and (2) *penetration* twins.[1] These are illustrated by

Fig. 284.

Fig. 285.

Figs. 285 and 284, respectively. Contact twins consist of two individuals so placed that if one be rotated through 180° about the twinning axis the simple crystal results. In penetration twins two individuals have interpenetrated one another. If one of the individuals be rotated

[1] Also designated as *reflection* and *rotation* twins, because they are symmetrical to a plane or an axis, respectively.

through 180° about the twinning axis, both individuals will occupy the same position.

Contact and penetration twins are comparatively common in all systems. In studying twins, it must be borne in mind, as pointed out on page 19, that owing to distortion the two individuals may not be morphologically symmetrical. Re-entrant angles are commonly indicative of twinning.

Common Twinning Laws.—Only those twinning laws which are most frequently observed on the minerals described in this text will be considered.

FIG. 286.   FIG. 287.

Cubic System.—The most common law in the cubic system is known as the *spinel law*, the twinning plane being parallel to a face of an octahedron, $(a : a : a)$, $\{111\}$. Figure 285 shows such a twin crystal of the mineral spinel. A penetration twin of fluorite is shown in Fig. 286. Here, two cubes interpenetrate according to this law.

Figure 287 shows a penetration twin of two pyritohedrons of the mineral pyrite. These twins are often known as crystals of the *iron cross*. A plane parallel to a face of the rhombic dodecahedron, $(a : a : \infty a)$, $\{110\}$, is the twinning plane.

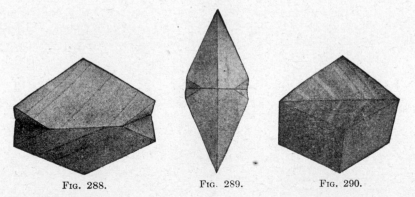

FIG. 288.   FIG. 289.   FIG. 290.

Hexagonal System.—Calcite and quartz are the only common minerals belonging to this system which furnish good examples of twinning.

Upon calcite the basal pinacoid, $(\infty a : \infty a : \infty a : c)$, {0001}, is commonly a twinning plane. Figures 288 and 289 illustrate this law.[1] A plane parallel to a face of the negative rhombohedron, $-(\infty a : 2a : 2a : c)$,

FIG. 291.   FIG. 292.

{01$\bar{1}$2}, may also be a twinning plane as illustrated by Fig. 290. These are the most common laws on calcite.

The common or Dauphiné twinning law on quartz is shown in Fig. 291. Here either two right- or two left-hand crystals interpenetrate, after one has been revolved 180° about the c axis as the twinning axis.

FIG. 293.

The so-called *Brazilian law* is also common on twins of quartz (Fig. 292). Here, right and left crystals have interpenetrated so that the twin is now symmetrical to a plane parallel to a face of the prism of the second order, $(2a : 2a : a : \infty c)$, {11$\bar{2}$0} (see also Figs. 554 and 557), page 268).

Tetragonal System.—Most of the twin crystals of this system are to be observed on substances crystallizing in the ditetragonal bipyramidal class. A plane parallel to a face of the unit bipyramid of the second order, $(\infty a : a : c)$, {011}, commonly acts as the twinning plane. Figure 293 represents a crystal of cassiterite twinned according to this law, which is also frequently observed on zircon and rutile.

FIG. 294.   FIG. 295.   FIG. 296.

Orthorhombic System.—The most common twins of this system belong to the bipyramidal class in which any face aside from the pina-

[1] Compare with Figs. 139 and 144.

coids may act as the twinning plane. Figure 294 shows a penetration twin of staurolite, where the brachydome, $(\infty a : b : \frac{3}{2}c)$, {032}, acts as the twinning plane. Figure 295 shows the same mineral with the bipyramid, $(\frac{3}{2}a : b : \frac{3}{2}c)$, {232}, as the twinning plane. Figure 296 represents a contact twin of aragonite. Here the unit prism, $(a : b : \infty c)$, {110}, is the twinning plane.

Fig. 297.   Fig. 298.   Fig. 299.

Monoclinic System.—In this system, gypsum and orthoclase furnish some of the best examples. Figure 297 shows a contact twin of gypsum

Fig. 300.   Fig. 301.

in which the orthopinacoid, $(a : \infty b : \infty c)$, {100}, is the twinning plane. Penetration twins of orthoclase are shown in Figs. 298 (left) and 299 (right). Here, the c axis acts as twinning axis. This is known as the *Karlsbad law* on orthoclase. Two other twinning laws are also fre-

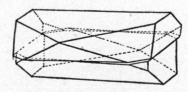

Fig. 302.   Fig. 303.

quently observed on orthoclase, namely, the *Baveno* and *Manebach* laws, where the clinodome, $(\infty a : b : 2c)$, {021} (Fig. 300) and the basal pinacoid, $(\infty a : \infty b : c)$, {001} (Fig. 301), respectively, act as the twinning planes.

Triclinic System.—Since there are no planes of symmetry in this system, any plane may act as the twinning plane. The mineral albite furnishes good examples. In Fig. 302, the brachypinacoid, ($\infty a : b : \infty c$), {010}, is the twinning plane. This is the *albite law*. Another common law is shown by Fig. 303. Here, the basal pinacoids of both individuals are parallel, the crystallographic b axis acting as the twinning axis. This is known as the *pericline law*.

Summary of the Common Twinning Laws.—The following table gives the important twinning laws in the different systems and the names of the minerals on which they may be observed:

System	Twinning plane or axis, and type of twin	Mineral
Cubic	1. Octahedron, contact and penetration. ($a:a:a$). *Spinel law.* 2. Rhombic dodecahedron, penetration. ($a:a:\infty a$). *Iron cross law.*	Spinel, fluorite. Pyrite.
Hexagonal	1. Basal pinacoid, contact. ($\infty a: \infty a: \infty a:c$). 2. Rhombohedral, contact. $-(\infty a:2a:2a:c)$, $-\frac{1}{2}R$. 3. c is twinning axis, penetration. *Dauphiné law.* 4. Prism of the second order, penetration. ($2a:2a:a: \infty c$). *Brazilian law.*	Calcite. Calcite. Quartz. (Two right or two left individuals). Quartz. (Right and left individuals).
Tetragonal	Bipyramid of the second order, contact. ($a: \infty a:c$).	Cassiterite, rutile, zircon.
Orthorhombic	1. Prism, contact and penetration. ($a:b: \infty c$). 2. Brachydome, penetration. ($\infty a:b:\frac{3}{2}c$). 3. Brachybipyramid, penetration. ($\frac{3}{2}a:b:\frac{3}{2}c$).	Aragonite, cerussite, macrasite, arseno- pyrite. Staurolite (*cross* or *plus* (+) shape). Staurolite (x shape).
Monoclinic	1. Orthopinacoid, contact and penetration. ($a: \infty b: \infty c$). 2. c is twinning axis, penetration. *Karlsbad law.* 3. Clinodome, contact. ($\infty a:b:2c$). *Baveno law.* 4. Basal pinacoid, contact. ($\infty a: \infty b:c$). *Manebach law.*	Gypsum, pyroxenes, amphiboles. Orthoclase. Orthoclase. Orthoclase.
Triclinic	1. Brachypinacoid, contact. ($\infty a:b: \infty c$). *Albite law.* 2. b is twinning axis, contact. *Pericline law.*	Microcline and plagioclase feldspars. Microcline and plagioclase feldspars.

Repeated Twinning.—In the foregoing, crystals consisting of but two individuals have been discussed. Intergrowths of three, four, five, or more individuals are termed *threelings, fourlings, fivelings,* and so on. *Polysynthetic* and *cyclic* twins are the result of repeated twinning. In the polysynthetic twins, the twinning planes between adjacent individuals are parallel. This is illustrated by Figs. 304 and 305 showing

FIG. 304.

FIG. 305.

FIG. 306.

polysynthetic twins of albite and aragonite, respectively.[1] If the individuals are very thin, the re-entrant angles are usually indicated by striations. Cyclic twins result when the twinning planes do not remain parallel, as, for example, when adjacent or opposite faces of a form act as twinning planes. This is shown by the cyclic twins of rutile (Fig. 306) in which adjacent faces of the unit bipyramid of the second order, $(\infty a : a : c)$, $\{011\}$, act as twinning planes.

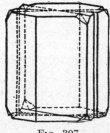

FIG. 307.

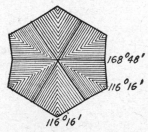

FIG. 308.

Mimicry.—As a result of repeated twinning, forms of an apparently higher grade of symmetry often result. This is especially true of those substances possessing pseudosymmetry (page 64). Figure 307 shows a *trilling* or *threeling* of the orthorhombic mineral aragonite, which is apparently hexagonal in its outline. In Fig. 308 the cross section is shown. This phenomenon is called *mimicry*.

[1] Compare with Figs. 302 and 296.

CHAPTER X

PHYSICAL PROPERTIES

Those physical properties which are easily recognized or determined and are important in the rapid determination of minerals will be discussed in this chapter. The optical properties involving the use of the microscope will be treated later.

Luster.—The luster of a mineral is the appearance of its surface in reflected light and is a property of fundamental importance in the recognition of minerals. Luster is a function of the transparency, refractivity, and structure of a mineral. It is in no way related to hardness. There are two principal types of luster, *metallic* and *nonmetallic*.

Metallic luster is exhibited by metals and by minerals of a metallic appearance. Substances with a metallic luster are opaque or nearly so and quite heavy. The common minerals pyrite and galena possess metallic luster.

All other kinds of luster are referred to as being nonmetallic. Some of the more important nonmetallic lusters are

Vitreous.—The luster of glass or quartz.

Adamantine.—The exceedingly brilliant luster of minerals with high indices of refraction, as the diamond and pyromorphite.

Resinous.—The luster or appearance of resin. This is well shown by sphalerite.

Greasy.—The appearance of an oiled surface. Example, nephelite.

Pearly.—This is similar to the luster of mother of pearl. It is commonly shown by minerals with a lamellar or platy structure and by those with pronounced cleavages. Example, talc.

Silky.—This luster is the result of a fibrous structure and is well shown by fibrous gypsum (satin spar) and asbestos.

Dull.—Not bright or shiny, good examples being chalk and kaolin. Sometimes called *earthy* luster.

The terms *splendent, shining, glistening*, and *glimmering* are sometimes used. They have reference to the intensity or quantity of light reflected. In some instances the luster is not the same on all faces of a crystal. Thus, on apophyllite it is pearly on the basal pinacoid and vitreous elsewhere. When a luster is intermediate between metallic and nonmetallic it is frequently called *metalloidal* or *submetallic*.

Color.—The color of a mineral is one of the first physical properties to be observed. Some minerals have a fairly constant color and are called *idiochromatic.* Other minerals have colors that vary greatly. This variation in color may be due to the presence of pigments, inclusions, or other impurities. Such minerals are termed *allochromatic.*

In idiochromatic minerals the color is an inherent property, for some essential constituent of the mineral is the pigmenting agent. Common examples of idiochromatic minerals are: sulphur, yellow; malachite, green; azurite, blue; pyrite, yellow; magnetite, black. In these minerals the color is constant and, therefore, may be of material assistance in their identification.

In allochromatic minerals the color may vary greatly. These minerals are colorless or white, when pure. The variation in color is due to pigmenting impurities that may be present in submicroscopic particles or as inclusions of other colored minerals. For example, quartz is entirely colorless when pure, but it is more often colored and among its varieties practically every hue is represented. Some of the colored varieties are the purple amethyst, the brown to black smoky quartz, the pink rose quartz, and the golden yellow citrine.

FIG. 309.—Albin Weisbach (1833–1901). Professor of mineralogy in the Saxon School of Mines, Freiberg, Germany. Pioneer in the use of physical properties for the determination of minerals.

Color is a poor aid in the identification of allochromatic minerals.

The pigment of allochromatic minerals is often irregularly distributed. The color may, hence, occur in patches or blotches, as in amethyst or sapphire. On the other hand, the color may be distributed in regular

FIG. 310.   FIG. 311.

FIG. 310.—Tourmaline showing zonal distribution of color and spherical triangular outline. San Diego County, California.
FIG. 311.—Agate. Brazil.

and sharply bounded zones or bands, as, for example, in tourmaline. The zonal distribution of color in tourmaline may be such that it occurs in horizontal bands across the length of the crystal, or in concentric zones parallel to the spherical triangular outline (Fig. 310). Agate, a variety of quartz, is commonly banded with colors (Fig. 311). Moreover, the coloring may be so distributed as to produce interesting and attractive markings, as in moss agate (Fig. 312) and in chiastolite (Fig. 313).

FIG. 312.—Moss agate.

FIG. 313.—Andalusite: Variety, chiastolite.   Lancaster, Massachusetts.

Play or Change of Colors.—Some minerals exhibit different colors as the specimen is slowly turned, or as the direction of observation is changed.   This is well illustrated by labradorite and precious opal.

Opalescence.—This consists of milky or pearly reflections from the interior of the specimen, as is seen in some opals and in moonstone. Opalescence is usually observed to best advantage on specimens with rounded and polished surfaces.

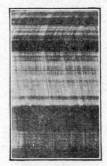

FIG. 314.—Gypsum: Variety, satin spar. Montmartre, Paris, France.

FIG.   315.—Tiger's-eye.   Griqualand West, South Africa.

Chatoyancy.—The changeable, wavy, silky sheen shown by some minerals with a fibrous structure is known as *chatoyancy*.   The satin spar variety of gypsum (Fig. 314) and tiger's-eye, a variety of quartz, (Fig. 315) are excellent examples of minerals showing chatoyancy.

Minerals with this property cut with a convex surface, called the *cabochon* cut, are frequently used as gems.

Iridescence.—Some minerals show a play of bright colors due to a thin coating or film on the surface of the specimen, as is often the case with limonite. In some cases it is due to cleavage cracks.

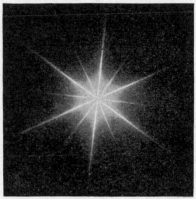

Fig. 316.—Asterism shown by phlogopite from South Burgess, Canada.[1] (*After Hauswaldt.*)

Tarnish.—After certain minerals have been exposed to air, the color of the exposed portions differs distinctly from that of the freshly fractured surfaces. Example, bornite.

Asterism.—Some minerals, like certain sapphires and rubies, exhibit a starlike light effect when viewed in reflected light. Other minerals show a similar effect in transmitted light, that is, when a source of light is viewed by holding the specimen close to the eye, for example, phlogopite (Fig. 316).

Fig. 317.—Rock crystal. Dauphiné, France.

Transparency or Diaphaneity.—This is the ability of a mineral to transmit light. This property, along with color and luster, can usually be recognized upon first sight. Substances through which objects can be easily and distinctly seen are said to be *transparent*. Rock crystal or colorless quartz (Fig. 317) is an excellent example of a transparent

[1] Figures 316, 371 to 373, 381 to 384, 387 to 390, and 393 to 397 are from Hauswaldt's "Interferenzerscheinungen im polarisirten Lichte."

mineral. When some light passes through the substance and objects are seen only indistinctly, the mineral is *translucent*. Relatively thin slabs of Mexican onyx and jade are translucent. Substances are *opaque* when no light is transmitted even through thin edges or layers, for example, graphite. The terms *subtransparent* and *subtranslucent* indicate intermediate stages.

Streak.—This is the color of the fine powder of a mineral and is frequently made use of in the determination of minerals. Although the color of minerals may vary greatly, the streak is often fairly constant. The color of the streak may be determined by crushing, filing, or scratching. The usual and most satisfactory method, however, is to rub the mineral on a piece of white, unglazed porcelain, called the *streak plate*. A streak of $\frac{1}{4}$ inch in length is generally sufficient to determine its color. The ease or difficulty with which the streak can be obtained with the plate is to some extent indicative of the hardness of the mineral. The streak plate cannot be used with minerals with a hardness of 7 or more, for these minerals are harder than the plate. The streak-plate method is the one commonly used in the laboratory.

When a streak plate is not available, the streak can be determined by crushing a small fragment to a fine powder and examining it for color, either unaided or with a hand lens, on a light background, such as a piece of paper, or on a finger nail. Obviously, when a mineral is filed or scratched as in determining the hardness, a fine powder is produced, which may be examined for color as just indicated.

Some minerals having the same color possess streaks which differ materially. Thus, the following three iron minerals may all be black, but they can be readily distinguished by their streaks: hematite (Fe_2O_3), red brown streak; limonite ($Fe_2O_3.nH_2O$), yellow brown streak; magnetite ($Fe(FeO_2)_2$) black streak.

Hardness.—The resistance offered by a mineral to abrasion or scratching is termed *hardness*. It is of great importance in the rapid recognition of minerals, for the approximate hardness of a specimen can be very easily determined. Hardness is indicated relatively in terms of Mohs's scale, which consists of 10 common minerals arranged in order of increasing hardness, as follows:

1. Talc.		6. Feldspar.	
2. Gypsum.		7. Quartz.	
3. Calcite.		8. Topaz.	
4. Fluorite.		9. Corundum.	
5. Apatite.		10. Diamond.	

Beryl, 7.5 to 8 in hardness, is often substituted for topaz in the above scale. The values assigned to the members of this scale indicate simply the *relative* hardness.

Substances scratched by, and which in turn scratch, some one member of the scale are said to have the hardness assigned to that member. If a mineral is scratched by quartz (7) but not by feldspar (6), it is said to have a hardness of 6½. In determining the hardness of a mineral the scratch made should be as short as possible, not over ¼ inch, and care exercised to distinguish between a scratch and a chalk mark. The latter is easily removed by rubbing.

The determination of the approximate hardness is greatly simplified by using a finger nail, copper coin, knife blade, a piece of window glass, or a steel file, which possess the following values:

Finger nail, up to 2.5.
Copper coin, up to 3.
Knife blade, up to 5.5.
Window glass, 5.5.
Steel file, 6 to 7.

FIG. 318.—Edward S. Dana (1849–1935). Noted American mineralogist. For many years professor in Yale University and editor of the *American Journal of Science.*

Since the majority of the minerals are less than 6 in hardness, this simplified scale is of great convenience in determining the approximate hardness in the laboratory and field.

The hardness of crystals and of small specimens, as well as of rough and uncut gems, is best determined by using *hardness pencils.* These are holders with conical-shaped fragments of the test minerals mounted on the ends (Fig. 319). A set of four pencils in a leather case contains

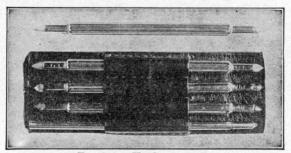

FIG. 319.—Hardness pencils.

the following seven test minerals: feldspar, 6; quartz, 7; zircon, 7½; topaz, 8; chrysoberyl, 8½; corundum, 9; diamond, 10. The *hardness wheel* is a very convenient arrangement of the hardness pencils. The wheel shown in Fig. 320 contains the following six test minerals: olivine, 6¾; quartz, 7; zircon, 7½; topaz, 8; chrysoberyl, 8½; corundum, 9. The pencils and the wheel obviously permit of very easy manipulation.

In testing gems many jewelers first use the steel file. If the file "bites" the tested material, the latter's hardness is below 7. The file will not bite stones harder than 7 but will slide over the edge being tested, often leaving a steel streak. Since many imitation gems, especially those of glass, have a hardness less than 7, while the real precious stones are much harder, this simple test with the steel file is helpful in distinguishing between them.

FIG. 320.—Hardness wheel.

Since hardness is expressed in terms of a numerical scale, it might well be inferred that the hardness of a mineral is a constant quantity. This is, however, not correct, for the hardness of a mineral varies with the crystallographic direction. Ordinarily the variation is so slight as not to be detected by the usual methods; but in some minerals it is quite marked. Thus, cyanite, which occurs in elongated crystals, has a hardness of 4 to 5 parallel to the length of the crystals, while at right angles to the elongation it is much higher, 6 to 7. Moreover, specimens of one and the same mineral from different localities may show some variation in hardness. This is well known to diamond cutters.

In the tables for the determination of minerals, which follow on pages 454 to 621, minerals have been divided into three groups based upon the hardness of calcite and feldspar, thus: (1) 1 to 3, softer than or as hard as calcite; (2) 3 to 6, harder than calcite but not harder than feldspar; (3) over 6, harder than feldspar.

FIG. 321.—Cubical cleavage, halite. Stassfurt, Germany.

FIG. 322.—Octahedral cleavage, fluorite. Near Rosiclare, Illinois.

Cleavage.—Many minerals split or separate easily along definite planes. This property is called *cleavage*. It is frequently very conspicuous and highly characteristic. A mineral can be cleaved either by striking it a properly directed blow with a hammer or by pressing upon it in a definite direction with the sharp edge of a knife blade. The planes along which the separation takes place are called *cleavage planes*. These planes are parallel to possible crystal faces and are so designated. Thus, cubical cleavage, that is, parallel to the faces of the cube, is shown by galena and halite (Fig. 321); octahedral cleavage, by fluorite (Fig. 322) and the diamond (Fig. 323); rhombic dodecahedral cleavage, by sphalerite; rhombohedral cleavage, by calcite; prismatic cleavage, by barite and celestite; basal cleavage, by topaz and mica; clinopinacoidal cleavage, by gypsum. The ease and perfection with which cleavages are obtained are indicated by such terms as *perfect, imperfect, distinct, easy,* and so forth. Thus, calcite is said to have a perfect rhombohedral cleavage.

The cleavage of minerals, and especially of crystals, can often be recognized by the presence and direction of cleavage cracks. Cleavage

Fig. 323.—Famous Cullinan diamond after being cleaved parallel to face of octahedron.

may also be frequently determined by carefully studying the outline and character of the surfaces of the specimen. In such cases, it is not necessary to resort to striking the specimen a blow and, hence, shattering it somewhat, or to the use of a knife-edge. Moreover, when the shape and character of the small particles resulting from the crushing of fragments or from scratching the specimen are examined with a hand lens, the cleavage of the mineral may often be recognized. As cleavage is dependent upon regularity of structure, it is observed only on crystallized substances. Amorphous substances do not possess cleavage.

The important cleavages in the various systems and the common minerals upon which they may be observed are given in the following table:

Cleavage	Mineral
Cubic System	
Cubical	Galena, halite
Rhombic dodecahedral	Sphalerite, sodalite
Octahedral	Fluorite, diamond, cuprite
Hexagonal System	
Rhombohedral	Calcite, dolomite, siderite
Basal	Beryl, apatite, nephelite
Prismatic	Apatite, nephelite

Cleavage	Mineral
	Tetragonal System
Basal	Apophyllite
Prismatic, first order	Rutile, zircon, scapolite
Prismatic, second order	Rutile, scapolite
Pyramidal, first order	Scheelite, wulfenite
Pyramidal, second order	Scheelite
	Orthorhombic System
Basal	Anhydrite (pearly), barite, celestite, topaz
Brachypinacoidal	Anhydrite (vitreous), stibnite, orthorhombic pyroxenes
Macropinacoidal	Anhydrite (greasy to dull)
Prismatic	Barite, celestite, orthorhombic pyroxenes
	Monoclinic System
Basal	Orthoclase, micas, chlorites, epidote
Clinopinacoidal	Orthoclase, gypsum, stilbite
Orthopinacoidal	Epidote
Prismatic	Amphiboles, pyroxenes
	Triclinic System
Basal	Plagioclases, microcline
Brachypinacoidal	Plagioclases, cyanite
Macropinacoidal	Cyanite

Parting.—This is a separation somewhat similar to cleavage and is sometimes called *false cleavage*. It is frequently the result of polysynthetic twinning. It may also be due to pressure applied in definite directions. Corundum has basal, rhombohedral, and prismatic partings.

Fracture.—The fracture of a mineral refers to the character of the surface obtained when crystalline substances are broken in directions other than those along which cleavage or parting may take place. Minerals with no cleavage or with only a poor cleavage yield fracture surfaces very easily. As amorphous substances are devoid of cleavage, they always show fracture surfaces when shattered by a blow. The following types of fracture may be distinguished:

Conchoidal.—The surfaces are curved and shell-like in character. Example, quartz.

Even.—The fracture surfaces are flat or nearly so, that is, they are approximately even planes. Example, lithographic limestone.

Uneven.—The surfaces are more uneven. Example, rhodonite.

Hackly.—The fracture surfaces have many sharp points and are rough and irregular. Example, copper.

Splintery.—The mineral breaks into splinters or fibers. Example, pectolite.

Earthy.—The irregular fracture characteristic of earthy substances like chalk, kaolin, and bauxite.

Fracture is best determined by examining carefully the character of the surfaces of the mineral. By using a hand lens, as indicated under cleavage, the fracture may be observed even when the specimen is in small fragments.

Tenacity.—Under this heading is included the behavior of minerals when an attempt is made to break, cut, hammer, crush, bend, or tear them. The most important kinds of tenacity are the following:

Brittle.—Easily broken or powdered and cannot be cut into slices. Example, quartz.

Sectile.—Can be cut and yields shavings, which crumble when struck with a hammer. Example, gypsum.

Malleable.—Can be hammered out into thin sheets. Examples, gold and copper.

Ductile.—Can be easily drawn into wire. Examples, copper and silver.

Flexible.—Thin layers of the mineral can be bent without breaking, and they remain bent after the pressure has been removed. Example, foliated talc.

Elastic.—Thin layers of the mineral may be bent without breaking, but they resume their positions when the pressure is removed. Example, mica.

Taste.—Minerals soluble in water or the saliva generally possess a characteristic taste, which may be designated as follows:

Acid.—The sour taste of sulphuric acid.

Alkaline.—The taste of soda or potash.

Astringent.—This causes a contraction or puckering. Example, alum.

Bitter.—The taste of Epsom or bitter salts.

Cooling.—The taste of potassium or sodium nitrate.

Metallic.—A very disagreeable, brassy, metallic taste. Example, decomposed pyrite.

Pungent.—A sharp and biting taste. Example, ammonium chloride.

Saline.—The salty taste of halite or sodium chloride.

Although the taste of a mineral is not a property of great importance, it is sometimes very useful in the rapid determination of minerals.

Odor.—Some minerals give off characteristic odors when breathed upon, rubbed, scratched, pounded, or heated, which are designated as follows:

Argillaceous.—The claylike odor obtained by breathing upon kaolin.

Bituminous.—The odor produced by minerals containing bituminous or organic matter. Usually it is easily obtained by striking the specimen with a hammer. Example, asphalt.

Fetid.—The odor of rotten eggs, due to the liberation of hydrogen sulphide. Example, barite.

Garlic.—The odor of the vapors evolved when arsenical minerals are heated. Also called *alliaceous* or *arsenical* odor. Example, arsenopyrite.

Horse-radish.—The very disagreeable odor of decaying horse-radish, obtained by heating compounds of selenium.

Sulphurous.—The odor of sulphur dioxide, which is liberated when sulphur or sulphides are heated or roasted. Example, pyrite.

Feel or Touch.—The impression one receives by handling or touching a mineral is designated as its *feel* or *touch.* The following terms are in common use:

Cold.—The feel of good conductors of heat. Examples, metallic minerals like copper and silver, and gems.

Greasy or Soapy.—The slippery feel of talc.

Harsh or Meager.—Rough to the touch. Example, chalk.

Smooth.—Without projections or irregularities. Example, sepiolite.

Some porous minerals like chalk, kaolin, and diatomaceous earth adhere readily to the tongue.

Specific Gravity.—The specific gravity of a solid substance is its weight in air compared with the weight of an equal volume of water. The specific gravity of a mineral is constant, provided its composition does not vary. Many minerals with strikingly similar physical properties often possess specific gravities which differ materially. Thus, celestite ($SrSO_4$) with a specific gravity of 3.95 can be easily distinguished from barite ($BaSO_4$) having a specific gravity of 4.5.

The specific gravity of minerals can be determined most conveniently by means of the spiral spring balance, often known as the *Jolly balance.* An improved, recording model of this balance is illustrated in Fig. 325.[1] This balance consists of an upright tube to which the inner fixed vernier and the movable, doubly graduated scale are attached. Within this large tube there is a second, smaller tube which can be moved by the large milled head. To this second tube the outer movable vernier is fastened. A movement of the inner tube upward carries the second vernier and the graduated scale with it. Within the second tube there is a rod of adjustable length, which carries the spiral spring, index, and scale pans. With this form of balance, only two readings and a simple division are necessary to determine the specific gravity.

In using the balance it is necessary that the graduated scale, the two verniers, and the index, which is attached to the spiral spring, all be at zero, the lower scale pan being immersed in water. This is accomplished by adjusting approximately, by hand, the length of the rod carrying the spring and then introducing the necessary correction by means of the micrometer screw shown directly below the spring in the illustration (Fig. 325). A fragment is then placed on the upper scale pan, and by turning the large milled head, the inner tube, graduated scale, and outer vernier are all driven upward until the index on the spring is again at

[1] This balance is manufactured by Eberbach and Son Company, Ann Arbor, Michigan.

zero. The fixed inner vernier W (Fig. 326) now records the elongation of the spring due to the weight of the fragment in air. The scale is then clamped by means of the screw at the lower end of it (Fig. 325). The fragment is now transferred to the lower scale pan, immersed in water, and the round tube lowered by the large milled head until the index again reads at zero. During this operation, the outer vernier moves downward on the graduated scale, and its position may now be indicated by

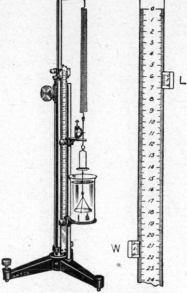

Fig. 324.   Fig. 325.   Fig. 326.

Fig. 324.—Philipp von Jolly (1809–1884). Professor of physics in the University of Munich (1854–1884). Inventor of the spiral spring balance, often called the *Jolly balance*, for the determination of specific gravity.

Figs. 325 and 326.—Improved and recording Jolly balance.

L (Fig. 326). This is obviously the decrease in the elongation of the spring due to the immersion of the fragment in water. The readings at W and L are all the data necessary for the calculation of the specific gravity. For

$$\text{Specific gravity} = \frac{\text{weight in air}}{\text{loss of weight in water}} = \frac{W}{L}.$$

It is also obvious that these readings are recorded so that they may be checked, if necessary, after the operations and calculation are completed.

By means of this balance, specific gravity determinations can be readily made in about two minutes, using for the purpose a crystal or larger mineral fragment as free from impurities as possible. In order to determine the specific gravity of minerals in smaller fragments or grains, it is necessary to make use of the *pycnometer* or *specific gravity flask*.

Fig. 327.

The pycnometer in its simplest form consists of a small glass flask (Fig. 327) fitted with a ground-glass stopper, which is pierced lengthwise by a capillary opening. The pycnometer is first weighed empty (A) and then when filled with distilled water (B). The pycnometer is then emptied and, after being thoroughly dried, the mineral powder, fragments, or grains are introduced and the whole weighed (C). The pycnometer is again filled with water and a fourth weighing made (D). The specific gravity can then be determined as follows:

$$\text{Specific gravity} = \frac{C - A}{B + C - A - D}.$$

Care must be exercised to remove all the air bubbles, which can usually be done by boiling the water and then allowing it to cool. When this

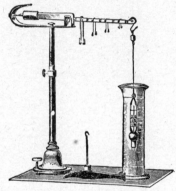

method is carefully carried out, very accurate results may be obtained. When substances are soluble in water, the determination may be made by using some liquid in which they are insoluble, for example, alcohol, and then multiplying the result by the specific gravity of the liquid employed.

The chemical balance and also certain heavy liquids in connection with the Westphal balance (Fig. 328) are sometimes used for the determination of specific gravity. These methods are very accurate but time consuming. They are generally employed in mineralogical research and but rarely by

FIG. 328.—Westphal balance.

students of elementary mineralogy.

Magnetism.—Comparatively strong magnetism is shown by a few iron-bearing minerals, their powders or small fragments being readily attracted by a magnet. A convenient method to test the presence or absence of magnetism in a mineral, without crushing it, is to suspend a small horseshoe magnet from the finger, so that it may swing freely, and then bring the specimen under consideration close to the magnet. If the specimen is magnetic, the magnet will be deviated from its vertical position, the amount of the deviation indicating roughly the relative strength of the magnetism; examples, magnetite and pyrrhotite. Some minerals even act as natural magnets or lodestones and will attract considerable quantities of iron filings, tacks, and nails; examples, certain varieties of magnetite (see Fig. 650, page 321).

Luminescence.—When heated or exposed, in the dark, to the influence of ultraviolet rays, as produced by the iron arc, some minerals glow or become luminescent. Such luminescence may also be produced by exposure to X rays, cathode rays, radiations from radium preparations, and sunlight. Even the mere scratching or pounding of some substances may cause them to show luminescence. The luminescent colors are frequently markedly different from those of the unexcited minerals. The display of these colors is not only interesting but may be even quite spectacular.

A substance is said to *fluoresce*, if it is luminescent during the period of excitation, and to *phosphoresce*, if the luminescence continues after the cause of excitation has been removed. Fluorescence or phosphorescence, or both, are exhibited by fluorite, calcite, opal, sphalerite, willemite, and other substances.

The luminescence caused by scratching, rubbing, or pounding is called *triboluminescence*. This is often well shown by some varieties of sphalerite. When the luminescence is the result of the application of heat, as is often observed on fluorite, it is termed *thermoluminescence*.

Fluorescence and phosphorescence can be readily induced by the use of mercury vapor and argon lamps or by an iron arc apparatus, all of which are available in convenient forms.

FIG. 329.—Leonard J. Spencer (1870–   ). Long associated with the British Museum. Distinguished for his many contributions to mineralogy, and as editor of the *Mineralogical Magazine*.

Electrical Properties.—Some minerals possess interesting electric properties. These properties are frequently classified as (1) *frictional electricity*, (2) *pyroelectricity*, (3) *piezoelectricity*, (4) *electrical conductivity*, and (5) *thermoelectricity*. The first three types will be discussed briefly.

Frictional Electricity.—Vigorous rubbing with a cloth or piece of fur will cause some minerals to become electrified. They will then attract bits of paper. The diamond, tourmaline, and topaz will frequently exhibit frictional electricity.

Pyroelectricity.—Minerals which crystallize in classes of symmetry with polar axes of symmetry may become electrified when subjected to a marked change in temperature. They are then said to exhibit *pyroelectricity*. Tourmaline is an excellent example of a pyroelectric mineral, for, if a light-colored crystal is heated, positive and negative charges develop on the opposite ends. As can be seen from Fig. 330, crystals of tourmaline are usually elongated along the *c* axis, which is polar in character.

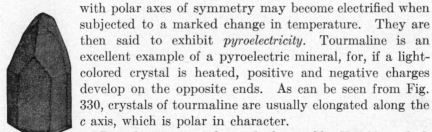

FIG. 330.

Pyroelectricity can be easily detected by *Kundt's method*. The crystal to be tested is gently heated and allowed to cool on an insulated support. It is then dusted with a finely powdered mixture of red lead and sulphur, the particles of which are electrified by friction in their passage through a fine sieve in the nozzle of the bellows containing the mixed powders. The red lead, having been positively electrified, collects at the negative end of the crystal, the negatively charged sulphur is attracted to the positive end. That is, the negative end of the crystal becomes, on cooling, reddish in color, the positive end yellowish.

Piezoelectricity.—By means of pressure, electrical charges may be developed in some minerals. This electrification, called *piezoelectricity*, is most marked along the axes of symmetry that have a polar develop-

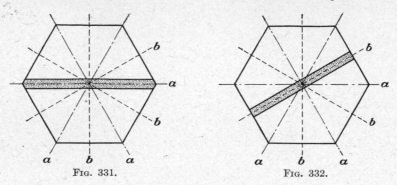

Fig. 331.   Fig. 332.

ment. Quartz is an important piezoelectric mineral. Properly oriented sections or plates of quartz (Figs. 331 and 332) are used for frequency control in electric and radio apparatus. These plates are cut through a crystal of quartz parallel to the crystallographic *c* axis, so that the length of the plate is also parallel to one of the horizontal axes, *a* or *b*. Figure 331 shows the Y cut. It is parallel to an *a* axis and hence is perpendicular to an intermediate *b* axis, which is called a Y or *mechanical* axis. The X cut is shown in Fig. 332. This cut is parallel to one of the *b* axes and hence is perpendicular to an *a* axis, which is termed an X or *electric* axis.

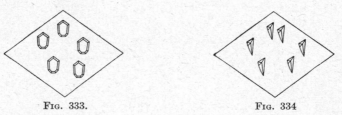

Fig. 333.   Fig. 334

Etch Figures.—When crystals of either minerals or chemical substances are subjected to the solvent action of certain liquids or gases, small geometrical depressions or elevations appear on their surfaces. The shape of these figures, called *etch* or *etching figures*, is intimately associated with the internal structure of the crystal. A study of the shape and position of these figures in relation to the faces on which they occur, and to the geometrical development of the crystal as a whole, is of assistance in determining the symmetry of the crystal. Thus, calcite

($CaCO_3$) and dolomite ($CaMg(CO_3)_2$), both, crystallize in rhombo-hedrons. The symmetry of calcite is, however, higher than that of dolomite, as revealed by the etch figures. On calcite (Fig. 333) the shape and position of the figures are such that a plane symmetry may be passed through the figures, from top to bottom, which corresponds in direction to a plane of symmetry through the crystal face, that is, to the short diagonal. On dolomite (Fig. 334), on the other hand, the shape and position of the figures reveal that no such plane of symmetry is possible. Not infrequently crystals of minerals show natural etch figures. For an accurate determination of crystal symmetry, etch figures should be studied in conjunction with the findings of X-ray analysis (see page 163).

In the production of etch figures in the laboratory, care must be exercised in the selection of the solvents and in the time they are per-mitted to act. Considerable skill in manipulation is also necessary.[1] See also page 31.

Structure.—Many minerals occur frequently in good crystals, as is the case with calcite and quartz. But for the most part minerals are found in masses of various types which may be either crystalline or amor-phous in character. In fact, the general structure of minerals may be classified as follows:

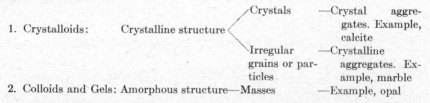

The term *crystalloid* refers to well-developed isolated crystals or to groups or *aggregates of crystals* (Fig. 560, page 269) and also to grains or particles possessing crystal structure but devoid of natural plane sur-faces, which are one of the outward expressions of crystallinity. Masses of grains or particles are called *crystalline aggregates* (Fig. 602, page 293). Colloids or gels do not crystallize and therefore yield only *amor-phous masses*, which are without definite form and internal structure. Those masses which appear to the unaided eye to be amorphous but are, in reality, crystalline, as revealed by the microscope, are called *cryptocrystalline*.

As was shown in Chaps. III to IX, crystals occur in a great diversity of form. These forms are very useful in the determination of minerals. There are also many types of crystalline aggregates and amorphous masses, of which the following are the most important:

[1] For further information, consult A. P. Honess, "The Nature, Origin, and Inter-pretation of the Etch Figures on Crystals." John Wiley & Sons, Inc., New York, 1927.

Acicular.—Composed of delicate and slender, needle-like crystals (Fig. 767, page 386).

Amygdaloidal.—Almond-shaped mineral masses occurring in small cavities in lavas (Fig. 499, page 242).

Arborescent.—Branching or treelike aggregates of crystals (Fig. 335).

Fig. 335.—Arborescent copper. Phoenix Mine, Lake Superior district.

Fig. 336.—Dendritic manganite on sandstone. Malone, New York.

Bladed.—A tabular or platy structure, the individuals resembling grass or knife blades. The blades may be parallel or divergent (Fig. 677, page 340).

Botryoidal.—Closely united, spherical masses, resembling a bunch of grapes (Fig. 616, page 304).

Capillary.—Composed of exceedingly slender or hairlike crystals.

Cellular.—Made up of pores, like a sponge. Porous.

Clastic.—Made up of fragments.

Columnar.—Composed of thick fibers or columns, often in parallel groups (Fig. 643, page 315).

Concentric.—Spherical layers about a common center, similar to the layers of an onion (Fig. 563, page 270).

Concretionary.—Rounded or nodular masses (Fig. 569, page 271).

Dendritic.—Branching and fernlike structure (Fig. 336).

Drusy.—A rough surface due to a large number of small, closely crowded crystals (Fig. 632, page 310).

Fibrous.—Consisting of slender fibers or filaments (Fig. 660, page 329).

Filiform.—Composed of thin wires, often twisted or bent (Fig. 505, page 243).

Foliated.—Made up of plates or leaves which are easily separated.

Globular.—Spherical, or nearly so.

Granular.—Composed of closely packed grains, which may be either coarse or fine (Fig. 697, page 347).

Lamellar.—Made of thin plates or layers.

Lenticular.—Lens shaped.

Mammillary.—Large and rounded masses, larger than grapes.

Micaceous.—Composed of very thin plates or scales, like those of mica.

Nodular.—Rounded masses of irregular shape (Fig. 569, page 271).

Oölitic.—Composed of small, rounded particles the size of fish eggs (Fig. 337).

Phanerocrystalline.—Crystals or coarsely crystalline (Fig. 744, page 374).

Pisolitic.—Composed of rounded particles, the size of peas or buckshot (Fig. 588, page 282).

FIG. 337.—Oölitic limestone. Bedford, Indiana.

FIG. 338.—Reticulated silver. Silver King Mine, Arizona.

Plumose.—Feathery structure, sometimes observed on mica.

Reniform.—Composed of large, rounded masses resembling a kidney in shape (Fig. 581, page 278).

Reticulated.—Composed of fibers crossing in meshes as in a net (Fig. 338).

Scaly.—Composed of small, thin scales or plates.

Sheaflike.—Aggregates resembling a sheaf of wheat in outline (Fig. 770, page 388).

Stalactitic.—Cylindrical or conical masses resembling icicles (Fig. 562, page 269).

Stellate.—Radiating crystals or fibers producing starlike forms.

Tabular.—Composed of broad, flat surfaces, tablet-like (Fig. 619, page 306).

Less frequently used terms are listed in the glossary (page 439). These are employed only when finer distinctions in structure are made.

CHAPTER XI

THE POLARIZING MICROSCOPE

Optical Methods.—Relatively simple methods have been devised for the easy and rapid determination of some of the more important optical constants of solids. These methods are especially adapted to the determination of the optical properties of substances that are available as crystals, in thin sections, or in limited quantities as small fragments or powders. Many of these methods involve the use of the mineralogical or polarizing microscope, which differs materially from the microscope ordinarily used by biologists, pathologists, and other scientists in that it is equipped with a rotating stage and various devices permitting the study of objects in polarized light. In fact, in determining solids by

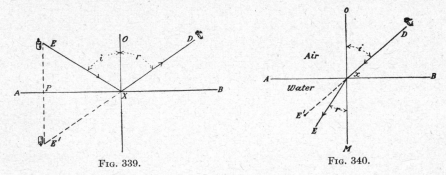

Fig. 339.　　　　　　　　　　Fig. 340.

optical methods polarized light is indispensable. It will, therefore, be necessary to review briefly some of the essential properties of light.

Reflection of Light.—It is well known that when a ray of light falls upon a polished surface, such as a mirror, it is reflected according to the law of reflection, which states that: *the angle of reflection is equal to the angle of incidence, and the reflected and incident rays lie in the same plane.* That is, in Fig. 339, the ray of light EX, from the candle at E, impinges upon the polished surface AB at X with the angle of incidence EXO or i, and is reflected to the eye at D, the angle of reflection being DXO or r. The angles i and r are equal. To the eye the object appears at E'. The line EE' is perpendicular to AB, and the distances EP and PE' are equal.

Refraction of Light—Single Refraction.—When light passes obliquely from one medium into another, for example, from air into water, the path of the ray is not straight but bent. That is, the ray is refracted.

114

We know this from the appearance of a rod or pencil placed in an inclined position in a glass or beaker of water. The phenomenon of refraction is clearly shown by Fig. 340. The ray Dx in air impinges at x upon the surface AB and in passing into the water does not continue in the direction XE' but is bent or refracted toward the normal OM, because the velocity of light is less in water than in air. If the angle of incidence DxO be represented by i and the angle of refraction MxE by r, then the law of refraction may be stated as follows: *the ratios between the velocities of light V and V' in the two media, and between the sines of the angles of incidence and refraction, are equal and constant for the media concerned;* thus, in the case of air and water,

$$n \text{ (index of refraction)} = \frac{V(\text{air})}{V'(\text{water})} = \frac{\sin i}{\sin r} = 1.333.$$

The constant n is called the index of refraction, the velocity of light in air being taken as unity. Thus, the index of refraction of water in terms of air is 1.333; of the garnet 1.75, and of the diamond 2.42. It is evident that the velocity of light in a given substance is proportional to the reciprocal of its index of refraction. Hence, the larger the index, the slower the velocity, and *vice versa*.

In determining these values, white light should not be used, for, when white light passes through a prism, it is resolved into its component colors —a spectrum is produced. Of these component colors, red light is refracted least and violet most. That is, the velocity of light from the red end of the spectrum is greatest, and least from the violet end. Indices of refraction must therefore be determined for a definite type of monochromatic light, commonly expressed in wave lengths, mμ (see page 150). Thus, the indices of the diamond may be given as follows:

$$
\begin{aligned}
n_{\text{red}} \quad & 687\text{m}\mu = 2.407 \\
n_{\text{yellow}} \quad & 589 \quad\;\; = 2.417 \\
n_{\text{green}} \quad & 527 \quad\;\; = 2.427 \\
n_{\text{violet}} \quad & 397 \quad\;\; = 2.465
\end{aligned}
$$

The indices of refraction for a certain variety of glass are $n_{\text{red}} = 1.524$ and $n_{\text{violet}} = 1.545$.

As sources of monochromatic light, the mineralogist commonly uses nonluminous gas flames colored by some volatile salt of the following elements:

Lithium, red,   670mμ

Sodium, yellow,   589

Thallium, green,   535

Dispersion.—The above examples are sufficient to show that the indices of refraction for a given substance vary considerably for the two extremes of the spectrum.   This difference in velocity is called *dispersion*, and in the case of the diamond it is unusually high $(2.465 - 2.407 = 0.058)$. The difference in the indices between opposite ends of the spectrum indicates the strength of the dispersion. The dispersion of glass is much lower $(1.545 - 1.524 = 0.021)$.

Total Reflection and Critical Angle.—When light passes from a denser into a rarer medium, for example, from water into air, the refracted ray is bent away from the normal (Fig. 341). That is, the angle of incidence I is now smaller than the angle of refraction R. It is therefore obvious that for a definite angle of incidence i the angle of refraction r may equal 90°. This angle i is called the *critical* angle, for when the angle of incidence exceeds i in value, as for example, I', the ray is totally reflected; that is, it does not enter the second medium but is reflected

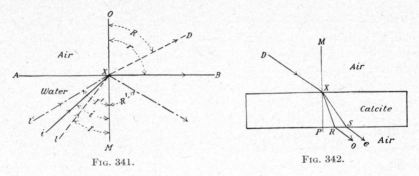

Fig. 341.   Fig. 342.

back into the first, so that angle R' equals angle I'. The value of the critical angle may be expressed as

$$\sin i = \frac{1}{n}$$

where n is the usual index of refraction and i the angle of the incident ray in the denser medium. Hence, it follows that substances with high indices of refraction have smaller critical angles than those with low indices. The critical angle of the diamond $(n = 2.42)$ in terms of air is only 24° 26′, while that of water $(n = 1.333)$ is 48° 36′. The phenomenon of total reflection is of great importance in crystal optics.

Double Refraction.—When an oblique ray of light passes through many solids it is not only refracted but is also resolved into two rays, which travel with different velocities. This phenomenon is designated as double refraction and is characteristic of all crystallized substances other than those of the cubic system. Single refraction has been discussed on page 114.

Double refraction is illustrated in Fig. 342. The ray DX is represented as impinging upon a section of the mineral calcite ($CaCO_3$). DX

is resolved into two rays, *o* and *e*, of which *o* is the slower ray and is refracted more than the faster ray *e*. The velocity of the *o* ray is the same for all directions in the crystal and is called the *ordinary* ray. The other ray, *e*, is termed the *extraordinary* ray. Its velocity varies with direction. In the case of calcite, illustrated in Fig. 342, the ordinary ray is slower than the extraordinary ray, but in other substances the conditions may be reversed; for example, zircon.

Optical Groups.—Substances showing single refraction are called *singly refractive* or *isotropic*, while those with double refraction are designated as *doubly refractive* or *anisotropic*. In isotropic substances the velocity of light of a given wave length does not vary with direction. There is, hence, but one index of refraction for such substances. Amorphous substances and crystals of the cubic system are isotropic. Examples: diamond (cubic), $n_y = 2.42$; garnet (cubic), $n_y = 1.75$; opal (amorphous), $n_y = 1.45$.

Anisotropic substances are subdivided into two groups, depending upon whether they possess one or two isotropic directions. These isotropic directions are called *optic axes*. Those with one isotropic direction possess two principal indices of refraction, ω and ϵ, and include crystals of the hexagonal and tetragonal systems. Examples: calcite (hexagonal), $\omega = 1.65$, $\epsilon = 1.48$; zircon (tetragonal), $\omega = 1.924$, $\epsilon = 1.968$. These substances have one optic axis and are called *uniaxial*. The direction of the optic axis is that of the *c* crystallographic axis. If the index ω is greater than ϵ, the crystal is said to be optically *negative*, and optically *positive* when ϵ has the larger value. Compare the values above for calcite and zircon. The difference between the indices of the ordinary and extraordinary rays gives the strength of *double refraction* or *birefringence*. Thus for calcite it is (ω) $1.65 - (\epsilon)$ $1.48 = 0.17$; for quartz it is (ϵ) $1.553 - (\omega)$ $1.544 = 0.009$. The birefringence is characterized as *strong* or *weak*, depending upon the values obtained.

Those anisotropic crystals which possess two isotropic directions, or optic axes, are called *biaxial*. They include all crystals belonging to the orthorhombic, monoclinic, and triclinic systems. In these crystals there are three principal optical directions at right angles to each other, parallel to which light is propagated with velocities indicated by the three indices, α, β, γ. Examples: topaz (orthorhombic), $\alpha = 1.607$, $\beta = 1.610$, $\gamma = 1.618$; epidote (monoclinic), $\alpha = 1.730$, $\beta = 1.754$ $\gamma = 1.768$; axinite (triclinic), $\alpha = 1.672$, $\beta = 1.678$, $\gamma = 1.681$. When β approaches in value α more than it does γ, as in the case of topaz, the substance is optically *positive*. In optically *negative* crystals the value of β lies nearer to γ, as is shown by the indices of epidote and axinite. The *double refraction* or *birefringence* of biaxial crystals is indicated by $\gamma - \alpha$; thus, for topaz it is $1.618 - 1.607 = 0.011$.

These optical properties may be summarized as follows:

Singly refractive or Isotropic $\begin{cases} \text{Amorphous substances and} \\ \text{cubic crystals} \end{cases}$ $\begin{cases} \text{One index of refraction, } n. \end{cases}$

Doubly refractive or Anisotropic

$\begin{cases} \text{Hexagonal} \\[2ex] \text{Tetragonal} \end{cases}$ Uniaxial $\begin{cases} \text{Two indices of refraction, } \omega \text{ and } \epsilon. \\[1ex] \text{Positive, } \omega < \epsilon \\ \text{Negative, } \epsilon < \omega \end{cases}$

$\begin{cases} \text{Orthorhombic} \\ \text{Monoclinic} \\ \text{Triclinic crystals} \end{cases}$ Biaxial $\begin{cases} \text{Three indices of refraction, } \alpha, \beta, \gamma. \\[1ex] \text{Positive, } \alpha\beta, \gamma \\ \text{Negative, } \alpha, \beta\gamma \end{cases}$

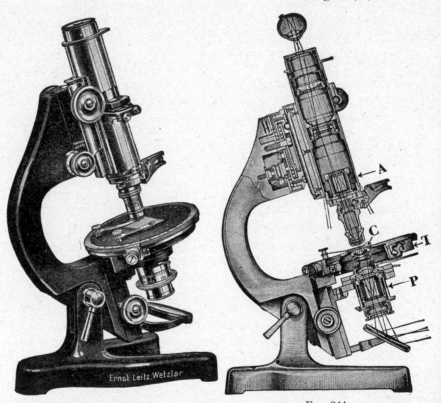

FIG. 343.   FIG. 344.

Polarizing Microscope.—As indicated on page 114, the microscope used by mineralogists (Fig. 343) differs materially from that commonly used by biologists and other scientists in that the stage rotates in the horizontal plane. It is also equipped with devices, called *Nicol prisms*, which permit objects to be studied in polarized light. Figure 344 shows a polarizing microscope in cross section. *T* is the rotating stage. Below the stage is *P*, a Nicol prism for the production of polarized light (see page 124). It is called the *polarizer*. Another Nicol prism, *A*, is placed above the stage in the tube of the microscope. This is called the *analyzer*. This second Nicol prism is mounted upon a slide so that it may be easily removed from the tube. Usually both Nicols can be rotated.

There are several classes of observations which can be made with a mineralogical microscope, namely:

    I. General observations in ordinary light.
   II. Observations in polarized light.
      a. Parallel polarized light.
      b. Convergent polarized light.

By inserting or removing the condensing lens *C* placed below the microscope stage, the change from parallel to convergent light, and *vice versa*, is easily made.

I. GENERAL OBSERVATIONS IN ORDINARY LIGHT

Centering.—In order to use the rotating stage to advantage, its center must obviously lie on the vertical axis passing through the tube when the stage is rotated. To permit of centering, the tube is provided with two screws placed at right angles to each other directly above the objective. These screws displace the tube laterally.

Centering is most readily accomplished by placing on the stage an object glass with a dark speck or small spot of ink, and noting the position of the speck with respect to the dark lines crossing the field. These are called *cross hairs*, and their intersection indicates the center of the field of vision. The object glass should then be carefully moved until the speck is at the intersection of the cross hairs. If the stage is centered, the speck will remain at the intersection when the stage is rotated. If it is not centered, the speck will move in a circular path, the center of which, *o*, lies to one side of the center of the

Fig. 345.—Frederick E. Wright (1877–   ). Geophysical Laboratory, Washington, D.C. American authority on the polarizing microscope and its applications.

field of vision *I* (Fig. 346). The stage should then be rotated until the speck appears to lie upon one of the cross hairs, *AA'*, and the screw parallel to it, *C*, should then be turned until the speck has moved from *X* to *Y*, that is, one-half the distance to the intersection of the cross hairs. The object glass is now moved so that the speck is again at the center of the field, and the stage rotated. The speck will describe the path indicated by the smaller circle. When it apparently lies on the second cross hair PP', the screw D should be turned until it has moved from X' to Y', again one-half the distance to the center of the field. Upon bringing the speck to the center of the field and rotating the stage, it will be found that it has been centered; that is, the spot will remain

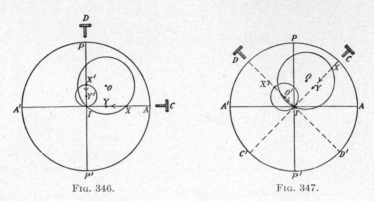

FIG. 346.   FIG. 347.

stationary. Ordinarily, it is necessary to repeat this process several times before the stage is perfectly centered.

On some microscopes, the centering screws are not parallel to the cross hairs, as in Fig. 346, but are placed diagonally, as shown in Fig. 347. When this is the case, the speck should be brought into the diagonal positions indicated by X and X' and the adjustments made by the screws C and D, as described above.

Measurement of Angles.—In measuring plane angles between crystal edges or between cleavage directions, the intersection of the edges is

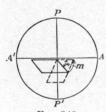

FIG. 348.

brought to the center of the cross hairs and the microscope centered, as described above. The stage is now rotated until one edge is parallel to one cross hair AA' and a reading made on the graduated scale of the stage (see Fig. 348). The stage is then rotated until the other edge is parallel with the same cross hair AA'. The difference between the two readings, angle m, is the supplement of the plane angle under consideration drawn in heavy lines.

Becke Method.—The indices of refraction of solids, in the form of either rock or mineral sections or fragments, may be easily determined by using the method devised by Becke (Fig. 349). This method depends upon refraction and total reflection of light, as illustrated in Fig. 350. Let A and B be two solids in contact, B having a higher index of refraction than A. If the microscope be focused upon the contact, a band or line of light will be observed at SO, which will move toward B when the tube is raised. On lowering the tube, it moves toward A. This band or zone is caused by the concentration of light on one side of the contact, for all rays of light in A, which impinge upon the contact, will pass into B, irrespective of the angle of incidence i. Thus, the ray X will emerge as OM. But when light passing through B impinges upon the contact, the size of the angle of incidence is of great importance, for here the passage is from a denser to a rarer medium. In all such cases, total reflection will take place if the angle of incidence i is larger than the critical angle. That is, the ray R will emerge as ST. As indicated, the raising of the microscope

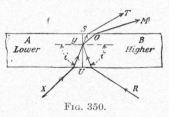

FIG. 350.

tube will displace the band of light, due to this concentration of rays, toward the substance with the higher index. The intensity of this line of light is often accentuated by lowering the substage or by partly closing the substage diaphragm. Whether or not the index of the substance under investigation is higher or lower than

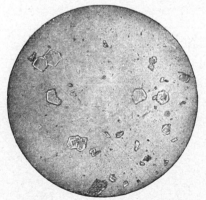

FIG. 351.—Crystal has higher index. FIG. 352.—Crystal has lower index.

Crystals embedded in Canada balsam, showing Becke line with raised tube. (*After Weinschenk-Clark.*)

that of a known substance can thus be easily determined (Figs. 351 and 352).

The indices of refraction of fragments can be determined by immersing them in liquids of known indices and the movement of the band of light noted. The operation is repeated with different liquids, until one is found with an index equal to that of the fragment. In this case, the fragment is invisible, or only slightly visible. When the difference between the indices of the fragment and the liquid is small, the fragment appears smooth and thin and is said to have *low relief.* If this difference is quite large, then the fragment has a dark border and appears rough and thick and is said to have *high relief.* To determine the indices of refraction by this method, the following liquids are serviceable:

Water	1.3336
Petroleum	1.45
Turpentine	1.4721
Xylol, meta	1.502
Clove oil	1.544
Cinnamon oil	1.6026
α Monobromnaphthalene	1.6495
Methylene iodide	1.7421
Sulphur in methylene iodide	1.8

FIG. 353.—Set of standardized refractive index liquids, as arranged by Hawkins.

A set of standardized index liquids[1] with fixed intervals is practically indispensable in determining the indices of refraction of small fragments. Wright (Fig. 345, page 119) suggests the use of the following, mixed in proper proportions:

Mixture of	Index
Petroleum and turpentine	1.450–1.475
Turpentine and clove oil	1.480–1.535
Clove oil and α monobromnaphthalene	1.540–1.635
α monobromnaphthalene and α monochlornaphthalene	1.640–1.655
Monochlornaphthalene and methylene iodide	1.660–1.740
Sulphur dissolved in methylene iodide	1.740–1.790
Methylene iodide, antimony iodide, arsenic sulphide, antimony sulphide, and sulphur	1.790–1.960

II. OBSERVATIONS IN POLARIZED LIGHT

Nature of Polarized Light.—According to the undulatory theory, light is assumed to be a form of energy transmitted in waves in the ether, which pervades all things and space. The propagation of light takes place

[1] Sold by J. T. Rooney, 30 Calumet Building, Buffalo, N. Y.

according to the laws of wave motion, the ether particles vibrating at right angles to the direction of propagation. The velocity of propagation has been determined to be about 186,000 miles per second.

In the case of ordinary light, the vibration of the ether particles takes place in a plane at right angles to the direction in which the light is propagated, but the vibration direction in this plane is constantly changing. If, in Fig. 354, a ray of light is considered as being propagated perpendicular to the plane of this page, then the vibration of the

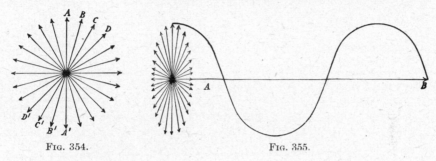

FIG. 354.   FIG. 355.

ether particles will be successively in the directions AA', BB', CC', and so forth. This is shown in perspective in Fig. 355, which must be conceived as revolving about AB as an axis.

In plane polarized light, the vibrations take place in a definite direction within the plane and at right angles to the direction of propagation. Plane polarized light may be produced in three ways: (1) by absorption, (2) by reflection, and (3) by refraction.

Polarized Light by Absorption.—When ordinary light passes through a plate of colored tourmaline cut parallel to the c axis, the light which

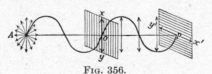

FIG. 356.

emerges is plane polarized. Its vibrations are commonly assumed to be parallel to the c axis. This is illustrated in Fig. 356. Ordinary light emanating from A vibrates in all directions, but, in order to pass through the tourmaline plate xy, it must vibrate parallel to the c axis, that is, parallel to xy. Light vibrating in other directions is absorbed by the tourmaline. Hence, op represents a ray of plane polarized light produced by absorption.

If a second plate of tourmaline $x'y'$ be placed in the path of op so that the direction of its c axis is perpendicular to that of the first plate xy, we observe that the ray op vibrating vertically is now entirely absorbed by the second tourmaline, the favorable direction for the passage of light, $x'y'$, being horizontal. This method for the production of polarized light is not commonly used in scientific instruments.

Polarized Light by Reflection.—When ordinary light is reflected from a smooth surface, it is found to be partially plane polarized, the vibration

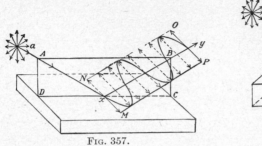

Fig. 357.

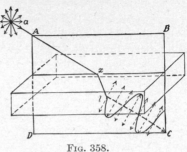

Fig. 358.

directions being at right angles to the direction of propagation. In Fig. 357, the plane $ABCD$, containing the incident and reflected rays ax and xy, is called the plane of *polarization*. The plane $MPON$, in which the polarized ray xy vibrates, is called the plane of *vibration*. It is perpendicular to the plane of polarization. This method of producing polarized light was formerly used much more extensively than at present.

Polarized Light by Refraction.—A portion of the ray ax in Fig. 358 may enter the plate at x and be refracted. Upon emerging as the ray lC, it is partially plane polarized. The vibrations are now executed in the plane of polarization and are perpendicular to the vibration directions characteristic of polarization by reflection. The polarized light used in the mineralogical microscope is commonly produced by refraction. For this purpose, the Nicol prism has long been employed, but in recent years it has been largely replaced by the Ahrens prism (see page 125).

Nicol Prism.—This consists of a cleavage piece of clear, transparent calcite, commonly called Iceland or double spar. It is usually somewhat elongated, as shown in Fig. 359. The natural angles of 71° at A and F are reduced by grinding to 68°. The prism is then cut in two along the plane CD, which is at right angles to the new end faces BC and DE. After the two parts have been polished, they are cemented together, DC, with Canada balsam or thickened linseed oil, which have indices of refraction of about 1.545.

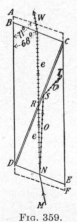

Fig. 359.

If ordinary light be allowed to fall upon DE in the direction of MN, it will be resolved into two rays, since calcite is a doubly refractive substance. Each of these rays is plane polarized. One of the rays is called the ordinary ray *o*. It has a constant index of refraction of 1.658. The other ray is termed the extraordinary ray *e*, and its index of refraction varies from 1.486, when propagated at right angles to the *c* axis, to 1.658, when parallel to the *c* axis. In the direction *NR*, its index of refraction approximates that of the Canada balsam.

The ordinary ray *o* with an index of refraction 1.658 impinges upon the film of Canada balsam at *S* with an angle of incidence which is greater than the critical angle. It is, hence, totally reflected in the direction of *ST*. It, therefore, does not emerge at the upper end of the Nicol prism but is absorbed by the side of the case in which the Nicol is mounted.

The extraordinary ray *e*, however, pursues a path in the Nicol indicated by *NR*. For this direction, the index of refraction of the extraordinary ray is approximately the same as that of the Canada balsam, and the ray, therefore, passes through the balsam with little, if any, deviation. It emerges from the prism at *W* and is plane polarized with vibrations parallel to the short diagonal of the end rhombohedral face of the Nicol. This simple device is very efficient for producing plane polarized light by refraction.

Nicol prisms have been used very extensively in polarizing microscopes and other crystallographic-optical instruments. In microscopes, a Nicol prism, called the *polarizer*, is placed below the stage, while a second, the *analyzer*, is mounted in the tube above the objective (see page 118). The Nicols can be rotated in the horizontal plane. Observations may be made with the vibration directions of both Nicols either parallel or at right angles to each other. When the directions are perpendicular to each other, the Nicols are said to be *crossed*. Observations with crossed Nicols are much more important than those made with *parallel* Nicols.

Ahrens Prism.—The prism devised by C. D. Ahrens permits of a more economical use of calcite than is possible in making the Nicol prism. Accordingly manufacturers of mineralogical microscopes quite generally use the Ahrens instead of the Nicol prism.

The Ahrens prism consists of a rectangular piece of calcite with square ends. The ratio between the lengths of the end and the side edges varies but is often about 1 : 1.8 (Fig. 360). In general the crystallographic *c* axis of the crystal is perpendicular to the front and rear sides. This square prism is cut as shown, *aaáá*, and cemented together with Canada balsam or thickened linseed oil. A section through the prism parallel to the *c* axis is shown in Fig. 361. Rays of ordinary light *m* entering the prism from below are resolved into ordinary, *o*, and extraordinary, *e*, rays. The ordinary rays are totally reflected by the cementing films *aá*, as in the case of the Nicol prism, while the extraordinary *e* rays pass through. In describing the construction and use of the polarizing microscope the devices employed for the production of polarized light, whether they be Nicol or Ahrens prisms, are generally referred to as Nicols.

Parallel and Convergent Polarized Light.—Observations may be carried out with the rays of polarized light passing through the substances parallel to the axis of the microscope tube, or the rays may be made to converge in the substance by means of suitable condensing lenses (Fig. 362). We may, hence, speak of observations in (*a*) *parallel polarized light* and in (*b*) *convergent polarized light.*

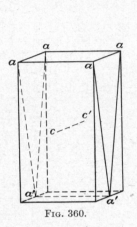

Fig. 360.

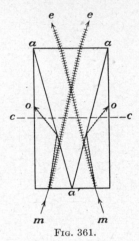

Fig. 361.

Since solids may be classified optically as isotropic and anisotropic, the effects of parallel and convergent polarized light upon each of these groups will be considered. It must be remembered that anisotropic substances can be subdivided into uniaxial and biaxial groups.

Behavior of Isotropic Substances. *a. In Parallel Polarized Light with Crossed Nicols.*—If the analyzer is removed from the microscope

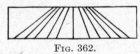

Fig. 362.

tube and an isotropic substance, either an amorphous substance or a crystal of the cubic system, be viewed on the microscope stage, it will be noted that the field of vision is illuminated. It remains illuminated for all positions of the stage, for the polarized light emerging from the polarizer passes through an isotropic substance and to the eye without change. But, when the analyzer is replaced with its vibration direction perpendicular to that of the polarizer, the field of vision is dark and remains so upon rotating the stage. This is due to the fact that the light emerging from the object on the stage vibrates parallel to the vibration direction of the polarizer. This direction, however, is at right angles to that of the analyzer, the Nicols being crossed, and, hence, no light passes through the upper Nicol. All unstrained isotropic substances, therefore, appear dark between crossed Nicols. This observation is very easily made and serves to distinguish isotropic substances from those which are optically anisotropic or doubly refractive.

b. In Convergent Polarized Light with Crossed Nicols.—When substances are studied in convergent polarized light, the rays of light pass through the substance inclined to the axis of the microscope; that is, they tend to converge (Fig. 362). Convergent light is easily obtained by using an objective of high magnification and inserting a condensing lens *C* below the microscope stage (see Fig. 344, page 118).

Isotropic substances appear dark in convergent light between crossed Nicols for the same reasons as given above. That is, between crossed Nicols they are always dark in both parallel and convergent light.

Behavior of Uniaxial Substances in Parallel Polarized Light with Crossed Nicols. *a. Sections Perpendicular to the c Axis.*—When the analyzer is removed, these sections of uniaxial crystals, that is, either crystals of the hexagonal or tetragonal systems, will appear light and remain so for all positions of the stage. When the analyzer is replaced with its vibration direction perpendicular to that of the polarizer, the field is dark and remains so when the stage is rotated. This behavior of hexagonal and tetragonal crystals is the same as for isotropic substances, as discussed above. This is due to the fact that the light is passing through the crystal or the section parallel to the *c* axis, which is an isotropic direction. For this particular direction, uniaxial substances behave in parallel polarized light as though they were isotropic.

b. Sections Parallel or Inclined to the c Axis.—When these sections are viewed with the analyzer removed, the field of vision is illuminated. When the analyzer is replaced and the stage rotated, the field is four times light and four times dark during a complete rotation, provided the Nicols are crossed. That is, when viewed in daylight or white artificial light, interference colors are seen four times during a complete rotation. The positions of greatest darkness or extinction indicate the vibration directions of the rays passing through the section or crystal. When the vibration directions of the crystal are parallel to those of the Nicols, the field of vision is dark. This is illustrated in Fig. 363, where *PP'* and *AA'* are the vibration directions of the polarizer and analyzer, respectively, and *RR'* and *SS'* those of the crystal. *PP'* and *RR'* being parallel, light from the polarizer passes through the crystal without change in vibration direction and enters the analyzer but does not emerge, the favorable direction for passage through the upper Nicol being *AA'*.

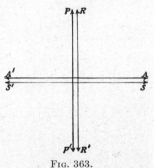

Fig. 363.

The cross hairs of the microscope are parallel to the vibration directions of the Nicols and are used for the determination of the extinction or vibration directions in the crystal or section. Extinction may take place when the cross hairs are parallel or perpendicular to the edges of the specimen, as in Fig. 364.   When this is the case, the crystal is said to have *parallel extinction*.   Uniaxial substances may also possess *symmetrical extinction*, as illustrated in Fig. 365.

   c. Determination of Indices of Refraction.—The position of extinction is found as indicated above.   The analyzer is then removed, and the

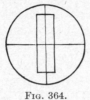

FIG. 364.   FIG. 365.

Becke test applied (see page 120).   In this way, the index of refraction of the ray vibrating parallel to the vibration direction of the polarizer is determined.   On rotating the stage through 90°, the index of refraction for the second vibration direction can be determined.   The ray vibrating parallel to the *c* axis is termed the *extraordinary* ray *e;* the one vibrating at right angles to it, the *ordinary* ray *o.*   When the index of refraction of *e* is larger than that of *o,* the crystal is said to be optically *positive;* when smaller, optically *negative,* (see page 117).

FIG. 366.—R e i n h a r d Brauns (1861–1937).   Professor of Mineralogy in the University of Bonn (1907–1932).   Eminent investigator, author, and editor.

   d. Interference Colors.—When the vibration directions in the crystal are not parallel to those of the Nicols, the field shows, in general, an interference color, provided the crystal is viewed in either daylight or artificial white light.   The color is due to the fact that the light from the polarizer *PP'* is resolved into two rays vibrating parallel to *xx'* and *yy',* the vibration directions of the crystal (Figs. 367 and 368).   The two rays in the crystal travel with different velocities, and, when they emerge, the slow ray naturally lags behind the faster.   On entering the upper Nicol, each of these rays is further resolved into two rays vibrating parallel to the vibration directions of the *o* and *e* rays of the analyzer.   As indicated on page 127, only the latter of these, namely, the two vibrating parallel to the *e* ray, emerge from the analyzer.   But these two emergent rays *OS* and *OR,* vibrating in the same plane, traveled with different velocities.   Interference of light is thus brought about, and with crossed Nicols, when the phasal difference of the two rays is equal to a whole wave length λ, or some whole multiple thereof, destructive interference results (Fig. 367). When the phasal difference is a half wave length, $\frac{1}{2}\lambda$, or some odd multiple thereof, the rays reinforce each other (Fig. 368).

As the phasal differences for the component colors of white light will be of both these types, certain portions of the white light passing through the crystal are destroyed, while other portions are intensified, causing the light which emerges to be colored. The field of vision shows, therefore, what is commonly designated as an interference color. The

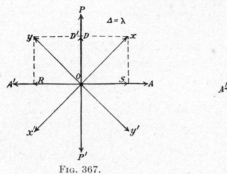

Fig. 367.

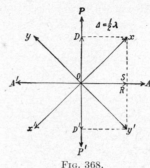

Fig. 368.

character of the color depends upon (1) *the strength of double refraction of the substance,* (2) *the position of the plate with regard to the c axis, and* (3) *the thickness of the plate.* When monochromatic light instead of daylight is used, the field will be dark, as before, if the vibration directions in the substance and Nicols correspond. In intermediate positions, the field will be illuminated by light of the particular color employed.

e. Determination of the Fast and Slow Rays.—The position of extinction is first determined, and the stage then rotated so that the extinction directions cross the field diagonally; that is, they make angles of 45° with the cross hairs (Fig. 369). This is the position of most intense illumination and color. Into the slot of the microscope tube, which is directly above the objective, a gypsum or selenite test plate is now inserted. When viewed alone between crossed Nicols, the test plate yields an interference color which is usually designated as the *sensitive red tint.* By the action of the crystal on the

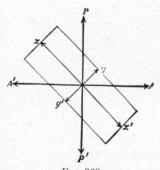

Fig. 369.

stage, the red tint is changed to either a bluish or yellowish color. If the tint is changed to a bluish color, it means that the vibration directions of the test plate and those of the crystal correspond; that is, the slow ray in the test plate is over the slow ray in the crystal and the fast over the fast. Now note the direction of the marked ray on the test plate, which is usually given as α or X. This is the fast ray, and the vibration direction at right angles to it is obviously that of the slow ray, which is commonly designated as c or Z. In this way, the directions of the corresponding rays are easily recognized in the crystal. If, however, the sensitive red tint is changed to a yellowish color, instead of a bluish, it means that the fast ray of the test plate is over the slow ray of the crystal, and *vice versa*.

If the mineral has high double refraction, the directions of the fast and slow rays can be more conveniently determined by the use of the quartz wedge. If the wedge is inserted so that the vibration directions of the wedge and of the mineral are of unlike character, the interference colors of the mineral are reduced, that is, they pass to those of a lower order; but, if the vibration directions are the same, the interference colors are increased, that is, they pass to those of a higher order.

f. Order of Interference Colors.—The interference colors may be bright and vivid and are then said to be of a *low* or *medium order*, or they may be hazy and dull and are of the *higher orders*. It is well in determining the order of interference colors to study an interference color chart. When the color approximates white, it is characterized as being *white of the higher order*. When sections of different substances have the same thickness and orientation, some indication of the strength of double refraction, or birefringence, can be obtained from the character of the interference colors, for the stronger the double refraction the higher the resultant order of colors. When dealing with one and the same substance, the thicker sections or crystals will show colors of higher order.

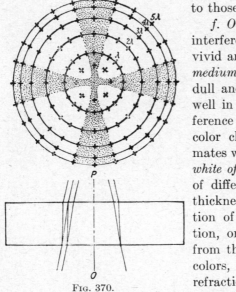

Fig. 370.

The Behavior of Uniaxial Crystals in Convergent Polarized Light with Crossed Nicols. *a. Sections Perpendicular to the c Axis.*—In uniaxial substances, all rays of light inclined to the c axis are resolved into two rays, *o* and *e*, which travel with unequal velocities. These rays interfere, therefore, on emerging from the substance, as indicated in Fig. 370. The phasal difference between these rays increases with the inclination of the incident rays to the c axis. Hence, at *OP*, which corresponds to the direction of the c axis, the phasal difference will be zero. Accordingly, the phasal difference increases as the distance of emergence from *P* grows larger. The increase is the same for all directions.   Wherever the phasal difference $\Delta = \frac{n}{2}\lambda$, where n is odd, reinforcement of light takes place.   Where $\Delta = n\lambda$, n being any whole number, destructive interference results.   Along any diameter through the field of vision, therefore, we shall observe darkness at the center P, and at equal distances on either side of P the same interference colors will appear when daylight or artificial white light is used.   In uniaxial crystals, all directions equally inclined to the c axis are optically the same.   Hence, the interference colors appear as a series of concentric rings.   The colors are brighter and more vivid near the center of the field and gradually fade as the distance from the center increases.   These isochromatic circles are farther apart near the center of the field and closer together

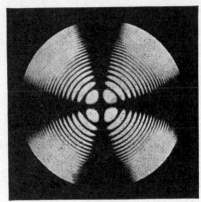

FIG. 371.[1]   FIG. 372.[1]

toward the periphery.   In monochromatic light, a series of light and dark circles will be observed (Figs. 371 and 372).

It will be further observed that a dark cross lies superimposed upon the isochromatic circles.   The cross occurs where the vibration directions of the substance correspond to those of the Nicols, for, as has been pointed out previously, in such instances the field is dark.   The isochromatic circles and the dark cross constitute what is called the *uniaxial interference figure*.

The uniaxial interference figure remains unchanged when the stage is rotated, for all directions through the substance equally inclined to the c axis are alike optically.   In order to observe interference figures, it is necessary to use an objective of high magnification, and either to remove the eyepiece of the microscope or to insert an auxiliary lens called the *Bertrand lens* into the tube above the analyzer.   In the first case, the figure is small and appears far down in the tube.   It is, however, usually

[1] After Hauswaldt.

quite distinct.   In the second case, the figure is much larger but generally more hazy.

b. Sections Inclined to the c Axis.—Sections of this character show only a partial interference figure in convergent light.   The more nearly the section is parallel to the base the more will the observed figure approximate the normal figure; and the greater the departure from this parallelism the more the figure will be eccentric and incomplete.   This is shown by Fig. 373.   When the stage is rotated, the arms of the dark cross move across the field parallel to the cross hairs and in the same direction as the movement of the stage.   This observation is of great importance in distinguishing certain uniaxial from biaxial figures (see pages 136 and 137).

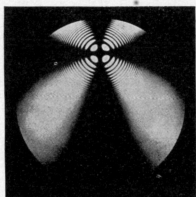

FIG. 373.[1]

c. Strength of Double Refraction Determined from Uniaxial Interference Figures.—The number of isochromatic circles may serve to estimate the strength of double refraction or birefringence.   When sections have the same thickness, substances with strong double refraction will show more rings than those possessing weak birefringence.   Thickness also increases the number of rings (Figs. 371 and 372).   In extremely thin sections these rings may not be visible.   This is especially true of substances with very weak birefringence.

d. Character of Double Refraction Determined from Uniaxial Interference Figures.—The optical character of uniaxial substances cut perpendicular to the *c* axis can usually be determined by using the following test plates: (1) *mica test plate,* (2) *gypsum or selenite test plate,* and (3) the *quartz wedge.*

1. Mica Test Plate.—If the mica test plate be inserted in the slot of the microscope tube, it will be observed that the interference figure breaks up and two distinct black spots appear near the center of the field.   The position of these spots with respect to the vibration direction

[1] After Hauswaldt.

marked on the test plate should be noted. If a line joining these spots is parallel to the c direction (vibration direction of the slow ray in test plate), the substance is optically *negative* (Fig. 374). In optically *positive* substances, the line joining the black spots is perpendicular to the c direction (Fig. 375).

2. Gypsum or Selenite Test Plate.—When the gypsum or selenite test plate is used, two blue spots appear. If the line joining these

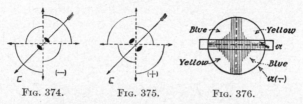

FIG. 374.   FIG. 375.   FIG. 376.

blue spots is parallel to the α direction of the gypsum test plate (fast ray in test plate), the substance is said to be optically *negative* (Fig. 376) and optically *positive* if it crosses the α direction of the test plate.

3. Quartz Wedge.—If the quartz wedge is slowly pushed into the slot, it will be observed that the interference figure is broken up into two pairs of moving arcs which lie in opposite quadrants. One pair of these arcs will move *outward* or away from the center of the figure, while the other pair moves in the opposite direction, that is, *inward* or toward the center. If the outward movement of the arcs is parallel to the c direction of the wedge, when the wedge is slowly inserted beginning at the thin

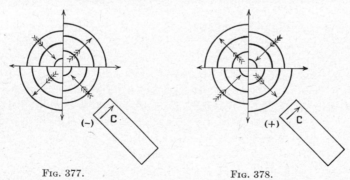

FIG. 377.   FIG. 378.

end, the substance is optically *negative* (Fig. 377). In optically *positive* substances, the outward movement of the arcs is across or perpendicular to the c direction (Fig. 378).

These observations are based upon the fact that when like directions in the test plates and in the substances are over one another, the double refraction is increased. When the corresponding directions are unlike, for example, fast ray over slow ray, and *vice versa*, a reduction in double refraction results.

General Statement Regarding Biaxial Crystals.—As indicated on page 117, all crystals of the orthorhombic, monoclinic, and triclinic systems are biaxial and possess three principal optical directions at right angles to each other. The principal optical direction which bisects the acute angle between the two isotropic directions, or the optic axes AA', is called the *acute bisectrix* Bx_a (Fig. 379). The *obtuse bisectrix* Bx_o bisects the obtuse angle of the optic axes. These bisectrices are the

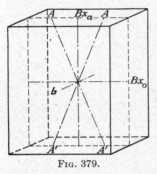

FIG. 379.

vibration directions of the rays traveling with the greatest and least velocities. The acute and obtuse bisectrices and the optic axes lie in the same plane, called the *plane of the optic axes*. The direction at right angles to the plane is termed the *optic normal* b or Y. In the orthorhombic system, the three optical directions, acute bisectrix, obtuse bisectrix, and optical normal (Fig. 379) correspond to the three crystallographic axes. Monoclinic crystals have only one of these directions fixed, namely, by the b crystallographic axis. In the triclinic system, there is no fixed relationship between the orientation of the principal optical directions and the crystallographic axes.

Crystals are said to be optically *positive* or *negative*, depending upon whether the acute bisectrix is the vibration direction of the slow (c or Z) or fast (a or X) ray, respectively. The direction of the optic normal is commonly designated as b or Y. Also consult pages 117 and 118.

Behavior of Biaxial Crystals. *A. In Parallel Polarized Light with Crossed Nicols. a. Any Section.*—All sections of biaxial crystals, with the exception of those perpendicular to an optic axis, are four times light and four times dark during a complete rotation of the stage. The extinction may be either parallel, symmetrical, or inclined to an edge or cleavage of the crystal or section (Figs. 364, 365, and 380). In the case of orthorhombic substances, the extinction is usually parallel or symmetrical. Monoclinic substances possess

FIG. 380.

both parallel and inclined extinctions; that is, sections parallel to the b axis have parallel extinction, while all other sections have inclined or oblique extinction. Maximum obliquity is observed on sections perpendicular to the b axis. In triclinic substances, all extinctions are inclined.

b. Sections Perpendicular to an Optic Axis.—These sections do not extinguish when the stage is rotated between crossed Nicols but remain uniformly illuminated. In convergent light, an interference figure is observed (see Figs. 389 and 390, page 137).

B. In Convergent Polarized Light with Crossed Nicols. a. Sections Perpendicular to the Acute Bisectrix Bx_a.—These sections show an interference figure consisting of two series of oval-like curves upon which two dark brushes are superimposed. In the *normal* position, that is, when the plane including the optic axes and the direction at right angles to it are parallel with the cross hairs, the interference figure resembles Fig. 381. In white light the curves are colored, while in monochromatic light they are alternately light and dark. The distance between the optic axes or "eyes" gives some indication of the size of the angle of the

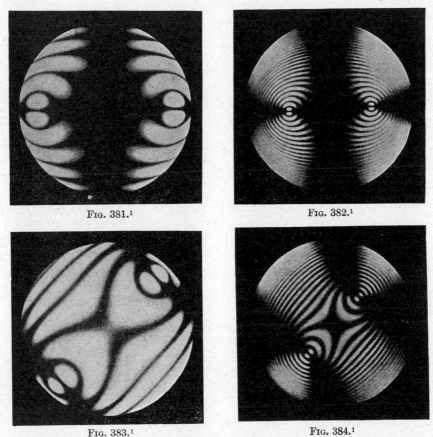

Fig. 381.[1]

Fig. 382.[1]

Fig. 383.[1]

Fig. 384.[1]

optic axes. The closer together the "eyes" are the smaller is the angle (Fig. 382), and *vice versa*. The angle of the optic axes is constant for any given substance and is independent of the thickness of the section, provided the temperature remains the same. From the number of curves in the interference figure, some idea of the double refraction may be obtained, for the stronger the double refraction the larger the number of the curves in the field of vision, provided the sections are the same thickness.

[1] After Hauswaldt.

The optical properties of biaxial crystals are very complex, and only an elementary and incomplete explanation of the formation of these interference figures will be given. The black cross or hyperbolic brushes appear wherever the vibration directions of the emergent rays are parallel to those of the Nicols. At all other points of the section, the emergent rays have vibration directions which are inclined to those of the Nicols, and interference of light, as explained on page 129, will, therefore, take place. As these vibration directions change most rapidly around the optic axes, the curves there will be smaller and closer together than elsewhere. These curves are unaltered as the stage is rotated. The dark brushes, however, change. Figures 383 and 384 show biaxial interference figures in the 45° or *diagonal* position.

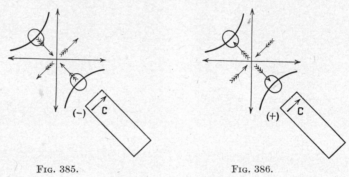

FIG. 385.   FIG. 386.

The positive and negative character of biaxial crystals may be determined from the interference figure by using the mica or gypsum test plates, as described on page 132. When the spots are in the same quadrants as the marked directions on the test plate (c, mica; or α, gypsum) the substance is negative, and positive in the opposite quadrants.

The quartz wedge may be used to advantage when the biaxial figure is in the 45° or *diagonal* position (Figs. 383 and 384). The wedge should be slowly inserted, beginning at the thin end. In optically *negative* substances the outward movement of the arcs is parallel to the c direction of the wedge (Fig. 385), while in optically *positive* substances it is across or perpendicular to the c direction (Fig. 386).

b. Sections Inclined to the Acute Bisectrix Bx_a.—These sections show a partial interference figure, usually only one optic axis or "eye" and a portion of the brushes being visible (Figs. 387 and 388). The brushes always move in a direction opposite to that of the stage.

c. Sections Perpendicular to an Optic Axis.—These sections show the emergence of an optic axis, the observed interference figure being illustrated by Fig. 389. This figure does not remain stationary when the stage is rotated, as is the case with interference figures of uniaxial substances (page 131). Figures 389 and 390 show the interference figure in the normal and diagonal positions, respectively. When the interference figure is in the 45° or diagonal position, the convex side of the hyperbolic brush and the more pointed portions of the curves about the optic axis are directed toward the acute bisectrix.

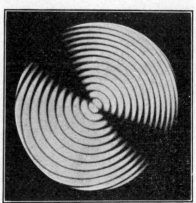

FIG. 387.[1]   FIG. 388.[1]

The gypsum test plate may be used to advantage in determining the optical character of the substance when the interference figure is in the diagonal position. If the substance is optically positive, a blue spot appears on the convex side of the hyperbolic brush, provided the test plate is inserted with its α direction parallel to the plane of the optic

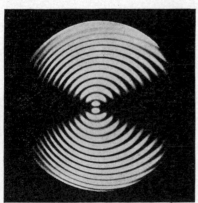

FIG. 389.[1]   FIG. 390.[1]

axes. In the case of optically negative substances, the blue spot will be observed on the concave side of the brush.

d. Sections Parallel to the Plane of the Optic Axes.—Sections of this character do not, in general, show distinct interference figures, especially if studied in white light.

[1] After Hauswaldt.

e. Dispersion of the Optic Axes, $r > v$ or $r < v$.—In Fig. 384 illustrating biaxial interference figures, the size of the angle of the optic axes is indicated by the distance between the centers of the eyes. When white light is used and the interference figures are viewed in the 45° or diagonal position, the hyperbolic brushes show red and blue or violet fringes. These fringes are especially distinct at r and v, as shown in Figs. 391 and 392. This is due to the fact that the size of the angle of the optic axes varies with the color. In some cases, the angle for red is larger than for violet, and *vice versa*. If red appears on the convex side of the hyperbolic brushes, it means that the optic angle for red is larger than for blue or violet; that is, $r > v$. On the other hand, if violet is observed on the convex side of the brushes, the angle for violet is the larger, namely, $v > r$. That is, the dispersion of the optic axes is directly opposite to what appears to be the case from the position of the colors

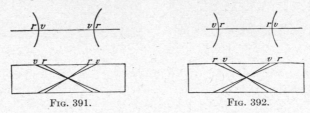

FIG. 391.   FIG. 392.

in the interference figure. This is due to the fact that from the white light traveling along the optic axes of the various colors, certain components are eliminated and others intensified. Hence, where the axes for red light emerge, say, at r in Figs. 391 and 392, red will have been eliminated and the resultant light will be violet. At v, violet has been lost, and in the interference figure red will appear at the corresponding positions. The observation of the character of the dispersion of the optic axes is best made with the interference figure in the diagonal position on any section where a portion of a hyperbolic brush is distinctly visible near the center of the field. The determination of the character of the dispersion aids materially in identifying biaxial substances.

Circular Polarization.—Some substances show circular polarization; that is, they rotate the plane of polarization. The most notable of such substances among the common minerals is quartz. As is well known, quartz occurs in enantiomorphous crystals; that is, in right- and left-handed crystals (see Figs. 190 and 191, page 59). This type of development is also observed on crystals of tartaric acid, cane sugar, and sodium chlorate. In some particulars, the behavior of substances possessing circular polarization is unique. The effect of circular polarization in uniaxial crystals only will be considered.

A. Parallel Polarized Light and Crossed Nicols. a. Sections Cut Perpendicular to the c Axis.—As the c axis in these substances is not an isotropic direction, sections cut perpendicular to it do not extinguish between crossed Nicols but remain uniformly illuminated when the stage is rotated.

b. Sections Cut Parallel or Inclined to the c Axis.—These sections behave in the same way as those described on page 132.

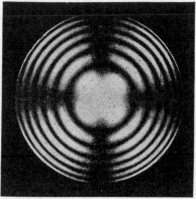

FIG. 393.[1]

B. Convergent Polarized Light and Crossed Nicols. Sections Cut Perpendicular to the c Axis.—An interference figure quite analogous to the regular uniaxial interference figure is obtained (Fig. 393). It will be observed that the dark brushes do not extend entirely across the

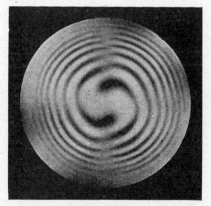

FIG. 394.[1]

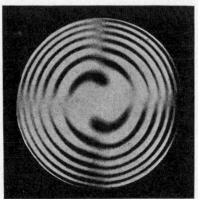

FIG. 395.[1]

center of the figure. By rotating the upper Nicol, the character of the rotation of polarization may be determined, that is, whether it is to the right or left. If the upper Nicol is rotated in the same direction as that of the rotation of the plane of polarization, the circles of the figure enlarge; but, if it is rotated in the opposite direction, the circles contract.

[1] After Hauswaldt.

By using the mica test plate, a two-armed spiral is obtained, the direction of rotation being indicated by the directions of the arms (Figs. 394 and 395). By placing two sections of quartz of the same thickness over one another, a figure with a four-armed spiral results. These are the spirals of Airy (Figs. 396 and 397). The direction of the arms of the spirals indicates the character of the rotation in the lower section.

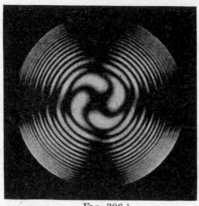

FIG. 396.[1]   FIG. 397.[1]

Twin Crystals.—The fact that crystals are twinned is easily recognized in polarized light, especially if they are anisotropic.

a. Parallel Light and Crossed Nicols.—Anisotropic crystals showing twinning do not extinguish uniformly. Certain portions of the crystal may be dark, while other portions are light, when the stage is rotated. Figures 398 and 399 show the behavior of contact twins and Fig. 400

FIG. 398.   FIG. 399.   FIG. 400.   FIG. 401.

that of a section with polysynthetic twinning. Obviously, twinned crystals of isotropic substances will have no effect upon polarized light.

b. Convergent Light and Crossed Nicols.—In properly oriented sections, interference figures may be observed, as shown in Fig. 401.

Pleochroism.—The absorption of light in colored sections and crystals of uniaxial and biaxial substances varies with direction. In the case of uniaxial substances, there are two principal colors for transmitted light. These colors are obtained when the light vibrates either parallel or perpendicular to the *c* axis. Uniaxial substances are, therefore, said to be *dichroic*. In biaxial crystals there are three principal colors cor-

[1] After Hauswaldt.

responding to the three principal optical directions at right angles to each other. Biaxial substances are therefore *trichroic*.

Pleochroism is easily recognized under the microscope by first determining the extinction directions of the section or crystal under consideration. The stage of the microscope should be then rotated so that one of the extinction directions is parallel to a vibration direction of the lower Nicol or polarizer. The upper Nicol should now be removed and the color observed, and then the stage rotated 90° and the change in color noted. Strongly pleochroic substances show marked changes in color when studied in this way.

Isotropic substances, that is, those which are amorphous or belong to the cubic system, do not show pleochroism.

Summary.

BEHAVIOR OF SECTIONS, CRYSTALS, OR FRAGMENTS IN PARALLEL LIGHT BETWEEN CROSSED NICOLS

All sections remain dark through 360° — Isotropic
- (*a*) No regular outline, structure, cleavage, or etch figures. — Amorphous.
- (*b*) Regular outline, structure, cleavage, and etch figures. — Cubic.

Not all sections remain dark through 360°. Some are four times light and dark, others remain uniformly light. — Anisotropic
- (*a*) Isotropic and doubly refractive sections. The first show an uniaxial interference figure in convergent light.
  - Hexagonal. Isotropic sections are trigonal or hexagonal in outline.
  - Tetragonal. Isotropic sections are tetragonal or ditetragonal in outline.
- (*b*) Sections either extinguish regularly or remain uniformly light. The latter show the emergence of an optic axis in convergent light.
  - Orthorhombic. Most sections show parallel or symmetrical extinction.
  - Monoclinic. Sections show parallel, symmetrical, or inclined extinction.
  - Triclinic. All sections show inclined extinction.

Order of Procedure and Methods for Recording Observations.—In studying sections, crystals, or fragments under the polarizing microscope, the following order for making determinations is suggested:

Parallel Polarized Light

1. Isotropic or anisotropic.
2. Index of refraction; higher or lower than Canada balsam or the liquid in which substance is embedded, if in fragments.
3. Outline of section or crystal. Cleavage cracks.
4. Extinction directions—parallel, symmetrical, or inclined. Measurement of extinction angles.
5. Determination of fast and slow rays.
6. Order of interference colors. Double refraction.
7. Pleochroism.

Convergent Polarized Light

1. Uniaxial or biaxial figure. Orientation.
2. If biaxial, note size of optic angle.
3. Positive or negative character.
4. Double refraction.
5. Dispersion.
6. Circular polarization.
7. System. See summary.

Figures 402 and 403 indicate a very good method, suggested by Weinschenk, for recording the various optical properties of substances,

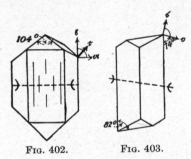

Fig. 402.			Fig. 403.

as determined under the microscope. In both figures the material represented was in the form of small crystals. The outline of the substance should be sketched and important angles measured and their sizes indicated. The direction of cleavage cracks may be shown as in Fig. 402. The various extinction directions are shown by arrows. The approximate value of the indices of refraction for these directions can be indicated by lines of different widths; that is, light lines indicate low indices, heavy lines high indices. The strength of double refraction is given by the arc enclosing the vibration directions, which may be drawn light or heavy in accordance with the variation from weak to strong double refraction, or one or more arcs may be used. Pleochroism may be shown in connection with the vibration directions, the observed colors being designated. The location of the optic axes, size of the optic angle, and dispersion are all easily indicated.

CHAPTER XII

CRYSTAL STRUCTURE AND X-RAY ANALYSIS

Crystals and Crystal Structure.—Crystals are ordinarily defined as solids bounded by natural plane surfaces called *crystal faces*. Such is the definition given on page 6. Since the positions and spatial relations of the crystal faces of a given substance are definite, they cannot be regarded as accidental surface phenomena but must be considered the result of some underlying cause inherent in the crystal itself. Moreover, among the various properties of crystals, there are some which vary with direction. As was shown in Chap. XI, the properties of light are of this character. It is evident that such characteristic phenomena must be due to a regular internal structure. Accordingly, the crystallographer is interested not only in the geometrical arrangement of crystal faces but also in the more fundamental internal structure of the crystal.

Early Theories of Crystal Structure.—Although it was long surmised that crystals undoubtedly possess regular internal structure, it was not until toward the close of the seventeenth century that students of crystals began to formulate theories. Thus, Huygens, in 1678, in explaining the double refraction of calcite, advanced views that may be considered as having formed the basis for the development of the subsequent theories of crystal structure. By assuming calcite to be made up of small, ellipsoidal particles arranged or packed in a regular manner, Huygens endeavored to explain the crystal form and cleavage of the

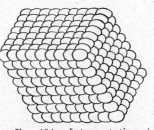

Fig. 404.—Interpretation of the internal structure of calcite according to Huygens.

mineral as well as the variations in its hardness and double refraction with direction. Figure 404 represents the internal structure of calcite as visualized by Huygens.

Later, in 1781, Haüy (Fig. 33, page 15) published a theory of crystal structure which was based principally on cleavage. Haüy assumed that a crystal is made up of a large number of small particles, similar in form and equal in size, which are arranged in parallel order and fill space without gaps. The occurrence of different crystal forms on a crystal, each with rational indices, Haüy explained by *decrescence*, according to which the successive layers decrease regularly, or stepwise, in area (Fig. 405). The particles were considered as being of infinitesimal size, and, hence, apparently smooth crystal faces resulted.

Space Lattices.—With the discovery of the compressibility of solids, it became necessary to assume that the ultimate particles of matter do not completely fill space. It was further assumed that the particles were in a state of motion varying with the temperature. Accordingly, the conception of Haüy was modified so that the particles were represented merely by points. These points were assumed to be the mean positions of the vibrating particles, which were no longer thought of as solid units completely filling space. The study of the possible arrangements of such points led to the development of the 14 space lattices.

A *space lattice* (Fig. 406) is a regular repetition of points in space, at constant intervals for a given direction. All parallel directions are

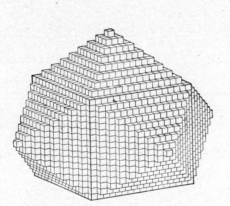

FIG. 405.—Crystal structure showing decresence according to Haüy.

FIG. 406.—Space lattice.

identical, and the environment about any one point is similar to that about every other point. It was definitely proved that only 14 lattices are geometrically possible, and that these 14 lattices are in harmony with the six crystal systems. Moreover, if a crystal is composed of units repeated according to a space-lattice pattern, a reasonable explanation is provided for the law of rational indices, as well as for the directional properties of the crystal.

If planes are passed through the points of a lattice, they divide space into identical parallelepipeds, known as *unit cells*. In Figs. 407 to 420 are shown the unit cells, representative of the 14 space lattices.

Point Systems.—Although the 14 elementary space lattices could account for the more important crystal structures in the six systems, the types of crystallization involving hemimorphism and enantiomorphism were not explained. *Regular point systems* were then theoretically evolved from the space lattices by assuming identical lattices to have interpenetrated one another either after definite rotations or after

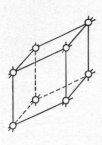

Fig. 407.—Triclinic.

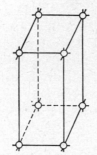

Fig. 408.—Simple monoclinic.

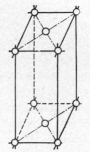

Fig. 409.—Base-centered monoclinic.

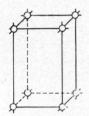

Fig. 410.—Simple orthorhombic.

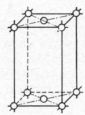

Fig. 411.—Base-centered orthorhombic.

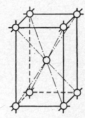

Fig. 412.—Body-centered orthorhombic.

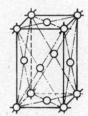

Fig. 413.—Face-centered orthorhombic.

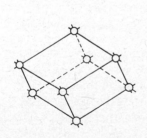

Fig. 414.—Rhombo-hedral.

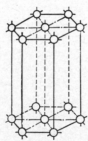

Fig. 415.—Hex-agonal.

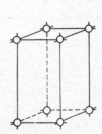

Fig. 416.—Simple tetragonal.

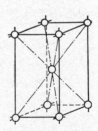

Fig. 417.—Body-centered tetragonal.

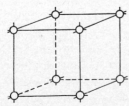

Fig. 418.—Simple cubic.

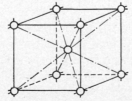

Fig. 419.—Body-centered cubic.

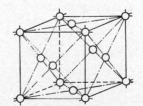

Fig. 420.—Face-centered cubic.

The 14 space lattices.

translations or glidings, or both. In this way, 65 regular point systems were developed.

Space Groups.—It was soon shown, however, that these 65 point systems did not account for all possible types of crystal symmetry. It then became necessary to extend the theory farther by assuming that the point systems in turn interpenetrate one another. As the result of purely theoretical and mathematical reasoning, it was soon demonstrated that 230 *space groups* of interpenetrating point systems are possible. It was also shown that these 230 groups possess the symmetry of the 32 classes and, further, that no other type of symmetry is possible among them.

In this theoretical work on crystal structure, Franckenheim, Bravais, Sohncke, Groth, Schoenflies, von Fedorov, and Barlow were most active.

FIG. 421.—Paul Heinrich von Groth (1843–1927). Professor of mineralogy in the University of Munich (1885–1923). Eminent for his many contributions on chemical and physical crystallography and on the structure of crystals.

By these investigators, the *points* were variously viewed as "crystal building stones," "molecules," "atoms," or even "crystal molecules."

Groth's Definition of a Crystal in Terms of Crystal Structure.—The foregoing discussion gives the salient features of the accepted views of crystal structure in 1904, when Groth defined a crystal as follows: *A crystal consists (1) of a number of interpenetrating point systems, each made up of similar atoms; (2) each point system consists of a number of interpenetrating space lattices made up of similar atoms arranged in a parallel manner; and (3) all space lattices of the resulting structure are congruent, that is, possess the same elementary parallelepiped.* Although this definition is based entirely upon theoretical and mathematical considerations, it is strikingly similar to the interpretations now placed upon the structure of crystals as the result of X-ray investigations, which, however, were not begun until a decade later (see also page 151).

Topical Axes.—With the development of the theory of point systems, various attempts were made, especially under the leadership of Groth, to apply the theory to the study of isomorphous substances. Thus, in 1893, Muthmann, in investigating the chemical-crystallographical properties of a series of phosphates and arsenates of ammonium and potassium, endeavored to show that the volumes of the elementary parallelepipeds, or unit cells, of these compounds are not identical but vary with the chemical composition. In order to demonstrate this, Muthmann computed the molecular volumes of the unit cells of the several compounds by combining the specific gravity and the chemical composition, as represented by the molecular weight, with the elements of crystallization (see page 14). In this way, he was able to determine the relative lengths of the edges of the elementary parallelepipeds and note the variations in them for the various compounds of the series. The lengths of the edges Muthmann called the *topical axes*. They were represented by the letters χ, ψ, ω. These axes correspond in direction to the crystallographic axes a, b, c.

At about the same time, and quite independently of Muthmann, Becke and Tutton introduced similar ideas. By Tutton the lengths of the edges of the unit cells were called *molecular distance ratios*. Formulas were developed by these investigators for the calculation of the topical axes for several of the crystal systems. Later, in 1901, Kraus and Mez developed the formulas[1] for all systems and defined the unit of the topical axes as the length of the edge of the cubical unit cell of a substance having a molecular volume of one.

Application of the Topical Axes.—The introduction of the idea of the topical axes stimulated interest in the study of structural relations between closely related compounds. As an example of one of the most interesting groups studied for the changes in the topical axes, the following series investigated by Slavik, in 1902, may be given:

NH_4I	$N(CH_3)_4I$	$N(C_2H_5)_4I$	$N(C_3H_7)_4I$
Cubic	Tetragonal	Tetragonal	Orthorhombic
$V^1 = 57.51$	108.70	162.91	235.95
$\chi = 3.860$	5.319	6.648	6.093
$\psi = 3.860$	5.319	6.648	7.851
$\omega = 3.860$	3.842	3.686	4.953

[1] The molecular volume V is equal to the molecular weight divided by the specific gravity (see p. 146).

These data show that, as the hydrogen in the first compound is successively replaced by CH_3, C_2H_5, and C_3H_7, the relationship between the topical axes is greatly altered. Furthermore, it is in the lengths of χ and ψ, corresponding to the crystallographic axes a and b, that the greatest changes take place. In other words, as the molecular volume becomes larger, χ and ψ change much more than does ω. Observations of this character seemed to confirm the ideas of crystal structure already referred to, and many similar studies were made during the first decade of the twentieth century. It was in this period that Barlow and Pope advanced the theory of *equivalent parameters*, which are obtained by substituting in the formulas for the calculation of the topical axes the total valency of the substance for its molecular weight.

[1] For these formulas, see GROTH-MARSHALL, "An Introduction to Chemical Crystallography," pp. 40–43, John Wiley & Sons, New York, 1906.

The topical axes proved very helpful in visualizing changes in the structure of chemically related compounds, but these changes could not be expressed precisely, for it was only the relative sizes and not the actual dimensions of the unit cells which were determined. Moreover, this procedure was based on the assumption that the true unit cell had dimensions proportional to the crystallographic axial ratio. While in many cases this relationship holds, there are frequent exceptions. Accordingly, topical axes have been entirely replaced by the accurate and absolute measurements made possible by X-ray methods.

Point Groups.—While the brief description of the historical development of the theory of crystal structure is of value in giving a background for the study of X-ray methods of structure analysis, the modern conception of a crystal can be best explained in terms of point groups. A *point group* may be defined as a group of symmetry elements, characteristic of one of the 32 crystal classes. For example, the hexoctahedral class of the cubic system has nine planes of symmetry, three fourfold, four threefold, and six twofold axes of symmetry, and a center of symmetry. These elements of symmetry constitute the point group of this class. The elements of symmetry, which comprise the point groups of each of the 32 crystal classes, are shown in the Tabular Classification of Crystal Forms, on pages 446 to 452.

The 14 space lattices represent the basic patterns according to which certain atomic groups are repeated throughout a crystal. These atomic groups are built up around the elements of symmetry of a point group. Thus, if an atom occurs in a general position in the hexoctahedral point group, the symmetry will require 47 additional atoms, making a total of 48 atoms. If the atom occupies a special position, such as on a plane, an axis, or a center of symmetry, or at the intersection of planes and axes, the number of additional atoms required by the symmetry is less. In the hexoctahedral class, instead of 48 atoms, as required in the general positions, there might be only 24, 16, 12, 8, 6, 4, 3, 2, or 1 in the special positions.

If more than one element is present, as in compounds, the atoms of each element will be arranged in individual groups. These groups interpenetrate each other, and each has the symmetry of the same point group.

If in the conception of the space lattice the points are replaced by point groups, space groups result. Thus in the cubic system, the five point groups, corresponding to the five symmetry classes, may occupy the positions of either (1) the simple cubic lattice, (2) the face-centered cubic lattice, or (3) the body-centered cubic lattice. This results in 15 cubic space groups. By the application of glide planes and screw axes of symmetry, additional point groups may be developed, which give rise to 21 more space groups, or a total of 36 in the cubic system. When this procedure is carried out in each of the six crystal systems,

230 space groups are found possible, which conform to those referred to on page 146.

In terms of the point group theory, *a crystal may be conceived as the result of the repetition of identical atomic groups at the positions of a space lattice.* Such groups may consist of a single atom, as in some of the elements, or of many atoms. In compounds the positions of the atoms of the different elements conform to the symmetry of a point group and are located in either special positions or general positions of the point group. This conception of a crystal is more easily visualized than the one given by Groth, on page 146.

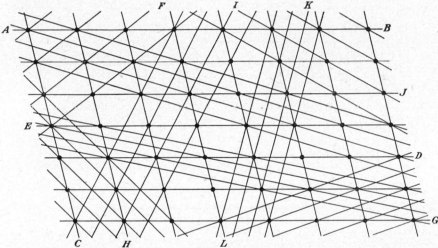

Fig. 422.—Two-dimensional network of points, showing various sets of parallel equidistant lines.

Atomic Planes.—In any regular two-dimensional arrangement of points, there can be drawn through the points many sets of parallel equidistant lines. Figure 422 shows a few of the possible sets of this kind. In addition to the lines of the original network parallel to AB and AC, there are shown sets of parallel equidistant lines as follows: AD, EG, EF, EH, HI, IJ, KL, and LD. In a similar manner, when atoms are repeated in a three-dimensional pattern, such as called for by the space-group theory, the atoms will lie on various sets of parallel equidistant planes. Crystal faces are always parallel to such planes. These planes obey the law of rational indices and can always be designated by Miller indices. Although the number of crystal faces observed on a given substance is usually small, the number of these sets of equidistant internal planes is unlimited. A knowledge of these planes is essential to the understanding of the X-ray methods of structure analysis to be described later.

Nature of X Rays.—Two years after the development of the idea of topical axes by Muthmann, X rays were discovered in 1895 by Roentgen, at that time professor of physics in the University of Würzburg. Although these new rays were intensively and critically studied, their exact nature remained in doubt for nearly two decades.

It had been noticed that in some respects X rays resemble light, while in others they seemed to differ from light. Of the various views which were held at that time only three will be referred to: (1) X rays are a wave motion like light, probably with very short wave lengths; (2) X rays constitute a corpuscular form of radiation, like the electrons; and (3) X rays are probably irregular ether pulses produced by the electrons striking a target from an X-ray tube. As the study of X rays progressed,

TABLE OF ELECTROMAGNETIC WAVES

Type of wave	Range of wave lengths
Cosmic	4 to 6.7 million millionths of 1 cm. $(4 \times 10^{-12}$ to 6.7×10^{-12} cm.$)$
γ rays	560 million millionths to 1 thousand millionths of 1 cm. $(560 \times 10^{-12}$ to 1×10^{-9} cm.$)$
X rays	1 to 450 thousand millionths of 1 cm. $(1 \times 10^{-9}$ to 450×10^{-9} cm.$)$
Extreme ultraviolet	0.45 to 1.3 millionths of 1 cm. $(0.45 \times 10^{-6}$ to 1.3×10^{-6} cm.$)$
Ultraviolet	1.3 to 35 millionths of 1 cm. $(1.3 \times 10^{-6}$ to 35×10^{-6} cm.$)$
Visible light	35 to 77 millionths of 1 cm.* $(35 \times 10^{-6}$ to 77×10^{-6} cm.$)$
Heat	77 millionths to 3 hundredths of 1 cm. $(77 \times 10^{-6}$ to 3×10^{-2} cm.$)$
Short electromagnetic	3 hundredths of 1 cm. to 1 meter $(3 \times 10^{-2}$ to 1×10^{2} cm.$)$
Radio	1 to 30,000 meters $(1 \times 10^{2}$ to 3×10^{6} cm.$)$
Long electromagnetic	30,000 meters to thousands of kilometers.

* The wave lengths of visible light are generally expressed in *millimicrons*, mμ (millionths of a millimeter). Thus, these wave lengths vary from 350mμ for violet light to 770mμ for red light at the extreme ends of the visible spectrum. The wave lengths of X rays are given in terms of Ångström units, Å (10 millionths of a millimeter).

it became evident that if some method could be devised whereby they could be diffracted and reflected it might then be possible to determine their fundamental character.

Studies involving the passage of X rays through small openings seemed to indicate that if they consist of transverse waves like light, they must possess extremely short wave lengths, in fact, much shorter than those of light. The wave lengths of light are of the order of 1×10^{-5} cm., and it was thought that those of X rays must be either of the order 1×10^{-8} or 1×10^{-9} cm., that is, about 10,000 times smaller than the waves of sodium light.

In the table shown on page 150 the different types of electromagnetic waves are given with the *approximate* ranges of the wave lengths as determined at present. The classification is somewhat arbitrary, definite dividing lines being impossible since the different types of waves may overlap greatly. It will be noted that the waves of visible light occupy a very small section of this so-called wave spectrum.

Laue's Discovery.—In studying the nature of X rays, Laue came to the conclusion that: (1) if the points in the space lattices are to be considered as atoms, and (2) if X rays are like light but possess very short wave lengths, comparable to the distances between the atoms, a crystal should act toward X rays as a three-dimensional diffraction grating. In this case, diffraction effects should take place and interference phenomena result when X rays are transmitted through a crystal. In 1912, Laue, in conjunction with Friedrich and Knipping, tried this epoch-making experiment.[1] Its success showed that the assumption of a regular internal atomic arrangement in crystals was justified, and that it might be possible to develop methods for investigating this arrangement. Moreover, the experience proved that X rays and light are fundamentally the same, but differ in wave lengths (see Table of Electromagnetic Waves, page 150), and demonstrated that there was now a means available for studying this radiation.

Laue Method.—In the Laue experiment a beam of heterogeneous or polychromatic X rays was transmitted through an oriented section of a crystal (Fig. 424). The emergent rays consist of a strong undeviated beam and of fainter beams, diffracted by the different layers of atoms which act as gratings. These beams were allowed to fall upon a photographic plate, forming spot photographs or what are now known as *Laue photographs* or *Laue diagrams* (Figs. 425 and 426). The spots are caused by diffraction or "reflection" of the incident beam by internal atomic planes, such as are called for by the space-lattice theory.

[1] The experiment was made in Munich, where Sohncke and Groth had long been active in developing and teaching theories of crystal structure, and where the noted physicists Roentgen and Sommerfeld were also located as professors in the university. Furthermore, it was in Munich that the researches were made by Muthmann, which, in 1893, led to the development of the idea of the topical axes.

Symmetry of Laue Photographs.—Since the positions of the internal planes depend upon the symmetry of the crystal, the arrangement of the reflections from these planes, as shown by the spots in the photograph, must possess a corresponding symmetry (Fig. 427). Investigation has

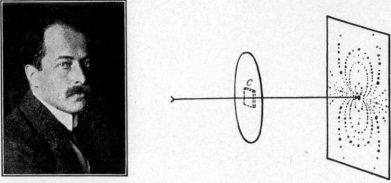

Fig. 423.   Fig. 424.

Fig. 423.—Max F. F. von Laue (1879–   ). Professor of theoretical physics in the University of Berlin (1919–   ). Winner of the Nobel prize for physics in 1914. Pioneer investigator of crystal structure by X-ray methods.
Fig. 424.—General plan for obtaining Laue diagrams. (*Adapted from Rinne.*)

shown, however, that a center of symmetry is always indicated by a Laue photograph, whether or not it is present in the crystal. Thus, while there are 32 classes of symmetry, only 11 classes can be distinguished in Laue photographs. Other X-ray methods must be resorted to for distinctions between the other classes. Likewise, the supple-

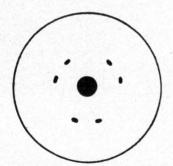

Fig. 425.—Laue diagram of sphalerite parallel to a threefold axis.

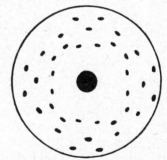

Fig. 426.—Laue diagram of sphalerite parallel to a fourfold axis.

mentary evidence of face development, etch figures, optical activity, and piezoelectricity may be utilized in doubtful cases.

Bragg Method.—Shortly after Laue announced that X rays could be diffracted by crystals, W. H. Bragg and W. L. Bragg (father and son) studied the effect of reflecting a beam of monochromatic X rays from a crystal face. They determined the position of the reflected beam by means of an ionization chamber, although now photographic plates are frequently used for this purpose. The apparatus is called an *X-ray*

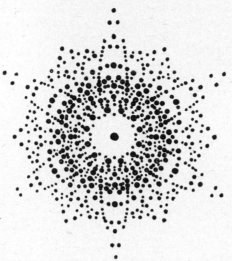

Fig. 427.—Laue photograph of beryl parallel to the vertical sixfold axis. (*After Rinne.*)

spectrometer. In this method the X-ray beam falls upon a crystal face at a small glancing angle, and the crystal is slowly turned. The angles at which reflections occur are determined. By means of the formula given below, the Braggs showed that it was possible to calculate the actual distance between the successive layers of atoms parallel to the crystal face.

In Fig. 429, let a and a' represent part of a beam of X rays, of wave length λ, impinging at an angle θ upon successive atomic layers NN, $N'N'$, $N''N''$. The distance between these layers is d. The incident beam may penetrate hundreds of thousands of these layers, and a very small portion of the beam will be diffracted or reflected by each layer. If, in a particular direction Ob, the reflections from successive layers are all in phase, they will reinforce one another and together make up a beam of sufficient intensity to be detected. The conditions under which this will occur are as follows: Let Ob and $O'b$ represent reflections from the first two layers. The difference in path between aOb and $a'O'b$ is $P'O$, for

$$aO = a'O' + O'P = a'O' + O'P',$$

but

$$P'O = Pm = Om \sin \theta = 2d \sin \theta.$$

Fig. 428.—Sir William Henry Bragg (1862–   ). Director of the Royal Institution of Great Britain. Fullerian professor of chemistry in the Royal Institution, and director of the Davy-Faraday Research Laboratory, London. Winner (with his son, W. L. Bragg) of the Nobel prize for physics in 1915. Eminent for researches in the field of crystal structure.

Thus the path difference between the reflections from the first two layers is equal to $2d \sin \theta$. This same relationship holds for the reflections from all succeeding layers. Accordingly, when the path difference of the superimposed reflections, such as Ob and $O'Ob$, is λ or $n\lambda$, they will all be in phase and the reflected beam will have a maximum intensity. This can be expressed by

$$n\lambda = 2d \sin \theta.$$

The path difference between reflections from successive layers becomes greater as the angle θ increases. Accordingly, there is a series of angles for which the path difference will be, successively, λ, 2λ, 3λ and so forth. The reflections occurring at these angles are known as reflections of the first, second, and third orders, respectively. In the above equation, the

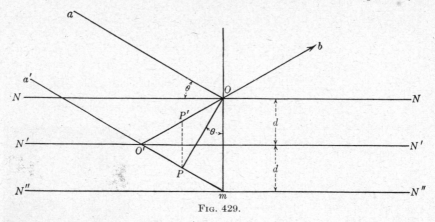

Fig. 429.

order of reflection is indicated by n, which is always a whole number. If the path difference varies even very slightly from $n\lambda$, complete destructive interference occurs. For this reason, these reflections do not represent merely positions of maximum intensity, but they are sharply defined and are separated by regions in which no reflections are observed.

The procedure used by the Braggs was to obtain reflections of several orders from a few simple faces, such as the cube, dodecahedron, and the octahedron, and calculate the spacings for each of these planes. With this information, together with the relative intensities of the various reflections, the spatial relations of the atoms within the crystal could be deduced with considerable certainty.

This method by itself is applicable only to the analysis of rather simple structures. Among the crystals studied by the Braggs were halite (NaCl), fluorite (CaF_2), sphalerite (ZnS), diamond (C), and pyrite (FeS_2). The method requires oriented single crystals of moderate size, free from twinning and imperfections.

Crystal Structure of Halite.—By applying the method just described to the study of halite (NaCl), the Braggs were able to show that the

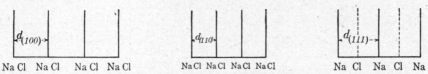

NaCl NaCl   NaCl NaCl   NaCl NaCl NaCl NaCl   Na Cl Na Cl Na

FIG. 430.—Relative distances between successive layers of atoms in halite (NaCl) parallel to faces of the cube (100), rhombic dodecahedron (110), and octahedron (111), respectively.

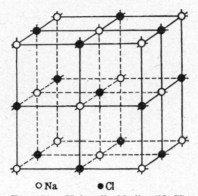

○ Na   ● Cl
FIG. 431.—Unit cell of halite (NaCl).

distances between the successive and identical layers of atoms parallel to the faces of the cube (100), rhombic dodecahedron (110), and octahedron (111) differ in the following ratio:

$$d_{(100)} : d_{(110)} : d_{(111)} = 1 : \frac{1}{\sqrt{2}} : \frac{2}{\sqrt{3}}.$$

This is clearly shown by Fig. 430.

These observations led to the conclusion that the structure of halite can be represented by Fig. 431, where the atoms of sodium are indicated by ○ and those of chlorine by ●. This structure can be interpreted as consisting of two interpenetrating face-centered cubic space lattices, the one composed entirely of sodium, the other entirely of chlorine atoms. Furthermore, it could be shown that the distances between like atoms along the edges of the cube is 5.628×10^{-8} cm., or 5.628 Å (Ångströms).

FIG. 432.—William Lawrence Bragg (1890–). Langworthy professor of physics in Victoria University, Manchester, England. Distinguished investigator of crystal structure by X-ray methods.

The unit cell of halite, as described, contains the equivalent of four molecules of NaCl, for, although more atoms are indicated in the above diagram of this unit cell, some are shared by adjacent cells. Thus, the only atom belonging entirely to this unit cell is the one in the center of the figure. The atoms at the centers of the faces, in the middle of the edges, and those at the corners are shared by two, four, and eight adjacent cells, respectively. Hence, as far as this unit cell is concerned, the influence of these atoms should be rated as one-half, one-fourth, and one-eighth of their full value, respectively.

Hull, Debye–Scherrer, or Powder Method.—This method, devised independently by Hull in this country and by Debye and Scherrer in

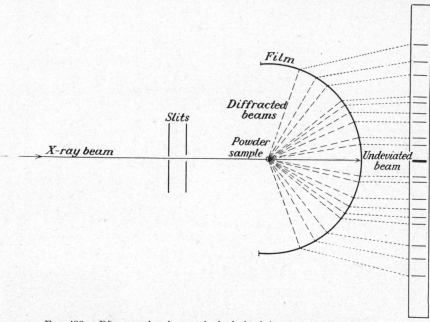

Fig. 433.—Diagram showing method of obtaining powder photographs.

Fig. 434.—Powder photographs of the dimorphous forms of FeS_2. Pyrite above, marcasite below.

Europe, differs from those of Laue and the Braggs in that an oriented specimen is not necessary. Monochromatic X rays are passed through a thin layer of finely powdered material (Fig. 433), and the reflected rays are recorded on a semicircular photographic film, producing a diffraction pattern (Fig. 434). The lines of the pattern are due to reflections from various crystal planes, for in a fine powder, with a random arrangement of a large number of particles, the orientations necessary for such reflections will be present. Hence, each line of the pattern corresponds to a definite crystal plane with its own characteristic spacing. Accordingly, a determination of the structure may be possible if these planes can be identified. This is usually quite simple in the cubic, hexagonal, and tetragonal systems, but great difficulties are encountered in the remaining systems.

With the powder method it is possible to obtain reflections from many more planes than with the Bragg method. Moreover, the method is applicable to many substances which are not well crystallized. In fact, there need be no development of crystal faces at all. The diffraction patterns obtained from most substances are characteristic and are, therefore, of great value for identification purposes. The method, moreover, permits direct comparison to be made of the patterns of different speci-

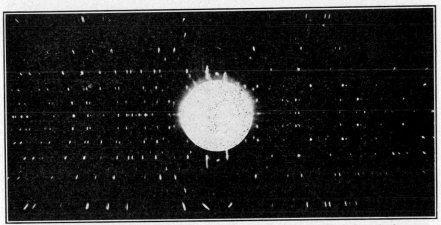

FIG. 435.—X-ray photograph of single crystal by rotating crystal method.

mens of the same substance or of different substances. Figure 434 shows the patterns for pyrite and marcasite. Both have the same composition FeS_2 but give distinctly different patterns.

Rotation and Oscillation Methods.—In these methods a single small crystal is rotated or oscillated through a definite angle about some important crystallographic direction. Monochromatic X rays are used. As the crystal rotates, reflections will occur from all planes that come into proper position. The number of reflections obtained is large (Fig. 435). Graphical methods have been developed for identifying the planes responsible for the reflections.

In the *Weissenberg* method, which is a modification of the rotation method, the number of reflections permitted to reach the photographic film is limited to a single row. During the exposure the cylindrical film is moved parallel to the axis of the cylinder and the axis of rotation, which coincide. This movement of the film is synchronized with the rotation of the crystal. Thus the position of each spot is related to the angular position of the crystal at the instant reflection occurred, and the more accurate assignment of indices to the planes is made possible. These two methods are the only ones which are readily adapted to the interpretation of complex crystal structures, or of those of low symmetry.

Summary of X-ray Methods.—The essential features of the methods of X-ray analysis just described may be summarized as follows:

A. Oriented Crystals or Crystal Plates Are Used

1. *Laue Method.*—Transmission of white X rays through stationary oriented specimen, yielding spot photographs. Of special value in determining symmetry.

2. *Bragg Method.*—Reflection of monochromatic X rays from a single rotating crystal face. Of special value in the accurate determination of interplanar spacings.

3. *Rotation and Oscillation Methods.*—Reflection of monochromatic X rays from a large number of internal crystal planes, which are brought into proper position for reflection by rotation of the crystal. Very important in the structure analysis of crystals with complex chemical compositions and those of the orthorhombic, monoclinic, and triclinic systems.

B. Unoriented Powdered Specimens Are Used

1. *Hull, Debye–Scherrer, or Powder Method.*—Transmission of monochromatic X rays through finely powdered specimens, yielding line diffraction patterns. The random positions of the powder particles furnish the proper orientations for reflections from many planes. Very important in identification and in the determination of structures of substances not occurring in good crystals.

Interpretation of X-ray Data.—With the above methods, data of four kinds may be obtained:

1. Crystal symmetry.
2. Interplanar spacings of known planes.
3. Relative intensities of the various orders of reflections from different planes.
4. Absence of reflections from certain planes.

Ordinarily the crystal system of a substance is known before an analysis of the structure is attempted. The symmetry, as revealed by a Laue photograph, may confirm the choice of the crystal system, or it may show that the assumed system is incorrect. Likewise, as indicated on page 152, Laue photographs may distinguish between certain of the symmetry classes. It is obvious that the crystal system must be known before the shape of the unit cell can be determined.

From the interplanar spacings it is possible to determine the actual dimensions of the unit cell. With these dimensions, together with the density of the substance and the weight of a single molecule, the number of molecules (n) in the unit cell can be calculated by means of the formula

$$\text{Density} = n \frac{\text{molecular weight} \times 1.649 \times 10^{-24*}}{\text{volume of unit cell (in Ångström units)}}.$$

* The value of 1.649×10^{-24} is the weight in grams of one unit of molecular (or atomic) weight.

When the number of molecules in the unit cell is known, the number of atoms of each element present in the cell is readily determined.

The next step is to determine the space lattice, then the space group, and finally the actual atomic arrangement. The general principles underlying this determination can be summarized briefly as follows: A space lattice may be a simple lattice, or it may be more complex because of body centering or face centering. Likewise, the atomic group at the lattice points may consist of a single atom or of a complex group of atoms of different elements.

A simple lattice, with a single atom at each point, will give reflections from every possible internal atomic plane. In more complex structures which are based on (1) body-centered or face-centered lattices, or in which (2) atomic groups, instead of single atoms, are located at the lattice points, no additional reflections are possible. The only effect of this increased complexity is to eliminate entirely reflections from certain planes, or to modify their intensities. Thus, the change from a simple cubic lattice to a face-centered or body-centered cubic lattice introduces additional atomic planes, located halfway between certain of the original planes. The odd-order reflections from these planes are eliminated, and the even-order reflections are intensified. The particular planes thus affected are different for the face-centered and for the body-centered lattices, and hence direct evidence is given as to which space lattice is involved.

Fig. 436.—Friedrich Rinne (1863–1933). Professor of mineralogy in the University of Leipzig (1909–1928). Noted investigator of the internal structure of crystals.

The substitution of atomic groups for single atoms introduces additional planes of varied composition at fractional distances between the original planes, and consequently complex interference relations result. Here, likewise, the effects on certain planes may be characteristic and indicate a definite space group, or at least limit the choice to several groups. Various atomic arrangements that are in harmony with the possible space groups are then considered. The atoms of the different elements must be assigned to symmetrical positions which are in accord with atomic sizes, interatomic forces, and characteristic atomic groupings. The theoretical intensities of reflection to be expected from such arrangements must then be calculated for a large number of planes. The structure finally chosen is the one for which the theoretical intensities are in best agreement with the observed intensities.

Crystal-structure Types.—In most of the crystals of inorganic substances, it has been found that the atoms are not grouped into definite molecules. Thus in halite (NaCl) the sodium and chlorine are present as positive and negative ions, respectively, each being surrounded at equal distances by six ions of opposite charge (Fig. 431, page 155). In quartz (SiO_2), however, at room temperature, there is an association of two oxygen atoms with each silicon atom. Between these two types of structures, which are termed *ionic* and *molecular*, respectively, there are all gradations. Although the molecular type is not common among inorganic compounds, certain atomic groupings are frequent, such as the radicals OH, CO_3, NO_3, and SO_4. These occur in well-defined groups which vary but little in different structures. The bonding in metals, such as gold, silver, and copper, is neither ionic nor molecular and represents a distinct type of structure.

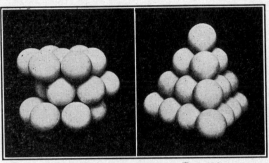

FIG. 437.   FIG. 438.

Crystal Structures of Elements.—Many of the elements have simple structures. The face-centered cubic arrangement (Fig. 420, page 145) is observed on 21 elements, including copper, silver, gold, and platinum. A body-centered cubic structure (Fig. 419, page 145) has been found for 14 elements. Iron at ordinary temperatures has this type of structure. Twelve elements, including zinc, have an hexagonal arrangement. This hexagonal type and the face-centered cubic arrangement represent the two ways in which spheres of equal size may be most closely packed together. These are referred to as hexagonal and cubic close packing, respectively (Figs. 437 and 438).

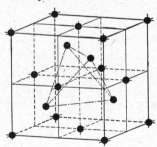

FIG. 439.—Unit cell of the diamond, C.

The submetallic elements arsenic, antimony, and bismuth, all occurring as minerals, have more complicated structures, based on rhombohedral lattices.

Three nonmetallic elements occur as minerals, namely, the two forms of carbon, diamond and graphite, and sulphur. Diamond is cubic and has a structure in which the carbon atoms are located both at the positions of a face-centered cube and at the corners of a tetrahedron within the cube (Fig. 439). The length of the edge of the unit cell containing the equivalent of eight atoms of carbon is 3.55×10^{-8} cm. or 3.55 Å.

Graphite has a related structure, which is hexagonal in symmetry. Sulphur has a very complex structure, with a large orthorhombic unit cell, which is supposed to contain 128 atoms.

Structures of Compounds.—The number of different types of structures among the minerals is large. A few of the more common types, observed on important minerals, will be described.

Galena (PbS).—The lead atoms occupy the corners and face centers of the cubic cell, while the sulphur atoms are located at the middle of the edges and at the cube center (Fig. 440). This arrangement is similar to that of the sodium and chlorine atoms in halite (NaCl), which has already been described on page 155. This type of structure is also observed on the minerals alabandite (MnS) and cerargyrite (AgCl), as well as on numerous compounds not occurring as minerals. In galena

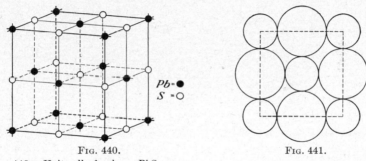

$$Pb = \bullet$$
$$S = \circ$$

FIG. 440.   FIG. 441.

FIG. 440.—Unit cell of galena, PbS.

FIG. 441.—Diagram showing arrangement of lead atoms (small) and sulphur atoms (large) in galena, parallel to a cube face.

the side of the unit cube has a length of 5.97 Å., in alabandite it is 5.21 Å., and in cerargyrite 5.54 Å.

In these structure diagrams no attempt is made to show the relative sizes of the atoms. The symbols $\circ$ and $\bullet$ merely represent the centers of the atoms. If relative sizes were to be shown, the structure of galena, for example, as given in Fig. 440, would appear as in Fig. 441, which indicates the arrangement of the smaller lead atoms and the larger sulphur atoms parallel to the unit cube face.

Fluorite (CaF$_2$).—The crystal structure of fluorite is illustrated by Fig. 442. The calcium atoms have the same positions in this structure as those of lead in galena (Fig. 440), while the atoms of fluorine occupy the centers of the eight smaller cubes into which the unit cell as a whole is divided by the planes parallel to the three intersecting sides. As shown in the figure, the fluorine atoms form a small cube within the face-centered cube lattice of calcium. The length of the edge of the unit cell containing the equivalent of four molecules of CaF$_2$ is 5.455 Å.

Sphalerite (ZnS).—Figure 443 illustrates the crystal structure of the mineral sphalerite, the zinc atoms being placed in the same manner as those of lead and calcium in Figs. 440 and 442, respectively. The four sulphur atoms occupy the alternate centers of the eight smaller cells into which the unit cell as a whole can be divided (see Fluorite). The sulphur atoms form a tetrahedron within the face-centered cube lattice of zinc atoms. The length of the unit cell containing the equivalent of four molecules of ZnS is 5.43 Å.

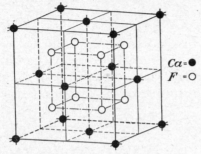

Fig. 442.—Unit cell of fluorite, CaF₂. Fig. 443.—Unit cell of sphalerite, ZnS.

Pyrite (FeS₂).—The iron atoms in pyrite are in the cubic face-centered positions (Fig. 444), just as are the lead, calcium, and zinc atoms in Figs. 440, 442, and 443, respectively. Since the formula is FeS₂, the unit cube must contain twice as many sulphur atoms as iron. Pairs of sulphur atoms are located at the middle of the edges and at the center of the cube. The unit cube contains the equivalent of four molecules of

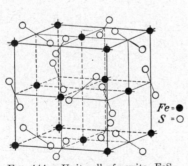

Fig. 444.—Unit cell of pyrite, FeS₂.

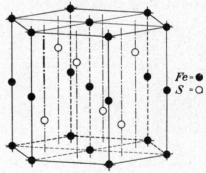

Fig. 445.—Unit cell of pyrrhotite, FeS.

FeS₂, and the length of the cube edge is 5.41 Å. This structure is common to all the members of the pyrite group (see page 257).

Pyrrhotite (FeS).—Pyrrhotite is hexagonal, and the atomic arrangement is shown in Fig. 445. The complete hexagonal prism is not taken as the unit cell but rather the parallelepipeds indicated by the lines crossing the basal pinacoid. Thus two entire cells, and two half-cells are shown. The iron atoms are located at the corners and at the middle of the vertical edges of the unit cells, and two sulphur atoms are within each cell. Each unit contains the equivalent of two molecules of FeS, and the lengths of the horizontal and vertical edges are 3.43 Å. and 5.79 Å., respectively.

Cassiterite (SnO_2).—The unit cell of cassiterite is tetragonal. The tin atoms have a body-centered arrangement, and the oxygen atoms are located within the cell, as shown in Fig. 446. This tetragonal cell contains the equivalent of two molecules of SnO_2, and the length of the horizontal edge is 4.72 Å. and that of the vertical edge 3.16 Å. Rutile (TiO_2) has a similar structure, with the length of the horizontal and vertical edges 4.58 Å. and 2.98 Å., respectively.

Value of X-ray Analysis.—The earlier investigations of crystal structure were limited to the elements and to comparatively simple compounds. With the newer methods and greatly improved technique, together with the

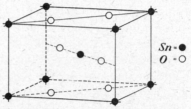

Fig. 446.—Unit cell of cassiterite, SnO_2.

rapidly accumulating knowledge concerning structural relationships, it is now possible to investigate crystals with complex chemical compositions and those of low symmetry. The X-ray methods obviously have certain limitations, but it is now generally agreed that with their proper use it is possible to obtain accurate and dependable results. Since the crystallographic properties are dependent upon the structure, it is evident that there should be complete agreement between crystallographic and X-ray data. In the few cases where such agreement is lacking, it is yet uncertain wherein lies the true interpretation.

During the years which have passed since Laue's discovery, great progress has been made. Many inorganic compounds, metals, and minerals have been investigated. Not only have the general theories of crystal structure based upon space groups been confirmed, but important relationships between crystal structure and the chemical and physical properties of crystalline solids have been established. Many problems in mineralogy have been studied. Important data concerning isomorphism, polymorphism, solid solution, hardness, cleavage, twinning, indices of refraction, and crystal growth have been obtained. Crystal structure data have been of value in verifying and in correcting formulas of some minerals. X-ray analysis is also being used in research and industry in the study of the structure, composition, and properties of many substances, such as metals, alloys, textile fibers, resins, glass, cement, sugars, rubber, greases, porcelains, and pigments.

Through this new branch of study, not only has crystallography become an exact science, but it has also become the basis for the interpretation of many of the phenomena characteristic of the solid state.

CHAPTER XIII

CHEMICAL PROPERTIES

As indicated earlier, minerals have characteristic chemical compositions; that is, when pure they may be either elements or chemical compounds. If minerals are elements, the elements are said to occur *native*. We may thus speak of *native* gold, *native* silver, and *native* copper. Obviously, most of the minerals are chemical compounds.

Chemical Formulas.—The determination of the principal chemical constituents of a mineral can frequently be made most rapidly by blowpipe methods. These methods are discussed in detail in the next chapter. The determination of the quantitative composition of minerals belongs to the domain of chemistry, the usual methods of the analytical chemist being employed. The formulas representing the chemical composition of minerals are calculated in exactly the same way as for any other chemical substance. For example, an analysis of chalcopyrite from Müsen, Germany, gave Laspeyres the following results:

	I Analysis, Per Cent.		II Atomic Weights		III Combining Ratios	IV	V
Cu	34.89	÷	63.57	=	0.5488	1.020	1
Fe	30.04	÷	55.84	=	0.5379	1.000	1
S	34.51	÷	32.06	=	1.0767	2.002	2

FIG. 447.—Samuel L. Penfield (1856–1906). Professor of mineralogy in Yale University (1893–1906). Distinguished American chemical mineralogist.

By dividing the percentages (I) of the various constituents by the atomic weights (II) of the same, their combining ratios (III) are obtained. These can then be expressed in approximate whole numbers (IV and V), from which the following ratio results: Cu : Fe : S = 1 : 1 : 2.

This gives $CuFeS_2$ as the *empirical formula* for chalcopyrite; that is, the types and numbers of atoms present in chalcopyrite without attempting to show the manner in which the atoms are combined.

In the case of more complex minerals where the composition is indicated by giving the percentages of the various oxides present, the procedure is the same, with the exception that the molecular weights of the oxides, that is, the sum

164

of the atomic weights of the elements in the same, are used. Thus, Brax in analyzing a beryl from Paavo, Finland, obtained the following:

	I Analysis, Per Cent.		II Molecular Weights		III Combining Ratios	IV	V
SiO_2	66.37	÷	60.1	=	1.1043	5.846	6
Al_2O_3	19.26	÷	101.9	=	0.1889	1.000	1
BeO	14.01	÷	25.0	=	0.5604	2.967	3

These oxides therefore combine in the following ratio:

$BeO:Al_2O_3:SiO_2 = 3:1:6$, from which the formula $3BeO.Al_2O_3.6SiO_2$ or $Be_3Al_2Si_6O_{18}$ is obtained.

Percentage Composition.—When the formula of a mineral has been established, it is possible to calculate what percentages of the various constituents should theoretically be present. Indeed, the degree of purity of a mineral may often be easily estimated by comparing an analysis with the theoretical percentage composition, calculated from the generally accepted formula. Referring again to the mineral chalcopyrite, the formula of which was calculated above as $CuFeS_2$, we may determine its theoretical percentage composition by ascertaining the percentage the combining weight of a given constituent is of the molecular weight of the mineral as a whole. Thus,

Constituents	Atomic Weights	Combining Ratios	Combining Weights	Proportion of Molecular Weight of Mineral	Theoretical Percentage Composition
Cu	63.57	1	63.57	$\dfrac{63.57}{183.53}=$	34.64
Fe	55.84	1	55.84	$\dfrac{55.84}{183.53}=$	30.42
S	32.06	2	64.12	$\dfrac{64.12}{183.53}=$	34.94
			183.53 (Molecular weight of mineral)		100.00

Using $Be_3Al_2Si_6O_{18}$ as the formula for beryl, the theoretical percentage composition of the various constituents may be calculated as follows:

Constituents	Molecular Weights of Radicals	Combining Ratio	Combining Weights of Radicals	Proportion of Molecular Weight of Mineral	Theoretical Percentage Composition
SiO_2	60.1	6	360.6	$\dfrac{360.6}{537.5}=$	67.09
Al_2O_3	101.9	1	101.9	$\dfrac{101.9}{537.5}=$	18.96
BeO	25.0	3	$\dfrac{75.0}{537.5}$ (Molecular weight of mineral)	$\dfrac{75}{537.5}=$	$\dfrac{13.95}{100.00}$

PERIODIC CLASSIFICATION OF THE ELEMENTS

Periods	Group O	Group I	Group II	Group III	Group IV	Group V	Group VI	Group VII	Group VIII
1		Hydrogen H = 1.008							
2	Helium He = 4.00	Lithium Li = 6.94	Beryllium Be = 9.02	Boron B = 10.82	Carbon C = 12.00	Nitrogen N = 14.01	Oxygen O = 16.00	Fluorine F = 19.0	—
3	Neon Ne = 20.2	Sodium Na = 23.00	Magnesium Mg = 24.32	Aluminum Al = 26.97	Silicon Si = 28.06	Phosphorus P = 31.02	Sulphur S = 32.06	Chlorine Cl = 35.46	—
4	Argon A = 39.94	Potassium K = 39.10	Calcium Ca = 40.08	Scandium Sc = 45.1	Titanium Ti = 47.9	Vanadium V = 50.95	Chromium Cr = 52.0	Manganese Mn = 54.93	Iron Fe = 55.84 Cobalt Co = 58.94 Nickel Ni = 58.69
5	—	Copper Cu = 63.57	Zinc Zn = 65.38	Gallium Ga = 69.72	Germanium Ge = 72.6	Arsenic As = 74.93	Selenium Se = 79.2	Bromine Br = 79.92	—
6	Krypton Kr = 82.92	Rubidium Rb = 85.44	Strontium Sr = 87.63	Yttrium Y = 88.92	Zirconium Zr = 91.2	Columbium Cb = 93.3	Molybdenum Mo = 96.0	Masurium Ma = ?	Ruthenium Ru = 101.7 Rhodium Rh = 102.9 Palladium Pd = 106.7
7	—	Silver Ag = 107.88	Cadmium Cd = 112.41	Indium In = 114.8	Tin Sn = 118.7	Antimony Sb = 121.76	Tellurium Te = 127.5	Iodine I = 126.93	—
8	Xenon Xe = 130.2	Cæsium Cs = 132.81	Barium Ba = 137.36	Lanthanum La = 138.9	Cerium Ce = 140.13	—	—	—	—
9	—	—	—	—	—	—	—	—	—
10	—	—	—	Ytterbium Yb = 173.5	Hafnium Hf = 178.6	Tantalum Ta = 181.4	Tungsten W = 184.0	Rhenium Re = 186.31	Osmium Os = 190.8 Iridium Ir = 193.1 Platinum Pt = 195.2
11	—	Gold Au = 197.2	Mercury Hg = 200.6	Thallium Tl = 204.4	Lead Pb = 207.22	Bismuth Bi = 209.0	—	—	—
12	Radon Rn = 222	—	Radium Ra = 225.97		Thorium Th = 232.1		Uranium U = 238.14	—	

Names.—Although chemical names may be assigned to minerals, it has long been common practice to designate them by special or mineralogical names. These mineral names are given for various reasons. In some instances, as in the case of *celestite*, the name refers to the light blue color which is commonly observed on this mineral. *Azurite* also has reference to color, namely a deep azure blue; *vesuvianite* to Mount Vesuvius, where first found; and *tetrahedrite* to its crystallization in tetrahedrons. *Argentite* is so called because it is a compound of silver (argentum). *Magnesite* is a compound of magnesium. *Scheelite* is named after Scheele, a Swedish chemist, and *wollastonite* after Wollaston, an English scientist. It is thus seen that in some instances outstanding physical or chemical properties have been incorporated in the names, whereas in other cases the minerals have been named after distinguished scientists or after the locality where first found.

Fig. 448.—Gustav Tschermak (1836–1927). For many years professor of mineralogy and petrography in the University of Vienna. Distinguished for his numerous contributions, especially for those on the isomorphism of the feldspars.

Isomorphism.—It can be easily shown that the various properties of minerals vary in general with the chemical composition. In order to emphasize this, it will be well to review briefly the periodic system of chemical elements. In 1869 the Russian chemist Mendelyeev published a classification of elements in which they were arranged in order of their increasing atomic weights. This classification is given on page 166. After certain intervals or periods, elements are observed which possess similar properties. For example, in group II calcium, strontium, and barium, are found directly under one another. These elements are very closely related to each other chemically. Obviously then, the carbonates of these three elements, $CaCO_3$, $SrCO_3$, and $BaCO_3$, will possess strikingly similar physical and chemical properties. These carbonates occur in nature as the minerals aragonite, strontianite, and witherite, respectively. All of them crystallize in the orthorhombic system.

The tabulation shown on page 168 gives the molecular weights, the specific gravities, several important angles, and the elements of crystallization of the minerals aragonite, strontianite, and witherite.

It is observed that the specific gravities increase regularly with the molecular weights. The size of corresponding prism and dome angles on crystals of these three minerals is of the same character. A close examination, however, reveals small but regular differences. This is also true of the elements of crystallization. In both cases, nevertheless, the fact that the values, although among themselves slightly different, are of the same order, is at once noticed. Likewise the sulphates of Ca, Sr, and Ba—anhydrite, celestite, and barite—form another series of minerals with similar properties.

Formula	Molecular weights	Specific gravity	Angles		Elements of crystallization		
			Prism $110 \wedge 1\bar{1}0$	Dome $011 \wedge 0\bar{1}1$	a	b	c
Aragonite $CaCO_3$.......	100.1	2.9	63° 48′	71° 33′	0.6228	:1:	0.7204
Strontianite $SrCO_3$......	147.6	3.7	62° 41′	71° 48′	0.6089	:1:	0.7237
Witherite $BaCO_3$.......	197.4	4.3	62° 12′	72° 16′	0.5949	:1:	0.7413

Substances with analogous chemical compositions which crystallize in forms that are strikingly similar are commonly said to be isomorphous. Such substances may also crystallize together, that is, an analysis of strontianite will not infrequently show the presence of considerable calcium and barium replacing the strontium. Indeed, there are a number of instances where two chemical compounds may crystallize together in varying proportions. A striking illustration is the plagioclase series of feldspars in which albite ($NaAlSi_3O_8$) and anorthite ($CaAl_2Si_2O_8$) are the end members. Between them are intermediate members whose composition and properties vary regularly from that of albite on the one hand to that of anorthite on the other. This is clearly shown by the following table:

Albite,	$NaAlSi_3O_8(Ab)$........................	Ab_9An_1
Oligoclase,	Ab_9An_1............................	Ab_7An_3
Andesine,	Ab_7An_3............................	Ab_1An_1
Labradorite,	Ab_1An_1............................	Ab_3An_7
Bytownite,	Ab_3An_7............................	Ab_1An_9
Anorthite,	Ab_1An_9............................	$CaAl_2Si_2O_8(An)$

Isomorphism is one of the most important principles in chemical mineralogy, for only in rare instances are minerals absolutely pure. Usually, as already indicated, one or more of the constituents have been replaced by others of analogous character. Thus, in the case of the garnet group, the general composition is best expressed by the formula $M''_3M'''_2(SiO_4)_3$. In this formula, M'' may be either calcium, magnesium, ferrous iron, or manganese. M''' indicates ferric iron, aluminum, or chromium. Usually one of the elements in each of these groups predominates, the others being present in varying amounts. It is common practice to differentiate six distinct varieties of garnet depending upon the elements which predominate, as shown in the following table:

Grossularite..	$Ca_3Al_2(SiO_4)_3$
Pyrope...	$Mg_3Al_2(SiO_4)_3$
Spessartite..	$Mn_3Al_2(SiO_4)_3$
Almandite...	$Fe_3Al_2(SiO_4)_3$
Uvarovite...	$Ca_3Cr_2(SiO_4)_3$
Andradite...	$Ca_3Fe_2(SiO_4)_3$

Between these compositions there are all possible gradations, but in every instance the composition can be referred to the general formula $M''_3M'''_2(SiO_4)_3$.

Dimorphism.—Some chemical substances occur in different modifications with distinct physical and chemical properties. Thus, calcium carbonate is found in nature as the minerals calcite and aragonite. The following table gives the common characteristics of each.

	Name	Crystallization	Specific Gravity	Hardness	Optical Character
$CaCO_3$	Calcite	Hexagonal	2.7	3	Uniaxial
	Aragonite	Orthorhombic	2.9–3	3.5–4	Biaxial

When a chemical substance occurs in two distinct modifications, it is said to be *dimorphous;* in three modifications, *trimorphous;* in many, *polymorphous.* Among the minerals, carbon as the diamond and graphite, FeS_2 as pyrite and marcasite, and $KAlSi_3O_8$ as orthoclase and microcline, are good examples of dimorphism. TiO_2 is trimorphous, for it occurs as the minerals rutile, brookite, and anatase. The element sulphur is an excellent example of a polymorphous substance, having at least six modifications, although the stable form is orthorhombic.

CHAPTER XIV

FORMATION AND OCCURRENCE OF MINERALS

In general, minerals may have been formed in four ways:

1. From solution.
2. From fusion.
3. By sublimation.
4. By metamorphism.

Of these methods, those involving solution and fusion are the most important. Most of the best crystals observed on minerals are the result of solidification from solution.

Solutions that exist in the earth's crust are derived from one of two possible sources. Surface water which in its passage through rocks dissolves varying amounts of the more soluble mineral constituents is called *meteoric water*. The mineral constituents are commonly later deposited on or near the surface. Water of deep-seated origin is known as *magmatic water* and is the liquid derived from large igneous intrusions. Mineral deposits from magmatic solutions are generally found at considerable depths.

FORMATION FROM SOLUTION

Minerals may form from solution in various ways. The following are some of the most important methods.

a. Evaporation of the Solvent.—Anhydrite and halite are commonly the result of the simple evaporation of the solution in which they were dissolved. In many instances these deposits are of great thickness. This is especially true of those occurring in central New York, Michigan, Kansas, and Iowa. Many minerals have been formed in this way.

b. Loss of Gases Acting as Solvents.—When water containing a considerable amount of carbon dioxide in solution comes in contact with limestone, calcium carbonate readily passes into solution as the acid or bicarbonate $(CaH_2(CO_3)_2)$. This is, however, an unstable compound, and due to various factors, the carbon dioxide in solution may be lost causing the bicarbonate to revert to the more insoluble normal carbonate $(CaCO_3)$, which is at once deposited. In limestone districts calcium carbonate is thus frequently dissolved in large quantities and subsequently deposited in caves in the form of *stalactites*, suspended from the roof, or as *stalagmites*, found upon the floor of the caves. Unusually translucent or attractively banded calcite found in caves is called in the trade *onyx marble* or *cave onyx*. It is also frequently deposited in this way around springs and in the beds of the streams resulting from them. Here it is generally observed as mosslike deposits, often enclosing twigs and leaves, and is called *calcareous tufa*. *Travertine* has a similar origin but is somewhat more compact. Deposits of travertine at Tivoli, near Rome, Italy, have been worked for centuries. By virtue of the presence of carbon dioxide, calcium carbonate passed into solution but was later deposited when the carbon dioxide escaped.

Fig. 449.—Charles Palache (1869–). Professor of mineralogy in Harvard University. Eminent American crystallographer and mineralogist.

c. *Change of Temperature and Pressure.*—In regions of geysers and hot springs the solubility of the circulating water is commonly greatly increased because of its high temperature and the pressure to which it is subjected. These waters therefore frequently contain much more mineral matter in solution than can be retained after they reach the surface, where the temperature is lowered and the pressure reduced. In these localities considerable quantities of *siliceous sinter* or *geyserite* are observed, which have formed in this way.

d. *Interaction of Solutions.*—As is commonly observed in the chemical laboratory, two solutions may interact and form an insoluble compound which is at once precipitated or deposited. Thus, a solution of calcium sulphate ($CaSO_4$), when brought into contact with one of a soluble barium compound such as $BaCl_2$, yields at once the insoluble barium sulphate ($BaSO_4$). When found in nature, barium sulphate is called *barite*. This mineral has undoubtedly been frequently formed in this way. Likewise, important ore deposits at times are formed near the contact of two different types of rocks, where the circulating waters of each type mingle and react chemically to form new minerals. Reactions between surface waters and those of deep-seated origin may also form new mineral constituents.

e. *Interaction of Solutions and Solids.*—A solution containing zinc sulphate may interact with limestone ($CaCO_3$) to cause the formation of smithsonite ($ZnCO_3$) and calcium sulphate. Frequently a solution dissolves one mineral and simultaneously deposits another in its place. Thus, galena (PbS) and other sulphides are deposited from solution and at the same time replace the limestone with which the solution is in contact. The texture or structure of the original mineral is often retained by the replacing substances. Opalized wood is another good example of replacement. Here the siliceous solutions have completely replaced the cellulose material with opal, retaining however the original woody structure. This process is called *metasomatism*, and has been of great importance in the formation of ore deposits.

f. Interaction of Gases with Solutions.—Waters charged with hydrogen sulphide precipitate sulphides from mine and quarry waters containing copper or iron. Presumably, many of the sulphide minerals have thus been formed.

g. Action of Organisms upon Solutions.—Mollusks, corals, crinoids, and other organisms secrete calcium carbonate from ocean water in the formation of shells and the hard parts of their bodies. This calcium carbonate may be in the form of either calcite or aragonite. Sponges, radiolaria, and diatoms similarly secrete silica. Diatomaceous earth, chert, and other forms of chalcedony may be formed in this manner. Limonite and sulphur may result from the action of certain bacteria upon water containing iron or sulphates in solution. The large deposits of soda niter in Chile are thought by some to be the result of the action of organisms.

FUSION

The minerals composing the igneous rocks are the result of solidification from a molten mass called the *magma*. Only rarely, however, does such a molten mass contain the constituents of a single mineral, so that generally several minerals are formed on cooling. In reality, crystallization from a magma takes place following the laws of solution, in which the least soluble constituent separates out first and the most soluble one last. Large crystals can result only if the process of cooling is comparatively slow. Hence, some portion of the molten or fused mass is apt to form amorphous or glassy material. Water and other active mineralizers are frequently contained in the magma and are of great importance in determining the character and size of the resulting minerals. Such igneous rocks as granite, syenite, diorite, and basalt, for example, are composed of minerals formed in this way. For a further description of the character and composition of such rocks, see pages 177 to 183.

Also, at times, important ore deposits of magnetite, ilmenite, chromite, pyrrhotite, and chalcopyrite have been formed by the segregations of these minerals directly from the molten magma due to their insolubility in the silicate melt.

When the temperature drops below that known as the *critical temperature* point, high-temperature aqueous solutions (mother liquors) are formed that are very active chemical agents in dissolving and concentrating some of the metallic constituents of the magma which are then deposited in the fissures and other openings in the rocks. These ore-bearing mother liquors may also react with the walls that enclose the fissured rock, and by hydrothermal alteration and replacement the earlier formed veins are frequently considerably enlarged.

SUBLIMATION

Under this heading are included not only the minerals which are the result of having passed from a solid state through the vapor and back to the solid state again, but also those which are the result of the interaction of gases upon one another and upon the country rock. Among the gaseous constituents of magmas are water vapor, which usually predominates, chlorine, boron, fluorine, sulphur, and volatile compounds of these gases with various metallic elements. While the temperature of a magma remains above the critical temperatures of these substances, they must be present as gases. If they escape to the surface, as in volcanic eruptions or in fumaroles, the minerals may be deposited by direct sublimation. Halite ($NaCl$), sal-ammoniac (NH_4Cl), sulphur, boric acid, ferric chloride, etc., may be formed in this manner. In the vicinity of volcanoes small scales of hematite (Fe_2O_3) are frequently found in the cavities of lava, resulting from the interaction of volatile $FeCl_3$ and water vapor. Thus, $2FeCl_3 + 3H_2O = Fe_2O_3 + 6HCl$.

Of greater importance are the minerals formed through the reaction of such gases with the rock adjacent to the intrusions of granitic magmas. Minerals formed in this way are usually said to be the result of *pneumatolytic action* or *pneumatolysis*. One of the most prominent examples of this character is the formation of cassiterite (SnO_2), which is frequently associated with fluorite (CaF_2).

$$SnF_4 + 2H_2O = SnO_2 + 4HF$$
(Cassiterite)

$$4HF + 2CaCO_3 = 2CaF_2 + 2H_2O + 2CO_2$$
(Limestone   (Fluorite)
or calcite)

In this case, it is assumed that volatile SnF_4 and water vapor interact to form SnO_2 (cassiterite) and hydrofluoric acid. The latter, however, is an exceedingly active chemical compound and hence tends to react with whatever it comes in contact, which in the above reaction is supposed to be limestone or the calcite of the adjacent rock. Fluorite is thus formed as the result of this reaction.

The following minerals are frequently regarded as being the result of pneumatolytic action: tourmaline, fluorite, cassiterite, topaz, apatite, scapolite, and phlogopite.

METAMORPHISM

Under the influence of certain processes involving principally heat, water vapor, pressure, and the chemical action of solutions, profound changes in the character, structure, and mineral constituents of rocks are frequently wrought. In this way sedimentary and igneous rocks may be changed. When such changes are limited in extent, the results constitute what is commonly called *local* or *contact metamorphism*. This type of metamorphism is most pronounced in the vicinity of dikes, intrusive sheets, and lava streams, that is, wherever older rocks, especially limestones and shales, have been subjected to the action of magmas. Similar changes may, however, take place over large areas, due to what are generally known as mountain-making processes. Such changes generally are the result of *regional* or *dynamic metamorphism*.

a. *Local or Contact Metamorphism.*—A considerable number of minerals are commonly the result of contact metamorphism. Wollastonite, garnet, graphite, vesuvianite, and epidote are frequently formed when impure limestone is metamorphosed by contact action. If considerable

Fig. 450.—Disseminated crystals   Fig. 451.—Attached
of orthoclase in trachyte.   crystal of quartz.

amounts of magnesium are present, diopside, tremolite, spinel, phlogopite, chondrodite, and olivine may be formed in addition to calcite and dolomite. In a similar manner andalusite and cordierite are often formed in shales under the influence of an igneous intrusion.

b. *Regional or Dynamic Metamorphism.*—Here large areas have been affected, and the structure of the rocks may be profoundly changed. This type of metamorphism is, however, not so productive of new minerals as is local or contact metamorphism. By regional metamorphism, soft or bituminous coal has been changed to hard or anthracite coal, sedimentary limestone to recrystallized limestone or marble, and igneous granite to a gneiss. By this action sandstone is converted into quartzite, and shale into slate or mica schist.

OCCURRENCE OF MINERALS

Minerals may be found either *disseminated* throughout other minerals or rocks (Fig. 450), or they may occur *attached* as crystals (Fig. 451) or adhering as crusts or in layers on other minerals or rocks. When found disseminated they sometimes exhibit crystal forms, although they are most frequently observed in irregular particles or grains. Disseminated crystals are generally *doubly* or *fully terminated.* Crusts of compact calcite, so commonly observed coating the exposed surfaces of limestone in cracks or coating pebbles in stream beds, are illustrative of the attached occurrence. Under favorable conditions crystals frequently

FIG. 452.—Vein of asbestos in serpentine.

FIG. 453.—Banded vein of sphalerite (dark), fluorite, and calcite.

form with one end well developed and with the other end adhering to the rock or mineral on which it was formed. Attached crystals are generally only *singly terminated* (Fig. 451).

Cracks or crevices filled with mineral matter are spoken of as *veins* (Fig. 452). When a vein consists of several minerals deposited in

FIG. 454.—Quartz vein with copper (dark).

FIG. 455.—Vein of smaltite and calcite (light).

layers or bands, it is termed a *banded vein* (Fig. 453). Veins may be *symmetrically* or *unsymmetrically banded*, depending upon whether or not the same minerals are encountered in passing from opposite walls of the vein to the center. The character of veins, as to their width and constituents, varies greatly in different localities. In some instances the width and mineral contents will continue practically unchanged over considerable distances laterally and vertically, whereas in other cases marked changes take place (Figs. 454 and 455). When a vein consists principally of unimportant or valueless material, which however contains some mineral of value disseminated throughout it, the former is spoken of as the *gangue*. Thus, in a gold-bearing quartz vein, quartz is obviously the gangue mineral (also see Figs. 454 and 455). The term *lode* is used for a highly mineralized area consisting of a series of parallel or branching veins.

Veins have been formed principally as the result of solidification of mineral matter from solution. These solutions may have been descending or ascending in character, while in some instances their flow

Fig. 456.—Broken geode of quartz crystals.

may have been largely lateral. Where veins trending in different directions cross, due to a possible difference in the character of the solutions from which they were formed, mineralization is usually most pronounced. In fact, it is well known that the richest mineral deposits, or what are frequently called *bonanza ores*, are to be expected at the intersection of veins. An *ore* may be defined as a mineral deposit of economic importance.

Geodes are cavities lined with mineral matter, which frequently consists of well-developed crystals. Quartz and calcite geodes are not uncommon (Fig. 456). Some geodes are large enough to be designated as caves. Thus, the "crystal" cave on the island of Put-in-Bay in Lake Erie is a huge geode containing crystals of celestite ($SrSO_4$). Similarly, large geodes lined with quartz crystals are found in the Alps of Switzerland. The term *vug* is sometimes used for geode.

When crystals or minerals are found in the places where they were formed, we may speak of them as occurring *in situ*. They are also said to be found in the parent or mother rock. When found in the sands and gravels of streams or of other bodies of water, as the result of transportation, they are said to occur in *secondary deposits* or *placers*. When gold is found in a quartz vein, it may be said to be observed *in situ*, but, when it is recovered from the sands and gravels of a stream or lake, we refer to it as *placer* gold. There are also platinum, diamond, and cassiterite placers.

ROCKS

As was indicated on page 5, the earth's crust consists of solid material, commonly called rocks, and, as these are composed of minerals, it is obvious that rocks must be the source of most minerals. A brief description of the most common and important rocks will therefore be given.

Any mineral or aggregate of minerals comprising an important part of the earth's crust may be termed a *rock*. A rock may consist of a single component as, for example, a sandstone or limestone (see page 5). In the majority of rocks, however, two or more minerals are present as is illustrated in the case of the granite where the three principal constituents are quartz, orthoclase, and mica or hornblende. To illustrate the relationship between minerals and rocks, the minerals might be compared to the letters of the alphabet and the rocks to the words.

Depending upon origin, three main groups of rocks may be differentiated. The *igneous* rocks are those which have resulted from the solidification of a molten or liquid mass, commonly called a magma. The *sedimentary* rocks, on the other hand, were deposited in water, either as fragments carried mechanically or as chemical precipitates, while the *metamorphic* rocks were developed from either the igneous or sedimentary types by geological agencies including heat, pressure, and circulating waters.

Igneous Rocks

If the magma be permitted to cool slowly it will in time become supersaturated with reference to certain chemical compounds which then separate or crystallize out to form the various minerals. The important rock-forming minerals of igneous rocks comprise (*a*) the *essential* and (*b*) the *accessory* minerals. The former are those whose presence has a direct influence upon the character and name of the rock. This division would include feldspars, pyroxenes, amphiboles, micas, nephelite, leucite, olivine, and quartz. The accessory minerals, as the name indicates, are those present in smaller amounts. They do not affect appreciably the character of the rock. The more important ones would include magnetite, ilmenite, pyrite, pyrrhotite, apatite, zircon, rutile, and titanite.

The order of crystallization from the magma, while not constant in all cases, tends to proceed in a more or less definite manner. The accessory minerals, being the first to form, usually show very good crystal outlines. The ferromagnesium minerals (olivine, biotite, hornblende, or augite) follow the accessory constituents and these in turn are followed by the feldspars. If the original magma contained a large amount of silica, the excess, if any remains after combining to form the above mentioned minerals, separates out as quartz. From this sequence it will be seen that, in general, the more basic minerals—those low in silica—crystallize out first to be followed by those more acid in composition.

Those igneous rocks which are the result of magmas that have reached the surface are termed *extrusive* or *volcanic*. Due to the escape of dissolved gases and the rapid rate of cooling, rocks of this type are characterized by fragmental, glassy, cellular, or extremely fine-grained (felsitic) textures. Magmas, on the other hand, that have solidified at depths produce rocks that are spoken of as *plutonic* or *intrusive*. These have cooled very slowly and consequently possess larger and better developed crystal grains. They are said to have a granular texture. In many instances the texture of an intrusive rock is sufficiently coarse to permit of the identification of all the essential minerals with the naked eye.

Fig. 457.—Auguste Michel-Levy (1844–1911). For many years professor in the Collège de France, Paris. Distinguished for his researches on rock-forming and synthetic minerals.

The field classification of igneous rocks is based primarily upon grain or texture and mineral composition. The latter depends, however, upon the chemical composition of the original magma. Magmas containing a total of 65 to 80 per cent. of SiO_2 produce *acid* or light-colored rocks. In these there is developed an abundance of orthoclase or microcline, some quartz, and a subordinate amount of ferro-magnesium minerals. Examples of this type are granite, rhyolite, aplite, and pegmatite. The *basic* or dark-colored rocks result from magmas containing less than 52 per cent. of SiO_2. In these we have an excess of the ferro-magnesium minerals, some feldspar (plagioclase), and olivine, but little or no quartz. Gabbro, peridotite, pyroxenite, and basalt are a few examples of basic rocks. The intermediate types must then result from those magmas whose SiO_2 content is somewhere between 65 and 52 per cent. and are represented by syenite, diorite, trachyte, and andesite. A summary of some of the more important igneous rocks is given in the table shown on page 179. It should be noted, however, that in nature the transition from one type of rock into another is gradual. The various types do not show the sharp distinctions which might be inferred from the rulings in the diagram.

From an inspection of the chart it will be seen that a rock with a granular texture is called a *granite* when it contains orthoclase or microcline, a dark constituent, and quartz, while a rock with the same texture without the quartz is known as a *syenite*. Rhyolite and trachyte are mineralogically the equivalents of granite and syenite but possess a felsitic rather than granular texture. Diorite, on the other hand, is a granular rock consisting essentially of acid plagioclase[1] and hornblende, while gabbro contains basic plagioclase, augite, and frequently some olivine. The term *dolerite* may be employed for those types of diorite-gabbro rocks when it is impossible to determine with the naked eye whether the dark constituent is hornblende or augite. Andesite and basalt are the felsitic equivalents of diorite and gabbro, respectively.

	Orthoclase		Plagioclase		Feldspar-free	
acid	←——— intermediate			———→		basic
Dark constituent	Mica or hornblende		Hornblende or augite		Augite or hornblende	
Distinguishing mineral	+ Quartz	− Quartz	− Quartz	± Olivine	− Olivine	+ Olivine
Granular texture	Granite[1]	Syenite	Diorite[2]	Gabbro Dolerite	Pyroxenite	Peridotite
Felsitic texture	Rhyolite	Trachyte Felsite	Andesite	Basalt	Augitite	Limburgite
Glassy texture	Obsidian Pitchstone			Tachylyte (Basaltic glass)		
Cellular texture	Pumice			Scoria		

[1] If considerable plagioclase accompanies orthoclase the term *granodiorite* is preferred.
[2] If quartz is present the rock is called *quartz diorite*.

Dike Rocks.—Frequently penetrating the larger rock bodies will be found fissures containing intrusions of igneous material. These occurrences are known as *dikes*. They are of later origin than the rock penetrated and may be either extremely acid or very basic in character. The acid or light-colored dikes include *aplite* and *pegmatite*, while the general term *lamprophyre* has been suggested for all the basic types. Aplite is an extremely fine and even-grained rock consisting largely of quartz and orthoclase with a very subordinate amount of dark material. Pegmatite, while possessing in general the same mineral composition as the aplite, has, on the contrary, an exceedingly coarse and uneven texture. In the formation of pegmatites it is believed that mineralizers have played an important role. The dissolved vapors would not only increase the fluidity of the magma, thus reducing internal friction and permitting the growth of crystals of unusual size, but also explain the size and concentration of certain accessory minerals which are so abundant in some pegmatites. Hydrothermal solutions frequently alter the original mineral components of a dike by dissolving some of the constituents

[1] The terms *acid* and *basic* plagioclase refer to silica content (see page 376). Thus oligoclase with 61.9 per cent. SiO_2 is an acid, while labradorite, containing 49.1 per cent. SiO_2, is a basic plagioclase.

and reacting with others, with the result that many new species are formed. A list of a few of the more common accessory minerals in pegmatites would include tourmaline, beryl, topaz, fluorite, spodumene, wolframite, and columbite. While in most cases aplite and pegmatite have the general mineral composition of granite, there are instances where they are more closely related to syenite, diorite, or gabbro. The basic dikes are not so well crystallized, nor do they, as a rule, contain the wealth of accessory minerals which characterizes the acid types.

Sedimentary Rocks

These are all of secondary origin, having been derived from the disintegration of older rocks through the action of agencies included under the comprehensive term of "weathering." That portion of the mineral matter which is carried away in solution may at some later period be deposited either through strictly chemical action, by slow evaporation, or through processes involving organic life.

Sedimentary rocks are characterized by a parallel or bedded structure. In these rocks the layers may vary in thickness, and the individual grains of the materials making up the rock may show considerable variation in composition and size. They form widely extended deposits which, generally speaking, are without great vertical dimensions, especially when compared with some of the massive igneous formations. A field classification based on origin would divide the sedimentary rocks into three main groups: (a) the *mechanical*, (b) the *chemical*, and (c) the *organic sediments*. The mechanical sediments would include shale, sandstone, conglomerate, and breccia; while formations of anhydrite, gypsum, and salt would be classified as chemical deposits. Those of organic origin would include coal, limestone, and dolomite.

Shale.—The finest particles carried mechanically by the water, and generally referred to as mud or silt, when reaching the sea, settle quickly, due to the action of the soluble salts in the ocean water. These deposits when consolidated, yield a very fine and even-grained rock—possessing a good parting parallel to the bedding—which is known as *shale*. The chief components are clay, quartz, and feldspar, although these constituents cannot be distinguished with the naked eye. As the amount of quartz and the size of the grain increase, the shale gradually passes over into a sandstone. The colors of shale may vary from green to gray and in some instances may even be black (*carbonaceous shale*). From some of the shales of northwestern Colorado and adjacent states oil has been extracted, and in several instances the quantity recovered amounted to 40 or 50 gallons per ton of rock. These are termed *oil shales*. The oil can be obtained by distillation at a low temperature (about 400°C.), and paraffine wax and ammonium sulphate recovered from the residue.

Sandstone.—When particles of sand of nearly uniform size become consolidated, *sandstone* results. The individual components are usually rounded and consist essentially of quartz. When considerable feldspar is present, the rock is spoken of as feldspathic sandstone or *arkose.* The cementing material varies greatly in both amount and character. In some instances it is silica, although calcium carbonate, clay, or iron oxide may serve as the binding material. The most durable sandstones for structural purposes are those with a siliceous cement. Those containing iron oxide show, however, the greatest variation in color. When a sandstone is used for structural purposes, it should always be placed with the bedding planes in a horizontal position, insuring thereby greater strength and durability. A thinly bedded argillaceous sandstone is called a *flagstone,* while the term *freestone* is applied to those homogeneous types which occur in thick beds and can be worked in all directions with equal ease.

A *conglomerate* is a rock term applied to rounded, water-worn pebbles of various sizes which are held in a matrix of finer materials. If the fragments are sharp and angular instead of rounded the term *breccia* is employed. Breccias are quite common in limestone regions where the movement along a fault plane has crushed the rock to various degrees of fineness. These are known as *friction breccias* in contrast to *volcanic breccias* which are composed of consolidated, angular fragments of igneous material.

Limestone and Dolomite.—A *limestone* is a sedimentary rock consisting essentially of calcium carbonate with minor amounts of magnesium carbonate, silica, clay, iron oxide, or carbonaceous material. The majority of limestones were formed by organisms such as Foraminifera, brachiopods, corals, mollusks, and crinoids, which have secreted calcium carbonate taken from the waters and utilized the material to form shells and skeletons. The pressure of superimposed rocks has, in many instances, largely destroyed its original fossiliferous character. The variety known as *oölitic limestone* is composed of small rounded grains of concretionary nature. With an increase in the content of magnesium carbonate, limestone gradually passes over to a *dolomitic limestone,* and finally to a *normal dolomite,* which theoretically contains 54.35 per cent. $CaCO_3$ and 45.65 per cent. $MgCO_3$. Normal dolomite is both slightly heavier and harder than the limestone and will not effervesce so freely when treated with cold, dilute acids. Many dolomites are believed to be the result of magnesium solutions reacting upon limestones as indicated by the equation $2CaCO_3 + MgCl_2 = CaMg(CO_3)_2 + CaCl_2$.

Metamorphic Rocks

Compressive or directional forces together with the heat, caused by the folding and crushing of the rock strata, and the chemical action of liquids, produce profound changes in both igneous and sedimentary rocks. The alterations noted are either mineralogical or chemical in character and frequently also include a change in the original structure. The resultant rocks, classified as *metamorphic*, possess certain features which resemble both the igneous and sedimentary types. Many are coarsely crystalline in character and in this respect are similar to intrusive igneous rocks. Others, on the other hand, possess a banded structure caused by certain minerals of like character being brought together in parallel layers. This parallel arrangement is termed *schistose* or *foliated structure*. Some of the important types resulting from the action of regional metamorphism (page 174) include gneiss, schists, quartzite, slate, and marble.

Gneiss.—This is a laminated rock which generally has the mineral composition of the granite. The intermingled grains of quartz and feldspar are separated by layers of the dark constituent. The banding may extend in straight parallel lines or be curved and bent. Gneisses differ from schists in that they are more coarsely laminated and contain a larger amount of feldspar. They usually represent an altered igneous rock, such as granite, although they may also have originated from a coarse feldspathic sandstone or conglomerate. Gneisses are of widespread occurrence, especially in the older geological formations.

Schists.—These are laminated metamorphic rocks which split readily along planes that are approximately parallel. Depending upon the character of the prevailing mineral, four types are easily differentiated, namely, mica, chlorite, talc, and hornblende schists. In the *mica schist* the scales are so arranged that the cleavage directions are all parallel, thus producing a rock of pronounced schistose structure. In addition to mica and more or less quartz and feldspar, well-developed crystals of garnet, cyanite, and staurolite are also frequently present. Next to the gneiss, mica schist is the most abundant metamorphic rock. Usually it is the result of the alteration of a fine-grained sedimentary deposit, such as clay or shale. In *chlorite schist* the chief component is the green, granular or scaly mineral chlorite. In many instances it has been formed from some basic igneous rock, such as gabbro or basalt. In the case of *talc schist*, the predominating mineral is talc, which gives the rock a characteristic soapy feel. As talc is a magnesium silicate it can only be developed from the feldspar-free igneous rocks or, if of sedimentary origin, from impure dolomites. A schist consisting largely of black slender prisms of hornblende is termed a *hornblende schist*. As the needles are all arranged with their long direction parallel to the schistosity, these schists cleave readily and show a marked silky luster. In many instances it has been derived from a basic igneous rock, such as a gabbro.

Quartzite.—This is a very firm compact rock consisting of interlocking quartz grains. It is the result of the intense metamorphism of a sandstone in which the silica cement has been recrystallized and becomes an integral part of the quartz grains. In an ordinary sandstone it will be seen that the fracture always follows the cement, while in a true quartzite it passes through the recrystallized grains.

Slate.—This is an exceedingly fine-grained rock which breaks very easily in thin broad sheets. The cleavage, as a rule, does not correspond to the bedding planes of the shale, from which most slates were derived, but cuts these planes at various angles. In mineral composition the slates consist essentially of quartz and mica with subordinate amounts of chlorite, hematite, or graphite, which contribute the green, red, and black colors, respectively. Purple slates owe their color to a combination of green chlorite and red hematite. Slates containing a considerable amount of iron carbonate have a tendency to develop a brown color (limonite) on exposure and are termed *fading slates* in the building trade.

Marble.—Strictly speaking, the term *marble* includes limestones or dolomites which have been recrystallized and are capable of taking a polish. The term, however, is used somewhat loosely and not infrequently includes any limestone that will take a polish and can be used for decorative purposes, irrespective of its recrystallized character. Scales of mica and chlorite, arranged in wavy streaks or bands, are frequently present which add to the attractiveness of the stone, but interfere with the continuity of the polish and lower its resistance to atmospheric agencies when placed in exposed positions. Marbles show great variation in texture and color. Statuary marbles demand the purest and whitest varieties, while ornamental types show strongly contrasted color effects. For structural purposes uniformity of color is rather essential. Marbles are not so widely distributed as limestones and are confined almost entirely to metamorphic areas.

DECOMPOSITION AND WEATHERING OF MINERALS

As soon as minerals are formed and are exposed to atmospheric conditions, they are subject to change. By the action of moisture, the oxygen of the air, various acids of the soil, and other agencies, profound changes are brought about. In some cases the alteration takes place rather rapidly while in others it may proceed very slowly. All minerals are, however, sooner or later acted upon. The changes are effected by the action of processes familiar to students of chemistry. Some of the more important are solution, oxidation, reduction, hydration, and carbonation. In most instances several of these processes may have been effective simultaneously or successively.

PSEUDOMORPHS

Not infrequently crystals alter in such a way that the external form of the original specimen is retained. For example, limonite ($Fe_2O_3.nH_2O$) is sometimes found in the form of crystals which were originally pyrite (FeS_2).   That is, by means of oxidation and hydration pyrite has been altered to limonite without destroying the crystal shape.   Such altered crystals are called *pseudomorphs,* and in the case, just referred to, they are known as pseudomorphs of *limonite after pyrite.*   There are several interesting types of pseudomorphs.

Paramorphs.—In these a molecular rearrangement has taken place, without the chemical composition being changed.   Paramorphs are possible only in the case of polymorphous substances.   Thus, rutile (TiO_2), tetragonal, after brookite (TiO_2), orthorhombic.   Also, calcite ($CaCO_3$), hexagonal, after aragonite ($CaCO_3$), orthorhombic.

Alteration Pseudomorphs.—The change in composition may involve the loss of some constituents, the addition of new ones, or there may be a partial exchange.   Anhydrite ($CaSO_4$) after gypsum ($CaSO_4.2H_2O$), malachite ($CuCO_3.Cu(OH)_2$) after cuprite (Cu_2O), kaolin ($H_4Al_2Si_2O_9$) after orthoclase ($KAlSi_3O_8$), and chlorite after garnet are excellent illustrations of pseudomorphs of this type.

Substitution Pseudomorphs.—Sometimes the replacing mineral has no chemical relation to the original substance.   Good illustrations are the pseudomorphs of quartz (SiO_2) after fluorite (CaF_2), and quartz after calcite ($CaCO_3$).

Incrustation Pseudomorphs.—At times a mineral may be deposited upon the crystal form of another and completely enclose it.   Thus, smithsonite ($ZnCO_3$) on calcite ($CaCO_3$) (Fig. 607, page 297).   Incrustation pseudomorphs of quartz on fluorite are sometimes of such a character as to permit the deposit of quartz with the cubical casts of fluorite to be removed intact.   In some cases the removal of the first mineral has taken place simultaneously with the deposition of the incrusting substance.

CHAPTER XV

QUALITATIVE BLOWPIPE METHODS

Whenever possible it is advisable to determine minerals at sight, that is, by means of their physical properties, occurrences, and associates. It frequently becomes necessary, however, to supplement these observations by simple, confirmatory, chemical tests. These reactions, obtained largely at high temperatures by the proper use of the blowpipe, are referred to as *blowpipe reactions*. The chemist in his laboratory can increase the number of his reagents at will, and naturally his field of operation is larger than that of the student equipped with a blowpipe, who relies upon a limited number of reagents and the effects produced when minerals are subjected to the oxidizing or reducing action of a flame. The ease with which many blowpipe tests are obtained and the small amount of apparatus and reagents required have made these reactions popular with both the mineralogist and geologist.

The equipment which is necessary may be limited to the following apparatus and reagents.

Fig. 458.—George J. Brush (1831–1912). For many years a professor in Yale University. Distinguished for the application of blowpipe and chemical methods in the determination of minerals.

APPARATUS

Blowpipe.—The best type consists of a brass or nickel-plated, slightly conical-shaped tube *a* (Fig. 459) about 18 cm. in length, into the larger end of which fits a mouthpiece of hardened rubber *b*. At the opposite end a hollow, cylindrical chamber *c* serves to collect the moisture which condenses in the tube. A side tube *d* joins the air chamber at right angles and is equipped with a platinum tip *e*, in the center of which is a smooth hole from 0.4 to 0.6 mm. in diameter.

Lamps.—Where illuminating gas is available, the most convenient form of lamp is the Bunsen burner equipped with an additional inner tube which is flattened at the upper end and cut off obliquely (Fig. 460). The supply of gas should be so regulated that a luminous flame about 4 cm. in height results. Where gas is not available, lamps may be secured which burn either liquid (alcohol, olive oil, lard oil) or solid (tallow, paraffin) fuel. By the addition of a small amount of turpentine to the alcohol the luminosity as well as the reducing power of the flame is greatly increased.   A candle flame may also be used to advantage.

Forceps.   Plain iron, or better still platinum-tipped, forceps are indispensable for testing the fusibility of minerals as well as for noting flame colorations.

Charcoal.—Rectangular blocks of charcoal about $10 \times 2\frac{1}{2} \times 2\frac{1}{2}$ cm. are useful supports during the fusion of the assay.   Likewise films are often condensed and deposited on the cooler portion of the support. Charcoal made from willow, pine, or basswood is usually recommended.

Plaster Tablets.—These are made by preparing a thin paste of plaster of Paris and water, and spreading it over an oiled glass plate until a uniform thickness of about 5 mm. is secured.   Before the plaster has hardened the surface is ruled by a knife into rectangular divisions 10 cm. long and about 5 cm. wide.   These tablets are especially well adapted for the condensation of iodide sublimates.

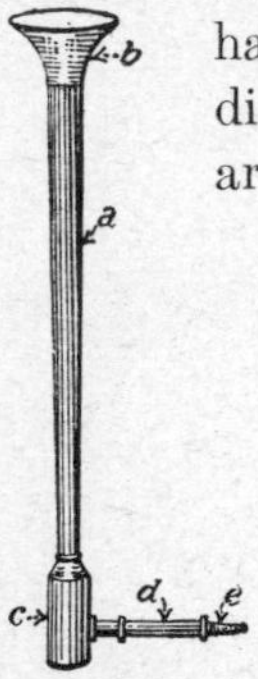

Platinum Wire.—No suitable substitute has been found to replace platinum wire for flame colorations and bead tests.   The wire should be No. 27 or 28 B. & S. gauge, about 10 cm. long. One end should be fused into a piece of glass tubing.

Fig. 459.— Blowpipe.

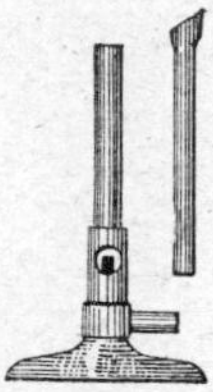

Fig. 460.— Bunsen burner with inner tube.

Hammer and Anvil.—A small hammer weighing about 75 g. with a wire handle is recommended.   Also a block of steel 4 cm. square and 1 cm. thick, for crushing material to be tested.

Agate Mortar and Pestle.—The mortar should be at least 4 cm. in diameter.   It is used for pulverizing material.

Diamond Mortar.—The mortar should be of tool steel, about 4 cm. square and possess a cylindrical cavity to receive the pestle.   It is indispensable in crushing minerals to a fairly fine powder.

Open and Closed Tubes.—Hard-glass tubing, 12 to 14 cm. in length and about 5 mm. inside diameter, is employed either open at both ends to note the effect of a current of heated air upon the mineral, or closed at one end for the detection of volatile acids.

Merwin Flame-color Screen.—This is a celluloid screen, $7\frac{1}{2}$ by $12\frac{1}{2}$ cm., consisting of three colored strips, one blue, one violet, and one blue over violet.   The strips are so stained as to absorb the orange and yellow portions of the spectrum.   This screen is extremely useful in the examination of flame colorations and is far superior to the "blue" and "green glass" formerly employed for the same purpose.

Other articles for blowpipe work which need no detailed description are the following:

Test Tubes.—12 cm. in length and 15 mm. in diameter.

Test-tube Stand, Test-tube Brush and Holder.

Magnet.—Horseshoe type.

Watch Glasses.—5 cm. in diameter.

Glass Funnel and Filter Paper.—Bunsen rapid-filtering funnel, 65 mm. in diameter.

File.—Triangular for cutting glass tubing.

Pliers.—Serviceable in breaking and cutting fragments of minerals.

Figure 461 shows an assembly of the more important blowpipe apparatus.

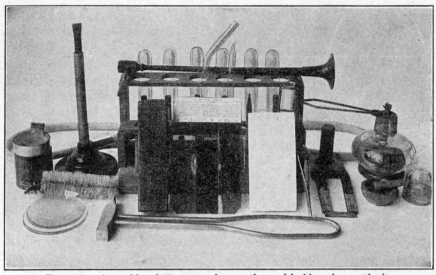

Fig. 461.—Assembly of apparatus frequently used in blowpipe methods.

DRY REAGENTS

These reagents should be kept in wide-mouthed glass bottles.

Sodium Carbonate, Na_2CO_3; or *Sodium Bicarbonate*, $NaHCO_3$.— Employed extensively in the decomposition of minerals.

Borax, $Na_2B_4O_7.10H_2O$.—When fused in a loop of platinum wire it is used for bead tests. Borax glass is fused and pulverized borax.

Microcosmic Salt or Salt of Phosphorus, $HNaNH_4PO_4.4H_2O$.—Also used for bead tests. Upon heating, water and ammonia are liberated and the salt is transformed to sodium metaphosphate, $NaPO_3$.

Test Papers.—Blue and red litmus for alkaline and acid reactions. Yellow turmeric paper for the detection of boracic acid and zirconium.

Potassium Bisulphate, $KHSO_4$.—Used in fusions for decomposing minerals.

Bismuth Flux.—An intimate mixture of 1 part by weight of KI, 1 part of $KHSO_4$, and 2 parts of S (*von Kobell's flux*). When used on the plaster support many elements yield highly colored iodide sublimates.

Boracic Acid Flux.—Consists of 3 parts of finely pulverized $KHSO_4$ and .1 part of powdered fluorite (CaF_2) (*Turner's flux*). Employed for the detection of boron in silicates.

Potassium Nitrate, KNO_3.—When used with a fusion mixture it accelerates oxidation.

Granulated Tin and Zinc.—Used in acid solutions to effect reduction.

Magnesium Ribbon.—For the detection of phosphoric acid.

LIQUID REAGENTS

Work in the field demands that the number of reagents, and especially those of the liquid type, be reduced to a minimum. Under these conditions it is possible to restrict the number of wet reagents to ammonia, a 10 per cent. solution of cobalt nitrate, and the common acids HCl, HNO_3, and H_2SO_4. In the laboratory it is far better to augment this number in order to extend materially the range of operations.

FIG. 462.—Wolfgang Franz von Kobell (1803–1882). For many years professor of mineralogy in the University of Munich. Noted for his contributions in the field of blowpipe methods.

Alcohol.—95 per cent. ethyl alcohol.

Ammonium Hydroxide, NH_4OH.—One part of the concentrated alkali diluted with 2 parts of water.

Ammonium Molybdate, $(NH_4)_2MoO_4$.—Dissolve 50 g. of MoO_3 in a mixture of 200 cc. of water and 40 cc. of NH_4OH (sp. gr. 0.90). The solution should be kept warm. The liquid is then filtered and poured with constant stirring into a mixture of 200 cc. of HNO_3 (sp. gr. 1.42) and 300 cc. of water.

Ammonium Oxalate, $(NH_4)_2C_2O_4.2H_2O$.—20 g. dissolved in 500 cc. of water.

Ammonium Polysulphide, $(NH_4)_2S_x$.—Add flowers of sulphur to fairly concentrated ammonia and saturate the solution with H_2S. The flask should be cooled with running water while being charged with H_2S. Keep stopper in bottle when not in use.

Barium Chloride, $BaCl_2.2H_2O$.—$30\frac{1}{2}$ g. dissolved in 500 cc. of water.

Calcium Hydroxide (Lime Water), $Ca(OH)_2$.—Prepared by shaking CaO with water and decanting the clear liquid.

Cobalt Nitrate, $Co(NO_3)_2.6H_2O$.—One part of the crystallized salt is dissolved in 10 parts of water and the solution kept in dropping bottles.

Dimethylglyoxime, $C_4H_8O_2N_2$.—Prepare a saturated solution in 50 per cent. alcohol to which a small amount of ammonia has been added.

Disodium Hydrogen Phosphate (Sodium Phosphate), $Na_2HPO_4.-12H_2O$.—30 g. dissolved in 500 cc. of water.

Ferrous Sulphate, $FeSO_4.7H_2O$.—Solution prepared as needed.

Hydrobromic Acid, HBr.—Prepared by passing H_2S through a solution of liquid bromine in water until the red color of the bromine disappears. The flask should be cooled with running water while being charged. Decant the clear solution.

Hydrochloric Acid, HCl.—The chemically pure concentrated acid is diluted with an equal volume of water.

Hydrogen Peroxide, H_2O_2.—3 per cent. solution. Keep in amber colored bottle.

Lead Acetate, $Pb(C_2H_3O_2)_2.3H_2O$.—$47\frac{1}{2}$ g. dissolved in 500 cc. of water.

Nitric Acid, HNO_3.—Used either in its concentrated form, or 1 part of the acid is diluted with 2 parts of water.

Fig. 463.—The Butler blowpipe set suitable for field use.*

Nitrohydrochloric Acid (Aqua Regia).—A mixture of 3 parts of concentrated HCl and 1 part of concentrated HNO_3.

Potassium Ferricyanide, $K_3Fe(CN)_6$.—$27\frac{1}{2}$ g. dissolved in 500 cc. of water.

Potassium Ferrocyanide, $K_4Fe(CN)_5.3H_2O$.—$26\frac{1}{2}$ g. dissolved in 500 cc. of water.

Potassium Hydroxide, KOH.—The "sticks" should be kept in well-stoppered bottles and dissolved in water when needed.

Silver Nitrate, $AgNO_3$.—$21\frac{1}{2}$ g. dissolved in 500 cc. of water. The solution should be kept in amber colored bottles.

Sodium Nitroferricyanide, $Na_2Fe(NO)(CN)_5$.—Solution should be prepared as needed.

Stannous Chloride, $SnCl_2.2H_2O$.—Solid reagent.

* Arranged by Prof. G. M. Butler and sold by the Denver Fire Clay Company, Denver, Colorado.

Sulphuric Acid, H_2SO_4.—Used at times in its concentrated form, also diluted with 6 parts of water. In diluting, the acid should be added very slowly to the water.

On account of the ease with which blowpipe reactions may be obtained and the simplicity of the equipment necessary, various portable sets suitable for field work have been arranged. One of the best is the Butler blowpipe set, illustrated in Fig. 463.

STRUCTURE AND USE OF THE FLAME

Structure of the Flame.—The structure of the flame is essentially the same whether produced by burning a gaseous, a liquid, or a solid fuel. If a small luminous flame of the Bunsen burner be examined carefully, it will be noted that four more or less distinct zones are present (Fig. 464).

Fig. 464.— Structure of luminous flame.

Immediately above the burner is a dark cone *a*, consisting primarily of unburned gases. Surrounding the dark zone and extending beneath the luminous mantle, is a small, blue, nonluminous zone *b*. The strongly luminous region *c*, which emits a bright yellow light, constitutes the largest portion of the luminous flame.

In general, luminosity may be due to three causes operating either separately or jointly in increasing the light-producing property of a flame. These causes are (1) the temperature of the flame, (2) the density of the flame gases, and (3) the presence of solid particles which are heated to incandescence. In the case of the Bunsen burner fed with ordinary coal gas the luminosity is unquestionably due to the presence of solid particles of carbon. The illuminants, which determine the light-giving property of a coal-gas flame, are the unsaturated hydrocarbons, such as ethylene (C_2H_4), acetylene (C_2H_2), and benzene (C_6H_6). Due to the heat of combustion these hydrocarbons undergo dissociation. Ethylene breaks down, giving acetylene and hydrogen, while the acetylene yields carbon and hydrogen, thus explaining the cause of the luminosity. The equations expressing this dissociation may be written as follows:

$$C_2H_4 \rightarrow C_2H_2 + H_2$$
$$C_2H_2 \rightarrow 2C + H_2$$

Finally surrounding the luminous mantle we have an outer, nonluminous, invisible zone *d*, in which, due to the oxygen of the air, there is almost complete oxidation yielding as end products CO_2 and H_2O.

The Bunsen flame may be modified by inserting an inner tube which is flattened at one end and cut off obliquely, so that the blowpipe flame can be directed downward. The tube also acts as a support for the blowpipe.

Oxidizing and Reducing Flames.—The oxidizing blowpipe flame is produced by inserting the tip of the blowpipe into the luminous flame, which should be about 4 cm. in height and blowing a gentle but steady current of air. The flame is directed slightly downward and immediately becomes nonluminous, with the possible exception of a very small luminous region above the blowpipe tip. Two well-defined nonluminous zones are readily produced, *a* and *b* (Fig. 465). The nonluminosity of this flame may be explained by the dilution and cooling effect of the air introduced into the flame gases, thus preventing the dissociation of the hydrocarbons which is so essential for the production of luminosity. Not only does the flame become nonluminous, but it is also reduced in size. Since the same amount of gas is consumed and the ultimate end products are the same in both cases, the heat liberated would likewise be the same in both instances. As the nonluminous flame is smaller, it follows that the average temperature of this flame must necessarily be higher than that of the luminous flame. The zone *a* is slightly reducing in character due to the presence of CO in this region. For oxidation purposes the substance to be tested should be placed as indicated

FIG. 465.—Oxidizing flame.

by the position of the loop *A* (Fig. 465). When placed in this position, the highly heated substance readily unites with the oxygen of the atmosphere.

The oxidizing blowpipe flame is also frequently employed in testing the fusibility of minerals. The hottest portion of this flame is to be found at *c*. In testing for fusibility, the fragment, which should extend beyond the tip of the forceps, should be thin, possess sharp edges, and be held in the hottest portion of the flame. If the sharp outlines are rounded, the mineral is said to be fusible. The degree of fusibility may be roughly determined by comparison with the fusibility of minerals comprising a standard scale. It is quite important that fragments should be chosen of approximately the same size. The generally accepted *scale of fusibility* is composed of the following six minerals beginning with the most fusible. This is Penfield's modification of von Kobell's scale.

Stibnite fuses readily in a candle flame, also in a closed tube.

Chalcopyrite fuses in the luminous gas flame but with difficulty in a closed tube.

Almandite (garnet) fuses readily in the blowpipe, flame, infusible in the luminous gas flame.

Actinolite, edges are readily rounded in the blowpipe flame.

Orthoclase, edges are fused with difficulty in the blowpipe flame.

Bronzite, only the sharpest splinters are rounded by fusion.

The reducing blowpipe flame is produced by placing the blowpipe tip just outside the flame while blowing a gentle current of air (Fig. 466). The flame is tilted sideways but retains its luminosity. A fragment held in the luminous portion of this flame will suffer reduction by virtue of the hot carbon particles of the flame. Thus, by simply shifting the position of the blowpipe and regulating the strength of the blast, entirely opposite chemical effects may be produced. The purity of the oxidizing and reducing flames may be readily tested by dissolving a few small

particles of MnO_2 in a borax bead on a platinum wire. In the oxidizing flame the color of the bead should be reddish violet, while in the reducing flame the color should entirely disappear.

F I G. 466.—Reducing flame.

Scope of the Chemical Reactions.—The reactions to be described will be presented in the following order:

1. Reactions on plaster of Paris tablet.
   a. Assay heated *per se.*
   b. Assay heated with reagents.
2. Reactions on charcoal support.
   a. Assay heated *per se.*
   b. Assay heated with reagents.
3. Flame colorations.
4. Bead tests.
5. Heating in open tube.
6. Heating in closed tube.
7. Special tests.
8. Summary of chemical and blowpipe tests.

I. REACTIONS ON PLASTER TABLET

On account of their smooth white surface, infusibility, conductivity, and porosity, plaster tablets are one of the most important supports for blowpipe work. They can be employed with both solid and liquid reagents. The tablets are cheaply and easily made, and their cleanliness in handling has added to their popularity.

Per Se Reactions.—A small depression to hold the assay is made in the lower portion of the tablet and the support held in an inclined position. Unless otherwise stated, the oxidizing blowpipe flame is then directed upon the assay. The volatile constituent, either the metal itself or an oxide of the metal, is driven off by the heat and deposited upon the cooler portions of the support. Should the material be difficult to retain on the support due to decrepitation, a paste should be made of the finely powdered substance with water, and the heat applied gradually. The more important *per se* tests are given as shown in table on page 193.

While some characteristic coatings are thus obtained by merely heating the substance *per se*, the use of reagents greatly increases the number of elements which can be easily differentiated. The reagents

Per Se Reactions on Plaster Tablet

Indication	Color of coating	Remarks
Cadmium	Near assay, reddish brown to greenish yellow, at times somewhat iridescent. At a distance brownish black.	Film is due to an oxide, is permanent, and is best obtained from metallic cadmium.
Carbon	Brownish black, non-volatile coating.	Obtained from those carbonaceous materials yielding sooty deposits. Example, asphalt.
Molybdenum	In oxidizing flame, near assay, yellowish white, crystalline coating of MoO_3.	When touched with reducing flame, white coating is immediately changed to deep blue. Example, ammonium molybdate.
Arsenic (metal)	White over brownish black, very volatile coating.	Garlic odor is also noted, due probably to small amount of arsine.
Arsenic (sulphide)	Yellowish to reddish brown coating. Not very distinct.	When heated too rapidly, coating becomes brownish black.
Mercury	Drab gray, extremely volatile sublimate.	Example, HgO.
Selenium	Cherry red to crimson in thin layers. Black near assay where coating is very thick.	Sublimate is due to metal, is volatile, and yields reddish fumes with odor of rotten horse-radish. Example, metallic selenium.
Tellurium	Volatile brown to black coating, at times with narrow fringe of blue near assay.	A drop of conc. H_2SO_4 added to brown coating and gently heated yields evanescent pink of tellurium sulphate. Example, metallic tellurium.
Silver	Yellowish coating near assay. When touched with reducing flame, becomes brownish and mottled.	Coating is permanent and requires high heat. Reduced metal may also be noted. Example, $AgNO_3$.
Gold	Slightly purple to rose colored coating near and under the assay.	Requires very intense heat and is best seen when tablet is cold.

usually employed on the plaster support are bismuth flux, ammonium polysulphide, hydrobromic acid, and cobalt nitrate.

Reactions with Bismuth Flux and Ammonium Polysulphide.—One part of the powdered mineral is intimately mixed with 3 parts of bismuth flux (consisting of 2 parts S, 1 part KI, and 1 part $KHSO_4$) and heated on a plaster support. In nearly every instance, highly colored, volatile iodide coatings are obtained which condense on the cooler parts of the tablet. Similarly colored sublimates can be easily differentiated by the use of ammonium polysulfide, which transforms the iodide films to sulphides. The accompanying table summarizes the most satisfactory iodide reactions.

IODIDE SUBLIMATES ON PLASTER TABLET

Indication	Color of coating	Remarks
Arsenic	Lemon to orange-yellow coating	A drop of $(NH_4)_2S_x$ on coating yields yellow ring. Single drop of NH_4OH dissolves ring completely.
Antimony	Orange to peach red sublimate.	A drop of $(NH_4)_2S_x$ on coating produces orange-red ring, which is not dissolved by single drop of NH_4OH.
Lead	Chrome-yellow coating.	$(NH_4)_2S_x$ applied to film yields black spot, often surrounded by reddish cloud.
Thallium	Orange-yellow film near assay, with purplish black band at distance. Entire coating ultimately changes to yellow.	$(NH_4)_2S_x$ applied to yellow coating gives chocolate-brown spot.
Bismuth	Chocolate-brown with underlying crimson. Yellowish on outer margins.	When subjected to ammonia fumes, brown coating changes to orange yellow and then to cherry red.
Mercury	Combination of scarlet, yellow, and greenish black.	If strongly heated, predominating color is greenish black.
Silver	Slightly yellowish coating near assay. Somewhat similar to the *per se* reaction.	Requires intense heat. When touched with reducing flame becomes pinkish brown and somewhat mottled.
Selenium	Reddish brown to scarlet. Similar to the *per se* reaction.	Reddish fumes given off. Flame is colored indigo blue.
Tellurium	Purplish brown to black coating. Similar to the *per se* reaction.	A drop of concentrated H_2SO_4 added to coating and gently heated yields an evanescent pink.

Combination of Elements.—On account of the difference in the degree of volatility of the iodides, it is not difficult at times to determine more than one element, capable of giving iodide coatings, at a single operation. Thus, in the case of jamesonite ($Pb_2Sb_2S_5$), when the powder is heated slowly with bismuth flux, the peach-red antimony iodide coating is the first to appear at a distance from the assay. As the temperature is increased, the less volatile chrome-yellow coating of lead iodide forms near the assay. The use of ammonium polysulphide can also be used to advantage to detect such a combination. Near the assay a black spot with a reddish cloud indicates the presence of lead, while at a distance a well-defined red antimony ring is obtained. Iodides of the same or nearly the same degree of volatility are deposited together producing a compound coating with a resultant color which may serve to indicate the individual components.

Reactions with Hydrobromic Acid.—The porosity of the plaster tablet lends itself readily to the application of the liquid reagent hydrobromic acid. To the assay, placed in a slight depression as heretofore, are slowly added 6 to 8 drops of the acid. The liquid is quickly absorbed by the support and returned as needed to the assay when the latter is heated with the blowpipe flame. Hydrobromic acid can be prepared by passing H_2S through a mixture of bromine in water until the red color of the liquid bromine disappears. The elements not previously recorded, which yield bromide reactions, are copper and iron.

BROMIDE REACTIONS ON PLASTER TABLET

Indication	Color of coating	Remarks
Copper	Volatile, purplish coating, mottled with black.	On standing frequently changes to yellow. Flame is colored green.
Iron	Rust-colored spots, color fades on standing.	Nonvolatile and deposited near assay.

Of the two reactions indicated above, that for copper is the more important, as the reagent alone develops a slight reddish stain on the tablet which may be mistaken for a trace of iron. In addition to the copper and iron reactions, molybdenum, bismuth, lead, and mercury may also produce the following colored films with HBr:

Molybdenum.—Volatile, blue to bluish green coating.

Bismuth.—Volatile, yellow or crimson sublimate.

Lead.—Canary-yellow film.

Mercury.—Volatile, yellow coating.

Cobalt Nitrate Reactions.—Crystallized cobalt nitrate is dissolved in 10 parts of water and kept in convenient dropping bottles. The application of this reagent is restricted to white or light-colored, infusible minerals. Fusible compounds would invariably yield blue cobalt glasses. The pulverized mineral is placed on a plaster tablet and strongly ignited with the oxidizing flame, a drop or two of cobalt nitrate is then added and the assay intensely heated a second time. Upon cooling, the assay may be seen to have assumed a definite color due to combination with the cobalt oxide. If the mineral is sufficiently porous to absorb the cobalt nitrate, the liquid can be applied directly to the fragment without previous pulverization. Cobalt nitrate reactions are especially serviceable in the detection of magnesium, aluminum, and zinc. Therefore, only the first three tests listed below are to be considered important.

COBALT NITRATE REACTIONS

Indication	Color	Remarks
MgO and minerals containing it.	Pink or pale-flesh red.	Best seen when cold. Example magnesite.
Al_2O_3 and compounds containing it. Zinc silicates.	Blue.	Examples, kaolinite, hemimorphite.
ZnO and minerals containing it.	Bright green.	Can be applied to fragment or to white coating on charcoal. Example, smithsonite.
SnO_2, Sb_2O_3	Bluish green.	Should be applied to white coating on charcoal.
TiO_2	Yellowish green.	Should be applied to the white powder.

II. REACTIONS ON CHARCOAL SUPPORT

When plaster tablets are not available or when it is desirable to verify the presence of an element, recourse may be had to the charcoal support, for the reactions obtained on plaster and charcoal supplement each other. Plaster is the better conductor, and the sublimates formed are found nearer the assay. Charcoal, on the other hand, aids the reducing flame whenever reduction is desired. Care must be exercised not to mistake the ash of the charcoal for a sublimate. The ash will form near the assay where the heat has been intense and will not obscure the grain of the charcoal; sublimates, on the other hand, tend to conceal the grain.

Per Se Reactions.—A small depression is made near the edge of the charcoal and the assay is heated slowly with the oxidizing flame, while the support is held in an inclined position to catch the sublimate formed. If the assay decrepitates (snaps) when heated, it should be finely pulverized and moistened with a drop of water. The films produced when heat is applied slowly are mainly oxides, as is shown by the accompanying table.

SUBLIMATES ON CHARCOAL

Indication	Color and character	Remarks
Arsenic	White (As_2O_3), very volatile coating.	Deposits at distance from assay. Garlic odor often noted.
Antimony	Near assay, dense white coating (Sb_2O_3, Sb_2O_4). At distance, bluish.	Less volatile than arsenic coating.
Cadmium	Near assay—black to reddish brown (CdO). At distance, yellowish green.	Very thin deposits are iridescent.
Molybdenum	Pale yellow (MoO_3), hot; white, cold; crystalline.	When touched with reducing flame, becomes dark blue. Copper red (MoO_2) coating surrounding assay.
Lead	Dark yellow (PbO) hot; pale yellow, cold. At distance bluish white.	At times mixed with white sulphite and sulphate of lead.
Bismuth	Orange yellow (Bi_2O_3), hot; lemon yellow, cold. At distance greenish white.	Distinguished from lead by bismuth flux test (see p. 198).
Zinc	Canary yellow (ZnO), hot; white, cold.	When moistened with $Co(NO_3)_2$ and heated, becomes grass green.
Tin	Faint yellow (SnO_2), hot; white, cold.	When moistened with $Co(NO_3)_2$ and heated, becomes bluish green.
Selenium	Near assay, steel gray with metallic luster. At distance, white (SeO_2) tinged with red (Se).	Coating colors the flame blue. Characteristic odor.
Tellurium	Near assay, white (TeO_2). At distance, gray (Te) or brownish.	Imparts pale green color to flame.
Thallium	White (Tl_2O), very volatile.	Coating colors flame bright green.

In addition to the above, white sublimates may result from the volatilization of the chlorides of copper, lead, mercury, ammonium, and the alkalies.

Since the charcoal support does not lend itself readily to the use of liquids, solid reagents such as bismuth flux and sodium carbonate are frequently employed.

Reactions with Bismuth Flux.—The reactions of the elements with bismuth flux on charcoal are, on the whole, rather unsatisfactory with the following two exceptions:

Lead.—Greenish yellow film.

Bismuth.—Yellowish white sublimate with crimson border.

Reactions with Sodium Carbonate.—The effect of heating the assay with Na_2CO_3 on charcoal is to increase the reducing action of the hot charcoal. This is due to the formation of reducing gases, such as CO and possibly gaseous sodium. Under this treatment a number of substances are reduced to the metallic condition. The assay is mixed with 3 parts of anhydrous Na_2CO_3 together with some powdered charcoal obtained from the pit made to support the assay. After heating with the reducing flame for several minutes the fusion is ground with water in an agate mortar and the color, malleability, or magnetism of the reduced particles noted. In addition to reduced metal, some substances yield a sublimate, while still others are volatilized so quickly that no reduced metal is formed.

Summary of Na_2CO_3 Reactions.—The reactions of the common elements fall under three divisions.

1. *Reduced Metal without Sublimate.*

a. Malleable buttons—Cu, Ag, Au.

Copper—confirm by dissolving in HNO_3 and note deep-blue color when solution is made alkaline with NH_4OH.

Silver—dissolve in HNO_3 and note white precipitate when a drop of HCl is added. The precipitate is soluble in NH_4OH.

Gold—confirm by dissolving in aqua regia, evaporate almost to dryness, and dissolve the residue in a little water. Add a few drops of freshly prepared $SnCl_2$. Finely divided precipitate is formed which renders the solution purple by transmitted light and brownish by reflected light (Cassius purple test).

b. Magnetic particles—Fe_3O_4, Co, Ni.

Iron—dissolve in HNO_3, add a few drops of potassium ferrocyanide. Dark-blue precipitate will be formed.

Cobalt—dissolve in borax bead on end of platinum wire. Note blue color.

Nickel—dissolve in HNO_3 and make alkaline with NH_4OH. Add several cubic centimeters of alcoholic solution of dimethylglyoxime. Bright-red precipitate is produced.

2. *Reduced Metal with Sublimate.*

Antimony—dense white coating near assay. Gray brittle button.

Lead—sulphur-yellow coating. Gray malleable button.

Bismuth—lemon-yellow sublimate. Reddish white, brittle button.

Tin—white coating near assay, yellow while hot. White malleable button.

3. *Sublimate without Metal.*

Arsenic—white volatile film. Garlic odor.

Zinc—white film, yellow while hot.

Cadmium—reddish brown to orange sublimate with tarnish colors.

Selenium—steel-gray coating and reddish fumes with characteristic odor.

Tellurium—white coating with reddish or dark-yellow border.

Molybdenum—white coating, changed to dark blue when exposed to the reducing flame.

Sodium carbonate can also be profitably employed in the detection of sulphur, manganese, chromium, and phosphorus.

Test for Sulphur.—The powdered sulphide, mixed with 3 to 4 parts of anhydrous Na_2CO_3, is thoroughly fused on a charcoal support. In the case of sulphates, some powdered charcoal should be added to the Na_2CO_3. After fusion, the mass (Na_2S) is removed from the support and crushed. One-half of the powder is then placed upon a clean silver coin, and several drops of water are added. A dark-brown or black stain (Ag_2S) indicates sulphur, provided selenium and tellurium are absent. To check this sulphur test, the remaining powder is placed on a watch glass. Several drops of water are then added; followed by a drop or two of freshly prepared sodium nitroferricyanide $Na_2Fe(NO)(CN)_5$. An intense red purple coloration is indicative of sulphur. It is preferable to use an alcohol flame for the fusion, if the gas flame contains sulphur compounds. Also, there is a tendency for the fusion to sink into the charcoal, and for this reason the same pit should be used but once.

Tests for Manganese and Chromium.—Powdered manganese compounds should be mixed with a small amount of KNO_3 and placed in a shallow depression made in a charcoal support. Sodium carbonate is then spread over this mixture. The blowpipe flame is directed for a brief period on a given spot until incipient fusion takes place. Upon cooling, this fused area assumes a bluish green color due to the formation of sodium manganate, Na_2MnO_4. Long fusion is to be avoided, as the manganate loses its color, due to reduction brought about by the charcoal. If copper is present, this test cannot be used for manganese.

Chromium compounds when fused with Na_2CO_3 and KNO_3 in a manner similar to that indicated for manganese yield yellow-colored fusions (Na_2CrO_4). This test for chromium is, however, unsatisfactory in the presence of lead or vanadium as these elements may also yield yellow masses. Instead of performing the fusion on charcoal, manganese or chromium compounds may be dissolved in a Na_2CO_3 bead held in a loop of platinum wire. Under the influence of the oxidizing flame of the blowpipe the bead will assume the color indicated above. If the platinum wire test is used, it is not necessary to add KNO_3 to the Na_2CO_3.

Test for Phosphorus.—Phosphates of aluminum and the heavy metals should be fused with 2 parts of Na_2CO_3 on charcoal, and the powdered fusion then ignited in a test tube with magnesium ribbon. The phosphorus is thereby converted into a phosphide (Mg_3P_2), which upon the addition of a few drops of water liberates the unpleasant, garlic-like odor of phosphine, PH_3, which produces a black coloration when brought in contact with filter paper moistened with $AgNO_3$. Phosphates of the alkalies and alkaline earths may be ignited with magnesium ribbon directly without previous fusion. This test for phosphorus cannot be relied upon in the presence of arsenic or antimony.

A more reliable test for phosphorus is the following: The phosphate is dissolved in HNO_3 (if insoluble, fusion with Na_2CO_3 should precede solution in acid) and a portion of the filtrate added to an equal volume of ammonium molybdate solution. Upon standing or upon slightly warming, a yellow precipitate of ammonium phosphomolybdate will be formed.

III. FLAME COLORATIONS

A number of compounds and especially those of the alkalies and alkaline earths impart to the nonluminous flame of the Bunsen burner, or to the oxidizing flame of the blowpipe, characteristic colors which may be used for their identification. As the intensity of the flame coloration depends upon the volatility of the salt used, and, inasmuch as chlorides are generally more volatile than other compounds, the best results are ordinarily obtained by moistening the powder with HCl. In a few instances moistening with H_2SO_4 is preferable. The powder is introduced into the Bunsen flame by means of a clean platinum wire, or a very thin splintery fragment of the mineral, moistened with acid, may be held by the forceps in the nonluminous portion of the oxidizing blowpipe flame. Fusible metals and arsenic should not, however, be heated in contact with platinum-tipped forceps. To detect alkalies in silicates, decomposition may be brought about by mixing the assay with an equal volume of powdered gypsum before introducing into the hottest portion of the Bunsen flame. It is even possible at times to detect the individual components when several flame-coloring elements occur together. This may be accomplished by making use of (1) the spectroscope, or (2) the difference in degree of volatility of the constituents present, or (3) colored screens.

Spectroscope.—For blowpipe work the direct-vision pocket spectroscope is very useful. The best instruments are provided with a scale and a comparison prism by means of which the spectrum of an unknown substance can be directly compared with that of a known substance. When a colored flame is observed through a spectroscope, light-colored lines are perceived upon a dark background. The color, position, and grouping of the lines are used as the basis for the recognition of the elements.

Difference in Volatility.—In a mixture the flame-coloring constituents can often be detected readily without the use of the spectroscope, by noting the *difference in the degree of volatility of the components*. In general the alkalies (Na, K, Li) are more volatile than the alkaline earths (Ca, Ba, Sr), and by holding the platinum wire about 1 mm. from the outer nonluminous Bunsen flame sufficient heat is encountered to volatilize the alkalies, while insertion in the hotter portion of the flame is necessary to detect the alkaline earths.

Colored Screens.—These are also extensively employed in analyzing flame mixtures. Screens composed of colored glass or celluloid transmit

FLAME COLORS

Indication	Flame color	Through Merwin screen	Remarks
*Calcium	Yellowish red	1. Flash of greenish yellow 2. Faint green 3. Flash of crimson	Invisible through green glass. Calcium minerals become alkaline upon ignition.
*Strontium	Crimson	1. Invisible 2. Invisible 3. Crimson	Strontium minerals become alkaline upon ignition. If to solution of Sr salt a few drops of $BaCl_2$ are added, red color (Sr) will appear *after* green of Ba. Sr solutions yield white precipitate when a few drops of H_2SO_4 are added. (Distinction from Li.)
*Lithium	Carmine	1. Invisible 2. Invisible 3. Crimson	Lithium minerals do not become alkaline upon ignition. If to solution of Li salt a few drops of $BaCl_2$ are added, red color (Li) will appear *before* green of Ba.
*Potassium	Pale violet	1. Blue violet 2. Deep red violet 3. Red violet	Purplish red through blue glass. Spectroscope is necessary to distinguish between potassium, rubidium, and caesium.
*Sodium	Intense yellow	1. Invisible 2. Invisible 3. Invisible	Flame color should be intense and persistent to indicate sodium mineral. Invisible through blue glass.

* Important reactions.

FLAME COLORS—(*Concluded*)

Indication	Flame color	Through Merwin screen	Remarks
Copper oxide ⎫ Copper iodide ⎭	Emerald green		Tinged with azure blue when moistened with HCl.
Manganese chloride	Yellowish green	1. Emerald 2. Pale blue green 3. Pale lavender	Coloration of short duration.
Tellurium ⎫ Antimony ⎭	Pale green		
Thallium	Grass green		
Phosphorus	Pale bluish green	1. Green 2. Invisible 3. Red violet	Should be moistened with concentrated H_2SO_4. Color not very distinct.
*Boron	Yellowish green	1. Bright green 2. Faint green 3. Faint green	For borates decomposed by H_2SO_4: To mineral placed in porcelain dish, add alcohol and concentrated H_2SO_4, apply match. Note yellowish green color of flame. For borates not decomposed by H_2SO_4: Mix powder with 3 parts of boracic acid flux (3 parts $KHSO_4$, 1 part CaF_2), introduce into flame by means of hot platinum wire. Flash of green will be seen, due to BF_3.
*Barium	Yellowish green	1. Bright green 2. Faint green 3. Faint green	Barium minerals become alkaline upon ignition. Have rather high specific gravity.
Molybdenum	Faint yellowish green		If in form of oxide or sulphide. Not very distinct.
Zinc	Bluish green		Appears as bright streaks in outer part of flame.
*Copper chloride	Azure blue	1. Bright green 2. Bluish green 3. Bluish green	Flame is tinged with emerald green.
Selenium	Indigo blue		Accompanied by characteristic odor.
Arsenic	Livid blue		Characteristic garlic odor
Lead	Pale azure blue		Tinged with green in outer parts.

* Important reactions.

certain rays while others are entirely absorbed. Thus, blue glass absorbs certain red and green rays together with those of yellow. One of the most effective screens on the market at present is the *Merwin Flame Color Screen*. This celluloid screen is composed of three colored divisions, one blue, one violet, and one blue over violet. The strips are stained so as to absorb the orange and yellow portions of the spectrum. Observations should be made through all three divisions of the screen. In the table shown on pages 201 and 202, flame colorations will be recorded as seen with and without the Merwin color screen. The numbers refer to the divisions of the screen. Observations are made against a dark background.

IV. BEAD TESTS

The oxides of many metals form complex compounds with characteristic colors when dissolved at a high temperature in borax, $Na_2B_4O_7.-10H_2O$, or microcosmic salt (salt of phosphorus), $HNaNH_4PO_4.4H_2O$.

BEAD COLORATION

Oxide of	Borax bead		Microcosmic salt bead	
	Oxidizing flame	Reducing flame	Oxidizing flame	Reducing flame
Mn	Reddish violet	Colorless	Violet	Colorless
Co	Blue	Blue	Blue	Blue
Cu	Blue-green	Opaque red	Blue-green	Opaque red
Ni	Reddish brown	Opaque gray	Straw to reddish yellow	Yellow to reddish yellow
Fe	Yellow	Pale green	Colorless to yellow	Colorless to pale violet
U	Yellow	Pale green to colorless	Yellowish green	Bright green
Cr	Yellowish green	Emerald green	Emerald green	Emerald green
V	Yellowish green	Emerald green	Light yellow	Emerald green
Ti	Colorless	Brownish violet	Colorless	Violet
Mo	Colorless	Brown	Colorless	Pure green
W	Colorless	Yellow to yellowish brown	Colorless	Fine blue
Si	Colorless	Colorless	Insoluble skeleton	Insoluble skeleton

The support usually employed for this work is a No. 28 B. & S. gauge platinum wire about 10 cm. long which has been fused into the end of a piece of glass tubing. Unoxidized metals as well as compounds of sulphur, arsenic, and antimony should be roasted until the volatile constituents have been removed and the residue converted into an oxide.

A small circular loop made at the end of the platinum wire is heated and then touched to the borax or microcosmic salt. Sufficient material will adhere to form a clear colorless glass, when heated before the blowpipe flame. In the case of the microcosmic salt bead the heat should be applied slowly as the material has a tendency to drop from the wire, due to the escape of water and ammonia. By touching the hot bead to a few particles of the finely crushed oxide, and again heating in the oxidizing flame of the blowpipe, solution and coloration of the fusion will frequently result. The color of the bead should be noted after it has been subjected to the oxidizing flame[1] and again after the reducing flame has been applied. The action of the reducing flame may be greatly accelerated by dissolving a small fragment of SnO or SnCl$_2$ in the bead. The colors observed with the microcosmic salt are not in every instance identical with those of the borax. In general the tests obtained with the borax flux are more delicate, while the microcosmic salt fusions yield a greater variety of colors. The removal of the bead from the support for preservation may be accomplished by simply straightening the wire. In the preceding table the colors listed are those of the cold beads obtained from the unmixed oxides.

Of the beads enumerated, the first eight are extremely serviceable. In order to detect Ni in the presence of Co, or any other oxide which ordinarily would obscure the nickel test, the procedure should be as follows: Dissolve several beads in HNO$_3$ and add NH$_4$OH until the solution becomes alkaline. To the filtrate add several cubic centimeters of an alcoholic solution of dimethylglyoxime. A scarlet precipitate indicates Ni. This is an extremely delicate test.

$$Ni(NO_3)_2 + 2NH_4OH + 2C_4H_8N_2O_2 =$$
$$(C_8H_{14}N_4O_4)Ni + 2NH_4NO_3 + 2H_2O.$$

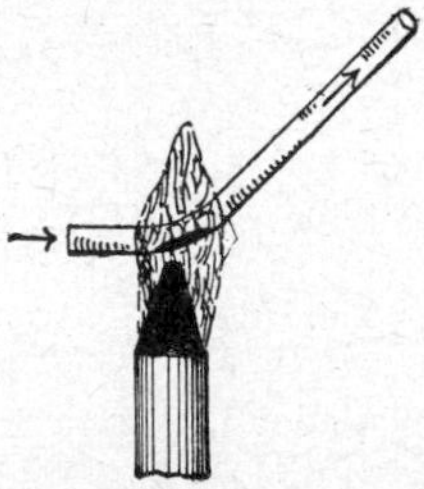

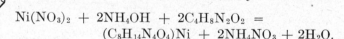

V. OPEN-TUBE REACTIONS

Hard-glass tubing, 15 to 20 cm. long and about 5 mm. in diameter, is employed in blowpipe work to note the effects of a current of air when permitted to pass over a highly heated substance. These open tubes should be bent slightly near one end in order to hold more conveniently the material which should be in a powdered condition to expose the maximum amount of surface. The tube is held in an

FIG. 467.—Heating in open tube.

[1] A particle of KNO$_3$ added to the bead aids oxidation.

inclined position in the flame; apply heat first above the assay to insure a good current of air through the tube and then directly under the mineral (Fig. 467). In most instances oxidation results and the volatile material either escapes in the form of a gas with a characteristic odor, or a sublimate is formed which deposits upon the cooler portions of the tube. The temperature should be increased gradually so as not to volatilize the substance in an unoxidized condition. The results of open-tube tests may be summarized as follows:

A. Gases with Characteristic Odors

1. *Odor of Burning Sulphur* with bleaching properties. The gas liberated is SO_2. The test is very delicate and is extremely useful in testing for sulphur or sulphides. If oxidation is not complete, due to too rapid heating or an insufficient air supply, free sulphur may also deposit on the sides of the tube.

2. *Garlic Odor.*—Produced when arsenic compounds are rapidly heated and not completely oxidized.

3. *Odor of Rotten Horse-radish.*—Obtained from selenium compounds when volatilized.

B. Sublimates

Indication	Character of the coating	Remarks
Arsenic Arsenides Sulphides of arsenic	White, crystalline, and volatile sublimate (As_2O_3). Crystals are minute octahedrons.	Metallic mirror of arsenic or yellow coating of arsenic sulphide indicates too rapid heating.
Antimony Sulphides of antimony	Dense white fumes which partly escape and partly condense as white powder. Both Sb_2O_3 and Sb_2O_4 are formed.	Sb_2O_3 is white, slowly volatile, and crystalline. Sb_2O_4 is non-volatile.
Bismuth sulphide	White, non-volatile powder ($Bi_2(SO_4)_3$).	Fusible to yellow drops.
Bismuth (free from sulphur)	Brown while hot; yellow when cold (Bi_2O_3).	Sublimate is fusible.
Tellurium Tellurides	Snow white, non-volatile sublimate (TeO_2).	Upon heating fuses to colorless drops.
Lead chloride	White, partially volatile sublimate (Pb_2OCl_2).	Fusible to yellow drops.
Lead sulphide	Non-volatile, white powder formed near assay ($PbSO_4$).	Fusible to yellow drops, white when cold.

B. Sublimates—(*Concluded*)

Indication	Character of the coating	Remarks
Selenium Selenides	Near assay, steel gray, volatile coating consisting of radiating needles (SeO_2).	At distance reddish due to finely divided Se.
Molybdenum oxide or sulphide	Yellow when hot, white when cold (MoO_3).	Collects near assay as mass of delicate crystals.
Mercury Amalgam	Minute, gray, metallic globules. Volatile (Hg).	Globules unite by rubbing with strip of paper.

VI. CLOSED-TUBE REACTIONS

Closed-tube reactions are carried out in hard-glass tubes about 4 inches long and 6 mm. in diameter, which are closed at one end. The assay is introduced in the form of small fragments and heat applied gradually. The object of this treatment is to note the effect of heat without oxidation as the air is practically entirely excluded (Fig. 468). These are known as the *per se* tests. Closed tubes may also be profitably employed in heating the assay with $KHSO_4$.

Fig. 468.— Heating in closed tube.

A. Per Se Tests

The application of heat alone may produce such phenomena as:

a. Change in Appearance or Character of Assay.

1. *Change in Color.*—The more important minerals thus affected are Copper minerals—blue or green, become black when hot; black, cold.

Zinc minerals—white or colorless, become pale yellow when hot; white, cold.

Manganese and cobalt minerals—pink, become black when hot; black, cold.

Lead and bismuth minerals—white or colorless, become dark yellow to brown when hot; pale yellow to white, cold.

Iron minerals—green or brown, become black when hot; black, cold.

Hematite—dark red, becomes black when hot; dark red, cold.

2. *Fusion*—Only minerals with a fusibility below one and one-half in the scale of fusibility melt when heated in a closed tube *per se*.

3. *Carbonization.*—Indicating organic substances.

4. *Luminescence.*—Some minerals when heated to a temperature below redness and viewed in a dark room will be seen to emit colored light. Many varieties of fluorite when heated to 150°C. emit a purple or green light.

5. *Decrepitation.*—Alkaline chlorides, galena, and many minerals snap and break down to a fine powder when heated. This behavior is usually the result of unequal expansion or due to the presence of water held mechanically.

6. *Magnetization.*—Iron minerals frequently become magnetic upon the application of heat.

b. Formation of Gases in the Tube.

1. *Carbon Dioxide.*—Colorless and odorless gas. A drop of lime water held in a loop of platinum wire becomes turbid. Indicates carbonates.

2. *Oxygen.*—A glowing splinter takes fire when held in the tube. Indicates peroxides, nitrates, chlorates, bromates, or iodates.

3. *Ammonia.*—Characteristic odor and alkaline reaction. More pronounced when heated with Na_2CO_3. Indicates ammonium salts or organic compounds containing nitrogen. If the latter, the mass usually chars.

c. Formation of Sublimates.

1. *Colorless or White Sublimates*

Indication	Character of sublimate	Remarks
Water	Colorless, volatile liquid which forms on the cooler part of the tube.	Indicates water of crystallization or hydroxyl. Neutral if pure, may show acid or alkaline reaction.
Ammonium salts	White, very volatile.	
Lead chloride	White, fusing to yellow drops.	
Mercurous chloride	White, yellow when hot.	Sublimate is infusible.
Mercuric chloride	White, yellow when hot.	Sublimate is fusible.
Antimony oxide	White, fusible.	Sublimate consists of needle-like crystals.
Arsenic oxide	White, volatile.	Sublimate consists of octahedral crystals.
Tellurium oxide	Pale yellow, hot; colorless to white globules, cold.	Obtained from tellurium and a few of its compounds.

2. *Colored Sublimates*

Indication	Character of sublimate	Remarks
Sulphur Some sulphides	Brownish red liquid, hot; pale yellow crystalline solid, cold.	Due to the formation of free sulphur.
Sulphides of arsenic	Dark red liquid, hot; reddish yellow solid, cold.	From realgar, orpiment and sulpharsenites.
Sulphides of antimony	Black when hot; reddish brown when cold. Sb_2OS_2 is formed.	From sulphides and sulphantimonites.
Sulphide of mercury	Brilliant black solid.	Yields a red powder when rubbed.
Selenium Selenides	Black fusible globules. Red when rubbed.	Sublimate forms only at high temperature.
Arsenic Arsenides	Brilliant black sublimate. Gray and crystalline near heated end.	Garlic odor noted when tube is broken below mirror and gently heated.
Mercury Amalgam	Minute, gray metallic globules.	Globules unite when rubbed
Tellurium Tellurides	Black fusible globules.	Sublimate forms at high temperature.

B. Reactions in Closed Tube with KHSO₄

The detection of volatile acids may be accomplished by gently heating the assay with an equal volume of $KHSO_4$.

1. *Colored Gas Evolved*

Indication	Character of gas	Remarks
Nitrates Nitrites	Reddish brown with pungent odor.	Gas liberated is NO_2.
Chlorates	Yellowish green fumes with odor of chlorine.	Gas liberated is ClO_2.
Iodides	Violet vapors accompanied by a black metallic sublimate.	Iodine is set free.
Bromides Bromates	Heavy brownish red vapor with pungent odor.	Bromine is liberated. Best seen when tube is held against a white background.

2. *Colorless, Odorous Gas Evolved*

Indication	Character of sublimate	Remarks
Sulphates Sulphites	Suffocating odor with bleaching properties.	Gas is SO_2.
Chlorides	Colorless gas which fumes strongly when in contact with NH_4OH.	Gas is HCl.
Fluorides	Gas which etches the tube above the assay.	Gas is HF.
Sulphides	Gas with odor of decayed eggs. Blackens lead acetate paper.	Gas is H_2S.
Acetates	Gas with odor of vinegar.	Gas is $C_2H_4O_2$.

3. *Colorless, Odorless Gas Evolved*

Indication	Character of sublimate	Remarks
Carbonates	A drop of lime water held in a loop of platinum wire becomes turbid.	Gas is CO_2.
Oxalates	A gas which burns with a blue flame.	Gas is CO.

VII. SPECIAL TESTS

In this section reactions will be listed which do not conveniently fall under any of the previous divisions. They are nevertheless extremely useful in mineralogical determinations. The reactions given below are to be considered as individual tests and not in any way related to one another.

1. Tests for Calcite and Aragonite.—*a.* Powdered calcite when boiled from 1 to 5 minutes in a 5 to 10 per cent. solution of cobalt nitrate remains white or in the presence of organic matter becomes yellowish, while aragonite turns violet due to the formation of a basic cobalt nitrate. This is commonly known as *Meigen's test.* The change in color is more readily detected by washing the powder by decantation after boiling. Inasmuch as barium or strontium carbonate and precipitated basic magnesium carbonate give the same reactions as aragonite, and dolomite the same as calcite, it is absolutely necessary first to establish the fact that one is dealing with one of the modifications of $CaCO_3$ before applying the cobalt nitrate test. This test cannot be applied to powdered mixtures of calcite and aragonite.

b. Leitmeier and Feigl have shown that a cold solution of $MnSO_4$ and Ag_2SO_4 produces a black color ($MnO_2 + Ag$) on powdered aragonite in a few seconds, but on calcite only after several minutes. The same reagent can be used on microsections, but the action is slower. Strontianite and witherite give the same reactions as aragonite; dolomite the same as calcite.

2. Tests for Calcite and Dolomite.—*a.* Calcite dissolves in acetic acid with a brisk evolution of CO_2, while dolomite is not appreciably affected by the cold acid.

b. J. Lemberg has noted that powdered calcite is colored violet within a few minutes when treated with a solution of aluminum chloride and extract of logwood, while dolomite remains unchanged. The reaction is caused by the precipitation upon the calcite of $Al(OH)_3$ which absorbs the dye and acts as a mordant. To observe the color change, the powder should be washed by decantation. The Lemberg solution is prepared by boiling for 20 minutes a mixture of 4 grams of $AlCl_3$, 6 grams extract of logwood, and 60 grams of water, with constant stirring and with the addition of the amount of water lost by evaporation. Aragonite gives same reaction as calcite.

c. According to F. Cornu, calcite and dolomite may be distinguished by covering the powder with a small amount of water and adding a few

Indication	Color of solution	Remarks
Titanium	Violet color.	Best seen when evolution of H_2 ceases.
Tungsten	Dark blue.	Color due to heavy precipitate which upon standing settles to bottom.
Columbium	Pale blue.	Color fades with addition of water.
Vanadium	Blue, green, finally blue violet.	Metallic zinc should be used instead of tin.

Instead of using a reducing agent for the detection of titanium and vanadium, H_2O_2 in an acid solution can be employed. The oxidation reactions are more delicate than the corresponding reduction tests.

Titanium	Amber colored solution.	The fused mass should be dissolved in $1:1$ H_2SO_4 solution.
Vanadium	Reddish brown solution.	Dissolve fusion in HNO_3.

drops of phenolpthalein solution.   Upon shaking, the aqueous solution above the calcite quickly assumes a pink to red color while the dolomite is not appreciably affected.   (Aragonite gives the same test as calcite.)

3. Test for Cassiterite (SnO_2).—As the usual colors of cassiterite are various shades of yellow, brown, or black, a change in the appearance of the mineral can be utilized for its detection.   This can readily be accomplished by placing fragments of cassiterite in a test tube on top of granulated metallic zinc and adding dilute HCl.   The nascent hydrogen liberated reduces the SnO_2, and after a few minutes the cassiterite becomes coated with a thin gray layer of metallic tin.

4. Reduction Tests with Metallic Tin and HCl.—Rapid tests for the elements titanium, tungsten, columbium, and vanadium may be carried out by dissolving the Na_2CO_3 fusion in HCl and adding a few fragments of metallic tin.   The hydrogen evolved reduces the salts of the rarer elements producing colored solutions or precipitates which are used to detect the presence of the element involved.   The table shown on page 210 indicates the changes referred to.

VIII. SUMMARY OF CHEMICAL AND BLOWPIPE TESTS FOR THE MORE IMPORTANT ELEMENTS

For convenience of reference the most reliable tests for the various elements are here summarized.   The wet chemical tests included in this summary are often extremely useful and supplement the dry reactions.

ALUMINUM (Al)

1. *Ignition with Cobalt Nitrate.*—Infusible light-colored aluminum minerals when moistened with a drop or two of cobalt nitrate and intensely ignited assume a blue color.   (Zinc silicates give a similar reaction but yield a white coating when heated with Na_2CO_3 on charcoal.)

2. *Precipitation with Ammonia.*—When an acid solution containing aluminum is rendered alkaline with NH_4OH, a white gelatinous precipitate of $Al(OH)_3$ is formed.   This precipitate is readily dissolved in a warm KOH solution.

AMMONIUM (NH₄)

Heating in Closed Tube.—When boiled with a solution of KOH, or heated with Na_2CO_3 or CaO, ammonia is evolved which is recognized by its odor, alkaline reaction, and white fumes when brought in contact with HCl.

ANTIMONY (Sb)

1. *Sublimate on Plaster Tablet.*—Antimony minerals mixed with bismuth flux and heated on a plaster support yield an orange- to peach-

red sublimate. A drop of $(NH_4)_2S_x$ upon the coating produces an orange red ring.

2. *Sublimate on Charcoal.*—When heated with the oxidizing flame on charcoal, a dense white sublimate of Sb_2O_3 is formed near the assay. The coating is volatile and bluish in thin layers. The fumes have no distinctive odor (difference from arsenic).

3. *Heating in Open Tube.*—Most antimony minerals yield dense white fumes which partly escape and partly condense as a white powder.

4. *Heating with Concentrated Nitric Acid.*—HNO_3 oxidizes antimony and its sulphides to metantimonic acid which is a white precipitate, insoluble in both water and HNO_3.

ARSENIC (As)

1. *Sublimate on Plaster Tablet.*—Arsenic minerals mixed with bismuth flux and heated on a plaster support yield a lemon-yellow sublimate. A drop of $(NH_4)_2S_x$ on the coating produces a yellow ring.

2. *Sublimate on Charcoal.*—Arsenic, arsenides, and sulphides of arsenic heated with the oxidizing flame on charcoal give a very volatile white coating of As_2O_3 which deposits at some distance from the assay. The fumes have a characteristic garlic odor.

3. *Heating in Open Tube.*—Arsenic, arsenides, and sulphides produce a white, volatile, and crystalline sublimate of As_2O_3. Too rapid heating may yield a metallic mirror instead of the oxide.

4. *Heating in Closed Tube.*—Arsenic and arsenides give a bright metallic mirror. When the tube is broken below the mirror and heated, a garlic odor will be noted. Arsenates should be mixed with powdered charcoal to cause reduction.

5. *Precipitation as Ammonium Magnesium Arsenate.*—With few exceptions arsenic minerals are oxidized to arsenic acid (H_3AsO_4), when boiled with concentrated HNO_3. Make the solution alkaline with NH_4OH and filter. To the filtrate add a few cubic centimeters of magnesia mixture ($MgCl_2$ and NH_4Cl), shake, and let stand. White crystalline $MgNH_4AsO_4$ will precipitate.

BARIUM (Ba)

1. *Flame Test.*—When moistened with HCl, many barium minerals impart a yellowish green color to the flame (coloration quite similar to boron).

2. *Alkaline Reaction and High Specific Gravity.*—Barium compounds are characterized by rather high specific gravities and alkaline reaction on moistened turmeric paper after strong ignition.

3. *Precipitation as Barium Sulphate.*—A few drops of dilute H_2SO_4 will precipitate white $BaSO_4$, insoluble in dilute acids. This test dis-

tinguishes barium from boron and phosphorus minerals which also color the flame green.

Beryllium (Be); also Called Glucinum

Beryllium compounds resemble very closely aluminum in their chemical reactions. A few distinguishing tests are:

1. *Precipitation as Basic Carbonate.*—Ammonium carbonate added to a solution of a beryllium salt produces a white precipitate of beryllium carbonate, readily soluble in an excess of the reagent (difference from Al). Upon boiling the solution, beryllium is precipitated as white basic carbonate.

2. *Oxine Test for Beryllium.*—Aluminum and beryllium can be separated with 8-hydroquinoline (oxine). A slightly acid solution of the NH_4OH precipitate of aluminum and beryllium is warmed to 60°C. and treated with an excess of acetic acid solution of oxine. Ammonium acetate is added until a permanent precipitate is obtained. After settling, the aluminum compound, $(C_9H_6ON)_3Al$, is filtered. The beryllium in the filtrate is precipitated from a hot solution with NH_4OH as beryllium hydroxide.

Bismuth (Bi)

1. *Sublimate on Plaster Tablet.*—When mixed with bismuth flux and heated on a plaster support, bismuth minerals yield a chocolate-brown coating, which is changed to a bright red when exposed to strong ammonia fumes.

2. *Bismuth Flux on Charcoal.*—Upon charcoal the mineral mixed with bismuth flux produces a yellowish sublimate with crimson border.

3. *Reduction on Charcoal.*—Bismuth compounds mixed with Na_2CO_3 on charcoal give a lemon-yellow coating with white border and reddish white brittle buttons.

4. *Precipitation as Bismuth Oxychloride.*—If water is added to an HCl solution, which has been evaporated almost to dryness, a white precipitate of BiOCl is formed.

Boron (B)

1. *Flame Test.*—Some boron minerals yield a yellowish green flame when heated alone, but the majority require the application of H_2SO_4 or boracic acid flux. If decomposable by H_2SO_4, boron compounds burn with a yellowish green flame due to the formation of basic acid methyl ester, $B(OCH_3)_3$, when placed in an evaporating dish with alcohol and concentrated H_2SO_4 and ignited. Borates not decomposable by H_2SO_4 should be mixed with 3 parts of boracic acid flux (3 parts $KHSO_4$, 1 part CaF_2) and introduced into the flame on a clean platinum wire.

A flash of green indicates the liberation of the volatile boron fluoride (BF_3).

2. *Turmeric Paper Test.*—If turmeric paper is moistened with a dilute HCl solution of boron and dried, it assumes a reddish brown color. If it is then moistened with NH_4OH a bluish black or grayish blue spot results, depending upon the amount of turmeric and boric acid present. It is advisable to run a blank test at the same time. As acid solutions of zirconic, titanic, tantalic, columbic, and molybdic acids also color turmeric paper brown, this test for boron can be employed only in their absence.

Bromine (Br)

1. *Heating in Closed Tube with Potassium Bisulphate.*—When a bromide is heated with $KHSO_4$, heavy brownish red vapors of bromine are liberated.

2. *Precipitation as Silver Bromide.*—A white precipitate of AgBr (soluble in NH_4OH) is formed when $AgNO_3$ is added to a dilute HNO_3 solution of a bromide.

Cadmium (Cd)

1. *Heating on Plaster Tablet per Se.*—Near the assay there is formed a reddish brown to greenish yellow coating. At a distance it is brownish black. It is best obtained from the metal.

2. *Heating on Charcoal.*—When heated on charcoal, cadmium yields a film which is reddish brown near the assay and yellowish green at a distance. Very thin deposits show an iridescent tarnish.

Calcium (Ca)

1. *Flame Test.*—After being pulverized and moistened with HCl, many calcium minerals color the nonluminous flame yellowish red. The color should not be confused with the redder and more persistent strontium flame. When viewed through the Merwin color screen, calcium appears as a flash of greenish yellow through division 1 (distinction from lithium and strontium).

2. *Precipitation as Calcium Oxalate.*—Ammonium oxalate added to an ammoniacal solution of calcium produces a white precipitate of calcium oxalate (CaC_2O_4). This precipitate will also form in a very slightly acid solution.

3. *Precipitation as Calcium Sulphate.*—A few drops of dilute H_2SO_4 added to a calcium salt dissolved in a small volume of dilute HCl precipitates $CaSO_4$. Upon the addition of water and the application of heat the precipitate dissolves (distinction from barium and strontium).

Carbon (C)

1. *Heating in Closed Tube.*—When heated, hydrocarbons such as asphaltum, albertite, or bituminous coals yield oils and tarry compounds

which condense on the sides of the tube. The residue, if any, is mainly carbon. If carbon is present as a carbonate, decomposition is effected with the liberation of CO_2 which renders a drop of lime water on a loop of platinum wire turbid.

2. *Effervescence with Acids.*—The solution of carbonates in dilute acids takes place with brisk evolution of CO_2. In some instances the acid should be heated, but care must be exercised not to mistake boiling for liberation of CO_2.

Cerium (Ce)

1. *Oxidation with Hydrogen Peroxide.*—If a cerous salt is treated with a slight excess of NH_4OH and then with H_2O_2, the white precipitate becomes reddish orange in color, due probably to $Ce(OH)_3O_2H$. To remove interfering elements proceed as follows: Fuse with Na_2CO_3 and evaporate the HCl solution to dryness. Take up with dilute HCl and filter. Precipitate the cerous oxalate from the dilute acid solution by means of ammonium oxalate. Filter and dissolve the precipitate in warm concentrated HCl. Make ammoniacal with NH_4OH, and white $Ce(OH)_3$ is formed. Upon oxidation with H_2O_2, its color is changed to reddish orange.

2. *Oxidation with Lead Peroxide and Nitric Acid.*—Boil and allow to settle; cerous salts yield orange-colored solutions due to the formation of ceric nitrate.

Chlorine (Cl)

1. *Flame Coloration with Copper Oxide.*—If a hot salt of phosphorus bead saturated with CuO is brought in contact with a chloride and then heated in the nonluminous flame, copper chloride will be formed which will tinge the flame azure blue. (Bromine gives a similar reaction.)

2. *Liberation of Chlorine.*—If a chloride is mixed with $KHSO_4$ and a small amount of MnO_2 and then heated in a closed tube, free chlorine is set free. AgCl and silicates containing chlorine require fusion with Na_2CO_3.

3. *Precipitation as Silver Chloride.*—A few drops of $AgNO_3$ added to a chloride in a dilute HNO_3 solution precipitates white curdy AgCl, soluble in NH_4OH. This is an extremely delicate test. Minerals insoluble in HNO_3 should be fused with Na_2CO_3. (Bromine gives a similar reaction.)

Chromium (Cr)

1. *Bead Tests.*—Chromium colors borax and microcosmic salt beads green, in both the oxidizing and reducing flames.

2. *Fusion with Sodium Carbonate on Platinum Wire.*—When chromium compounds are dissolved in a Na_2CO_3 bead under the influence of

the oxidizing flame, the fusion is colored a light yellow; yellowish green in reducing flame.

3. *Precipitation as Lead Chromate.*—Fuse with Na_2CO_3 and KNO_3 on charcoal. Leach with water, make slightly acid with acetic acid, and add a few drops of lead acetate. A yellow precipitate of lead chromate will be formed.

4. *Oxidation to Perchromic Acid.*—Dissolve the fusion in water and acidify with dilute H_2SO_4. To the cold solution add H_2O_2, and a blue color of H_3CrO_8 is obtained. Perchromic acid is very unstable and the color may last but a few seconds.

COBALT (Co)

Bead Tests.—Cobalt imparts a blue color to the borax and salt of phosphorus beads, in both the oxidizing and reducing flames. When copper and nickel interfere, fuse the bead on charcoal with a particle of metallic tin. Copper and nickel are reduced to the metallic condition, and the blue color of cobalt will appear.

COLUMBIUM (Cb); ALSO CALLED NIOBIUM

Reduction with Tin.—Finely powdered columbates are decomposed when heated to dull redness with $KHSO_4$ in a test tube. When decomposition is complete, rotate and incline the tube so that the melt may solidify as a thin crust on the sides. Add HCl, some metallic tin, and boil. Reduction takes place, and a light blue color due to columbium will appear. The color becomes much fainter upon the addition of water. With zinc instead of tin the blue color changes to brown.

COPPER (Cu)

1. *Sublimate on Plaster Tablet.*—When moistened with HBr and heated on a plaster support, copper minerals yield a volatile purplish coating, mottled with black.

2. *Flame Test.*—Oxides of copper color the flame emerald green, while moistening with HCl produces an intense azure blue.

3. *Bead Tests.*—Under the influence of the oxidizing flame, borax and microcosmic salt beads are green when hot and bluish green when cold. In the reducing flame, Cu_2O is formed which colors the beads an opaque red.

4. *Reduction to Metal on Charcoal.*—When heated on charcoal with a mixture of Na_2CO_3 and borax, copper minerals yield globules of metallic copper. Sulphides should first be roasted before reducing.

5. *Blue Solution with Ammonium Hydroxide.*—A copper solution made alkaline with NH_4OH assumes a deep-blue color. (Nickel solutions are light blue.)

FLUORINE (F)

1. *Etching Glass Tube.*—When mixed with 4 or 5 parts of $KHSO_4$ or with sodium metaphosphate (obtained by fusing salt of phosphorus), and then heated in a closed tube, many powdered fluorides liberate HF, which etches the glass. In addition a ring of SiO_2 may form in the upper part of the tube. The etching of the glass may be seen to best advantage by breaking the closed end of the tube, washing out its contents, and drying the tube over a flame when the glass will appear clouded.

2. *Flame Test.*—Fluorides mixed with $KHSO_4$ and tourmaline, and introduced into the Bunsen flame on a platinum wire, give a flash of green due to the volatilization of BF_3.

GLUCINUM (Gl). SEE BERYLLIUM

GOLD (Au)

1. *Sublimate on Plaster per Se.*—Upon intense and prolonged ignition on the plaster support, gold gives a slight purple to rose-colored coating near and under the assay. It is best seen when the tablet is cold.

2. *Cassius Purple Test.*—Gold dissolves readily in concentrated nitro-hydrochloric acid (aqua regia) with the formation of auric chloride ($AuCl_3$). Evaporate the solution almost to dryness and dissolve the residue in a little water. If a few drops of freshly prepared stannous chloride are now added, a finely divided precipitate will form which is purplish in transmitted and brownish in reflected light. This is known as the *Cassius purple test* for gold and is extremely delicate. The color is due to a mixture of colloidal gold and tin hydroxide. Ferrous salts also precipitate gold at ordinary temperatures from neutral or acid solutions (distinction from platinum).

3. *Alloy with Silver.*—Yellow flakes are isolated, wrapped in silver foil and heated. Dissolve the silver in HNO_3, absorb the filtrate with filter paper, and heat residue in crucible. A spongy, yellow residue indicates gold.

HYDROGEN (H)

Water in Closed Tube.—When minerals containing water of crystallization or the hydroxyl radical are heated in a closed tube, water is set free which condenses on the cold portions of the tube. More intense heat is necessary to liberate the hydroxyl radical. The water which may be neutral towards test papers is often acid in reaction but rarely alkaline.

Iodine (I)

1. *Heating with Potassium Bisulphate.*—Iodides when heated in a closed tube with $KHSO_4$ liberate violet vapors, often accompanied by a metallic sublimate of iodine.

2. *Precipitation as Silver Iodide.*—A few drops of $AgNO_3$ added to an iodide in a dilute HNO_3 solution precipitates AgI, nearly insoluble in ammonia (distinction from chlorine and bromine).

Iron (Fe)

1. *Magnetic upon Ignition.*—Although a few iron minerals (magnetite, pyrrhotite) are magnetic before heating, the majority become magnetic when heated in the reducing flame and allowed to cool. (Cobalt and nickel minerals react in a similar manner.)

2. *Borax Bead Test.*—In the oxidizing flame iron colors the borax bead yellow when cold. In the reducing flame a pale green results.

3. *Precipitation as Ferric Hydroxide.*—If an acid solution containing ferric iron is made ammoniacal with NH_4OH, a reddish brown precipitate of $Fe(OH)_3$ is formed. To obtain the iron in the ferric condition, a few drops of HNO_3 should be added to the HCl when dissolving the mineral.

4. *Test for Ferrous and Ferric Iron.*—If an iron mineral is dissolved in a nonoxidizing acid as HCl or H_2SO_4, the valence of the iron in solution will be the same as in the original mineral. If a few drops of potassium ferricyanide are added to a solution of ferrous iron, a dark-blue precipitate will be formed. Ferric iron, on the other hand, gives a similar precipitate with potassium ferrocyanide. Potassium sulphocyanate (KCNS) gives a blood-red color but no precipitate, when added to a ferric solution. (Nitric and chloric acids give red color with KCNS, but color is destroyed by heat.)

Lead (Pb)

1. *Sublimate on Plaster Tablet.*—When mixed with bismuth flux and heated on a plaster support, lead minerals yield a chrome-yellow coating. A drop of $(NH_4)_2S_x$ applied to the film gives a black spot.

2. *Bismuth Flux on Charcoal.*—Upon charcoal, lead minerals, mixed with bismuth flux, produce a greenish yellow film.

3. *Reduction on Charcoal.*—Mixed with Na_2CO_3 on charcoal, lead compounds give a yellowish coating and gray malleable globules.

4. *Precipitation as Lead Sulphate.*—From a dilute HNO_3 solution, lead may be precipitated as white insoluble $PbSO_4$ upon the addition of a few drops of H_2SO_4.

Lithium (Li)

Flame Test.—Lithium imparts a carmine-red coloration to the flame. The color is not so persistent as that of strontium. If to a solution of a lithium salt a few drops of $BaCl_2$ are added, the red color of lithium will appear before the green of barium. (Strontium will appear after the green.) Lithium minerals do not become alkaline upon ignition (distinction from strontium). In testing silicates, it is necessary to mix the assay with powdered gypsum and introduce it into the flame on a platinum wire.

MAGNESIUM (Mg)

1. *Ignition with Cobalt Nitrate.*—Infusible and light-colored magnesium minerals assume a pink color when moistened with a drop or two of cobalt nitrate and intensely ignited. This test is unsatisfactory at times, and the following wet reaction must then be employed.

2. *Precipitation as Ammonium Magnesium Phosphate.*—If hydrogen sodium phosphate (Na_2HPO_4) is added to a strongly ammoniacal solution, magnesium is precipitated as ammonium magnesium phosphate (NH_4MgPO_4). The precipitate is white and crystalline and may appear only after shaking and standing for a short time. In order to remove interfering elements proceed as follows: The HCl solution containing a few drops of HNO_3 is boiled and then made alkaline with NH_4OH. This will precipitate Fe, Al, and Cr, if present. To the ammoniacal filtrate add ammonium oxalate to remove Ca, Ba, and Sr. To the filtrate, Na_2HPO_4 is then added to test for magnesium.

MANGANESE (Mn)

1. *Borax Bead Test.*—Manganese colors the borax bead reddish violet in the oxidizing flame but becomes colorless in the reducing flame. Salt of phosphorus gives a similar reaction, but the test is not so sensitive.

2. *Fusion with Sodium Carbonate on Platinum Wire.*—When dissolved in a Na_2CO_3 bead in the oxidizing flame, manganese compounds color the fusion a bluish green due to the formation of sodium manganate (Na_2MnO_4). If a charcoal support is used instead of platinum wire, a small amount of KNO_3 should be added to the Na_2CO_3 to offset the reducing action of the support.

3. *Heating in Closed Tube.*—Some of the higher oxides yield oxygen, or when dissolved in HCl evolve chlorine.

4. *Oxidation to Permanganic Acid.*—Boil with HNO_3 and Pb_3O_4, and allow the lead oxide to settle. The supernatant solution will be purplish from the permanganic acid formed. The same result may be obtained by the use of potassium periodate (KIO_4) in a nitric acid solution.

MERCURY (Hg)

1. *Sublimate on Plaster Tablet.*—When mixed with bismuth flux and heated on a plaster support, mercury minerals produce a coating which is usually a combination of scarlet, yellow, and greenish black.

2. *Heating in a Closed Tube.*—When mixed with 3 parts of dry Na_2CO_3 and heated, metallic mercury will volatilize and condense as globules on the sides of the tube.

3. *Precipitation by Copper.*—A clean copper wire immersed in a mercury solution becomes covered with a deposit of metallic mercury.

MOLYBDENUM (Mo)

1. *Sublimate on Plaster and Charcoal.*—When heated *per se* with the oxidizing flame, some molybdenum compounds yield MoO_3, which is yellow when hot and white when cold. When touched with the reducing flame, the white coating is changed to a deep blue. If a charcoal support is used, a copper-red sublimate will also be noted surrounding the assay which is best seen in reflected light.

2. *Treatment with Concentrated Sulphuric Acid.*—If a molybdate is treated with a few drops of concentrated H_2SO_4 in a porcelain dish and evaporated until it fumes strongly, the mass upon cooling is colored intensely blue. A drop of alcohol added at this point will hasten the color reaction. The color will disappear upon the addition of water. Molybdenite (MoS_2) must be oxidized, either by boiling to dryness with HNO_3 or by roasting, before it can be tested in this manner.

3. *Formation of Molybdenum Thiocyanate.*—Fuse with Na_2CO_3, adding a small amount of KNO_3. Extract with H_2O and acidify the filtrate. KCNS causes little or no change when added to HCl solution of molybdenum, but, if it is then treated with zinc or $SnCl_2$, a blood-red coloration is produced. The reaction takes place in the presence of phosphoric acid (distinction from iron). If H_2O_2 is added to the solution immediately after the red color has developed, the color disappears, returning as soon as the H_2O_2 has been reduced. By shaking with ether, the color can be concentrated in the extract.

4. *Bead Test.*—The salt of phosphorus bead in the reducing flame is colored green.

NICKEL (Ni)

1. *Bead Tests.*—Nickel colors the borax bead in the oxidizing flame a reddish brown, while the salt of phosphorus bead is yellow.

2. *Pale-blue Solution with Ammonium Hydroxide.*—A fairly concentrated acid solution of nickel will become pale blue upon adding an excess of NH_4OH. The color is not so dark a shade as that produced by copper.

3. *Precipitation with Dimethylglyoxime.*—Dissolve the mineral in HNO_3 and make the solution alkaline with NH_4OH. Filter if necessary, and to the filtrate add several cubic centimeters of an alcoholic solution of dimethylglyoxime. A scarlet precipitate ($C_8H_{14}N_4O_4Ni$) indicates nickel.

Niobium (Nb). See Columbium

Nitrogen (N)

1. *Heating in Closed Tube.*—Nitrates heated in a closed tube with $KHSO_4$ liberate reddish brown fumes of NO_2.

2. *Brown-ring Test.*—Acidify the solution with a few cubic centimeters of dilute H_2SO_4, then add twice its volume of concentrated H_2SO_4. Cool and add fresh $FeSO_4$ solution so that it forms a separate layer on top.   A brown ring will form at the junction of the two liquids.   (Iodides give a ring of free iodine which interferes with the test.)

Oxygen (O)

1. *Heating in Closed Tube.*—Some of the higher oxides as MnO_2 and $KClO_3$ liberate oxygen which causes a glowing splinter to take fire.

2. *Evolution of Chlorine.*—If HCl is added to some of the higher oxides, free chlorine is liberated which is recognized by its odor and bleaching properties.

Phosphorus (P)

1. *Reduction with Magnesium Ribbon.*— Phosphides of aluminum and the heavy metals should be fused with Na_2CO_3 and the powdered fusion ignited in a test tube with Mg ribbon.   The phosphorus is converted into a phosphide which upon the addition of a few drops of water liberates phosphine (PH_3), recognized by its unpleasant garlic odor and ability to produce a black coloration when brought in contact with filter paper moistened with $AgNO_3$.   Phosphates of the alkalies and alkaline earths may be ignited with Mg ribbon directly without previous fusion. This test is not satisfactory if arsenic or antimony is present.

2. *Precipitation with Ammonium Molybdate.*—The phosphate is dissolved in HNO_3 (if insoluble, fusion with Na_2CO_3 should precede solution in acid) and a portion of the filtrate added to an excess of ammonium molybdate solution.   Upon standing or slightly warming, a yellow precipitate of ammonium phosphomolybdate will be formed.

Platinum (Pt)

1. *Brownish Red Solution with Potassium Iodide.*—Isolate and dissolve several scales of platinum in concentrated aqua regia and evaporate to dryness.   Redissolve in HCl and evaporate to a thick paste.   Dilute with water and then add a few drops of H_2SO_4 and a crystal of KI.   The solution assumes a wine-red color.   This test will not detect traces of platinum in the presence of large quantities of iron.

2. *Precipitation of Potassium Platinic Chloride.*—Add KCl to a concentrated portion of the paste obtained, as indicated in 1.   Yellow crystals of K_2PtCl_6, insoluble in 80 per cent. alcohol, will be precipitated.

Potassium (K)

Flame Test.—Volatile potassium compounds impart a pale-violet color to the nonluminous flame. If obscured by sodium, view the flame through a thick blue glass or a Merwin color screen. Through blue glass the flame appears purplish red, while through the Merwin screen the coloration is blue-violet through division 1, and red-violet through divisions 2 and 3. In testing silicates it will be necessary to mix the assay with powdered gypsum and introduce it into the flame on a platinum wire.

Selenium (Se)

1. *Sublimate on Plaster Tablet.*—When heated on the plaster tablet *per se*, selenium gives a coating which is cherry-red to crimson in thin layers and nearly black in thick deposits. When volatilized, the fumes are reddish and have the odor of rotten horse-radish.

2. *Flame Test.*—When volatilized, selenium imparts an indigo-blue coloration to the flame.

Silicon (Si)

1. *Salt of Phosphorus Bead.*—Silica does not dissoive readily in the salt of phosphorus bead but forms an insoluble translucent skeleton.

2. *Gelatinization with Acid.*—Finely powdered silicates, which are completely soluble in HNO_3 or HCl, form a gelatinous mass of silicic acid when evaporated almost to dryness.

3. *Fusion with Sodium Carbonate.*—Insoluble silicates should be fused with 3 to 4 parts of Na_2CO_3 and dissolved in HCl. Evaporate to complete dryness and redissolve the bases with fairly concentrated HCl. SiO_2 remains insoluble and may be removed by filtering the solution.

Silver (Ag)

1. *Reduction on Charcoal.*—When silver minerals are heated on charcoal with 3 parts of Na_2CO_3 they are readily reduced to malleable, metallic globules. If sulphur, arsenic, or antimony is present, roasting should precede reduction in order to volatilize these constituents.

2. *Precipitation as Silver Chloride.*—If to an HNO_3 solution of a silver mineral a few drops of HCl are added, a white curdy precipitate of AgCl will be formed. This precipitate is soluble in ammonia.

Sodium (Na)

Flame Test.—Sodium imparts an intense and prolonged yellow color to the flame. The color is invisible through a thick dark-blue glass or the Merwin screen. Silicates of sodium should be mixed with gypsum and introduced into the flame on a platinum wire.

STRONTIUM (Sr)

1. *Flame Test.*—Strontium imparts a crimson color to the flame, which is more persistent than that of lithium and is invisible through division 1 of the Merwin screen (distinction from calcium). If a few drops of $BaCl_2$ are added to a solution of a Sr salt, the red color (Sr) will appear after the green of Ba. (Lithium will appear before the green.)

2. *Alkaline Reaction upon Ignition.*—With the exception of silicates and phosphates, strontium minerals give upon ignition an alkaline reaction with turmeric paper (distinction from lithium).

3. *Precipitation as Strontium Sulphate.*—From a strontium bearing solution, $SrSO_4$ is precipitated upon the addition of a few drops of dilute H_2SO_4 (distinction from lithium).

SULPHUR (S)

When Present as Sulphides

1. *Heating in Open Tube.*—Powdered sulphides are oxidized when heated in an open tube. SO_2 is set free and is recognized by its pungent odor and acid reaction with litmus paper.

2. *Heating in Closed Tube.*—When heated in a closed tube, some sulphides liberate a portion of their sulphur which condenses as a dark-red liquid when hot and changes to a crystalline yellow solid when cold.

3. *Fusion with Sodium Carbonate.*—Fuse with 3 to 4 parts of Na_2CO_3 and place a portion of the fusion on a silver coin. Moisten with a few drops of water. A dark-brown to black spot indicates sulphur, provided selenium and tellurium are absent. To another portion of the fusion placed in a watch glass, add several drops of water and a drop or two of freshly prepared sodium nitroferricyanide. An intense purple color is indicative of sulphur.

4. *Oxidation with Nitric Acid.*—Hot concentrated HNO_3 oxidizes sulphides to sulphates, liberating some free sulphur which rises to the surface. A few drops of $BaCl_2$ added to the filtrate precipitate the sulphur as white $BaSO_4$.

When Present as Sulphates

5. *Fusion with Sodium Carbonate.*—Mix the sulphate with an equal volume of powdered charcoal and 3 volumes of Na_2CO_3. Fuse and test as indicated in 3.

6. *Precipitation as Barium Sulphate.*—Sulphates soluble in HCl are precipitated as $BaSO_4$ upon the addition of $BaCl_2$.

TELLURIUM (Te)

1. *Sublimate on Plaster Tablet.*—Tellurides heated *per se*, or with bismuth flux on a plaster support, yield a purplish brown coating.

A drop of concentrated H_2SO_4 added to the film and gently heated forms a pink spot.

2. *Sublimate on Charcoal.*—When heated on charcoal, a white sublimate of TeO_2 is formed near the assay which resembles Sb_2O_3. The coating is volatile and, when touched with the reducing flame, it colors the flame a pale green.

3. *Test with Concentrated Sulphuric Acid.*—When gently warmed with concentrated H_2SO_4, powdered tellurides produce a reddish violet solution. Too intense heat or the addition of water will cause the color to disappear. Manganese may also give a purple color, but it is permanent.

Tin (Sn)

1. *Reduction on Charcoal.*—If fused with an equal volume of powdered charcoal and 2 volumes of Na_2CO_3, tin minerals are reduced, forming minute metallic globules. Upon prolonged ignition, the tin is volatilized and deposits as a white coating of SnO_2. Add a drop of $Co(NO_3)_2$ to the coating and heat. A bluish green spot results.

2. *Reaction with Metallic Zinc.*—Place a fragment of cassiterite (SnO_2) in a test tube on top of granulated metallic zinc and add dilute HCl. After a few minutes the mineral becomes coated with a thin gray layer of metallic tin.

Titanium (Ti)

1. *Reduction with Tin.*—After fusion with 3 volumes of Na_2CO_3, the titanium will dissolve in HCl forming $TiCl_4$. Upon boiling with metallic tin, the titanium is reduced to $TiCl_3$, the solution assuming a violet color. If only a small amount of titanium is present, test 2 should be employed.

2. *Oxidation with Hydrogen Peroxide.*—Dissolve the Na_2CO_3 fusion in 1:1 solution of H_2O and H_2SO_4, and, when cold, add water and a few drops of H_2O_2. The solution is colored a pale yellow to orange red, depending upon the amount of Ti in the solution. This reaction depends upon the formation of $TiO_3.xH_2O$ and is exceedingly delicate. Hydrofluoric acid destroys the color.

Tungsten (W)

1. *Reduction with Tin.*—After fusion with Na_2CO_3, the sodium tungstate is dissolved in hot water. (Columbates are insoluble in water.) Filter if necessary and acidify the filtrate with concentrated HCl. An insoluble white precipitate of hydrated tungstic acid ($H_2WO_4.H_2O$) is formed in the cold, which upon boiling turns yellow (H_2WO_4). Upon adding metallic tin and boiling, a dark-blue solution results, which is due to a heavy precipitate ($WO_3 + WO_2$) held in suspension. Dilution

with water will not cause the color to disappear (distinction from columbium). Prolonged reduction finally produces a brown color (WO_2).

2. *Salt of Phosphorus Bead.*—Colorless in oxidizing flame, blue in reducing flame, becoming red upon addition of $FeSO_4$.

URANIUM (U)

1. *Salt of Phosphorus Bead.*—Uranium colors the salt of phosphorus bead a yellowish green in the oxidizing flame and a bright green in the reducing flame. In the borax bead, uranium cannot be distinguished from iron.

2. *Precipitation as Potassium Urante.*—Potassium ferrocyanide produces a brown precipitate $(UO_2)_2[Fe(CN)_6]$ in a slightly acid solution, which upon the addition of KOH is changed to the yellow potassium uranate ($K_2U_2O_7$) (distinction from cupric ferrocyanide). If iron is present proceed as follows: Dissolve the fusion in aqua regia. Make alkaline with NH_4OH which will precipitate the Fe and U as $Fe(OH)_3$ and $(NH_4)_2U_2O_7$. Upon adding $(NH_4)_2CO_3$ and shaking, the uranium forms a soluble complex salt. Filter and acidify with HCl. Add NH_4OH until alkaline and the uranium is precipitated free from iron. Test precipitate as indicated in 1.

VANADIUM (V)

1. *Bead Tests.*—Vanadium can usually be detected by the bead colorations. In the borax bead the color is yellowish green in the oxidizing flame and emerald green in the reducing flame, while the microcosmic salt bead is colored light yellow and emerald green, respectively.

2. *Oxidation with Hydrogen Peroxide.*—If to an HNO_3 solution of vanadium H_2O_2 is added, pervanadic acid (HVO_4) is formed, which colors the solution orange to reddish brown, not destroyed by hydrofluoric acid (see Titanium). A very delicate reaction.

3. *Reduction with Zinc.*—Zinc in an acid medium causes reduction of vanadic acid so that the solution turns blue, then green, and finally violet. (This test is not so delicate as test 2).

ZINC (Zn)

1. *Sublimate on Charcoal.*—When the finely powdered mineral is mixed with Na_2CO_3 and a small amount of charcoal and ignited, zinc is reduced and then quickly oxidized forming an oxide coating near the assay which is pale yellow when hot, white when cold. A drop of cobalt nitrate added to the sublimate and heated produces a green spot.

2. *Heating with Cobalt Nitrate.*—When moistened with a drop of cobalt nitrate and intensely ignited, infusible and light-colored silicates of zinc usually assume a blue color. ZnO or minerals forming the oxide upon heating, such as $ZnCO_3$, become green.

Zirconium (Zr)

1. *Turmeric-paper Test.*—Fuse with Na_2CO_3 and dissolve in dilute HCl. Turmeric paper dipped in this solution and dried is colored reddish brown (see Boron). It is well to compare the turmeric paper with another strip treated only with HCl and dried.

2. *Precipitation as Phosphate in Acid Solution.*—Dissolve the Na_2CO_3 fusion in HCl, boil, and filter. To the acid filtrate add several drops of Na_2HPO_4, and a white precipitate of zirconium phosphate will be formed. No other common metal, except titanium, yields a phosphate insoluble in an acid solution.

CHAPTER XVI

DESCRIPTIVE MINERALOGY

INTRODUCTION

Descriptive mineralogy includes a detailed discussion in some systematic order of the crystallographic, physical, and chemical properties of minerals. Characterizing features, associations, occurrences, and uses are also given. Two general methods of classification of minerals are in common use. In one of these methods, all minerals possessing some element as an important constituent are grouped together irrespec-

Fig. 469.—James D. Dana (1813–1895). Professor in Yale University (1850–1890). Author of "System of Mineralogy," the standard reference work on descriptive mineralogy.

tive of their chemical and crystallographic relationships. Thus, the important iron minerals would be grouped together, as follows:

1. Pyrrhotite, FeS		4. Magnetite, $Fe(FeO_2)_2$	
2. Pyrite, FeS_2		5. Limonite, $Fe_2O_3.nH_2O$	
3. Hematite, Fe_2O_3		6. Siderite, $FeCO_3$	

The second method of classification is considered more scientific and is followed in this text, the minerals being grouped according to their chemical composition and the principle of isomorphism. Minerals with the simplest composition are discussed first, while those of greatest complexity are treated last. Nine classes are easily arranged.

1. Elements.
2. Sulphides, arsenides, sulpho minerals.
3. Oxides, hydroxides.
4. Haloids.
5. Nitrates, carbonates, manganites.
6. Sulphates, chromates, molybdates, tungstates, uranates.
7. Aluminates, borates, ferrites.
8. Phosphates, vanadates.
9. Silicates.

Within each of these classes the various minerals are arranged, as far as possible, in isomorphous series, thus bringing together those minerals with analogous chemical compositions and strikingly similar crystal forms. In all, 150 minerals are described. The 100 minerals

FIG. 470.—Alfred Lacroix (1863–   ).   Professor of mineralogy in the Muséum d'Histoire Naturelle de France, Paris (1893–   ).   Authority on the minerals of France.

which are considered as the most important are designated by large, heavy type, thus **QUARTZ**. For the remaining 50 minerals, smaller type is used, thus **Scheelite**. In describing the individual minerals, the following order is used:

a. Name and formula.

b. Crystallographic features and structure.

c. Important physical properties, such as cleavage, fracture, hardness, specific gravity, luster, color, indices of refraction, etc.

d. Chemical composition and properties.

e. Varieties, if important.

f. Occurrence, associations, and important localities.

g. Uses.

I. ELEMENTS

Of the 90 and more known elements, only the following eight occur uncombined in nature in sufficient quantities to warrant description:

NONMETALS

DIAMOND	C	Cubic
GRAPHITE	C	Hexagonal
SULPHUR	S	Orthorhombic

SEMIMETALS
Arsenic Group

| Arsenic | As | Hexagonal |
| Bismuth | Bi | Hexagonal |

METALS

| PLATINUM | Pt | Cubic |

Copper Group

COPPER	Cu	Cubic
SILVER	Ag	Cubic
GOLD	Au	Cubic

The specific gravities of the nonmetals are low, those of the semimetals range from 5.6 to 10, while those of the metals may be as high as 22. The metals are malleable and ductile.

Nonmetals

The three minerals to be described here are of great value in commerce and industry.

DIAMOND (*Bortz, Ballas, Carbonado*), C.

Cubic, hexoctahedral class. Usually in crystals or crystal fragments, microscopically small or over 3,000 carats[1] in weight. Most common forms are the octahedron (Fig. 471), rhombic dodecahedron, and hexoctahedron; rarer, the cube. Crystals are often rounded and distorted. Contact twins according to the spinel law, the twinning plane being parallel to a face of the octahedron, are frequently noted. Sometimes massive.

FIG. 471.—Diamond in blue ground. Kimberley, South Africa.

Highly perfect octahedral cleavage. Hardness, 10 (hardest known mineral). Specific gravity, 3.15 to 3.53. Greasy adamantine luster (carbonado, dull). Commonly colorless, or slightly yellowish; also yellow, red, green, blue; more rarely black. Transparent to translucent and opaque. Very high index of refraction ($n_{B\ line} = 2.407$, $n_{D\ line} = 2.417$, $n_{H\ line} = 2.465$). The *fire* so character-

[1] The metric carat is 200 mg. It has been in use in the United States since July 1, 1913. See also p. 394.

istic of the diamond is due to the exceptionally strong dispersion (2.465 − 2.407 = 0.058). Transparent to X rays, while lead glass imitations, such as *paste* and *strass*, are not (Fig. 472). Exposure to sunlight or to electric discharges may cause some diamonds to phosphoresce, while radium emanations may produce fluorescence or a change in color.

Colorless diamonds are pure carbon, for on combustion in an atmosphere of oxygen only carbon dioxide is obtained. Colored stones yield small residues. Unaffected by acids. Inclusions, especially of carbonaceous matter, are frequent.

There are four varieties of the diamond, (1) *diamond proper*, (2) *bortz* or *bort*, (3) *ballas*, and (4) *carbonado*.

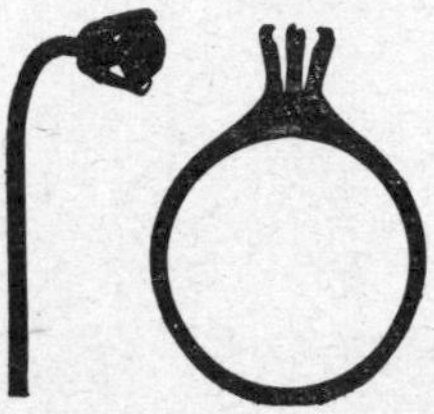

Fig. 472.—X-ray photograph of lead-glass imitation (pin) and of diamond (ring).

1. *Diamond Proper*.—This variety has been known from the earliest times and was called *adamas* by the ancients. These older stones were obtained from secondary deposits in eastern and southern India. These localities furnished some of the world's famous diamonds, but their output at present is very small.

According to tradition, diamonds were discovered in the gold washings in Brazil as early as 1670, but were not positively identified as such until 1721. The provinces of Minas Geraes and Bahia are the most important producers. These deposits are secondary in character, the diamond occurring in stream sands and gravels associated with gold, cyanite, tourmaline, zircon, pyrope, and some heavy ore minerals. From 1721 to 1870, the Brazilian deposits were relatively heavy producers, but at present the yield is small.

In 1867, diamonds were discovered on the south shore of the Orange River, near Hopetown in southern Africa, and at present, Africa, as a whole, furnishes over 95 per cent. of the world's production. At first, they were found in the "river diggings," that is, in the sands and gravels of the streams, especially the Orange, Vaal, and Modder rivers. About three years later, diamonds were discovered in primary deposits, known as "dry diggings," upon the plateau between the Vaal and Modder rivers. Here the occurrence of the diamond is restricted to limited areas, elliptical or circular in outline and varying from 20 to 700 and more meters in diameter (Figs. 473 and 474). On the surface the diamonds were found in a soft, decomposed material known as the *yellow ground*. At depth the diamond-bearing areas constrict, and the yellow ground is underlaid by a hard, basic magnesian rock, known as kimberlite (variety of peridotite) or the *blue ground*. These areas are volcanic pipes. Originally, the diamonds were easily recovered from the soft yellow ground by simply washing away the lighter constituents and sorting the diamonds from the concentrates. Formerly, the harder blue ground was brought to the surface in large lumps and generally exposed in the open fields, "depositing floors," to the action of the atmospheric agencies. In due time, the material could be easily crushed. It was then washed and concentrated and passed over oscillating tables covered with grease, called "sorters" or "greasers." The use of these tables is based upon the fact that of all the minerals in the concentrates grease sticks most tenaciously to the diamond. At present, at most of the large mines, the blue ground is crushed and concentrated immediately after being mined.

In general, the diamond content of a load of blue ground (1,600 pounds) is less than ¼ carat.

Kimberley is the diamond center for South Africa, four important mines, the Kimberley, Du Toitspan, De Beers, and Bultfontein, being

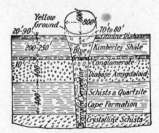

FIG. 473.—Section through the Kimberley Mine.

FIG. 474.—Kimberley Diamond Mine.

located in its immediate vicinity. Other important mines are the Jagersfontein, in the Orange Free State, and the Premier, in the Transvaal near Pretoria. The Premier is the largest known diamond mine and covers about 80 acres (see Fig. 802, page 411).

Diamonds also occur in secondary deposits in various parts of Africa, thus, near Lüderitz Bay on the west coast, along the Kasai River in the Belgian Congo, in Angola, and in the district known as the Gold Coast. The value of the diamonds mined annually in Africa has exceeded $75,000,000, about one-third of the stones being obtained from the mines and two-thirds from alluvial deposits.

Diamonds have also been found in Australia, the Ural Mountains, British Guiana, Colombia, Mexico, and British Columbia. In the United States occasional diamonds have been discovered in Wisconsin, Indiana, Michigan, California, Georgia, and North Carolina. The most important find of diamonds in the United States was made on Aug. 1, 1906, near Murfreesboro, Pike County, Arkansas. The occurrence here is strikingly similar to that of the principal South African "pipe" mines, and up to January, 1932, about 40,000 stones have been recovered; 10 per cent were of gem quality. See also page 410.

Microscopic diamonds have been reported in meteorites (Cañon Diablo, Arizona).

The diamond has long been used as a gem, but the ancients were content to polish the natural crystal faces. It is generally claimed that

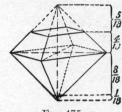

Fig. 475.

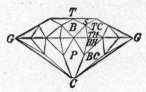

Fig. 476.

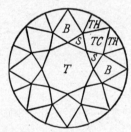

Fig. 477.

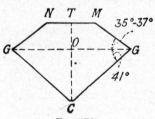

Fig. 478.

about 1456, the art of cutting facets upon the diamond was invented whereby the *fire* was greatly increased. Many different styles of cutting have been in use at various times, but the *brilliant* and *emerald* cuts have been the most common. At present, various fancy cuts are also used, such as, *baguette, cut corner triangle, epaulet, half-moon, hexagon, keystone, kite, lozenge, marquise, pentagon* or *bullet, square, trapeze, triangle.* These newer cuts are well adapted to the designing of modernistic jewelry.

As illustrated in Fig. 475, the octahedron, either natural or obtained by cleaving or sawing, is made the basis for the *brilliant* style of cutting. Figures 476, 477, and 478 are side and top views of the cut stones. Usually there are 58 facets, but in some cases as high as 74 are cut. Depending upon the character of the rough stone, from a third to one-half of its weight is lost in cutting. Amsterdam and Antwerp are the most important diamond-cutting centers. See also pages 396 to 399.

The largest diamond ever found was the *Cullinan* or *Premier*, also called the *Star of Africa* (Fig. 479), discovered on Jan. 25, 1905, at the Premier Mine, in the Transvaal. This stone weighed 621.2 grams or 3,106 carats. It measured about 10 × 6.5 × 5 cm. and was a cleavage fragment of a larger stone. It was purchased by the Assembly of Transvaal and presented to King Edward VII and sub-sequently cut into nine large (Fig. 480) and 96 smaller stones. The largest two stones are called *Cullinan I* and *II* and weigh 530.2 and 317.4 carats, respectively. Some of the other famous cut diamonds and their approximate weights are: the *Jubilee*, 245.3 carats; *Kohinoor*, 106 carats; *Orloff*, 195 carats; *Regent*, 137 carats; *Tiffany* (yellow), 128.5 carats; *Hope* (blue), 44.5 carats; *Dresden* (green), 40 carats; *Star of the South*, 125.5 carats (Fig. 481). In January, 1934, the *Jonker* diamond, weighing 726 carats, was found in alluvial diggings at Elandsfontein, near Pretoria.

Fig. 479.—Cullinan diamond. Premier Mine, South Africa. Weight 3,106 carats.
(Three-fourths original size.)

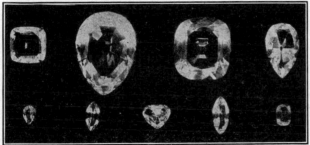

Fig. 480.—The largest nine stones cut from the Cullinan diamond.
(One-third original size.)

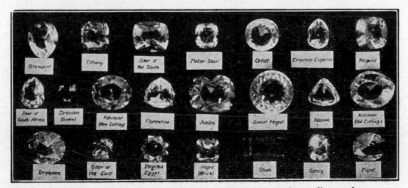

Fig. 481.—Photograph of glass models of famous large diamonds.
(Approximately one-third original size.)

2. *Bortz.*—Also called *bort* and *boart*. Dark-colored, poorly crystallized variety, often with a radial fibrous structure. Translucent to opaque. Crystals and fragments of an inferior quality, hence unfit for

FIG. 482.—Bortz suitable for diamond drills.

FIG. 483.—Diamond drill bit, set with bortz.

gem purposes, are also called bortz. Bits used in diamond drills are frequently set with bortz (Figs. 482 and 483).

3. *Ballas.*—Spherical masses of minute diamond crystals arranged

more or less concentrically are called *ballas* (Fig. 484). On account of the structure, these masses do not cleave easily. Ballas is very tough and well suited for drilling and industrial purposes. It is obtained principally from Brazil and the Jagersfontein mine, South Africa. Spherical white or grayish diamonds are sometimes called ballas, although they are more properly classified as bortz, because of their cleavage.

FIG. 484.—Ballas, 110 carats, original size.

4. *Carbonado.*—Often called *black diamond*, or simply *carbon*. This variety is compact, opaque, and usually black to gray in color (Fig. 485). Specific gravity, 3.15 to 3.29. No cleavage.

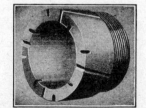

FIG. 485.—Carbonado. Brazil.

FIG. 486.—Diamond drill bit.

Found in placer deposits in the Province of Bahia, Brazil. The largest carbonado ever found weighed 3,078 carats (Fig. 803, page 412).

Diamond proper is used extensively as a gem. Inferior stones and *bortz* are used as an abrasive, glass cutters, and as dies for wire drawing. *Carbonado*, broken into small cubes, finds application in diamond drilling, the small cubes being set in the bit (Fig. 486). The number of stones in the bit depends upon its size and varies from 2 to 50. In prospecting for oil, bits with 6 to 16 stones are generally used. Bortz is also used in diamond drill bits (Figs. 482 and 483). Diamond drilling is employed extensively to determine the location and size of ore bodies, and the character of the rocks to be penetrated and, hence, is of the utmost importance in mining and structural engineering. Carbonado and bortz are also used in "diamond-set" lathe tools and saws which now find wide application in many industries.

GRAPHITE (*Plumbago, Black Lead*), C.

Hexagonal, ditrigonal scalenohedral class. Crystals are small, tabular, and hexagonal in outline but very rare. Usually found in foliated, scaly, granular and compact, or earthy masses (Fig. 487).

Perfect basal cleavage, yielding very thin and flexible laminæ. Hardness, 1 to 2; marks paper and soils the fingers. Greasy feel. Specific gravity, 1.9 to 2.3. Iron black to dark gray in color. Shiny black streak. (Rubbed streak black; molybdenite, greenish.) Opaque. Metallic luster, sometimes dull or earthy. Good conductor of electricity. Transparent to X rays.

Fig. 487.—Graphite with calcite. Ticonderoga, New York.

Essentially carbon, but not so pure as the diamond. On combustion may yield as much as 20 per cent. ash. Not attacked by acids. Graphite brought in contact with metallic zinc in a solution of copper sulphate is quickly copper plated, while molybdenite treated in the same way is only slowly coated. Infusible.

Graphite occurs in large masses and disseminated scales, also in dikes and veins in granites, gneisses, mica schists, and crystalline limestones. In some cases, it is the result of metamorphic action on carbonaceous matter, as in Rhode Island, or it may be due to the reduction of carburetted vapors, as in Ceylon, or of the oxides of carbon, as at Ticonderoga and vicinity in the eastern part of New York State. Common associates are calcite, orthoclase, quartz, pyroxene, garnet, spinel, and amphibole. The principal sources are Ceylon; Madagascar; Chosen (Korea); Sonora, Mexico; Austria; Czechoslovakia; eastern New York; Chester County, Pennsylvania; Clay County, Alabama; Dillon, Montana; Burnet, Texas.

Artificial graphite is manufactured in large quantities from anthracite coal or petroleum coke in electric furnaces at Niagara Falls, New York.

Graphite is used extensively in the manufacture of crucibles, stove polish, foundry facings, lead pencils, paint, lubricants, and electrodes. See page 412.

SULPHUR (*Brimstone*), S.

Orthorhombic, bipyramidal class, if formed below 96°C. Crystals are common, showing mostly pyramidal or tabular habits (Figs. 488 and 489); also in granular, fibrous, earthy, powdery, or stalactitic masses (Fig. 490).

Indistinct cleavages. Pronounced conchoidal to uneven fracture. Hardness, 1.5 to 2.5. Specific gravity, 1.9 to 2.1. Adamantine luster on crystal faces, otherwise resinous to greasy. Transparent to trans-

Fig. 488.　　Fig. 489.—Sulphur with calcite. Racalmuto, Sicily.　　Fig. 490.—Banded sulphur in limestone. Racalmuto, Sicily.

lucent. White to yellow streak. Usually sulphur yellow in color; also honey yellow or yellow brown; and, due to impurities, reddish, greenish, or grayish. High indices of refraction, α 1.950, β 2.043, γ 2.240, (+); $2V = 69°$; $r < v$. Nonconductor of electricity and heat. On account of the low conductivity and unequal distribution of heat, cold crystals often crack when held in the hand. When held to the ear, a crackling sound may be heard.

Usually, practically pure sulphur; sometimes mixed with bitumen and clay. Melts at 112.8°C., and at 270°C. burns with a bluish flame to sulphur dioxide. Insoluble in water and acids. Soluble in carbon disulphide.

The large and commercially important deposits occur in sedimentary rocks and are generally the result of the reduction of sulphate minerals, notably gypsum. The common associates are celestite, gypsum, aragonite, and calcite. In the United States commercial deposits of sulphur occur in the cap rocks of salt domes in the Texas and Louisiana coastal plain. Practically all of the American production of sulphur is from this

area.   The two most important producing localities are the Boling dome
in Wharton County, Texas, and the Lake Washington dome, Louisiana.
Other important deposits occur in Brazoria, Fort Bend, Matagorda,
Palangana, and Duval counties, Texas, and in Iberia Parish, Louisiana.
Many other salt domes with workable deposits of sulphur are known,
but they are not being mined at present.   In these domes the sulphur

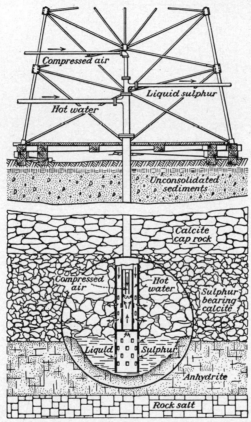

Fig. 491.—Cross section of sulphur deposit showing Frasch method, Texas Gulf Sulphur
Company.

occurs disseminated and in lenses and cavities at considerable depths
below the surface.   By means of superheated water and compressed
air the sulphur is melted and forced to the surface, and allowed to
solidify in large vats (Figs. 491 and 492).   It is then ready for ship-
ment, being 99.5 per cent. pure sulphur.   Girgenti, Sicily, has for many
years been the chief center of the sulphur industry of Sicily.   Sulphur
is also found in small quantities around volcanoes, the result of sublimation or interaction of sulphurous vapors; thus, on Mounts Vesuvius and

Etna, also in Iceland, Japan, and Hawaii. Furthermore, it occurs as the result of decomposition of pyrite and other sulphide minerals.

Important in the manufacture of sulphuric acid, matches, gunpowder, fertilizer, vulcanized rubber, insecticides, medicines, the bleaching of silk, straw, and woolen materials, and in the preparation of wood pulp used in the manufacture of paper. See page 432.

Fig. 492.—Sulphur discharge into vats by the Frasch method. Texas Gulf Sulphur Company, Gulf, Matagorda County, Texas.

Semimetals

Arsenic Group

The members of this group crystallize in the hexagonal system in pseudocubical rhombohedrons. They are brittle and nonmalleable.

Arsenic (*Native Arsenic*), **As.**

Hexagonal, ditrigonal scalenohedral class. Crystals are pseudo-cubical rhombohedrons, but very rare. Commonly in compact, scaly, granular, or fine-grained masses with reniform and botryoidal structures (Fig. 493). Often breaks into concentric or onion-like layers.

Basal cleavage but usually not conspicuous. Uneven and fine-grained fracture. Hardness, 3 to 4. Specific gravity, 5.6 to 5.8. Metallic luster. Opaque. Tin-white color on fresh fracture surface, tarnishes dark gray to black on exposure. Grayish streak.

Fig. 493.—Arsenic. Andreasberg, Harz Mountains, Germany.

Native arsenic often contains antimony, also bismuth, cobalt, nickel, silver, iron, or gold.

Found principally in veins with silver, cobalt, and nickel ores; thus, in the Freiberg mining district of Saxony; Joachimsthal, Bohemia;

Kongsberg, Norway; Mexico; Chile; China Creek, Vancouver Island, British Columbia.

Native arsenic furnishes but a small portion of the arsenic used in commerce and industry. Metallic arsenic is a constituent of shot metal. See page 405.

Bismuth (*Native Bismuth*), **Bi.**

Hexagonal, ditrigonal scalenohedral class. Rarely in rhombohedral crystals. Usually in reticulated, arborescent, platy, or compact masses (Fig. 494).

Fig. 494.—Bismuth with calcite and smaltite. Cobalt, Ontario.

Basal cleavage, generally conspicuous. Hardness, 2 to 2.5. Specific gravity, 9.7. Brittle, slightly malleable when heated. Metallic luster. Opaque. Reddish white color, often with brassy tarnish colors. Shiny lead-gray streak.

Native bismuth often contains traces of arsenic, sulphur, and tellurium.

Not especially abundant but usually in veins associated with silver, cobalt, lead, zinc, and tin ores. Important localities are Freiberg, Saxony; Joachimsthal, Bohemia; Bolivia; Cornwall, England; Cobalt, Ontario; Great Bear Lake, Canada.

Metallic bismuth is obtained either from native bismuth or as a by-product in the electrolytic refining of lead. The metal is used in the manufacture of easily fusible alloys, such as find application in automatic sprinklers and safety plugs in boilers; also in rifle bullets and thermopiles. The salts of bismuth are used in pharmaceutical preparations, calico printing, and in the manufacture of highly refractive glass. See page 407.

Metals

Only the four very important metallic elements, platinum, copper, silver, and gold will be described. The internal structures of these elements are discussed on page 160.

PLATINUM (*Native Platinum*), **Pt.**

Cubic, hexoctahedral class. Small crystals, generally cubes, but very rare. Usually in scales or grains; also in nuggets.

Hackly fracture. Metallic luster. Opaque. Hardness, 4 to 6. Specific gravity, 14 to 19; melted platinum is 19.7, hammered 21.23. Malleable, ductile, sectile. Silver white to dark gray or black in color. May be magnetic if much iron is present.

Native platinum usually contains iron (up to 19.5 per cent.) and smaller amounts of iridium, rhodium, palladium, osmium, copper, and, at times, gold. Infusible at ordinary temperatures, but may be fused and welded with the oxyhydrogen blowpipe. Soluble in hot concentrated nitrohydrochloric acid.

Platinum was first discovered in 1735 in the gold placers of the Pinto River in Colombia, associated with gold, zircon, magnetite, chromite, and so forth. In 1822, it was found in the alluvial deposits of Nizhne Tagilski in the Ural Mountains. Although practically all of the world's supply is obtained from placer deposits, platinum also occurs in veins associated with chromite and disseminated in peridotite rocks. Russia is one of the chief producers and largely controls the market. Platinum is recovered in considerable quantities from the copper ores in the Sudbury district, Ontario. In the United States, small amounts are found in the black sands of the rivers along the Pacific Coast. Other occurrences are in various districts in the Transvaal and southern Rhodesia, South Africa; Colombia, and other South American countries; near Bunkerville, Clark County, Nevada, and in Westphalia, Germany.

Platinum is used very extensively as a catalytic agent in the manufacture of sulphuric, acetic, and nitric acids and in physical, chemical, and electrical apparatus; also in jewelry, pyrography, dentistry, nonmagnetic watches, and surgical instruments. The price of refined platinum has fluctuated greatly. In 1905, it was only $0.35 per gram but gradually increased to $5.55 in 1918. During the next 10 years, it slowly declined and in 1928 was about $2.80 and in 1936 about $1.95 per gram. Also see page 427.

Copper Group

The very important metals copper, silver, and gold belong to this group. They crystallize in the cubic system and are rather soft, heavy, and very malleable.

COPPER (*Native Copper*), Cu.

Cubic, hexoctahedral class. Crystals are rather common but usually distorted and in parallel groups. Tetrahexahedrons, rhombic dodecahedron, and cube are the most commonly observed forms (Figs. 495, 496, and 497). Generally in scales, grains, plates, and masses, oftentimes weighing many tons (Fig. 498); less frequently arborescent and filiform.

Hackly fracture.   Hardness, 2.5 to 3.   Specific gravity, 8.5 to 9.
Metallic luster.   Ductile and malleable.   Color copper red on fresh fracture.   Due to tarnish and decomposition products, color may be super-

FIG. 495.—Crystallized copper (tetrahexahedron).   Phoenix
Mine, Lake Superior district.

FIG. 496.—Crystallized copper
(rhombic dodecahedron).   Lake
Superior district.

FIG. 497.—Crystallized copper.   Lake Superior district.

FIG. 498.—Mining *mass* copper.   Quincy Mine, Lake Superior district.

ficially black (CuO), red (Cu_2O), green ($CuCO_3.Cu(OH)_2$), or blue
($2CuCO_3.Cu(OH)_2$).   Streak copper red, metallic and shiny.   Excellent
conductor of heat and electricity.

Native copper is generally almost pure copper; sometimes contains
small amounts of silver or arsenic.

The most important locality for the occurrence of native copper is Keweenaw Peninsula in northern Michigan, where it occurs disseminated, principally in fine grains or scales, or in veins in (1) dark-colored igneous rocks, called *melaphyre amygdaloids* (variety of basalt) (Figs. 499 and 500); (2) in reddish quartz porphyry conglomerates (Fig. 501);

Fig. 499.—Copper in amygdaloid. Lake Superior district.

Fig. 500.—"Shot" copper. Adventure Mine, Lake Superior district.

(3) in sandstones; (4) in epidotic beds; (5) in felsitic rocks. The first two occurrences are at present the most important. These ores average about 1.65 per cent. of copper and are easy to treat. By means of crushing, washing, and concentrating with jigs and tables, the metallic copper is readily extracted. It is then smelted and refined and cast into ingots and sold as "lake" copper. This district has produced about

Fig. 501.—Copper conglomerate. Lake Superior district.

175,000,000 pounds annually. At present about 60 per cent. of the ore handled is conglomerate rock. The common associates are calcite, quartz (Fig. 502), datolite (Fig. 503), epidote, silver, analcite, and other zeolites.

Native copper also occurs in smaller quantities associated with the other copper minerals—malachite, azurite, cuprite, chalcopyrite, bornite, and chalcocite—especially in Arizona and New Mexico.

Metallic copper is used very extensively in commerce and industry. Large amounts are used in the manufacture of copper wire, nails, and sheets, brass, bronze, electrical and radio apparatus, munitions of war; also for coinage purposes and chemical reagents. It is said that there are about six hundred uses for copper where it is practically indispensable (see page 415). The price of metallic copper fluctuates greatly. In 1929, it was 18 cents, in 1932 as low as 5 cents and in 1936, $9\frac{1}{2}$ cents a pound.

FIG. 502.—Copper with calcite and quartz. Lake Superior district.

FIG. 503.—Copper with datolite (white). Lake Superior district.

SILVER (*Native Silver*), **Ag.**

Cubic, hexoctahedral class. Crystals usually small and distorted, and in parallel groups. Cube and octahedron most common. Also acicular, reticulated, or arborescent; fine threads or wires (Figs. 504 and 505), sometimes matted and resembling tufts or wads of hair; scales, plates, or large masses.

FIG. 504.—Wire silver with argentite. Porco, Bolivia.

FIG. 505.—Wire silver. Cliff Mine, Lake Superior district.

Malleable and ductile. Hardness, 2.5 to 3. Specific gravity, 10 to 12. Metallic luster. Color silver white, usually with yellow-brown, gray, or black tarnish colors. Silver-white streak, shiny. Excellent conductor of heat and electricity.

Native silver; often contains varying amounts of gold, up to 28 per cent.; also copper, arsenic, antimony, mercury, iron, or platinum.

Occurs commonly with ores of silver, lead, copper, arsenic, cobalt, and nickel, associated with calcite, quartz, barite, or fluorite. Kongsberg, Norway, has furnished a great deal of silver in the form of crystals and large masses, some weighing 750 pounds. The Saxon mines at Freiberg, Marienberg, and Annaberg were for a long time heavy producers; also Mexico, especially Sonora, Durango, Sinaloa; Chile; Peru; and Bolivia. Several of the more important localities in the United States are the

Fig. 506.—Silver (white) and copper "Half Breed." Lake Superior district.

Fig. 507.—Silver with calcite. La Rose Mine, Cobalt, Ontario

Bingham and Tintic districts, Utah; Butte, Montana (from copper ores); Tonopah, Nevada; Coeur d'Alene, Idaho; Aspen, Colorado; Lake Superior copper district, associated with copper, forming "half breeds" (Fig. 506). In large deposits, disseminated and in veins, at Cobalt and vicinity, Ontario, associated with niccolite, smaltite, erythrite, annabergite, bismuth, and calcite (Fig. 507). A mass of silver weighing 4,402 pounds was removed from the Keeley mine, South Lorrain, Ontario. Many masses contained 95 per cent. silver. Rarely found as nuggets.

Native silver is used for coinage, jewelry, and ornamental purposes; also in physical, chemical, and surgical apparatus. The price varies greatly. In 1920 it was about $1.00, in 1932 about 25 cents, and in 1936 about 45 cents an ounce. Also see page 429.

GOLD (*Native Gold*), **Au.**

Cubic, hexoctahedral class. Crystals are small, more or less distorted, but only rarely found. The most common forms are the octahedron, cube, and rhombic dodecahedron, occurring either independently or in combination. Skeletal development frequent. Usually in disseminated or rolled scales or grains; also filiform, reticulated, and in large lumps or nuggets (Fig. 508).

Malleable and ductile. No cleavage, hackly fracture. Hardness, 2.5 to 3. Specific gravity, 15.6 to 19.3. Metallic luster. Golden to brassy or light yellow in color depending upon the amount of silver present. Opaque.

Native gold. Generally contains varying amounts of silver (up to 40 per cent.); also iron, copper, bismuth, and so forth. Readily fusible, and soluble in nitrohydrochloric acid. Readily acted upon by chlorine and potassium or sodium cyanide. Forms an amalgam with mercury.

Gold occurs widely distributed, but in only a comparatively few places in sufficient quantities to be of economic importance. There are two general types of occurrence, namely, (1) *in situ* and (2) in *secondary deposits*, called *placers*.

FIG. 508.—Gold in conglomerate. Western Sonora, Mexico.

FIG. 509.—Gold in quartz. Tuolumne County, California.

FIG. 510.—Gold-bearing conglomerate. Rand mines, Transvaal.

Gold occurring *in situ* is usually found disseminated in quartz veins and associated with various sulphide minerals, of which pyrite is the most important. Owing to the decomposition of the associated sulphides, the quartz, where exposed on the surface to the action of percolating water—zone of oxidation—is usually more or less cellular and of a rusty appearance. Such quartz is often called "porous" or "rusty." quartz. Gold is also found disseminated in granites, trachytes, andesites, crystalline schists, sandstones, and conglomerates. The most common associates, aside from quartz and pyrite, are chalcopyrite, galena, stibnite, tetrahedrite, sphalerite, arsenopyrite, tourmaline, and molybdenite, some of which are frequently auriferous (Figs. 509 and 510).

Free milling gold is usually present in distinctly visible particles and is easily recovered by crushing and washing in a stamp mill and subsequent amalgamation with mercury, the finely crushed material from the mill being allowed to flow over copper plates coated with mercury. Where gold is associated with considerable quantities of the sulphides, the chlorination or cyanide processes may be used, either alone or in connection with amalgamation. In the chlorination process, the auriferous ores are roasted and then subjected to the action of chlorine, which causes the gold to pass into solution. In the cyanide process, the crushed ores, either raw or roasted, are treated with solutions of potassium or sodium cyanide, whereby a soluble double cyanide is formed. The gold can be separated from these solutions by means of electrolysis or zinc dust.

Fig. 511.—Hydraulic mining. La Clara Mine, Porce River, Colombia.

These processes permit ores carrying very small amounts of gold, sometimes as low as $1.50 per ton, to be worked with a profit.

Important localities for the occurrence of gold *in situ* are California, Nevada, South Dakota, Utah, Alaska; the Rand in the Transvaal, South Africa; Western Australia, New South Wales, the Ural Mountains; Porcupine district, Ontario.

Placer gold is the result of the disintegration of rocks containing gold *in situ*, that is, disseminated or in veins. As these rocks are reduced by the action of the atmospheric agencies and erosion to sand and gravel, the gold, on account of its very high specific gravity, becomes concentrated in the stream beds in auriferous regions and is found as scales, grains, and nuggets. Especially rich deposits are likely to be found where the velocity of the stream has been checked by a bend in its course or by some obstruction. Placer gold is readily recovered by washing, the sand and gravel being thrown into long wooden troughs called sluices.

Through these sluices water flows at a rather rapid rate in order to carry away the lighter rock material. At regular intervals, cross-bars, called riffles, are placed in the trough to check the velocity of the water. This causes the heavy particles to fall to the bottom of the sluices, and, since mercury is added from time to time and is also caught by the riffles, an amalgam of gold is formed. From this amalgam, the gold is easily recovered by volatilizing the mercury. In some localities, *hydraulic* mining is employed in working placer deposits. This does not differ essentially from the above method and consists in directing a large stream of water under high pressure against the bank of the placer in order to loosen the same and wash the sand and gravel down into the sluices (Fig. 511). This type of working placers is practicable only where there is an abundant water supply. In regions where the supply of water is limited, dredges are used to advantage.

Gold placers are common in California, Alaska, Colorado, Australia, and Siberia. In practically all noteworthy gold-producing districts, gold has usually been found first in placers, and by subsequent exploration the primary occurrences *in situ* have been located.

Gold is used chiefly for coinage and jewelry. Gold coins of the United States consist of 9 parts of gold and 1 part of copper. For jewelry purposes, copper and silver are alloyed with gold to increase its hardness. The gold content of such alloys is expressed in carats, thus 14 carat gold consists of 14 twenty-fourths gold and 10 twenty-fourths other metals. See page 417.

II. SULPHIDES, ARSENIDES, AND SULPHO MINERALS

This group, consisting of 23 members, includes some of the most important ore minerals.

A. Sulphides and Arsenides

REALGAR	AsS	Monoclinic
ORPIMENT	As_2S_3	Monoclinic
STIBNITE	Sb_2S_3	Orthorhombic
Molybdenite	MoS_2	Hexagonal
SPHALERITE	ZnS	Cubic
PYRRHOTITE	FeS	Hexagonal
Niccolite	$NiAs$	Hexagonal
GALENA	PbS	Cubic
Argentite	Ag_2S	Pseudocubic
CHALCOCITE	Cu_2S	Orthorhombic
CINNABAR	HgS	Hexagonal

PYRITE-MARCASITE GROUPS

PYRITE	FeS_2	Cubic
Cobaltite	$CoAsS$	Cubic
Smaltite	$CoAs_2$	Cubic
MARCASITE	FeS_2	Orthorhombic
ARSENOPYRITE	$FeAsS$	Orthorhombic

B. Sulpho Minerals

a. General Formula, $M'_xR'''S_y$

CHALCOPYRITE	$CuFeS_2$	Tetragonal
BORNITE	Cu_5FeS_4	Cubic
Proustite	Ag_3AsS_3	Hexagonal
Pyrargyrite	Ag_3SbS_3	Hexagonal
Bournonite	$PbCuSbS_3$	Orthorhombic
TETRAHEDRITE	$M'_3R'''S_3$	Cubic

b. General Formula, $M'_xR^VS_y$

Enargite	Cu_3AsS_4	Orthorhombic

These minerals generally possess a metallic luster and are opaque and heavy.

A. Sulphides and Arsenides

Only the important simple sulphides and arsenides will be described.

REALGAR, AsS.

Monoclinic, prismatic class. Crystals are usually short prismatic. Occurs also in granular and compact masses and as incrustations and coatings.

Cleavages parallel to clinopinacoid and orthoprism. Conchoidal fracture. Hardness, 1.5 to 2. Specific gravity, 3.5. Resinous luster.

Aurora-red to orange-yellow color. Orange-yellow streak. Transparent to translucent. α 2.46, β 2.59, γ 2.61, $(-)$; $2V = 40°$, all for lithium light; $r > v$, very strong.

AsS. Sometimes written As_2S_2. Alters to orpiment.

Occurs with ores of silver and antimony and is usually associated with orpiment. Frequently disseminated in clay or dolomite; also as a sublimation product and as a deposit from hot springs.

Some notable localities are Kapnik and Felsöbánya, Rumania; Joachimsthal, Bohemia; Allcahr, Macedonia; Binnenthal, Switzerland; Mount Vesuvius, Italy; Iron County, Utah; Yellowstone Park; San Bernardino and Trinity counties, California.

This mineral is usually found well represented by beautiful specimens in mineral collections but is of no economic importance. The artificial compound is used in the manufacture of fireworks and pigments.

ORPIMENT (*Auripigment, Arsenical Gold Ore*), As_2S_3.

Monoclinic, prismatic class. Crystals are short prismatic but not common. Usually in foliated or granular masses, sometimes as crusts.

Cleavage parallel to clinopinacoid. Flexible but not elastic. Hardness, 1.5 to 2. Specific gravity, 3.5. Resinous to pearly luster. Lemon-yellow color and streak. Translucent to opaque. Very much like realgar, but differs in color. $\beta' = 2.72_{Li}$, $(+)$; very strong double refraction; $2E = 70°$; $r > v$, strong.

As_2S_3. Often formed from realgar, with which it is commonly associated.

Formation and occurrence are the same as for realgar.

Excellent specimens are rather common, but the mineral is not important commercially. The artificial compound is used as a pigment and in dyeing and tanning.

STIBNITE (*Antimonite, Gray Antimony*), Sb_2S_3.

Orthorhombic, bipyramidal class. Crystals common, prismatic, and highly modified (Fig. 512), often vertically striated, bent, or twisted; also in radial aggregates; bladed (Fig. 513), columnar, granular, and compact masses.

Cleavage parallel to brachypinacoid. Slightly sectile. Metallic luster. Hardness, 2. Specific gravity, 4.65. Lead gray in color and streak. Often tarnishes black.

Sb_2S_3. Sometimes contains gold and silver. Fuses easily in candle flame.

Found in veins with quartz and various antimony minerals resulting from the decomposition of stibnite. Also with galena, barite, cinnabar, sphalerite, and gold. Occurs in Saxony, Bohemia, Siberia, Algeria, Mexico, and Hunan Province, China. Excellent crystals have been obtained from the Island of Shikoku, Japan.   The chief American localities are Idaho, Nevada, Utah, Alaska, California; also Washington and Arkansas.

Stibnite is the chief source of metallic antimony and its compounds. Since 1912, China has been the principal source of metallic antimony and

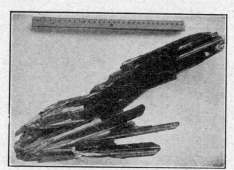

FIG. 512.—Stibnite.   Province of Iyo, Island of Shikoku, Japan.

FIG. 513.—Bladed stibnite. Kremnitz, Hungary.

now furnishes 70 per cent. of the world's supply.   Metallic antimony is used principally in the manufacture of antimonial lead for storage batteries, cable coverings, and in various alloys, such as type, babbitt, and britannia metals.   Some of the compounds are used in rubber goods, as pigments in paints and enamels, and in medicinal preparations (see also page 405).

Bismuthinite (Bi_2S_3) resembles stibnite very closely.   Not common.

Molybdenite, MoS_2.

Hexagonal, dihexagonal bipyramidal class.   Rarely in tabular or prismatic hexagonal crystals (Fig. 514).   Generally in disseminated scales or grains; sometimes in foliated or granular masses.

Excellent basal cleavage.   Flexible.   Greasy feel. Marks paper.   Blue-gray in color (graphite is black). Hardness, 1 to 1.5.   Specific gravity, 4.75 (graphite 1.9 to 2.3).   Greenish streak on glazed porcelain (graphite shiny black).

MoS_2.   Sometimes contains gold or silver.

FIG. 514.—Molybdenite. Wakefield, Quebec.

Generally disseminated in granites, especially those associated with tin ore deposits; also in syenites, gneisses, and crystalline limestones.   Commonly with cassiterite, wolframite, topaz, epidote, and chalcopyrite.   Large crystals occur in Renfrew County, Ontario.   Important occurrences in Saxony and Bohemia; Cornwall, England; Queensland and New South Wales, Australia; Copper and Blue Hill, Maine; Westmoreland, New Hampshire; Crown Point, Chelan County, Washington; Pitkin and Climax, Colorado; Sulphur Gulch, near Questa, New Mexico.

Chief source of molybdenum and its compounds. Used in the manufacture of steel and iron castings and in "high-speed" tools. See page 424.

SPHALERITE (*Blende, Zinc Blende, Blackjack*), ZnS.

Cubic, hextetrahedral class. Crystals are common; often highly modified, and distorted or rounded (Fig. 518). Tetrahedrons with cube

FIG. 515.   FIG. 516.   FIG. 517.—Sphalerite. Cleavage rhombic dodecahedron. Joplin, Missouri.

or rhombic dodecahedron are most commonly observed (Figs. 515, 516, and 518). Twins according to the spinel law. Generally in cleavable, fine to coarse granular, and compact masses; also fibrous and botryoidal. The internal structure of sphalerite is discussed on page 161.

FIG. 518.—Sphalerite. Joplin, Missouri.   FIG. 519.—Sphalerite with quartz and galena. Kapnik, Rumania.

Highly perfect, rhombic dodecahedral cleavage (Fig. 517). Brittle. Resinous to adamantine luster. Very high index of refraction, $n = 2.47$. Hardness, 3.5 to 4. Specific gravity, 3.9 to 4.2. Color varies greatly; when pure, white; commonly, yellow, red, black, or green.

Transparent to translucent. Streak white, pale yellow, or brown. Fluorescence or triboluminescence sometimes observed.

ZnS. Usually contains iron, up to 18 per cent., also manganese, cadmium, or mercury.

Occurs extensively in dolomitic limestones and other sedimentary rocks, and also in crystalline rocks. Usually associated with galena, chalcopyrite, pyrite, barite, fluorite, siderite, rhodochrosite, and quartz (Figs. 519, 520 and 521). Commonly in veins and cavities; also in extensive deposits. Important localities are Freiberg, Saxony; Přibram,

FIG. 520.—Sphalerite in chert. Galena, Illinois.

FIG. 521.—Sphalerite with galena and calcite. Webb City, Missouri.

Bohemia; Binnenthal, Switzerland; Cornwall, England; and Yechigo, Japan.

In the United States, sphalerite is very common in the limestones of Missouri, Kansas, Oklahoma, Wisconsin, Arkansas, Iowa, and Illinois; beautiful crystals at Joplin, Missouri. Also found with lead and silver ores, notably in Montana, Idaho, and Utah. Found in many places in smaller quantities.

Sphalerite is the chief source of zinc. Metallic zinc, known commercially as *spelter*, is used in large quantities in galvanizing iron and in the manufacture of brass, zinc wire and sheets, shot, dust zinc, and electric batteries. The various compounds of zinc are employed extensively as pigments and in chemistry and medicine. Sphalerite is one of the chief sources of cadmium and thallium. Also see page 436.

PYRRHOTITE (*Magnetic Pyrites*), FeS.

Hexagonal, ditrigonal pyramidal class. Crystals are tabular or pyramidal (Fig. 522) but not common. Usually massive, granular, or lamellar. For a discussion of the internal structure of pyrrhotite, see page 162.

Inferior basal cleavage. Brittle. Hardness, 3.5 to 4. Specific gravity, 4.5 to 4.6. Metallic luster. Opaque. Bronze yellow to bronze red in color, tarnishing easily to dark brown. Streak grayish black. Powder frequently attracted by the magnet.

FeS. May contain up to 6 per cent. of excess sulphur. Nickel, cobalt, and platinum are often present. *Troilite* is a variety of FeS without an excess of sulphur. It is usually found in meteorites.

FIG. 522.—Pyrrhotite with sphalerite. Near El Paso, Texas.

Usually as a magmatic segregation in basic igneous rocks such as gabbros, norites, and peridotites, and commonly associated with pyrite, chalcopyrite, pentlandite, and galena. Important localities are Kongsberg, Norway; Bodenmais, Bavaria; Sudbury, Canada; Stafford and Ely, Vermont; Ducktown, Tennessee; Gap Mine, Lancaster County, Pennsylvania.

An important source of nickel. See page 424.

FIG. 523.—Niccolite. Cobalt, Ontario.

Niccolite (*Copper Nickel*), **NiAs.**

Hexagonal, ditrigonal pyramidal class. Crystals are rare. Nearly always massive or disseminated (Fig. 523).

Uneven fracture. Hardness, 5.5. Specific gravity, 7.3 to 7.7. Metallic luster. Light copper red in color, tarnishes brown or grayish. Often coated with a green crust of annabergite ($Ni_3As_2O_8.8H_2O$). Streak brownish black.

NiAs. May contain small amounts of iron, cobalt, antimony, and sulphur.

Commonly associated with nickel, cobalt, and silver ores, thus in the Freiberg district of Saxony; Joachimsthal, Bohemia; the Cobalt district of Ontario; in smaller quantities at Franklin Furnace, New Jersey; Silver Cliff, Colorado.

A nickel ore. See page 424.

Breithauptite (NiSb) is isomorphous with pyrrhotite and niccolite.

GALENA (*Galenite, Lead Glance*), **PbS.**

Cubic, hexoctahedral class. Well-developed crystals are common. Usual forms are the cube (*h*) and octahedron (*o*), independently or in combination; also the rhombic dodecahedron (Figs. 524, 525, 526, and 527). Most generally in cleavable masses; also compact, coarse to fine granular; more rarely stalactitic or fibrous. The internal structure of galena is discussed on page 161

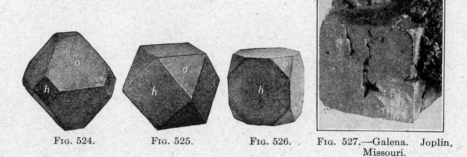

FIG. 524.   FIG. 525.   FIG. 526.   FIG. 527.—Galena.   Joplin, Missouri.

Perfect cubical cleavage (Fig. 528).   Hardness, 2.5.   Specific gravity, 7.3 to 7.6.   Metallic luster, especially on cleavage surfaces (Fig. 529); otherwise rather dull.   Lead-gray color.   Grayish black streak.

PbS.   Often with small amounts of silver.   On this account, galena is an important source of silver.   Galena with curved surfaces is apt to

FIG. 528.—Galena showing cubical cleavage.

FIG. 529.—Galena (light). Flat River, Missouri.

carry higher silver values than that with a good cubical cleavage.   Antimony, iron, zinc, gold, or bismuth may also be present.   Alters to cerussite, anglesite, and pyromorphite.

Found in veins in crystalline rocks associated with sphalerite, chalcocite, bournonite, quartz, various silver ores, calcite, and barite; often silver bearing. Thus, at Wallace, Idaho; Leadville, Colorado; Tintic and Park City districts, Utah; Freiberg, Saxony; Přibram, Bohemia; Cumberland, England; Mexico; Chile. Also in large quantities in Missouri, Illinois, Kansas, Wisconsin, and Iowa, in nonargentiferous veins, irregular deposits, or replacement deposits in limestones, with calcite, sphalerite, chalcopyrite, smithsonite, and marcasite. Excellent crystals occur at Joplin, Missouri, and Mineral Point, Wisconsin.

Galena is the chief source of metallic lead. It is also a valuable silver ore. Metallic lead is used extensively in the manufacture of paint, pipes and sheets, shot, solder, type metal, easily fusible alloys, and the various compounds of lead. Galena has been used as a detector in radio apparatus. Also see page 419.

Clausthalite ($PbSe$) and altaite ($PbTe$) are isomorphous with galena.

Argentite (*Silver Glance*), Ag_2S.

Cubic above 180°C.; orthorhombic (acanthite) at ordinary temperatures. Crystals are cubical or octahedral in habit, often distorted and in parallel groups (Fig. 530). Crystals are, however, not common. Generally disseminated, coatings, or arborescent.

Hardness, 2 to 2.5. Specific gravity, 7.2 to 7.4. Malleable, sectile; takes an impression. On fresh surface, high metallic luster; but on exposure, soon becomes dull and black. Dark lead-gray color. Shiny lead-gray streak.

Ag_2S. On charcoal fuses with intumescence yielding fumes of sulphur dioxide and a globule of silver.

Commonly in veins associated with silver, cobalt, and nickel minerals; proustite, pyrargyrite, smaltite, niccolite, native silver. Occurs at Com-

Fig. 530.—Argentite. Batopilas, Mexico.

stock Lode and Tonopah, Nevada; Aspen, Colorado; Cobalt district, Ontario; Guanajuata and Batopilas, Mexico; Freiberg, Saxony; Joachimsthal, Bohemia; Peru; and Chile.

An important ore of silver. See page 429.

CHALCOCITE (*Copper Glance*), Cu_2S.

Orthorhombic, bipyramidal class, if formed below 91°C. Crystals are tabular or thick prismatic and pseudohexagonal, the prism angle being 119° 35' (Figs. 531 and 532). Striated parallel to the *a* axis. Frequently twinned. Crystals not common. Usually massive—compact, granular, or disseminated.

Hardness, 2.5 to 3. Specific gravity, 5.5 to 5.8. High metallic luster on fresh surface, which soon becomes dull and black. Conchoidal fracture. Color dark lead-gray, often tarnished blue or greenish. Shiny lead-gray streak.

Cu_2S. Usually with varying amounts of iron; also gold and silver. Alters to covellite, malachite, and azurite.

Commonly found in veins with bornite, chalcopyrite, tetrahedrite, galena, enargite, pyrite, and covellite. Occurs in large quantities in the Butte district, Montana; Kennecott, Copper River district, Alaska; Nevada; Arizona; Sonora, Mexico; excellent crystals at Cornwall,

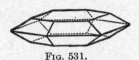

Fig. 531.

Fig. 532.—Chalcocite. Cornwall, England.

England, and Bristol, Connecticut; as an impregnation at Mansfeld, Germany.

Chalcocite is an important ore of copper. See page 415.

The following minerals are isomorphous with argentite and chalcocite: stromeyerite $((Cu, Ag)_2S)$, petzite $((Ag, Au)_2Te)$, and hessite (Ag_2Te).

CINNABAR (*Natural Vermilion*), HgS.

Hexagonal, trigonal trapezohedral class. Extremely small, highly modified crystals; rhombohedral or thick tabular in habit. Trigonal trapezohedral faces are rarely observed. Usually in fine-grained masses, crystalline crusts, or powdery coatings.

Hardness, 2 to 2.5. Specific gravity, 8 to 8.2. Adamantine to dull luster. Extremely high indices of refraction, ω 2.854, ϵ 3.201, (+). In thin plates transparent, otherwise opaque. Color varies with impurities and structure and may be scarlet, brownish red, brown, black, or lead-gray. Scarlet to reddish brown streak. If moistened with HCl and rubbed on clean copper, a silver-white streak is produced.

HgS. May contain bitumen, clay, ferric oxide, and so forth.

Cinnabar is found in veins, disseminated, or in irregular masses in sedimentary rocks, quartzites, trachytes, porphyries, and serpentine. Usual associates are native mercury, pyrite, marcasite, realgar, calcite, stibnite, quartz, and opal. In sandstones at Almaden, Spain; in shales and dolomites at Idria, Italy; Moschellandsberg, Bavaria; excellent crystals in Kweichow, China; Chile; Peru; in serpentine at New Almaden, Altoona, and New Idria, California; Terlinqua, Texas; Pike County, Arkansas.

Cinnabar is the chief source of metallic mercury which is used extensively in commerce, and industry.   See page 423.

Covellite (CuS), an indigo-blue copper mineral, is closely related to cinnabar in composition and crystallization.   Found with other copper minerals.   Other simple sulphides are wurtzite (ZnS), greenockite (CdS), alabandite (MnS), millerite (NiS), and pentlandite ((Fe,Ni)S).

Pyrite-marcasite Groups

These minerals form two isomorphous series, pyrite, cobaltite, and smaltite crystallizing in the cubic system, while marcasite and arsenopyrite possess the symmetry of the orthorhombic bipyramidal class.

PYRITE (*Fool's Gold, Iron Pyrites*), **FeS$_2$.**

Cubic, dyakisdodecahedral class.   Crystals are common, often large. The common forms are the cube, octahedron, and pyritohedron (Figs. 533 and 535); frequently distorted and highly modified.   Crystal faces, especially those of the cube, often show striations conforming to the

Fig. 533.—Pyrite crystals—octahedron, striated cube, cube and octahedron, pyritohedron.

Fig. 534.

symmetry of the dyakisdodecahedral class (Fig. 536).   Penetration twins of pyritohedrons with the twinning plane parallel to a face of the rhombic dodecahedron (Fig. 534) are sometimes called crystals of the "iron cross."   Also massive and disseminated; granular, reniform, botryoidal, stalactitic.   For a discussion of the internal structure of pyrite, see page 162.

Uneven fracture.   Hardness, 6 to 6.5.   Specific gravity, 4.9 to 5.2. Brittle.   Metallic luster.   Opaque.   Pale brassy to golden yellow in color, sometimes with brown or variegated tarnish colors.   Greenish to brownish black streak.

FeS$_2$.   May contain cobalt, nickel, copper, arsenic, and gold in varying accounts.   Decomposes readily, especially in a moist atmosphere. Limonite and goethite are the usual decomposition products, although various sulphates and sulphuric acid sometimes result.   Pseudomorphs of limonite after pyrite are quite common (Fig. 537).   Also see marcasite, page 259.

Pyrite is the most common sulphide mineral and, hence, is found very widely distributed. It occurs in rocks of all ages. Its mode of occurrence varies greatly. Usually associated with other sulphides, such as galena, chalcopyrite, sphalerite, and arsenopyrite; also with calcite, siderite, hematite and magnetite. Commonly found in quartz with

FIG. 535.—Pyrite. Bingham Canyon, Utah.

FIG. 536.—Pyrite. Striated cubes. Leadville, Colorado.

native gold. As nodules and concretions in many slates, sandstones, and coals.

Excellent crystals are found in the Freiberg district, Saxony; Přibram, Bohemia; Schemnitz, Czechoslovakia; enormous deposits carrying gold and silver at Rio Tinto, Spain. In the United States, especially good crystals occur at Franklin Furnace, New Jersey; Central City Mine, Gilpin County, and elsewhere in Colorado; French Creek, Pennsylvania. Large deposits of massive pyrite occur in Virginia, New York, California, Wisconsin, Massachusetts, and Georgia.

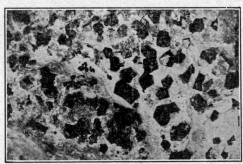

FIG. 537.—Limonite pseudomorphs after pyrite. Harz Mountains, Germany.

Pyrite is used principally as a source of sulphur dioxide in the manufacture of sulphuric acid, and of sulphate of iron, known as *copperas*. Pyrite is also a source of gold. It is *not* a source of iron. Small quantities of pyrite have been used as detectors in radio apparatus. See also page 432.

Cobaltite (*Cobalt Glance*), CoAsS.

Cubic, tetrahedral pentagonal dodecahedral class. Usually as small, well-developed crystals showing either the cube or pyritohedron. Sometimes both in combination. Cube faces striated, as shown in Fig. 536, (page 258). More rarely compact and granular.

Cubical cleavage. Uneven fracture. Brittle. Hardness, 5.5. Specific gravity, 6 to 6.4. Metallic luster. Opaque. Silver-white color, at times with a reddish tinge; grayish if much iron is present. Often with a pink coating of erythrite ($Co_3As_2O_8.8H_2O$). Grayish black streak.

CoAsS. Usually with iron up to 12 per cent.

Generally with other cobalt minerals; also with pyrrhotite, chalcopyrite, pyrite, galena, magnetite. Occurs at Tunaberg, Sweden, Skutterud and Nordmark, Norway; Cornwall, England; Cobalt district, Ontario.

A source of cobalt. See page 414.

Smaltite, CoAs₂.

Cubic, dyakisdodecahedral class. Crystals generally cubic in habit, but rare. Usually massive—compact, granular, lamellar, or fibrous.

Uneven fracture. Brittle. Hardness, 5.5. Specific gravity, 6.4 to 6.6. Metallic luster. Opaque. Tin-white to light steel-gray in color. Tarnishes dull. Often coated with erythrite ($Co_3As_2O_8.8H_2O$). Grayish black streak. Garlic odor when struck with a hammer. Difficult to distinguish by physical properties from chloanthite ($NiAs_2$).

FIG. 538.—Smaltite in veins of calcite (light). Cobalt, Ontario.

CoAs₂. Frequently approximates CoAs₃. Usually with varying amounts of nickel, iron, and sulphur. Iron may amount to 18 per cent., causing higher specific gravity.

Usually with cobalt, nickel, and silver ores; also with native bismuth, barite, siderite, quartz, arsenopyrite. Thus, in the Freiberg district, Saxony; Cornwall, England; Tunaberg, Sweden; La Motte Mine, Missouri; Cobalt district, Ontario (Fig. 538).

An important source of cobalt. See page 414.

Other members of the pyrite group are hauerite (MnS_2), gersdorffite ($NiAsS$), ullmannite ($NiSbS$), chloanthite, $NiAs_2$, and sperrylite ($PtAs_2$)

MARCASITE (*White Iron Pyrites, Spear Pyrites*), FeS₂.

Orthorhombic, bipyramidal class. Crystals usually tabular or short columnar; elongated and striated parallel to *a* axis. Often twinned, resembling cock's combs or spear heads (Figs. 530 and 531). Commonly massive; fine granular, stalactitic, reniform, and globular; often with radial structures.

Hardness, 6 to 6.5. Specific gravity, 4.6 to 4.8. Metallic luster. Pale-brass yellow to steel-gray in color, darker after exposure. Usually lighter in color than pyrite. Streak greenish black.

FeS_2. Contains at times arsenic and copper. Marcasite is formed from acid solutions at temperatures below 450°C., while pyrite has a greater temperature range of formation and may be deposited from either neutral or alkaline

FIG. 540.—Marcasite. Ossegg, Bohemia.

FIG. 539.—Marcasite.   Ossegg, Bohemia.

solutions. Marcasite alters more readily than pyrite, forming limonite and melanterite. Powdered marcasite dissolves in concentrated nitric acid with separation of sulphur, while pyrite does not.

Not so abundant as pyrite. When massive, difficult to distinguish from pyrite. Frequently with pyrite, galena, calcite, fluorite, and sphalerite. Common as concretions in marl, clay, limestone, and coal. In chalk marl at Folkestone, England; Bohemia; Saxony; with sphalerite, galena, and calcite at Joplin, Missouri; Mineral Point, Wisconsin; Galena, Illinois.

Uses same as for pyrite.

ARSENOPYRITE (*Mispickel*), FeAsS.

Orthorhombic, bipyramidal class. Often in disseminated, tabular or short

FIG. 542.—Arsenopyrite.   Freiberg, Saxony.

FIG. 541.

prismatic crystals (Fig. 541). Striated parallel to the *a* axis (Fig. 542). Sometimes twinned. More generally massive—compact, granular, columnar, or radial.

Hardness, 5.5 to 6. Specific gravity, 5.9 to 6.2. Color silver-white to light steel-gray, tarnishing brass yellow or gray. Streak black. Metallic luster.

$FeAsS$. Often contains cobalt, antimony, bismuth, gold, and silver.

Commonly with ores of tin, nickel, cobalt, silver, gold, and lead; also with pyrite, chalcopyrite, and sphalerite. Found at Freiberg, Saxony; in serpentine at Reichenstein, Silesia; Cornwall, England; Tunaberg, Sweden; in dolomite in Binnenthal, Switzerland; in gold-bearing quartz veins at Deloro, Ontario; Franconia, New Hampshire; Floyd and Montgomery counties, Virginia; Washington.

Used principally as a source of white arsenic or arsenious oxide, the arsenic of commerce. If present in paying quantities, gold, silver, and cobalt are recovered. See also page 405.

Other members of the marcasite group are löllingite ($FeAs_2$), glaucodote ((Co,Fe)AsS), safflorite ($CoAs_2$), wolfachite ($Ni(As,S,Sb)_2$), and rammelsbergite ($NiAs_2$).

B. Sulpho Minerals

Most of the important sulpho minerals can be referred to two general formulas:

$$(a)\ M_xR'''S_y \qquad\qquad (b)\ M_xR^VS_y$$

In these formulas, M is principally Cu, Ag, or Pb, while R''' may be ferric iron, arsenic, or antimony. In the second formula, R^V is pentavalent arsenic.

Fig. 543.   Fig. 544.

a. General Formula, $M_xR'''S_y$

Six minerals with these general compositions will be described.

CHALCOPYRITE (*Copper Pyrites, Yellow Copper Ore*), $CuFeS_2$.

Tetragonal, scalenohedral class. Bisphenoidal crystals resembling tetrahedrons and octahedrons, often distorted and difficult to interpret (Figs. 543, 544, and 545). Commonly in compact or disseminated masses (Fig. 546).

Uneven fracture. Hardness, 3.5 to 4. Specific gravity, 4.1 to 4.3. Brass to golden yellow in color. Tarnishes to various blue, purple, and blackish tints; often iridescent. Greenish black streak.

$CuFeS_2$. Contains at times small but valuable amounts of gold and silver; also selenium, thallium, and arsenic.

Most common copper mineral. Usually with pyrite, sphalerite, bornite, galena, tetrahedrite, chalcocite, malachite, azurite, quartz, and calcite. Occurs at Falun, Sweden; Rio Tinto, Spain; Cornwall, England; Sudbury district, Canada; Chile; Butte district, Montana; Bingham, Utah; Bisbee, Arizona; Ducktown, Tennessee; California; French Creek, Pennsylvania.

A very important ore of copper. See page 415.

FIG. 545.—Chalcopyrite. French Creek, Chester County, Pennsylvania.　　　FIG. 546.—Chalcopyrite (dark) with quartz. Bruce Mine, Canada.

BORNITE (*Purple Copper Ore, Horse Flesh Ore*), Cu_5FeS_4.

Cubic, hexoctahedral class. Cubic and rhombic dodecahedral crystals; very rare. Commonly in compact and granular masses.

Uneven fracture. Hardness, 3. Specific gravity, 4.9 to 5.2. Metallic luster. Color on fresh fracture surface is between bronze and copper red, tarnishing readily and showing brilliant peacock colors. Streak gray black.

Cu_5FeS_4. Frequently contains small amounts of gold and silver.

Occurs with chalcopyrite, chalcocite, enargite, and other copper minerals; also with cassiterite, pyrite, and siderite. Not very common in Europe. Good crystals at Cornwall, England, and Bristol, Connecticut. In large quantities in the Butte district, Montana; Virginia; North Carolina; Acton, Canada; Chile; Peru; Bolivia.

An important copper ore. See page 415.

Proustite (*Light-ruby Silver Ore, Light-red Silver Ore*), Ag_3AsS_3.

Hexagonal, ditrigonal pyramidal class. Crystals often small, highly modified, and difficult to interpret. Hemimorphic development sometimes distinct. Generally massive—disseminated, in crusts or bands.

Conchoidal fracture. Hardness, 2.5. Specific gravity, 5.5. Brilliant adamantine to dull luster. Translucent to transparent. Color and streak scarlet to vermilion.

Ag_3AsS_3. At times contains some antimony.

Occurs with pyrargyrite in veins with other silver minerals, galena, and calcite. Occurs at Freiberg, Saxony; Joachimsthal, Bohemia; Chañarcillo, Chile; Guanajuato, Mexico; Peru; Cobalt, Canada; various places in Colorado; Nevada; Idaho; Arizona.

An ore of silver. See page 429.

Pyrargyrite (*Dark-ruby Silver Ore, Dark-red Silver Ore*), Ag_3SbS_3.

Hexagonal, ditrigonal pyramidal class. Crystals resemble those of proustite; rare. Usually massive—compact, disseminated, crusts or bands.

Conchoidal fracture. Hardness, 2.5 to 3. Specific gravity, 5.8. Metallic adamantine luster. Dark red to lead gray in color; thin splinters in transmitted light are deep red. Cherry- to purple-red streak.

Ag_3SbS_3. Usually contains a little arsenic.

Occurrence similar to that of proustite but more abundant. Found in veins with other silver ores, calcite, and galena. Thus, in the Freiberg district, Saxony; Přibram, Bohemia; Guanajuato and Sonora, Mexico; Chile; Colorado; Nevada; Arizona; Cobalt, Ontario.

An important ore of silver. See page 429.

Bournonite (*Cog Wheel Ore*), $PbCuSbS_3$.

Orthorhombic, bipyramidal class. Thick tabular and prismatic crystals (Fig. 547). Frequently twinned, forming *cross* or *cogwheel* crystals (Fig. 548). Also in compact and granular masses.

Fig. 547.—Bournonite. Přibram, Bohemia.

Fig. 548.—Bournonite (cogwheel ore) and sphalerite. Kapnik, Rumania.

Hardness, 2.5 to 3. Specific gravity, 5.7 to 5.9. On fresh fracture, surface greasy. Metallic luster; crystals are sometimes dull. Steel gray to iron black in color. Dark-gray to black streak.

$PbCuSbS_3$.   Usually contains some arsenic.

Occurs in veins with galena, sphalerite, stibnite, chalcopyrite, tetrahedrite, siderite, and chalcocite at Freiberg, Saxony; Přibram, Bohemia; Kapnik, Rumania; Mexico; Chile; Boliva; excellent large crystals at Park City, Utah; Yavapai County, Arizona; Montgomery County, Arkansas.

An ore of copper and lead.   See pages 415 and 419.

The following minerals also belong to this group: miargyrite, $AgSbS_2$; jamesonite, $Pb_2Sb_2S_5$; stephanite, Ag_5SbS_4; pearceite, $(Ag, Cu)_{16}As_2S_{11}$; polybasite, $(Ag, Cu)_9SbS_6$.

TETRAHEDRITE (*Gray Copper Ore*), $M'_3R'''S_3$.

Cubic, hextetrahedral class.   Excellent crystals showing tetrahedral development (Figs. 549, 550, and 551), often highly modified.   Commonly massive—compact, granular, disseminated.

Fig. 549.   Fig. 550.   Fig. 551.—Tetrahedrite with quartz.   Kapnik, Rumania.

Uneven fracture.   Hardness, 3 to 4.   Specific gravity, 4.3 to 5.4. Metallic luster, sometimes dull.   Opaque.   Steel-gray to iron-black color, often with tarnish colors.   At times coated with chalcopyrite or sphalerite.   Streak black, or reddish brown.

Composition varies greatly. M' is usually copper; lead, silver, mercury, iron, or zinc may be present. R''' indicates antimony or arsenic.   An excess of sulphur is usually observed.   The following varieties are often differentiated—cupriferous and arsenical, *tennantite;* argentiferous, *freibergite;* mercurial, *schwatzite.*

Occurs commonly in veins with chalcopyrite, sphalerite, galena, bournonite, pyrite, quartz, siderite, and barite.   Found at Freiberg, Saxony; Clausthal, Harz Mountains, Germany; Přibram, Bohemia; Kapnik, Rumania; Mexico; Chile; Peru; Bolivia; excellent crystals at Bingham, Utah; many places in Colorado, Montana, Nevada, and Arizona.

An important ore of copper and silver.   See pages 415 and 429.

b. General Formula, $M_xR^vS_y$.

Only one mineral with a composition conforming to the above formula is sufficiently common to warrant a description.

Enargite, Cu₃AsS₄.

Orthorhombic, bipyramidal class. Small, prismatic crystals, vertically striated; rare. Usually in compact, granular, or columnar masses.

Perfect prismatic cleavage. Uneven fracture. Hardness, 3. Specific gravity, 4.4. Submetallic luster. Grayish black to iron black in color. In artificial light resembles sphalerite. Streak black. Opaque.

Cu_3AsS_4. May contain some iron, zinc, and antimony.

In veins with other copper minerals, such as chalcopyrite, bornite, chalcocite, tetrahedrite, also pyrite. Not common in Europe. More extensive in Peru; Argentina; Chile; Bolivia; Mexico; Island of Luzon, Philippines; in large quantities in the copper mines at Butte, Montana; also in San Juan Mountains, Colorado; Tintic district, Utah.

An important ore of copper. Also a source of arsenious oxide. See page 415.

III. OXIDES AND HYDROXIDES

Aside from water, 13 minerals of this group will be described.

A. OXIDES

WATER	H_2O	Hexagonal
QUARTZ	SiO_2	Hexagonal

Rutile Group

RUTILE	TiO_2	Tetragonal
CASSITERITE	SnO_2	Tetragonal

PYROLUSITE	MnO_2	
Zincite	ZnO	Hexagonal

Hematite Group

CORUNDUM	Al_2O_3	Hexagonal
HEMATITE	Fe_2O_3	Hexagonal
Ilmenite	$FeTiO_3$	Hexagonal

CUPRITE	Cu_2O	Cubic

B. HYDROXIDES

OPAL	$SiO_2.nH_2O$	Amorphous
MANGANITE	$Mn_2O_3.H_2O$	Orthorhombic
BAUXITE	$Al_2O_3.2H_2O$	
LIMONITE	$Fe_2O_3.nH_2O$	

A. Oxides

Many of these minerals are very common and of great economic importance.

WATER (*Snow, Ice*), H_2O.

Above 0°C., water is a liquid, hence, amorphous. It is almost colorless, but, in large quantities and when pure, it has a bluish tinge. Specific gravity, when pure, at 4°C. and 760 mm. barometric pressure is 1; that of ocean water may be as high as 1.028. When pure, it is without taste or odor. $n = 1.333$.

Water occurs very widely distributed in nature and is an important agency in the disintegration, decomposition, transportation, and formation of minerals. Nearly all minerals are more or less soluble in water, especially if it contains carbon dioxide, humus acid, hydrochloric acid, or oxygen in solution. The ocean water contains about 3.4 per cent. of solid matter in solution. Over 30 elements are found in ocean water, and, hence, water is frequently called the universal solvent. When water freezes, it expands, the increase in volume being about 9 to 10 per

cent. and the pressure exerted about 138 tons per square foot.   Due to
this enormous pressure, freezing water is a most important geological
agency, causing the widening of cracks and crevices, thereby extending
the zone of activity of water and oxygen and has-
tening weathering and disintegration.

On freezing, water forms snow or ice. Snow
crystals are often very beautiful. They are tabular and hexagonal in outline (Fig. 552) and show
great diversity in development. Lake or stream
ice consists of crystals arranged in a definite
manner, the *c* axes being perpendicular to the
extent of the sheet of ice. In glacier ice, however,
the ice particles do not possess a definite orientation.

Fig. 552.—Snow crystal.
(*After Bentley.*)

QUARTZ, SiO$_2$.

Hexagonal, trigonal trapezohedral class (below 573°C.).   Crystals are
very common.   They usually consist of an hexagonal prism, which predominates, terminated by faces of a positive and negative rhombohedron
so developed as to simulate the hexagonal bipyramid of the first order.
The pyramid habit is less frequent.   The prism faces are generally
horizontally striated.   Crystals are sometimes bent, twisted, or greatly
distorted.   Quartz forms right- and left-handed crystals, which are easily

Fig. 553.—Quartz crystals—pyramidal, prismatic, long prismatic, tabular, skeletal.

recognized when faces of the trigonal trapezohedron are present (Fig. 554
left, Fig. 555 right).   Twins are common.   Figure 556 illustrates the
common or Dauphiné law, the vertical axis being the twinning axis.
Here two right- or left-handed crystals interpenetrate so that the positive
rhombohedron of the one individual coincides with the negative of the
other, the *c* axis being the twinning axis.

Crystals twinned according to the Brazilian law (Fig. 557) consist of
a right- and a left-handed individual of the same sign so interpenetrated
that the twinned crystals are symmetrical to planes parallel to faces of
the prism of the second order.   Twins according to several other laws are
not uncommon.   Crystals sometimes show a skeletal development
(Fig. 558).

At times, crystals contain scales of mica or hematite distributed in a regular manner, so that they may be separated into sections or layers. Such crystals are called *cap quartz*. Parallel growths called *scepter quartz* (Fig. 559) are also observed. Although quartz is commonl found in distinct crystals, it also occurs in a great variety of massive forms.

According to Wright and Larsen, there are two modifications of quartz. One of these modifications, α quartz, is formed below 573°C. and crystal-

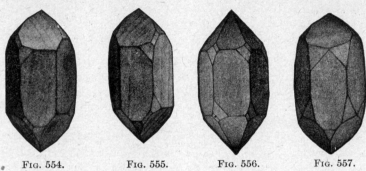

FIG. 554.   FIG. 555.   FIG. 556.   FIG. 557.

lizes in the trigonal trapezohedral class of the hexagonal system. This modification is the more common. It occurs in veins and geodes, and in some pegmatites, and is here described in detail. The second modification is called β quartz and is formed at temperatures between 573° and 870°C. β quartz crystallizes in the hexagonal trapezohedral class. It is found in granites and porphyries and in some pegmatites. These modifications are sometimes termed *low* and *high* quartz, respectively.

FIG. 558.—Skeletal quartz. Paris, Maine.

FIG. 559.—Scepter quartz with phantom. Mursink, Ural Mountains.

Indistinct rhombohedral cleavage. Conchoidal fracture. Hardness, 7. Specific gravity, 2.65. Vitreous luster. ω 1.544, ϵ 1.553, $(+)$. Transparent to opaque. Commonly colorless or white, also yellow, red, pink, amethystine, green, blue, brown, and black. Many colors disappear on heating. Streak white. Some varieties may show luminescence. Exhibits pyroelectric and piezoelectric properties (see pages 109 and 110).

SiO₂. Often contains inclusions of rutile, hematite, chlorite, mica, and liquid and gaseous carbon dioxide. Not attacked by the common acids and infusible before the blowpipe. Common as a pseudomorph after fluorite, calcite, siderite, and wood.

The many varieties of quartz are most conveniently classified as (a) *crystalline*, (b) *cryptocrystalline*, and (c) *clastic*.

a. Crystalline varieties are vitreous, either crystals or crystalline masses, and but slightly acted upon by potassium hydroxide.

1. *Rock Crystal.*—Colorless quartz. Excellent crystals are common (Fig. 560).

2. *Amethyst.*—Various shades of purple or violet.

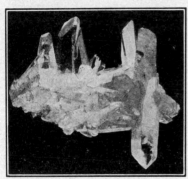

FIG. 560.—Quartz. Dauphiné, France.

FIG. 561.—Smoky quartz with muscovite. Paris, Maine.

3. *Rose Quartz.*—Pink to rose red in color, becoming paler on exposure to light. Usually massive.

4. *Smoky Quartz.*—Smoky yellow to dark brown. Often called *cairngorm stone* (Fig. 561).

5. *Milky Quartz.*—Milk white in color. Translucent or nearly opaque. Often with a greasy luster.

6. *Yellow Quartz.*—Light yellow in color, often called *false topaz*, *Spanish topaz*, or *citrine*.

7. *Aventurine.*—Contains glistening scales of mica or hematite.

8. *Ferruginous Quartz.*—Brown or red in color, due to the presence of either limonite or hematite.

9. *Rutilated Quartz.*—Contains fine inter-lacing needles of rutile.

FIG. 562.—Chalcedony (stalactitic). Havana, Cuba.

10. *Cat's-eye.*—Grayish or brownish, with an opalescence due to inclusions of fibers or to a fibrous structure.

11. *Tiger's-eye.*—Yellow brownish in color. Pseudomorphous after crocidolite. Pronounced chatoyant luster.

b. Cryptocrystalline varieties are compact and under the microscope show a crystalline structure. More readily acted upon by potassium hydroxide than the crystalline varieties.

FIG. 563.—Agate.　South America.

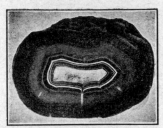

FIG. 564.—Agate.　Brazil.

1. *Chalcedony.*—A transparent to translucent variety having a waxy luster. Commonly stalactitic (Fig. 562), botryoidal, concretionary, and lining cavities. White, grayish, brown, blue, and black in color.

FIG. 565.—Moss agate.

FIG. 566.—Banded agate.

2. *Carnelian or Sard.*—Commonly reddish chalcedony.

3. *Chrysoprase.*—Apple-green chalcedony.

4. *Heliotrope.*—Bright or dark green chalcedony with small spots of red jasper resembling drops of blood. It is often called *bloodstone*.

FIG. 567.—Agate with onyx in center.

FIG. 568.—Agate—cameo.

5. *Agate.*—This is chalcedony made up of strata or bands indicating successive stages of deposition. The layers may be differently colored or clouded, giving rise to several varieties, such as *banded* and *clouded* agates. *Moss agate* contains visible inclusions, frequently dendritic or mosslike (Fig. 565).

The banding is usually in parallel but more or less wavy or irregular lines (Figs. 563, 564, and 566). Agates may be white, pale to dark brown, or bluish in color. They are frequently colored artificially.

6. *Onyx.*—Banded agate with the bands or layers in parallel straight lines, corresponding to layers in even planes (Fig. 567). Onyx is used for cameos (Fig. 568).

7. *Jasper.*—Opaque, and red, yellow, and grayish in color.

8. *Flint.*—Gray, smoky brown, or brownish black in color. Commonly in nodules with a white coating (Fig. 569). Translucent. Prominent conchoidal fracture.

9. *Chert.*—Includes varieties with a hornlike appearance, also impure flints and jaspers.

c. Clastic varieties of quartz include many of the siliceous fragmental rocks. In some cases, the individual particles are no longer distinct.

1. *Sand.*—Loose, unconsolidated grains or fragments of quartz.

2. *Sandstone.*—Consolidated sand. The cementing material may be silica, iron oxide, calcium carbonate, or clay. Occurs in a great variety of colors.

3. *Itacolumite.*—A flexible sandstone. Contains some mica.

4. *Quartzite or Granular Quartz.*—Metamorphosed sandstone in which the cement was silica. The individual quartz particles are generally not easily recognized by the naked eye.

Fig. 569.—Flint. Dover Cliffs, England.

Next to water, quartz is the most common of all oxides. It is a very important rock-forming mineral, being a constituent of many igneous and sedimentary rocks. It occurs in rocks of all ages and in many ore deposits. It is also found very abundantly as sand and gravel.

Rock crystal, amethyst, smoky and rose quartz, aventurine, cat's-eye, tiger's-eye, chalcedony, agate, and jasper are used extensively in jewelry and for ornamental purposes; agate and chalcedony for mortars and pestles; rock crystal for dishes, vases, optical instruments, spectacles, and chemical and radio apparatus; sand for mortar, plaster, and glass; sandstone and quartzite for building and paving purposes and grindstones; and ground or crushed quartz and flint in wood fillers, pottery, scouring and polishing soaps, and as an abrasive. Large quantities of quartz are also used as a flux in metallurgical processes and in the manufacture of refractories. See also page 429.

Rutile Group

This group contains the two common oxides of titanium and tin which crystallize in the tetragonal system.

RUTILE, TiO$_2$.

Tetragonal, ditetragonal bipyramidal class. Crystals are common. Usually prismatic or thick columnar, consisting of the prisms and bipyramids of the first and second orders (Fig. 570). Prism faces frequently striated vertically (Fig. 571a). Knee-shaped twins often observed, the twinning plane being parallel to a face of the bipyramid of the second order (Fig. 571b). Also trillings, sixlings, and eightlings (rosettes) according to this law (Fig. 571c). Also in compact, granular masses. Needle-like crystals of rutile occur frequently as inclusions in quartz.

Fig. 570.—Rutile. Georgia.

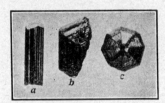

Fig. 571.—Rutile crystals—(a) prismatic and striated, (b) knee-shaped, (c) rosette (eightling).

Distinct prismatic and pyramidal cleavages. Hardness, 6 to 6.5. Specific gravity, 4.2 to 4.3. Metallic adamantine luster. Very high indices of refraction and extremely strong double refraction; ω 2.616, ϵ 2.903, (+). Opaque to transparent. Red brown, blood-red, and black in color. Streak yellow or pale brown.

TiO$_2$. Sometimes written TiTiO$_4$. Usually contains considerable iron. Occurs pseudomorphous after hematite, brookite, and anatase.

Rutile is the most common titanium mineral and occurs in gneiss, mica schist, granite, granular limestone, and dolomite. Commonly associated with quartz, hematite, and feldspar. Found at Arendal and Kragero, Norway; the Ural Mountains; Binnenthal and Saint Gotthard district, Switzerland; Nelson County, Virginia; Graves Mountain, Georgia; Magnet Cove, Arkansas. Occurs also in secondary deposits; thus, at Pablo Beach, Florida, in quartz, ilmenite, and zircon sand.

Used in coloring porcelain yellow and artificial teeth bluish white; also in special grades of steel and copper-bearing alloys; as a mordant in dyeing leather, and in carbons for arc lights. Also see page 433.

CASSITERITE (*Tin Stone*), SnO$_2$.

Tetragonal, ditetragonal bipyramidal class. Crystals are usually short prismatic, showing the prisms and bipyramids of the first and second orders. Knee-shaped twins are common, the bipyramid of the second order being the twinning plane. Frequently in disseminated granular, or reniform masses; also in grains and pebbles. Concentric and fibrous radial structure is frequently observed.

Hardness, 6 to 7. Specific gravity, 6.8 to 7. Adamantine to sub-metallic luster. High indices of refraction, ω 1.997, ϵ 2.093, (+). Reddish brown, brown, black; also yellow or white. Streak white to pale brown.

Three varieties may be distinguished:

1. *Ordinary Cassiterite or Tin Stone.*—Crystals and compact masses.

2. *Wood Tin.*—Botryoidal and reniform masses of varying colors, with concentric structure and commonly with a radial fibrous structure.

3. *Stream Tin.*—Angular and rounded grains or pebbles in sands and gravels of streams.

SnO_2. Sometimes written $SnSnO_4$. Generally contains iron. Infusible and insoluble in acids.

Cassiterite is commonly associated with quartz, topaz, fluorite (Fig. 572), apatite, and tourmaline. It occurs usually in veins cutting granites and rhyolites, which have gener-ally been greatly altered as the result of pneumatolytic action. Granitic rocks altered in this way are called *greisen,* while nongranitic rocks are termed *zwitter.* On account of its great resistance to weather-ing, cassiterite is also found extensively in secondary deposits. The Malay Pen-insula, the islands of Banca and Billiton near Borneo, Bolivia, China, Nigeria, and Siam are the chief producers of cassiterite.

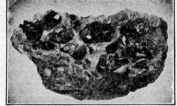

FIG. 572.—Cassiterite with fluorite. Saxony.

Other localities are Cornwall, England; Altenberg, Saxony; Buck Creek, Alaska; Black Hills, South Dakota; Gaffney, South Carolina; King's Mountain, North Carolina; El Paso, Texas.

Cassiterite is the only source of tin of commerce and industry. It is used extensively in the manufacture of tin plate or sheet tin (sheet iron or steel dipped in molten tin), solder, bronze, tin amalgam, gun metal, type metal, speculum metal, britannia metals, and pewter. Sodium stannate is used in calico printing. The artificial oxide is used as a polishing powder. Also see page 433.

PYROLUSITE (*Black Oxide of Manganese*), MnO_2.

Prismatic and needle-like, pseudomorphous after manganite; gen-erally compact, fibrous, columnar, stalactitic, dendritic, or powdery crusts (Fig. 573).

Hardness, 1 to 2.5; soils the fingers. Specific gravity, 4.8. Black or dark steel-gray in color. Black or bluish black streak. Metallic to dull luster. Opaque.

MnO_2. Usually contains small amounts of water and silica.

Pyrolusite is a secondary mineral resulting from the decomposition of manganite, rhodochrosite, and various manganiferous iron ores. Usually found with manganite, psilomelane, hematite, or limonite.

Occurs extensively in Thuringia and in the Harz Mountains, Germany; Bohemia; France; Brazil; Russia; Hungary; Cuba. The principal localities in the United States are the Crimora district, Augusta County, Virginia; Cave Spring and Cartersville, Georgia; Batesville, Arkansas; Livermore, Alameda County, California; Brandon, Vermont.

Fig. 573.—Pyrolusite. Ilfeld, Thuringia, Germany.

Pyrolusite is used in the manufacture of chlorine, oxygen, ferromanganese, manganese bronze, and spiegeleisen; as a coloring agent in calico printing and dyeing, glass, pottery, bricks, and paints; also as a decolorizer of green glass, and in dry batteries. Spiegeleisen is of great importance in the metallurgy of iron and steel. Also see page 422.

Zincite (*Red Zinc Ore*), ZnO.

Hexagonal, dihexagonal pyramidal class. Crystals are hemimorphic and consist of prisms, upper pyramid, and lower basal pinacoid. Natural crystals are very rare. Usually as compact, granular, or foliated masses (Fig. 574).

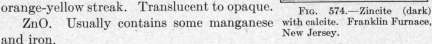

Perfect basal cleavage. Hardness, 4 to 4.5. Specific gravity, 5.4 to 5.7. Subadamantine to vitreous luster. High indices of refraction, ω 2.008, ϵ 2.029, (+). Dark red to orange or yellow in color. Reddish to orange-yellow streak. Translucent to opaque.

Fig. 574.—Zincite (dark) with calcite. Franklin Furnace, New Jersey.

ZnO. Usually contains some manganese and iron.

Occurs extensively at Franklin Furnace, Sussex County, New Jersey, in metamorphic limestones associated with franklinite, rhodonite, willemite, sphalerite, rhodochrosite, and calcite. Also in Schneeberg, Saxony; Tuscany; Poland.

An ore of zinc. It has been used for detectors in wireless apparatus. See page 436.

Hematite Group

This group includes the isomorphous minerals corundum, hematite, and ilmenite. These are sesquioxides of aluminum, iron, and titanium. They crystallize in the hexagonal system. Hematite is a very important economic mineral.

CORUNDUM (*Sapphire, Ruby, Emery*), Al_2O_3.

Hexagonal, ditrigonal scalenohedral class. Well-developed crystals are common and often rather large. The habit may be pyramidal, rhombohedral, prismatic, or tabular (Figs. 575 and 576). The most common forms are the prism of the second order, unit rhombohedron, bipyramid of the second order, and the basal pinacoid. Large crystals are sometimes rough or rounded, barrel shaped, and deeply furrowed or striated. Penetration and polysynthetic twins are common, the twinning being parallel to the unit rhombohedron. The basal pinacoid often shows triangular striations. Occurs also in compact, granular, and lamellar masses, showing frequently a nearly rectangular parting or pseudocleavage.

Fig. 575.—Corundum crystals —tabular, prismatic, pyramidal, long prismatic.

Fig. 576.—Corundum: variety, sapphire. Ceylon.

Basal and nearly rectangular rhombohedral partings. Conchoidal fracture. Hardness, 9. Specific gravity, 3.9 to 4.1. Commonly gray, brown, and bluish; also red, blue, yellow, and colorless. Sometimes multicolored. Transparent to translucent. Vitreous luster. ω 1.768, ϵ 1.760, ($-$). Luminescence is sometimes observed, especially on the gem varieties.

Al_2O_3. Crystals are usually quite pure. Small amounts of ferric oxide may be present as a pigment. Emery is generally quite impure.

Several varieties of corundum may be distinguished.

1. *Ruby.*—This is the transparent deep-red variety. It is highly prized as a gem.

2. *Sapphire.*—The sapphire proper is a transparent blue corundum. Transparent stones of other colors are called *yellow, golden,* or *white sapphires,* and so on. Sometimes the following terms are also used: when green, *oriental emerald;* yellow, *oriental topaz;* violet, *oriental amethyst.* Sapphires are used for gem purposes.

3. *Common Corundum.*—This includes crystals and compact masses with dull and irregularly distributed colors.

4. *Emery.*—This is an intimate mixture of corundum, magnetite, hematite, quartz, and spinel. Dark gray to black in color. It was first considered an iron ore. The admixture may be as high as 40 per cent. The hardness may be considerably lower than that of the other varieties, namely, 7 to 9.

Corundum usually occurs disseminated in crystalline limestone and dolomite (Fig. 577), gneiss, mica schist, chlorite schist, nepheline syenite, granite, and other crystalline rocks. It is commonly associated with magnetite, mica, chlorite, nephelite, serpentine, and spinel.

The gem varieties are found principally in placer deposits in Ceylon, Burma, Kashmir (Northern India), Siam, China, Queensland, Ural Moun-

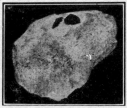

FIG. 577.—Corundum: variety, ruby. India.

tains, and near Helena, Montana. Rubies and sapphires are highly prized as gems. They are produced artificially in large quantities. Many of these synthetic corundums possess superior colors, and when small are often extremely difficult to distinguish from the natural stones (see page 401).

Common corundum is found in extensive deposits associated with peridotite in North and South Carolina and in Georgia; at Raglan and elsewhere in Renfrew County, Ontario, in nepheline syenite; also in Westchester County, New York; Chester County, Pennsylvania; and Chester, Massachusetts. Russia, Madagascar, India, and the Union of South Africa furnish most of the corundum used in industry.

Most of the world's supply of emery is obtained from the islands of Naxos and Samos in the Grecian archipelago and from Asia Minor. On Naxos and Samos it occurs in crystalline limestones and schists. It is also found in the Ural Mountains; Saxony; associated with chlorite and margarite in amphibolite schist at Chester, Massachusetts; in peridotite at Peekskill, New York. Pittsylvania County, Virginia, and Peekskill, New York, are the most important American producers of emery.

Ruby and sapphire are used extensively for gem purposes and as jewels in watches and various scientific instruments. Common corundum and emery, as well as artificial Al_2O_3, are important abrasive materials. Artificial Al_2O_3 is sold as *alundum, aloxite, exolon,* and *lionite* (see page 402).

HEMATITE (*Specularite, Specular Iron Ore, Red Iron Ore*), Fe_2O_3.

Hexagonal, ditrigonal scalenohedral class. Crystals are either thin or thick tabular, pyramidal, rhombohedral, or, more rarely, prismatic in habit (Figs. 578 and 579). Tabular crystals are often arranged in rosettes and are then called *iron roses.* The basal pinacoid is frequently striated, due to polysynthetic twinning. Occurs more abundantly in compact, granular (Fig. 580), columnar, fibrous, botryoidal (Fig. 581), reniform, stalactitic, micaceous (Fig. 582), oölitic, and earthy masses.

No cleavage, but a rhombohedral parting which is nearly cubical is sometimes observed. Conchoidal to uneven fracture. Hardness, 5.5 to 6.5; earthy varieties are very soft. Specific gravity, 4.9 to 5.3. Metallic, splendent, or dull luster. Opaque, except in very thin scales. Commonly steel gray, reddish brown, or iron black in color; sometimes with beautiful tarnish colors. Earthy varieties are red in color. Cherry-red or reddish brown streak. Sometimes slightly magnetic, due to the presence of a small amount of magnetite.

Fe_2O_3. May contain as much as 7 per cent. of titanium dioxide; also ferrous oxide, magnesium oxide, phosphoric acid, silica, and clay.

FIG. 578.   FIG. 579.—Hematite. Island of   FIG. 580.—Specular hematite.
                              Elba.   Lake Superior district.

Infusible. Becomes magnetic when heated on charcoal. When powdered, it is slowly soluble in acids. Occurs as a pseudomorph after calcite, siderite, pyrite, and magnetite.

There are several varieties of hematite.

1. *Specularite or Specular Iron Ore.*—This includes crystals, micaceous, and granular masses with a metallic or splendent luster (Figs. 580 and 582). Usually steel gray or iron black in color.

2. *Compact or Red Hematite.*—Compact masses, often with a radial fibrous structure. Submetallic to dull luster. Iron black or brownish red in color.

3. *Kidney Ore.*—Reniform masses, usually with smooth, shiny surfaces (Fig. 581).

4. *Red Ocher.*—This includes earthy varieties, which are very soft and have a dull luster. Often contains considerable clay or sand.

5. *Argillaceous Hematite.*—Hard and compact varieties, which are generally quite impure due to admixtures of much clay, sand, or jasper. Brownish black, reddish brown, or red in color.

6. *Oölitic or Fossil Iron Ore.*—This variety possesses an oölitic structure and frequently contains fossil remains.

7. *Martite.*—Hematite occurring in octahedrons, pseudomorphous after magnetite.

Hematite is the most important iron ore. It occurs (*a*) in independent deposits, sometimes of great thickness and extent; (*b*) as an accessory mineral in many igneous rocks, such as granite and syenite; (*c*) in cracks and crevices, usually with quartz; (*d*) as an inclusion in many minerals; thus, in feldspar, quartz, and carnallite; (*e*) as a sublimation product in lavas; thus, on Vesuvius and Etna; (*f*) sometimes it is the result of contact metamorphism.

Excellent crystals are found on the island of Elba, in the Mediterranean Sea; the Saint Gotthard district, Switzerland (iron roses); Arendal, Norway; Långban and Nordmark, Sweden; Cumberland, England.

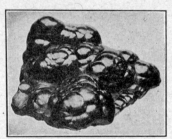

FIG. 581.—Hematite (kidney ore).
Cumberland, England.

FIG. 582.—Micaceous hematite.
Lake Superior district.

Enormous deposits of hematite occur in the rocks, chiefly of Huronian and Archean ages, in the Lake Superior region of northern Michigan, Minnesota, Wisconsin, and Canada. There are six well-defined iron ranges or districts in this region, *viz.; Marquette* in Michigan; *Menominee* and *Gogebic* in Michigan and Wisconsin; *Mesabi* and *Vermilion* in Minnesota; *Michipicoten* in Ontario, Canada. This region has produced about 55,000,000 long tons of iron ore annually, of which the greater part is mined by steam shovels operating in huge open pits. This ore includes both the hard and soft varieties. Oölitic or fossiliferous hematite occurs at Clinton, New York; and in large quantities in eastern Tennessee and northern Alabama. Birmingham, Alabama, is the center of an important district, which has furnished about 7,000,000 long tons annually. Important deposits of hematite also occur in Missouri, Wyoming, and Pennsylvania.

Hematite is the chief source of the iron of commerce and industry. About 95 per cent. of the iron ore mined annually is hematite. See also page 417.

Ilmenite (*Menaccanite, Titanic Iron Ore*), **$FeTiO_3$.**

Hexagonal, trigonal rhombohedral class. Crystals are tabular or rhombohedral in habit and resemble those of hematite. Occasionally rhombohedrons of the second and third orders are present. Generally in compact or granular masses, also in thin plates or disseminated grains, or as pebbles or sand.

No cleavage, but basal and rhombohedral partings. Conchoidal to uneven fracture. Hardness, 5 to 6. Specific gravity, 4.3 to 5.5. Iron to brownish black in color. Black to brownish red streak. Metallic to submetallic luster. Opaque; thin plates are brown in transmitted light. Slightly magnetic, greatly increased by heating.

$FeTiO_3$. Magnesium or manganese may replace some of the iron. Infusible. Yields a blue or violet solution after fusion with sodium carbonate and subsequent boiling with hydrochloric acid and tin foil.

As an accessory mineral it is common in many igneous and metamorphic rocks, such as granite, syenite, diorite, diabase, gneiss, and mica schist. Also found in large quantities in black sand; thus at Pablo Beach, Florida. Common associates are hematite, magnetite, apatite, serpentine, titanite, rutile, and quartz. Some localities are Kragerö, Snarum, and elsewhere, Norway; various places in Sweden; the Saint Gotthard district and Binnenthal, Switzerland; Province of Quebec, Canada; Orange County, New York; Magnet Cove, Arkansas.

It is used in the preparation of linings for puddling furnaces and in making ferrotitanium. On account of the difficulty in reducing it, ilmenite is not used to any extent as an ore of iron. Also see page 433.

Fig. 583.—Cuprite (cubes). Bisbee, Arizona.

CUPRITE (*Ruby Copper Ore*), **Cu_2O.**

Cubic, hexoctahedral class. Crystals are common, consisting usually of the cube (Fig. 583), octahedron, and rhombic dodecahedron, often in combination. Also, compact, granular, and earthy massive; fine slender aggregates are called *chalcotrichite* or *plush copper.*

Hardness, 3.5 to 4. Specific gravity, 5.7 to 6.1. Metallic adamantine to dull luster. Very high index of refraction, $n = 2.849$. Ruby red to almost black in color. Transparent to opaque. Brownish red to dirty brown streak.

Cu_2O. Usually quite pure. Alters readily to malachite, azurite, tenorite, and native copper. Pseudomorphs of malachite after cuprite are rather common.

Cuprite is a secondary mineral, resulting from the oxidation of various copper minerals. Commonly found with malachite, azurite, native copper, chrysocolla, limonite, and chalcopyrite.

At Chessy, France, it occurs in crystals, partially or completely altered to malachite; also found at Cornwall, England; Dobschau, Hungary; Chile; Peru; Bolivia; the Ural Mountains. Abundant with other copper ores at Bisbee, Clifton, and Morenci, Arizona; with native copper in the Lake Superior Copper district.

An important ore of copper.

B. Hydroxides

Only the four most important hydroxides will be described. These minerals are generally of secondary origin.

OPAL, $SiO_2.nH_2O$.

Amorphous. Usually compact, in veins or irregular masses, sometimes with botryoidal, reniform, stalactitic, or earthy structure.

Conchoidal fracture. Hardness, 5.5 to 6.5; earthy varieties may seem as low as 1. Specific gravity, 1.95 to 2.3. Vitreous, dull, or greasy luster. Index of refraction varies from 1.44 to 1.46. Transparent to opaque. Streak white. Color varies greatly; colorless, white, yellow, brown, red, green, gray, blue, and so forth. Often a beautiful play of colors may be observed. This is due to fine cracks filled with material possessing a slightly different index of refraction than the original substance and perhaps also to an unequal distribution of the water content. Some opaque opals show an opalescence, especially after immersion in H_2O. Luminescence is sometimes observed.

$SiO_2.nH_2O$. The amount of water present may vary from 1 to 21 per cent. but is usually between 3 and 13 per cent. Many opals are to be considered as dried and hardened gelatinous silica. Yields water when heated in a closed tube. Infusible. Soluble in hot caustic potash or soda.

The principal varieties of opal include

1. *Precious Opal.*—Yellowish white, dark gray, or bluish, with an excellent play of colors. Those with the lighter colors are called *white opals,* while the dark gray and blue opals are designated as *black opals.*

2. *Fire Opal.*—Orange yellow to red in color. Semitransparent.

3. *Common Opal.*—Translucent to opaque and shows many colors. When milk white, yellowish, bluish, or greenish it is called *milk opal.* With a resinous luster and wax, honey or other yellow in color, it is *resin opal.* Wood petrified by opaline material is called *wood opal*

(Fig. 584). *Opal jasper* is red, reddish brown, or yellow brown in color, with a resinous luster, and resembles jasper.

4. *Hyalite.*—Colorless and transparent masses of irregular outline. Looks like drops of melted glass (Fig. 585). Sometimes luminescent.

5. *Siliceous Sinter, Geyserite.*—These are opaline deposits from hot springs and geysers. May be porous, compact, fibrous, stalactitic, or botryoidal (Fig. 586) with a development like cauliflower; grayish, whitish, or brownish in color; sometimes with a pearly luster.

6. *Tripolite, Diatomaceous or Infusorial Earth.*—Porous, earthy, and chalk-like deposits of the siliceous remains of diatoms, radiolaria, and so forth. Light in weight.

Opal is commonly the result of the decomposition of silicate rocks and is hence frequently found in cracks and cavities in igneous and

| FIG. 584.—Wood opal. Storlein, Hungary. | FIG. 585.—Opal: variety, hyalite. Near Waltsch, Bohemia. | FIG. 586.—Opal: variety, geyserite. Yellowstone Park. |

sedimentary rocks. *Common opal* occurs rather widely distributed. *Precious opal* is found near Czerwenitz, Rumania; Queretaro and elsewhere in Mexico; Humboldt County, Nevada; Latah County, Idaho; Honduras; New South Wales, especially at White Cliffs, and at Lightning Ridge as black opal; Queensland; and South Australia.

Siliceous sinter or *geyserite* occurs abundatly in the Yellowstone Park, Iceland, and New Zealand. *Infusorial earth* is found in considerable deposits at Richmond, Virginia; Drakesville, New Jersey; Socorro, New Mexico. There are also extensive deposits in California, Nevada, Oregon; and at Oxford, Nova Scotia.

Precious and fire opals are used for gem purposes; wood opal for ornamental purposes. Tripolite is used in polishing powders, scouring soaps, artificial fertilizers, paint, wood fillers, in the filtering and refining of sugar, and as a nonconductor of heat.

MANGANITE, Mn₂O₃.H₂O.

Orthorhombic, bipyramidal class. Commonly in deeply striated prismatic crystals, arranged in groups or bundles (Fig. 587). Also in radial fibrous and columnar masses, more rarely granular and stalactitic.

Perfect brachypinacoidal cleavage. Uneven fracture. Hardness, 3.5 to 4. Specific gravity, 4.3. When fresh, manganite possesses a

submetallic luster, an iron-black color, and a reddish-brown to brownish-black streak. If more or less decomposed, it is steel gray in color with a black streak and metallic luster.

$Mn_2O_3.H_2O$. Soluble in concentrated hydrochloric acid with an evolution of chlorine. Occurs as a pseudomorph after calcite. Alters easily to pyrolusite.

Fig. 587.—Manganite. Il- menau, Thuringia, Germany.

Commonly associated with hematite, barite, calcite, siderite, pyrolusite, and other manganese minerals. Excellent crystals occur at Ilfeld, Harz Mountains; Ilmenau, Thuringia; Långban, Sweden; Marquette County, Michigan; Douglas County, Colorado; Nova Scotia; New Brunswick; Cornwall, England.

With pyrolusite it is used extensively in the preparation of oxygen and chlorine. See also page 422.

BAUXITE, Al₂O₃.2H₂O.

Crystallization unknown. Commonly shows a pisolitic or oölitic structure with rounded, concretionary grains embedded in an amorphous or claylike mass (Fig. 588).

Hardness 1 to 3. Specific gravity 2.55. White, brown, yellow, or reddish. Argillaceous odor. Variable streak. Dull to earthy luster.

$Al_2O_3.2H_2O$, essentially. Bauxite is probably a mixture of several hydrated aluminum oxide minerals, Al_2O_3 varying from 40 to 70 per cent. Ferric oxide, water, silica, and titanium oxide are usually present in varying amounts.

Bauxite is a decomposition product of feldspathic rocks, such as granites, syenites, gneisses, and so forth, the structure of the original rocks being sometimes well preserved. It is one of the principal

Fig. 588.—Pisolitic bauxite. Linwood, Georgia.

constituents of *laterite*, which is quite abundant in tropical regions. Bauxite is also found in nodules, grains, and pockets of irregular shape in limestones and dolomites, probably the result of deposition from hot solutions.

The most important deposits of bauxite in the United States are found in Pulaski and Saline counties, Arkansas, the town of Bauxite being the chief center; also in a belt extending from Jacksonville, Alabama, to Adamsville, Georgia; Tennessee; in the departments of Languedoc and Provence, southeastern France; Hessen-Nassau, Germany; British and Dutch Guiana; Jugoslavia.

Bauxite is the chief source of aluminum. It is also used in the manufacture of alum, bauxite brick, and the artificial abrasives called *alundum, aloxite, exolon,* and *lionite.* See also page 402.

LIMONITE (*Brown Hematite, Yellow Iron Ore*), $Fe_2O_3.nH_2O$.

Crystalline to amorphous. Nearly always found in compact, porous, or earthy masses. Often stalactitic (Fig. 589), botryoidal, or mammillary. Radial fibrous structure and black, varnish-like surfaces are quite characteristic (Fig. 590). Also concretionary.

Fig. 589.—Stalactitic limonite. White Marsh, Pennsylvania.

Fig. 590.—Limonite with varnish-like surface. Salisbury, Connecticut.

Hardness, 1 to 5.5. Specific gravity, 3.4 to 4. May be yellowish, brown, or black in color. Streak always yellow brown. Conchoidal to earthy fracture.

$Fe_2O_3.nH_2O$. Commonly a mixture of the iron oxides, hematite (Fe_2O_3) and goethite ($Fe_2O_3.H_2O$); at times jarosite ($K_2(Fe.2OH)_6(SO_4)_4$) is also present. May also contain silica, clay, manganese oxide, and organic matter. Common as a pseudomorph after iron minerals, especially pyrite, marcasite, and siderite.

The important varieties are:

1. *Compact Limonite.*—This includes the compact massive, stalactitic, botryoidal, and other varieties which often possess a radial fibrous structure and smooth, varnish-like surfaces.

2. *Bog Iron Ore.*—Found in marshy and swampy places. More or less loose and porous in texture and may contain organic remains.

3. *Ochreous Limonite.*—Here are placed the earthy, yellow or brownish varieties, which may be quite impure on account of the admixture of clay and sand. Often called *yellow ocher.*

Limonite is the usual decomposition product of iron minerals, resulting from the action of water, carbon dioxide, humus acid, and oxygen. It is hence found very extensively, and usually in association with such

minerals as pyrite, hematite, magnetite, and siderite and also with
many of the more strictly rock-forming minerals containing iron in small
quantities, as the amphiboles and pyroxenes. *Residual limonite* may be
the result of the decomposition of veins containing iron disulphide, or of
the weathering of iron-bearing rocks. Such limonite is usually associated
with slates, schists, or limestones. It occurs extensively in the United
States in a belt extending from Vermont to Alabama, the principal
mines being in Alabama, Virginia, West Virginia, Tennessee, and Georgia.
It is also found in Texas, Iowa, Wisconsin, Minnesota, and Oregon.
Very common as the yellow coloring matter of clays and soils and the
brownish, rusty stain on rocks.

Constitutes about 4 per cent. of the iron ore mined in the United
States (see page 417). Also used as yellow ocher, burnt umber, and
sienna in paints.

IV. HALOIDS

The following are the four most important halogen minerals:

HALITE	NaCl	Cubic
Cerargyrite	AgCl	Cubic
FLUORITE	CaF_2	Cubic
CRYOLITE	Na_3AlF_6	Monoclinic

Halite and cerargyrite are isomorphous. The internal structures of halite and fluorite are discussed on pages 155 and 161.

HALITE (*Common Salt, Rock Salt*), NaCl.

Cubic, hexoctahedral class. Crystals are generally cubes, sometimes in combination with the octahedron; also skeletal or hopper shaped.

Fig. 591.—Halite. Cleavage cube, Stassfurt, Germany; granular, Retsof, New York.

Usually in cleavable, fibrous, or granular masses (Fig. 591); as an efflorescence in arid regions.

Excellent cubical cleavage. Hardness, 2 to 2.5. Specific gravity, 2.1 to 2.3. Colorless or white; when impure, often reddish, blue, gray, greenish, or black. The color may be unevenly distributed. Easily soluble in water, 1 part in 2.8 parts of water. Saline taste. Vitreous luster. $n = 1.544$. Transparent to translucent.

NaCl. Sometimes very pure. May contain varying amounts of the chlorides and sulphates of calcium and magnesium, also admixtures of gypsum, anhydrite, organic matter, clay, and occluded liquids and gases. Colors the flame intensely yellow.

Halite occurs very widely distributed. There are four methods of occurrence: (1) *deposits*, often of great thickness and extent; (2) *in solution;* (3) *efflorescence;* (4) *sublimation product.*

1. *Deposits.*—Here salt is generally associated with gypsum, anhydrite, clay, or dolomite and is found in sedimentary rocks of all ages. Some of these deposits extend over large areas and may be of great thickness. Thus, the aggregate thickness of the salt layers in central New York is over 300 feet; near Detroit, Michigan, 400 feet; Stassfurt, Germany, over 1,200 feet; Petite Anse, Louisiana, over 2,000 feet.

Many explanations have been offered for the formation of extensive salt deposits, of which the *bar theory* of Ochsenius is perhaps in the larger number of cases the most satisfactory. This theory assumes that a portion of the ocean has been cut off from the main body of water by a bar, which rises almost to the surface. Evaporation within this bay would, on account of the shallowness of the water, be greatest on or near the bar. This would cause the water to become more dense, and a portion would settle to the bottom behind the bar, causing the water of the bay to become strongly saline. In due time, the concentration of this saline solution would be sufficient to cause the deposition of the various salts in order of their solubility. Calcium sulphate being one of the least soluble is generally deposited first, followed by rock salt. As the evaporation continues, more water would flow into the bay from the open ocean, thus furnishing a constant supply. If the bar emerges and cuts off the bay entirely, continued evaporation would cause the deposition not only of calcium sulphate and rock salt but also of the more soluble magnesium and potassium compounds, many of which are very complex. The salt deposits at Stassfurt, Germany, which cover an area of about 100 square miles, illustrate the order in which deposition will take place. These are underlain by clay and gypsum and contain over 30 different minerals. Of these minerals, aside from halite, carnallite ($KCl.MgCl_2.6H_2O$), sylvite (KCl), and kainite ($MgSO_4.KCl.3H_2O$) are the most important and in commerce and industry are frequently known as *potash salts*. Similar deposits also occur in the Hannover, Werre, Unstrut, and Mecklenburg districts of Germany. There are also important deposits in Alsace, France. Also see page 428.

In the United States, rock salt has been mined at Livonia, New York; Detroit, Michigan (see page 431); Petite Anse, Louisiana; Lyons, Kansas; and in Sevier County, Utah.

2. *In Solution.*—Common salt occurs abundantly in solution in the ocean, salt lakes, and saline springs and wells. Most of the large quantities of salt produced is usually obtained by the evaporation of saline solutions.

3. *Efflorescence.*—Earthy crusts of salt are frequently found in arid regions; thus, in the steppes near the Caspian Sea, and in Africa and Chile.

4. *Sublimation Product.*—Near volcanoes, salt is sometimes found as the result of sublimation.

Salt is used extensively for household and dairying purposes, in meat and fish packing, in the manufacture of sodium and its compounds, in various metallurgical processes, and to glaze pottery. Sodium carbonate or soda ash is used in large quantities in glass and soap making; sodium bicarbonate for cooking and baking and in medicine; and sodium cyanide in the cyanide process for the extraction of gold. Michigan, New York, Ohio, Kansas, Louisiana, Virginia, California, West Virginia, Texas, and Utah produce enormous quantities of salt annually. Of these, the first five furnish about 95 per cent. of the total production of the United States. See page 430.

Cerargyrite (*Horn Silver*), AgCl.

Cubic, hexoctahedral class. Crystals are rare and poorly developed. Generally found as a waxy crust or coating, also stalactitic and dendritic.

No cleavage. Highly sectile, cutting easily, and yielding shiny surfaces. Resembles wax. Very soft. Hardness, 1 to 1.5. Specific gravity, 5.5. Pearly gray, yellowish, greenish, or white in color; on exposure to light turns violet, brown, or black. Transparent to translucent. When rubbed becomes shiny. Waxy or resinous luster.

AgCl. May contain mercury, ferric oxide, or other impurities. Fuses easily on charcoal and yields a globule of silver.

Found as an alteration product in the upper levels of silver deposits. The usual associates are the various silver minerals, also galena, limonite, calcite, barite, and cerussite. It has been observed in Saxony, Norway, Mexico, Peru, Chile; also at Broken Hill, New South Wales; near Leadville, Colorado; Comstock Lode, Nevada; Poor Man's Lode, Idaho; Lake Valley, New Mexico, Cobalt, Ontario.

An important ore of silver.

FLUORITE (*Fluor Spar*), CaF₂.

Cubic, hexoctahedral class. Excellent crystals are common. The usual form is the cube (Fig. 592), either alone or in combination with

Fig. 592.—Fluorite, Cumberland, England.

Fig. 593.—Fluorite (penetration cubes). Durham, Weardale, England.

the tetrahexahedron or hexoctahedron. Penetration cubes twinned according to the spinel law are frequently observed (Fig. 593). Also in cleavable, granular, and fibrous masses. The internal structure is discussed on page 161.

Excellent octahedral cleavage (Fig. 594). Hardness, 4. Specific gravity, 3 to 3.2. Usually greenish, yellowish, or bluish in color; also various shades of red or brown, white, and colorless. Sometimes multi-colored. Transparent to nearly opaque. Vitreous luster. $n = 1.434$. Frequently strongly fluorescent and phosphorescent when heated or exposed to electric discharges.

CaF_2. Usually quite pure.

Fluorite is found in veins in limestones and dolomites, less frequently in granitic rocks and sandstones. It is also a common gangue mineral

FIG. 594.—Fluorite (octahedral cleavage). Near Rosiclare, Illinois.

with ores of lead, silver, copper, and especially tin. The common associates are galena, sphalerite, cassiterite, calcite, quartz, barite, pyrite, chalcopyrite, topaz, tourmaline, and apatite. Excellent crystals occur at Cumberland, Cornwall, and Derbyshire, England. Large quantities are mined annually in Hardin County, Illinois, and in Crittenden and Livingston counties, Kentucky. Smaller amounts have been obtained from Nevada, Colorado, New Mexico, and Arizona. Fluorite is a common mineral and occurs widely distributed.

Fluorite is used extensively in the manufacture of open-hearth steel, iron and steel enamel ware, opalescent glass, cyanamide, hydrofluoric acid, and in the electrolytic refining of antimony and lead. See also page 416.

CRYOLITE (*Ice Stone*), Na_3AlF_6.

Monoclinic, prismatic class. Crystals are cubical in habit. Usually observed in compact, granular, or cleavable masses (Fig. 595).

FIG. 595.—Cryolite (white) and siderite. Ivigtut, Greenland.

Basal and prismatic cleavages, three directions nearly at right angles. Uneven fracture. Hardness, 2.5 to 3. Specific gravity, 2.9 to 3. Colorless to snow white, more rarely reddish, brownish, or black. Pearly luster on the basal pinacoid, elsewhere vitreous to greasy. Often resembles snow-ice or paraffin. Transparent to translucent. $\beta = 1.364$, $(-)$; $2V = 43°$; $r < v$.

Na_3AlF_6. Usually quite pure. Fuses easily and imparts a yellow color to the flame.

The only important occurrence of cryolite is at Ivigtut on the southern coast of Greenland, where it is found in veins in granite and is associated with siderite, chalcopyrite, galena, pyrite, fluorite, sphalerite, columbite, cassiterite, and molybdenite. Found also at Miask in the Ilmen Mountains, Siberia, and in the Pikes Peak district, Colorado.

Used principally as a bath in the manufacture of aluminum by the electrolytic process; thus, at Niagara Falls, New York; also in opalescent glasses and enamels, and in white Portland cement. See also page 402.

V. NITRATES, CARBONATES, AND MANGANITES

A. Nitrates

Soda niter or Chile saltpeter is the only nitrate occurring in nature in sufficient quantities to warrant a description.

SODA NITER (*Chile Saltpeter*), **$NaNO_3$.**

Hexagonal, ditrigonal scalenohedral class. Crystals resemble those of calcite but are rare. Generally in crystalline aggregates or grains, also in crusts or deposits of great extent.

Perfect rhombohedral cleavage. Conchoidal fracture. Hardness, 1.5 to 2. Specific gravity, 2.1 to 2.3. Vitreous luster. Colorless, white, yellowish, gray, or reddish brown. Transparent to nearly opaque. Strong double refraction, ω 1.587, ϵ 1.336, $(-)$. Cooling and saline taste.

$NaNO_3$. Usually contains some sodium chloride and sodium sulphate. Easily soluble in water. Absorbs moisture. Colors flame intensely yellow. Mixed with rock salt, guano, gypsum, clay, and sand, it occurs in extensive deposits, 6 to 12 feet thick, in the deserts of Atacama and Tarapaca in northern Chile. The crude material is called *caliche* and must contain about 50 per cent. sodium nitrate to be considered high grade. Smaller quantities also occur in San Bernardino and Inyo counties, California; Humboldt County, Nevada; and in New Mexico.

Soda niter is a very important commercial mineral. It is used extensively as a fertilizer and in the manufacture of nitric acid and potassium nitrate. It is also a source of iodine, which is present in small amounts as lautarite $(Ca(IO_3)_2)$. Also see page 425.

B. Carbonates

Some of the most widely distributed minerals are carbonates. Several of them are of great importance commercially.

CALCITE GROUP

CALCITE	$CaCO_3$	Hexagonal
DOLOMITE	$CaMg(CO_3)_2$	Hexagonal
MAGNESITE	$MgCO_3$	Hexagonal
SMITHSONITE	$ZnCO_3$	Hexagonal
RHODOCHROSITE	$MnCO_3$	Hexagonal
SIDERITE	$FeCO_3$	Hexagonal

ARAGONITE GROUP

ARAGONITE	$CaCO_3$	Orthorhombic
STRONTIANITE	$SrCO_3$	Orthorhombic
WITHERITE	$BaCO_3$	Orthorhombic
CERUSSITE	$PbCO_3$	Orthorhombic

MALACHITE GROUP

MALACHITE	$CuCO_3 \cdot Cu(OH)_2$	Monoclinic
AZURITE	$2CuCO_3 \cdot Cu(OH)_2$	Monoclinic

$CaCO_3$ is dimorphous with modifications in the hexagonal and orthorhombic systems, known as calcite and aragonite, respectively.

Calcite Group

This isomorphous group contains six members, of which calcite is the most common and important. All of these minerals possess a perfect rhombohedral cleavage.

CALCITE (*Calcspar*), $CaCO_3$.

Hexagonal, ditrigonal scalenohedral class. Commonly in good crystals; often very complex. The habit varies greatly and may be obtuse or acute rhombohedral, tabular, long prismatic, or scalenohedral (Figs. 596 and 597). Over 300 forms have been observed. Twins are relatively common. The two most important laws involve twinning parallel to (1) the basal pinacoid (Fig. 598) and (2) the negative rhombohedron $(-\frac{1}{2}R)$ (Fig. 599). Calcite also occurs in granular, lamellar, fibrous, compact, porous, or earthy masses; less frequently it is oölitic, pisolitic, or stalactitic.

The highly perfect rhombohedral cleavage (105°) is very characteristic. Hardness, 3. Specific gravity, 2.72. Vitreous to earthy luster. Commonly colorless, white, or yellowish but may be any color. Transparent to opaque. Transparent varieties show strong double refraction (Fig. 600); ω 1.658, ϵ 1.486, $(-)$. Sometimes becomes luminescent.

$CaCO_3$. Sometimes very pure. May contain varying amounts of magnesium, iron, or manganese replacing the calcium. Often mixed with limonite, hematite, organic matter, sand, or clay. Easily soluble with a brisk effervescence in cold dilute acids. This test serves to distinguish calcite from dolomite, which does not effervesce freely in cold acid. Calcite may be distinguished from aragonite by *Meigen's test*, which consists of boiling the powdered minerals in a solution of cobalt nitrate. When calcite is treated in this way, the powder remains unchanged or turns a pale yellow, while aragonite assumes a lilac-red color.

The different varieties of calcite may be grouped as follows: (a) *ordinary calcites*, (b) *limestones*, (c) *marbles*, (d) *chalk and marl*, and (e) *spring, stream, and cave deposits*.

a. Ordinary Calcite.—These include crystals and cleavable, fibrous, and lamellar masses.

1. *Dog-tooth Spar.*—Scalenohedral crystals, often in beautiful aggregates (Fig. 596).

2. *Nail-head Spar.*—Prismatic crystals with obtuse rhombohedral terminations (Fig. 597).

3. *Iceland Spar.*—Colorless and transparent, showing strong double refraction (Fig. 600).

4. *Satin Spar.*—A fibrous variety with a silky luster. This term is also more frequently applied to fibrous gypsum (pages 315 and 316).

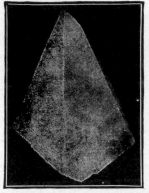

Fig. 596.—Calcite (scalenohedron). Joplin, Missouri.

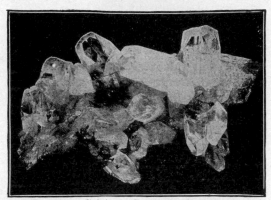

Fig. 597.—Calcite. Cumberland, England.

Fig. 598.—Calcite
(twinned parallel to the
base). Guanajuato,
Mexico.

Fig. 599.—Calcite (twinned parallel to $-\frac{1}{2}R$).
Joplin, Missouri.

Fig. 600.—Calcite: variety, Iceland spar, showing double refraction. Big Timber,
Montana.

b. Limestones.—Calcite is the chief constituent of limestone rocks, which occur so widely distributed. They are massive and may be dull and compact, coarse or fine granular, or composed of fragmental material.

1. *Compact Limestones.*—These may be nearly white, yellow, bluish gray, reddish, or black in color.

2. *Magnesian or Dolomitic Limestones.*—As the name indicates, these limestones contain varying percentages of magnesium carbonate.

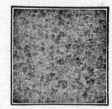

Fig. 601.—Calcite: variety, coquina. Anastasia Island, Florida.

Fig. 602.—Marble. Near Tate, Georgia.

3. *Lithographic Limestones.*—An even-grained, compact limestone, suitable for lithographic purposes. That from Solenhofen, Bavaria, is buff or drab in color.

4. *Hydraulic Limestones.*—These are impure limestones, containing from 10 to 14 per cent. of clayey impurities. They are used extensively in the manufacture of cement.

5. *Bituminous Limestones.*—Owing to the presence of much organic matter, these limestones yield the characteristic odor of bitumen when struck a blow with a hammer.

6. *Coquina.*—This is a mass of shell remains (Fig. 601). Found along the coast of Florida, near St. Augustine.

7. *Oölitic Limestones.*—These are composed of small, spherical concretions, resembling fish roe.

8. *Pisolitic Limestones.*—The concretions are larger and about the size of a pea.

c. Marbles.—These possess a fine to coarse crystalline structure and are generally metamorphosed limestones (Fig. 602). Commercially, however, any calcareous rock capable of taking a polish and suitable for decorative and structural purposes is termed a marble.

d. Chalk and Marl.—These are soft, earthy varieties.

1. *Chalk.*—Soft, white or grayish, earthy masses, consisting principally of the remains of Foraminifera. Found in large deposits at Dover, England.

2. *Marl.*—A soft, calcareous deposit mixed with clay and sand. Often contains shell or organic remains. It is used in the manufacture of cement.

e. Spring, Stream, and Cave Deposits.—These are due largely to the escape of carbon dioxide, which causes the soluble calcium bicarbonate, $CaH_2(CO_3)_2$, to pass over to the more insoluble normal carbonate, $CaCO_3$, and be deposited. It is thought that certain algæ aid in this process.

1. *Travertine, Calcareous Sinter, or Calcareous Tufa.*—These occur around springs and in stream beds and are usually porous and often contain twigs, leaves, and other organic remains.

2. *Stalactites.*—Icicle-like forms suspended from the roofs of caves.

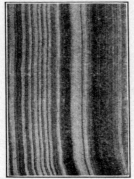

FIG. 603.—C a l c i t e : variety, Mexican onyx. Lehi City, Utah.

3. *Stalagmites.*—Deposits on the floors of caves, usually conical in shape.

4. *Onyx Marble.*—Compact deposits with a crystalline structure, often banded, translucent, and of colors suitable for decorative purposes (Fig. 603).

Calcite occurs very widely distributed. As limestone, marble, chalk, and marl it is found in large deposits, often of great thickness and extending over wide areas. It is also abundant as deposits around springs and in streams, and in cracks and cavities in igneous and sedimentary rocks. Often observed as an associate of metalliferous ore deposits. Excellent crystals are very common. A few of the most noted localities are Eskifiord, Iceland; Derbyshire, Cumberland, Devonshire, Durham, Lancashire, England; Andreasberg, Germany; Kapnik, Rumania; Guanajuato, Mexico; Joplin, Missouri; Rossie, St. Lawrence County, New York; Lake Superior copper district. Large and commercially important deposits of calcite marble occur in Vermont, Tennessee, Georgia, Alabama, and Colorado.

The different varieties of calcite are commercially of great value. Iceland spar is used in optical instruments; limestone for building purposes, quicklime, cement, flux in various metallurgical processes, railroad ballast, macadam, in lithography, and concrete; marble for building, ornamental, monumental, and statuary purposes, and as a source of carbon dioxide; chalk for whiting, crayon, scouring and polishing preparations, and as an adulterant; marl for cement. See also page 408.

DOLOMITE (*Pearl Spar*), $CaMg(CO_3)_2$.

Hexagonal, trigonal rhombohedral class. Rhombohedral crystals are common. The faces are frequently curved, forming saddle-shaped crystals (Fig. 604). Also in fine- to coarse-grained, cleavable, or compact masses.

Perfect rhombohedral cleavage. Hardness, 3.5 to 4. Specific gravity, 2.9. White, reddish, yellow, brown, or black; rarely colorless. Vitreous to pearly luster. Indices of refraction for pure dolomite are ω 1.681, ϵ 1.500, $(-)$; for dolomite containing calcium and iron they may be ω 1.695, ϵ 1.510, $(-)$. Transparent to translucent.

$CaMg(CO_3)_2$. In the crystals of dolomite, the carbonates of calcium and magnesium are usually present in the proportion of $1:1$; in massive varieties, this ratio varies greatly, but $CaCO_3$ generally predominates. In many instances, dolomite is believed to have been formed by the action

Fig. 604.—Dolomite.   Joplin, Missouri.

of soluble magnesium salts upon calcium carbonate, either before or after emergence from the sea.

$$2CaCO_3 + MgCl_2 = CaMg(CO_3)_2 + CaCl_2$$

Fragments of dolomite are but slightly acted upon by cold dilute acid; the powder effervesces briskly with hot dilute acids.

Dolomite occurs abundantly in many ore deposits and in cavities of various igneous and sedimentary rocks. Thus, at Joplin, Missouri; Lockport, New York; Austria; Switzerland; Freiberg, Saxony. The compact granular variety occurs in deposits of great thickness and extent. Thus, some of the mountain ranges of Central Europe are principally dolomite. These dolomites grade into dolomitic and magnesian limestones. The term *marble* includes metamorphosed dolomites (see page 183). Dolomitic marbles of commercial importance occur in New York, Maryland, and Massachusetts.

Dolomite is used for building, statuary, monumental, and ornamental purposes; as a source of magnesium compounds; and as refractory material. See also page 408.

MAGNESITE, $MgCO_3$.

Hexagonal, ditrigonal scalenohedral class. Rarely in rhombohedral crystals; usually in cleavable, granular, compact, or earthy masses with the appearance of unglazed porcelain (Fig. 605). Also coarsely crystalline, resembling coarse dolomite or marble in texture.

Crystals have a rhombohedral cleavage. Conchoidal fracture is conspicuous on massive varieties. Brittle. Hardness, 3.5. to 4.5. Specific gravity, 2.9 to 3.1. Colorless, white, yellow, brown, or blackish. Vitreous to dull luster. ω 1.700, ϵ 1.509, (−). Transparent to opaque.

$MgCO_3$. Iron or calcium may be present. Powdered magnesite is soluble in hot dilute acids.

Magnesite is commonly the result of the hydration and carbonation of magnesium minerals. Thus, olivine may alter to magnesite, serpentine, limonite, and opal. It is found in veins in talcose and chloritic schists and in serpentine. It occurs in Moravia and Styria, Austria;

Fig. 605.—Magnesite. Tulare County, California.

Fig. 606.—Longitudinal section through stalactite of smithsonite, showing banded structure. Masua, Sardinia.

Silesia; Zillerthal, Tirol; Greece; and very extensively in Santa Clara, Sonoma, Napa, Kern, Fresno, and San Benito counties, California, and in Stevens County, Washington.

Magnesite is used chiefly in the manufacture of refractory bricks, crucibles, furnace hearths, oxychloride or Sorel cement, and magnesium sulphite for the digestion and whitening of wood-pulp paper; as a source of carbon dioxide and magnesium compounds; when mixed with asbestos it serves as a boiler and steam-pipe covering; calcined magnesite is used for flooring, tiling, wainscoting, and sanitary finishes. See also page 421.

SMITHSONITE (*Calamine, Dry Bone*), $ZnCO_3$.

Hexagonal, ditrigonal scalenohedral class. Crystals are usually small and rough or curved. Generally found in reniform, botryoidal, stalactitic (Fig. 606), or compact granular masses. *Dry bone* is a term given to cellular and porous varieties.

Rhombohedral cleavage, observed on crystals. Uneven to splintery fracture. Hardness, 5. Specific gravity, 4.1 to 4.5. Color is commonly gray or brown; also white, yellow, blue, green, and pink. Greenish smithsonite is called *bonamite*. Translucent to opaque. Vitreous to pearly luster. ω 1.818, ϵ 1.618, $(-)$.

$ZnCO_3$. Iron, manganese, calcium, and magnesium may be present. *Turkey fat* is yellow smithsonite containing greenockite, CdS. Common as a pseudomorph after calcite, especially at Mineral Point, Wisconsin (Fig. 607).

Smithsonite is a secondary mineral and occurs extensively in the upper levels in limestones and dolomites. It is often the result of the action of

FIG. 607.—Smithsonite (pseudomorph after calcite). Mineral Point, Wisconsin.

carbonated waters on other zinc minerals. The common associates are sphalerite, hemimorphite, galena, limonite, and calcite. Sometimes it is mixed with sand and clay. Occurs at Broken Hill, New South Wales; Laurium, Greece; Altenberg, near Aachen, Germany; Scotland; Kelly, New Mexico; also extensively in Missouri, Arkansas, Iowa, Wisconsin, and Virginia, where it is mined as zinc ore. The term *calamine* is sometimes applied to smithsonite, but it refers more properly to hemimorphite ($H_2Zn_2SiO_5$) (page 337). These two minerals often occur in intimate association.

Chiefly used as an ore of zinc; green, blue, and yellowish varieties are sometimes polished for gem and ornamental purposes. See page 436.

RHODOCHROSITE, MnCO₃.

Hexagonal, ditrigonal scalenohedral class. Crystals are rhombohedral in habit, small, and quite rare (Fig. 608). Generally in cleavable, granular, and botryoidal masses; also in crusts.

Perfect rhombohedral cleavage. Uneven fracture. Hardness, 3.5 to 4.5. Specific gravity, 3.3 to 3.6. Usually rose red or pink in color; also gray, dark brown, and, more rarely, colorless. Vitreous to pearly luster. ω 1.826, ϵ 1.605, $(-)$. Translucent.

$MnCO_3$. Calcium, iron, zinc, and magnesium are often present replacing the manganese. Occurs as a pseudomorph after calcite and fluorite.

Usually found with iron, lead, gold, silver, and copper ores, and other manganese minerals. Most common associates are galena, sphalerite, pyrite, rhodonite, and psilomelane; thus, at Hucha, Spain; Freiberg, Saxony; Kapnik, Rumania; Franklin Furnace, New Jersey; Alicante, Colorado; Butte, Montana; Austin, Nevada.

Rhodochrosite is not a very common mineral. It is sometimes used as a source of manganese and its compounds. See page 422.

Fig. 608.—Rhodochrosite (rhombohedrons). Lake County, Colorado.

Fig. 609.—Siderite (dark) with dolomite. Salzburg, Austria.

SIDERITE (*Spathic Iron, Chalybite*), $FeCO_3$.

Hexagonal, ditrigonal scalenohedral class. Distorted and curved rhombohedral crystals (saddle shaped) are quite common (Fig. 609). Usually found in cleavable, granular, botryoidal, or fibrous masses.

Perfect rhombohedral cleavage. Conchoidal fracture. Hardness, 3.5 to 4.5. Specific gravity, 3.7 to 3.9. Vitreous to pearly luster. ω 1.830, ϵ 1.596, (—). Usually brownish to nearly black in color; also gray, green, and white. Translucent to nearly opaque. Streak white or yellowish.

$FeCO_3$. Usually contains some $CaCO_3$ and $MnCO_3$. Manganiferous varieties are termed *oligonite*. When mixed with clay, sand, and organic matter, it is often called *clay ironstone* or *blackband*. Occurs as a pseudomorph after calcite, aragonite, dolomite, barite, and fluorite. It alters to limonite, hematite, and magnetite.

Siderite occurs commonly with sulphide ore deposits, also in beds and as concretions in limestones and shales. The common associates are pyrite, chalcopyrite, galena, tetrahedrite, and cryolite. It occurs with ore deposits in the Harz Mountains; Přibram, Bohemia; Cornwall, England; Freiberg, Saxony; with cryolite and chalcopyrite in southern Greenland; in beds and as concretions in Westphalia; southern Wales; Silesia; Roxbury, Connecticut; St. Lawrence County, New York; in the coal measures in eastern Ohio, Kentucky, and western Pennsylvania.

A minor ore of iron. If it contains considerable manganese, it is used for spiegeleisen.

Aragonite Group

The members of this isomorphous group crystallize in the orthorhombic system. The prism angles of these minerals approximate 120°, so that crystals frequently have a pseudohexagonal development.

ARAGONITE, CaCO₃.

Orthorhombic, bipyramidal class. Crystals are quite common and show great diversity in development. They may be (1) domatic or chisel-like, (2) acute pyramidal or spear shaped, and (3) prismatic and pseudohexagonal, consisting of a prism and striated base. The prism

Fig. 610.—Aragonite (trillings).
Girgenti, Sicily.

Fig. 611.—Aragonite: variety, flos ferri.
Styria, Austria.

angle is 116° 16′. This pseudohexagonal symmetry is often accentuated by twinning parallel to a face of the unit prism (Fig. 610). Contact, cyclic, and penetration twins are common. Also occurs in radial, branching, columnar, and fibrous aggregates; oölitic, globular, stalactitic, and in crusts.

Imperfect brachypinacoidal and prismatic cleavages. Conchoidal fracture. Hardness, 3.5 to 4. Specific gravity, 2.9 to 3. Most commonly colorless, white, or yellow; also reddish, bluish, or black. Greasy luster on fracture surfaces, elsewhere vitreous. α 1.531, β 1.682, γ 1.686, (−); $2V = 19°$; $r < v$. Transparent to translucent. May show luminescence.

CaCO₃. May contain some strontium. Effervesces easily with acids but not so easily as calcite. Massive varieties are easily distinguished from calcite by Meigen's test (see page 209). Occurs as a pseudomorph after gypsum and calcite, but calcite pseudomorphs after aragonite are more abundant. At about 470°C., aragonite changes to calcite. Aragonite is usually deposited from hot solutions while calcite is formed from cold solutions. It may also be formed at ordinary temperatures through the action of organic agencies or by precipitation from saline waters containing sulphates or small amounts of the carbonates of strontium or lead.

Aragonite is found (1) in cracks and cavities, often associated with the zeolites; (2) in ore deposits, especially iron ore; the coralloidal variety occurring with siderite, as at Hüttenberg, Carinthia, is termed *flos ferri* (Fig. 611); (3) disseminated in clay, associated with gypsum, sulphur, and celestite; (4) as a deposit from hot springs and geysers, sometimes pisolitic and in crusts; (5) it constitutes the pearly layer of many shells and pearls. Aragonite is not nearly so common as calcite. Excellent crystals are found at Herrengrund, Hungary; Bilin, Karlsbad, and Horschenz, Bohemia; Aragon, Spain; Girgenti, Sicily; Alton Moor, England; other varieties at Hoboken, New Jersey; Lockport, New York; Warsaw, Illinois; Organ Mountains, New Mexico.

Aragonite is of no importance commercially.

STRONTIANITE, SrCO₃.

Orthorhombic, bipyramidal class. Crystals are usually spear shaped or acicular and arranged in radial aggregates. Forms and twinning are similar to those of aragonite. Pseudohexagonal with a prism angle of 117° 19′. Also granular and compact, sometimes with a divergent fibrous structure (Fig. 612).

Imperfect prismatic cleavage. Conchoidal fracture. Hardness, 3.5 to 4. Specific gravity, 3.6 to 3.8. Colorless, white, gray, yellow, and green. Vitreous luster, greasy on fracture surfaces. α 1.520, β 1.667, γ 1.667, $(-)$; $2V = 7°$; $r < v$. Transparent to translucent.

SrCO₃. Usually contains some calcium and barium. Occurs as a pseudomorph after celestite. Occurs in ore deposits, commonly with barite and galena. Important localities are Strontian, Argyllshire, Scotland; Hamm, Westphalia, Germany; Schoharie, New York; Ida, Michigan; near Austin, Texas; Skagit County, Washington.

Fig. 612.—Strontianite, Dreisteinfurt, Westphalia, Germany.

Strontianite is a source of strontium compounds, some of which are used extensively. The oxides and hydroxide are of importance in the precipitation of sugar from molasses; the nitrate, carbonate, and oxalate are used for red fire; and the iodide, bromide, and lactate in medicine. See page 431.

WITHERITE, BaCO₃.

Orthorhombic, bipyramidal class. Usually in pseudohexagonal bipyramids, resembling quartz (Fig. 613). These are penetration trillings with the twinning plane parallel to the unit prism. The prism angle is 117° 48′. Parallel groups not uncommon. Also in compact, botryoidal, reniform, or globular masses; sometimes with a lamellar or radial fibrous structure.

Imperfect prismatic cleavage. Uneven fracture. Hardness, 3.5. Specific gravity, 4.2 to 4.35. Colorless, grayish, white, or yellowish. Vitreous luster, on fracture surfaces somewhat greasy. α 1.529, β 1.676, γ 1.677, ($-$); $2V = 16°$; $r > v$. Translucent to transparent.

$BaCO_3$. Usually quite pure.

Occurs with deposits of galena in northwestern England; thus, at Fallowfield, Northumberland; Durfton, Westmoreland; Alston Moor,

Fig. 613.—Witherite (trillings). Northumberland, England.

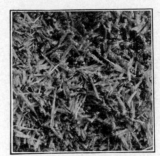

Fig. 614.—Cerussite. Leadville, Colorado.

Cumberland; with barite at Freiberg, Saxony; Lexington, Kentucky; Thunder Bay district, Lake Superior.

Witherite is used to adulterate white lead and in the extracting of sugar from sugar beets.

CERUSSITE (*White Lead Ore*), $PbCO_3$.

Orthorhombic, bipyramidal class. Crystals are generally tabular, prismatic, or pyramidal in habit; frequently arranged in clusters or star-shaped groups. Often very complex. Pronounced pseudohexagonal symmetry, the prism angle being 117° 14′. Twins are very common and similar to those of aragonite. Also in granular, fibrous, and compact masses, interlaced bundles (Fig. 614), and stalactitic.

Hardness, 3 to 3.5. Specific gravity, 6.4 to 6.6. Generally colorless, white, or gray. Adamantine luster, sometimes silky. High indices of refraction, α 1.804, β 2.076, γ 2.078, ($-$); $2V = 8°$; $r > v$. Transparent to almost opaque.

$PbCO_3$. At times, contains some silver and zinc. Occurs as a pseudomorph after galena and anglesite.

Found usually in the upper levels of galena deposits, from which it has resulted by the action of carbonated waters. Common associates are galena, pyromorphite, anglesite, malachite, and limonite.   Occurs at Broken Hill, New South Wales; Leadhills, Scotland; various places in Mexico; Leadville, Colorado; Pima and Yuma counties, Arizona; Park City, Utah; Coeur d'Alene district, Idaho.

An important ore of lead and silver.

Malachite Group

This group includes two basic carbonates of copper, which are of great importance commercially.

MALACHITE (*Green Carbonate of Copper*), $CuCO_3.Cu(OH)_2$.

Monoclinic, prismatic class.   Crystals are usually acicular, very slender, and without good terminations; often arranged in groups or tufts.   Commonly in reniform, botryoidal, and stalactitic masses with

smooth surfaces and a banded or radial fibrous structure (Fig. 615); also earthy and in velvety crusts.

Conchoidal to splintery fracture. Hardness, 3.5 to 4.   Specific gravity, 3.7 to 4.1.   Bright emerald green, grass green, to nearly black in color.   Translucent to opaque.   Silky, adamantine, or dull luster. α 1.665, β 1.875, γ 1.909, $(-)$; $2V = 43°$; $r < v$.   Light-green streak.

Fig. 615.—Malachite (polished). Rhodesia, Africa.

$CuCO_3.Cu(OH)_2$.   Masses may contain the oxides of iron and manganese, clay, and sand.   Occurs commonly as a pseudomorph after cuprite, azurite, and native copper.

Malachite is a common alteration product of copper minerals, resulting from the action of carbonated waters and, hence, is found in smaller or larger quantities in the upper levels of all copper mines.   Common associates are azurite, cuprite, native copper, chalcocite, chalcopyrite, and bornite.   Occurs in large quantities in the Ural Mountains; at Chessy, France, as pseudomorphs after cuprite; Cornwall, England; Rhodesia; Chile; Bisbee and Clifton districts, Arizona; Park City, Utah; as a coating on native copper in the Lake Superior copper district.

An important ore of copper, especially in Arizona.   Also used in jewelry and for ornamental purposes, such as table tops and vases. *Malachite matrix* is a term given to polished specimens with admixtures of gangue material.

AZURITE (*Chessylite, Blue Carbonate of Copper*), $2CuCO_3.Cu(OH)_2$.

Monoclinic, prismatic class.   Short prismatic or tabular crystals, often very complex, and arranged in spherical aggregates.   Commonly found in reniform or botryoidal masses, with a velvety, radial fibrous structure; also earthy and in crusts.

Hardness, 3.5. Specific gravity, 3.7 to 3.8. Vitreous to adamantine luster. α 1.730, β 1.758, γ 1.838, $(+)$; $2V = 68°$; $r > v$. Light azure to deep blue in color. Streak light blue. Translucent to opaque.

$2CuCO_3.Cu(OH)_2$. Occurs as a pseudomorph after cuprite and tetrahedrite. Alters to malachite.

Origin and occurrences are the same as for malachite; not so common as malachite. Excellent crystals occur at Chessy, France; in the Ural Mountains; Chile; the Bisbee and Clifton copper districts, Arizona; also in Utah and California.

Used as an ore of copper. When intimately mixed with malachite, it is sometimes polished for gem purposes and sold as *azurmalachite*.

C. Manganites

These minerals contain large percentages of manganese, but the composition of only one, hausmannite, is sufficiently constant to warrant the assigning of a chemical formula.

| Hausmannite | Mn_2MnO_4 | Tetragonal |
| Psilomelane | MnO_2, BaO, H_2O, etc. | Amorphous? |

Of these minerals, psilomelane is the more common and important.

Hausmannite, Mn_2MnO_4.

Tetragonal, scalenohedral class. Crystals are acute pyramidal and often form cyclic twins. Found generally in granular to compact masses.

Perfect basal cleavage. Hardness, 5 to 5.5. Specific gravity, 4.7 to 4.8. Brownish black to black in color. Chestnut-brown streak. Greasy metallic luster. Opaque.

Mn_2MnO_4. Soluble in hydrochloric acid with an evolution of chlorine.

A comparatively rare mineral. The common associates are pyrolusite, psilomelane, magnetite, barite, and hematite. Occurs at Ilfeld and Ilmenau, Germany; Pajsberg and Långban, Sweden.

Psilomelane (*Black Hematite*), MnO_2, BaO, H_2O, etc.

Occurs usually in botryoidal, reniform, or stalactitic masses, having smooth surfaces (Fig. 616).

Hardness, 5 to 6. Earthy varieties are very soft. Specific gravity, 3.7 to 4.7. Dark gray to iron black in color. Brownish black streak. Dull or submetallic luster. Opaque.

The composition varies greatly: MnO_2, 70 to 90 per cent.; BaO, 6 to 17 per cent.; H_2O, 1 to 6 per cent. It may also contain potassium, calcium, copper, and silicon. Evolves chlorine when treated with hydrochloric acid.

Psilomelane is a secondary mineral and is always associated with other manganese minerals, limonite, or barite. X-ray data indicate that the

Fig. 616.—Psilomelane. Ironwood, Michigan.

material classed as psilomelane includes several different species all of which have properties that are more or less similar. Found at Ilfeld and Ilmenau, Germany; Cornwall, England; Brandon, Vermont; Batesville, Arkansas; Blue Ridge region, Virginia; Cartersville, Georgia.

One of the important ores of manganese.

VI. SULPHATES, CHROMATES, MOLYBDATES, TUNGSTATES AND URANATES

The minerals belonging to this division may be conveniently arranged in the following groups:

BARITE GROUP

ANHYDRITE	$CaSO_4$	Orthorhombic
CELESTITE	$SrSO_4$	Orthorhombic
BARITE	$BaSO_4$	Orthorhombic
ANGLESITE	$PbSO_4$	Orthorhombic
Crocoite	$PbCrO_4$	Monoclinic

WOLFRAMITE GROUP

Wulfenite	$PbMoO_4$	Tetragonal
Scheelite	$CaWO_4$	Tetragonal
Huebnerite	$MnWO_4$	Monoclinic
WOLFRAMITE	$(Fe,Mn)WO_4$	Monoclinic
Ferberite	$FeWO_4$	Monoclinic

Uraninite	UO_3, UO_2, PbO, etc.	Cubic
ALUNITE	$K_2(Al.2OH)_6(SO_4)_4$	Hexagonal
Brochantite	$CuSO_4.3Cu(OH)_2$	Orthorhombic
GYPSUM	$CaSO_4.2H_2O$	Monoclinic
Epsomite	$MgSO_4.7H_2O$	Orthorhombic
Melanterite	$FeSO_4.7H_2O$	Monoclinic
Chalcanthite	$CuSO_4.5H_2O$	Triclinic

Most of these minerals possess nonmetallic lusters.

Barite Group

This group may be subdivided into two series. One of these series has orthorhombic crystallization, the other monoclinic. Crocoite is the only representative of the second series.

ANHYDRITE, $CaSO_4$.

Orthorhombic, bipyramidal class. Crystals are prismatic or thick tabular in habit, but not common. Generally in granular, cleavable, fibrous, or contorted masses. When granular, may resemble marble or lumps of sugar (Fig. 617).

Pinacoidal cleavages in three directions at right angles, yielding cubical or rectangular fragments. Conchoidal fracture.

FIG. 617.—Anhydrite. Oakwood Salt Shaft, Detroit, Michigan

Hardness, 3 to 3.5. Specific gravity, 2.7 to 3. Colorless, white, grayish, bluish, reddish, or black. Vitreous to pearly luster. α 1.571, β 1.576, γ 1.614, $(+)$; $2V = 42°$; $r < v$. Transparent to translucent.

CaSO₄. Often mixed with organic matter. Absorbs water and alters to gypsum ($CaSO_4.2H_2O$) causing an increase of 33 to 62 per cent. of the original volume. This hydration is, no doubt, the cause of the many local disturbances in the rock strata commonly observed in regions where gypsum occurs; thus, in central New York, and the Island of Put-in-Bay in Lake Erie. Occurs sometimes as a pseudomorph after gypsum.

Found commonly in limestones and shales associated with halite and gypsum. Some of the principal localities are the Stassfurt salt district, Germany; Hall, Tirol; Bex, Switzerland; Nova Scotia; New Brunswick; Lockport, New York; Detroit, Michigan; Ellsworth County, Kansas.

Anhydrite is of little use commercially. A siliceous variety is sometimes cut and polished for ornamental purposes.

CELESTITE, SrSO₄.

Orthorhombic, bipyramidal class. Tabular or prismatic crystals are common (Figs. 618, 619, and 620). Also in cleavable, granular, or fibrous masses.

Perfect basal and prismatic cleavages. Uneven fracture. Hardness, 3 to 3.5. Specific gravity, 3.9 to 4. Vitreous to pearly luster. α 1.622,

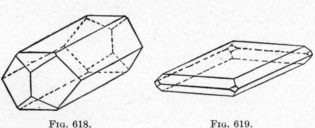

FIG. 618.   FIG. 619.   FIG. 620.—Celestite (tabular). Woolmith Quarry, Monroe County, Michigan.

β 1.624, γ 1.631, (+); $2V = 51°$; $r < v$. Generally possesses a faint blue tinge but may be white, yellow, and, more rarely, green or reddish. Transparent to translucent.

SrSO₄. Usually very pure but may contain small amounts of calcium and barium. Imparts a red color to the flame. More soluble in water than barite.

Celestite is usually associated with sulphur, gypsum, halite, aragonite, and, occasionally, galena and sphalerite. There are two principal types of occurrences:

1. *Disseminated* as crystals or irregular particles in shales, limestones, and dolomites. By the action of circulating water the celestite is dissolved and these rocks become more or less porous. They are often

called *gashed, acicular,* or *vermicular* limestones and dolomites. Such rocks occur near Syracuse, New York; and at various places in Michigan and northern Ohio.

2. *In cracks* and *cavities* in rocks of varying ages but principally of sedimentary origin. Most of the best known localities for the occurrence of celestite are of this type. It is found in association with sulphur, gypsum, and aragonite in the Girgenti sulphur district of Sicily; also at Maybee, Michigan; with halite at Bex, Switzerland; excellent crystals, some over 18 inches in length, are found on the Island of Put-in-Bay, Lake Erie; Mineral County, West Virginia; Kingston, Canada; San Bernardino County, California; Burnet County, Texas; Brown County, Kansas.

Used in the manufacture of strontium compounds. See page 431.

BARITE (*Heavy Spar, Barytes*), **BaSO₄.**

Orthorhombic, bipyramidal class. Tabular and prismatic crystals are very common, usually well developed (Figs. 621 to 626); often com-

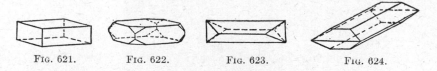

| Fig. 621. | Fig. 622. | Fig. 623. | Fig. 624. |

plex. Tabular crystals may be arranged in crested divergent groups (Fig. 627). Also in cleavable, granular, fibrous, or reniform masses; sometimes lamellar, nodular, or earthy.

Fig. 625.—Barite (light) with stibnite. Rumania.

Fig. 626.—Barite. Schemnitz, Czechoslovakia.

Perfect basal and prismatic cleavages. Uneven fracture. Hardness, 2.5 to 3.5. Specific gravity, 4.3 to 4.7. Colorless, white, yellow, blue, brown, or red. Transparent to opaque. Vitreous to pearly luster. α 1.636, β 1.637, γ 1.648, (+); $2V = 37°\ 30'$; $r < v$.

$BaSO_4$. May contain varying amounts of the oxides of strontium and calcium; also silica, clay, or organic matter. Colors the flame green.

Barite is a common and widely distributed mineral. It occurs in metalliferous veins associated with galena, sphalerite, fluorite, chalcopyrite, and the various manganese and iron minerals. This type of occurrence furnishes most of the finest crystals of barite. Thus, Cornwall, Cumberland, and Derbyshire, England; Kapnik, Rumania; Herrengrund, Hungary; Bohemia; Marquette County, Michigan; DeKalb, New York; Fort Wallace, New Mexico. Also in pockets and lenticular deposits in limestones and associated with calcite and celestite. Deposits of this character are mined at Cartersville, Georgia; also in Missouri, Tennessee, Kentucky, Virginia, and North and South Carolina.

FIG. 627.—Barite (crested).   Marquette County, Michigan.

Barite is used in large quantities in the manufacture of "ready-mixed" paint, lithopone, wall paper, glass, artificial ivory, and insecticides. It is the principal source of the various barium compounds. Some varieties are used for ornamental purposes. See also page 406.

ANGLESITE, $PbSO_4$.

Orthorhombic, bipyramidal class. Crystals are frequently highly modified and may be prismatic (Fig. 628), tabular, or pyramidal in habit. Massive varieties are compact, granular, or nodular.

Distinct basal and prismatic cleavages. Conchoidal fracture. Hardness, 3 to 3.5. Specific gravity, 6.1 to 6.4. Colorless, white, yellow, brown, green, or blue. Adamantine to greasy luster. High indices of refraction, α 1.877, β 1.882, γ 1.894, (+); $2V$ varies from 60° to 75°; $r < v$. Transparent to opaque.

$PbSO_4$. Usually quite pure. Fuses easily in a candle flame. Occurs as a pseudomorph after galena. Alters to cerussite.

Anglesite is a common oxidation product of lead minerals, especially galena. It is commonly found in cracks and cavities with galena and cerussite. Other associates are sphalerite, smithsonite, hemimorphite, and limonite. Excellent crystals are found at Monte Poni, Sardinia; Clausthal, Harz Mountains, Germany; Anglesea, England; Leadhills, Scotland; Phoenixville, Pennsylvania; Tintic district, Utah; various places in Colorado, Missouri, Wisconsin, Arizona, and California; in large deposits in Mexico and Australia.

Anglesite is an ore of lead.

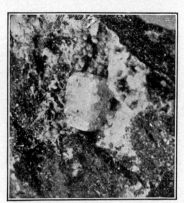

Fig. 628.—Anglesite (prismatic) in galena. Tintic district, Utah.

Fig. 629.—Crocoite. Near Dundas, Tasmania.

Crocoite, PbCrO₄.

Monoclinic, prismatic class. Commonly in prismatic or acicular crystals, often highly modified and striated (Fig. 629). Also columnar, granular, or in crusts.

Distinct basal and prismatic cleavages. Conchoidal to uneven fracture. Hardness, 2.5 to 3. Specific gravity, 5.9 to 6.1. Various shades of red, resembling potassium bichromate in color. Orange-yellow streak. Adamantine luster to greasy. Very high indices of refraction, α 2.31, β 2.37, γ 2.66 (all for lithium light), (+); $2V = 54°$; $r > v$, very strong. Translucent.

$PbCrO_4$. Usually quite pure.

An alteration product of galena and usually associated with galena, quartz, pyrite, vanadinite, wulfenite, and limonite. Found in excellent crystals near Dundas, Tasmania; Siberia; Maricopa County, Arizona.

Not a common mineral and of no commercial importance.

Wolframite Group

The members of this group crystallize in the tetragonal and monoclinic systems (see page 305). The various tungstates are of great commercial importance.

Wulfenite, PbMoO₄.

Tetragonal, tetragonal pyramidal class. Usually in square and thin tabular crystals (Fig. 630). Also pyramidal or short columnar. Sometimes with third-order forms. Hemimorphic development very rare. Also in coarse to fine granular masses.

Hardness, 3. Specific gravity, 6.3 to 7. Resinous to adamantine luster. ω 2.402, ε 2.304 (lithium), (−). Various shades of yellow, red, or green; also gray or white. Yellowish white streak. Transparent to translucent.

PbMoO₄. May contain some calcium, vanadium, molybdenum, or chromium. Occurs as a pseudomorph after galena.

Wulfenite is a secondary mineral, usually the result of the decomposition of lead minerals. It is commonly associated with galena, pyromorphite, and vanadinite. Occurs at Bleiberg, Carinthia, Austria, Přibram, Bohemia; Saxony; Phoenixville, Pennsylvania; various places in Yuma, Maricopa, and Pinal counties, Arizona; Searchlight, Nevada; also in Southampton, Massachusetts; Wisconsin, New Mexico, and California.

Fig. 630.—Wulfenite. Bleiberg, Carinthia, Austria.

A source of molybdenum and its compounds. See page 424.

Scheelite, CaWO₄.

Tetragonal, tetragonal bipyramidal class. Crystals are generally small and pyramidal in habit (Figs. 631 and 632); rarely tabular; some-

Fig. 631.

Fig. 632.—Scheelite on quartz. Zinnwald, Bohemia.

times with third-order forms. More often as crystalline crusts on quartz, or in reniform, disseminated, or granular masses.

Distinct pyramidal cleavage. Conchoidal to uneven fracture. Hardness, 4.5 to 5. Specific gravity, 5.9 to 6.2. White, yellow, brown, green, or reddish. Adamantine to greasy luster. ω 1.918, ϵ 1.934, $(+)$. Transparent to opaque.

$CaWO_4$. Usually contains some molybdenum. Occurs as a pseudomorph after wolframite.

Usually found with quartz, cassiterite, fluorite, topaz, molybdenite, wolframite, and apatite. Occurs in Cornwall and Cumberland, England; Schlaggenwald and Zinnwald, Bohemia; New South Wales; New Zealand; Tasmania; Monroe and Trumbull, Connecticut; San Bernardino and Kern counties, California; Cochise, Pinal, and Santa Cruz counties, Arizona; Jardine, Montana; White Pine and Humboldt counties, Nevada.

An important source of tungsten and its compounds. See page 434.

Huebnerite, $MnWO_4$.

Monoclinic, prismatic class. Generally in long fibrous, bladed, (Fig. 633) or stalky crystals without good terminations. Also in compact, lamellar, or cleavable masses.

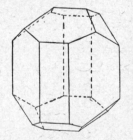

Fig. 633.—Huebnerite in quartz. Pima County, Arizona. Fig. 634. Fig. 635.—Wolframite. Zinnwald, Bohemia.

Clinopinacoidal cleavage. Hardness, 4.5 to 5.5. Specific gravity, 6.7 to 7.3. Brownish, red, brownish black, pale yellow, or nearly black in color; in transmitted light, pale ruby red to yellow. Submetallic to resinous luster. Translucent to opaque. Streak yellow to yellow brown.

$MnWO_4$. Usually contains iron and grades into wolframite.

Occurs in quartz veins with wolframite, fluorite, pyrite, scheelite, galena, tetrahedrite, and muscovite. Thus, in Lemhi County, Idaho; White Pine County, Nevada; Arivaca, Pima County, Arizona; Ouray and San Juan counties, Colorado.

WOLFRAMITE, $(Fe, Mn)WO_4$.

Monoclinic, prismatic class. Crystals are thick tabular or short columnar and often quite large (Figs. 634 and 635). Commonly in bladed, curved lamellar, or granular masses.

Perfect clinopinacoidal cleavage. Uneven fracture. Hardness, 5 to 5.5. Specific gravity, 7.1 to 7.5. Dark gray, reddish brown, brownish black, or iron black in color. Streak varies from dark red-brown for manganiferous varieties to black for those containing much iron. Greasy, submetallic luster. Opaque. Sometimes slightly magnetic.

$(Fe,Mn)WO_4$. An isomorphous mixture of $MnWO_4$ and $FeWO_4$ in which the composition of one of these constituents is not less than 20 per cent. and the other not over 80 per cent. Wolframite is therefore intermediate between huebnerite and ferberite. Occurs as a pseudomorph after scheelite.

Occurs with quartz, mica, fluorite, cassiterite, apatite, scheelite, molybdenite, huebnerite, ferberite, galena, and sphalerite. Some localities are Cornwall, England; various places in Saxony; Zinnwald, Bohemia; Siberia; New South Wales; Burma; the Malay States; Portugal; the Black Hills, South Dakota; Monroe and Trumbull, Connecticut.

Wolframite is a source of tungsten and its compounds. Tungsten is used in the manufacture of high-speed tool steels and as the filament in electric incandescent lamps; sodium tungstate as a mordant and to render cloth noninflammable; tungstic oxide to color glass; and calcium tungstate in X-ray apparatus. See page 434.

Ferberite, $FeWO_4$.

Monoclinic, prismatic class. Crystals are usually tabular and in crested aggregates. Also in compact and granular masses (Fig. 636).

Fig. 636.—Ferberite. Boulder County, Colorado.

Perfect clinopinacoidal cleavage. Uneven fracture. Hardness, 5. Specific gravity, 7.5. Brown to black in color and streak. Opaque.

$FeWO_4$. Usually contains manganese and passes over into wolframite, see above.

Occurs with quartz, hematite, limonite, molybdenite, pyrite, scheelite, wolframite, and sylvanite. The principal occurrences are in Boulder County, Colorado.

Uses are the same as for wolframite.

Uraninite (*Pitchblende*), UO_3, UO_2, PbO, etc.

Cubic, hexoctahedral class. Crystals generally show the octahedron and rhombic dodecahedron but are rare. Commonly in compact, botryoidal, reniform, curved lamellar, or granular masses. Often apparently amorphous (Fig. 637).

Conchoidal to uneven fracture. Hardness, 3 to 6. Specific gravity, 4.8 to 9.7; crystals, 9 to 9.7. Pitchy to submetallic luster on fresh fracture surfaces, otherwise dull. Brown to black in color. Dark green, brown, or black streak. Nonmagnetic.

FIG. 637.—Uraninite or pitchblende. Joachimsthal, Bohemia.

Composition is uncertain. Is considered an uranate of uranyl and lead with varying percentages of the rare earths thorium, cerium, yttrium, lanthanum, and erbium, and the gases nitrogen, argon, and helium. May also contain radium and be strongly radioactive. This element was discovered in uraninite from Joachimsthal, Bohemia. *Cleveite* is a variety from near Arendal, Norway, and contains thorium, argon, and helium. *Nivenite* is characterized by about 10 per cent. of the earths of the yttrium groups. It occurs in Llano County, Texas. *Bröggerite* occurs on the Island of Moss, near Oslo, Norway, and contains considerable thorium.

As a primary constituent of pegmatites and granites, associated with orthite, thorite, and fergusonite, it is found in the Arendal and Moss districts, Norway; Sweden; Branchville, Connecticut; Mitchell County, North Carolina; Llano County, Texas; the Black Hills, South Dakota. With lead, silver, bismuth, and tin minerals it occurs at Joachimsthal and Přibram, Bohemia; Johanngeorgenstadt, Saxony; Cornwall, England; Gilpin County, Colorado; LaBine Point, Great Bear Lake, Canada.

Uraninite is an important source of uranium and radium compounds. Uranium is used in the manufacture of special grades of steels; its compounds for coloring glass and as pigments for porcelain painting. As is well known, radium compounds possess important chemical, physical, and medicinal properties. See page 435.

ALUNITE (*Alum Stone*), $K_2(Al.2OH)_6(SO_4)_4$.

Hexagonal, ditrigonal scalenohedral class. Crystals are generally small rhombohedrons resembling cubes, often with curved surfaces; more rarely tabular. Commonly compact, granular, fibrous, or earthy (Fig. 638).

Perfect basal cleavage. Conchoidal, splintery, or earthy fracture. Hardness, 3.5 to 4; sometimes harder due to admixtures of quartz and feldspar. Tough. Specific gravity, 2.58 to 2.8. Colorless, white, yellowish, or reddish.　Pearly luster on cleavage surfaces, otherwise vitreous.　ω 1.572, ϵ 1.592, (+).　Transparent to translucent.

$K_2(Al.2OH)_6(SO_4)_4$.　May contain some sodium.　Insoluble in hydrochloric acid and water.

Alunite occurs in irregular deposits and in veins in altered feldspathic rocks, such as rhyolites, trachytes, and andesites.　Common associates are kaolin, pyrite, opal, and quartz.　Occurs in Czechoslovakia, Greece, France, Mexico, and Japan.　In the United States, it is found at Silverton and Cripple Creek, Colorado; Mariposa County, California; Morenci,

Fig. 638.—Alunite.
Talfa, Italy.

Fig. 639.—Brochantite. Chuquicamata, Chile.

Arizona; in large quantities with gold in the Goldfield district, Nevada; and Marysvale, Utah.

Alunite is a source of alum and potassium sulphate, which are obtained by roasting and subsequent leaching.　Some of the Hungarian varieties are so hard and tough as to be used for millstones.　Also page 428.

Brochantite, $CuSO_4.3Cu(OH)_2$.

Orthorhombic, bipyramidal class.　Short prismatic and acicular crystals with vertical striations.　Also reniform with fibrous structure, and as drusy crusts (Fig. 639).

Perfect brachypinacoidal cleavage.　Hardness, 3.5 to 4.　Specific gravity, 3.8 to 3.9.　Emerald to blackish green in color.　Light-green streak.　Transparent to translucent.　Vitreous to pearly luster.　α 1.730, β 1.778, γ 1.803, (−); $2V = 72°$; $r < v$.

$CuSO_4.3Cu(OH)_2$.　Loses water at 300°C.

A secondary copper mineral, commonly associated with malachite, azurite, cuprite, chalcopyrite, and limonite.　Occurs in Rumania; the Ural Mountains; Bolivia; Chile; Sonora, Mexico; in various copper districts of Arizona; Chaffee County, Colorado; the Tintic district, Utah.

Of minor importance as a copper mineral.

GYPSUM (*Selenite, Satin Spar, Alabaster*), **CaSO$_4$.2H$_2$O.**

Monoclinic, prismatic class.   Crystals are usually simple and either tabular or prismatic in habit.   Sometimes twinned parallel to the orthopinacoid yielding contact (swallowtail) and penetration twins (Figs.

Fig. 640.—Gypsum crystals—tabular, contact and penetration twins.

Fig. 641.

Fig. 642.

640, 641 and 642).   Very common in cleavable, columnar (Fig. 643), granular, fibrous, foliated, or carthy masses.

There are three cleavages parallel to (1) clinopinacoid, (2) positive unit hemipyramid, and (3) orthopinacoid, yielding very thin and smooth folia, and fibrous and conchoidal surfaces, respectively.   Hardness, 2.

Fig. 643.—Gypsum (columnar or "pencil rock").   Grand Rapids, Michigan.

Fig. 644.—Gypsum: variety, satin spar. Montmartre, P a r i s, France.

Specific gravity, 2.2 to 2.4.   Vitreous to pearly or silky luster. α 1.520, β 1.523, γ 1.530, (+); $2V = 58°; r > v$.   Colorless, white, gray, yellow, brown, reddish, or black.   Transparent to opaque.

CaSO$_4$.2H$_2$O.   Often mixed with clay, sand, or organic matter. Yields water when heated and becomes white and opaque.   Soluble in 380 to 460 parts of water.

There are five varieties of gypsum.

1. *Selenite.*—This includes crystals and cleavable masses and is usually colorless and transparent.

2. *Satin Spar.*—A fibrous variety with a pronounced silky luster (Fig. 644). Sometimes used in cheap jewelry.

3. *Alabaster.*—A massive and usually fine-grained variety (Fig. 645). Sometimes used for statuary and decorative purposes.

4. *Rock Gypsum.*—A compact scaly or granular variety, often very impure. It is frequently ground and used as a fertilizer under the name of *land plaster*.

5. *Gypsite.*—An impure, earthy or sandy variety occurring abundantly in Kansas, Arizona, New Mexico, and Oklahoma.

Gypsum is a common mineral and often occurs in extensive deposits of great thickness. It is usually found with limestones and shales and in connection with salt deposits. Deposits of this character are frequently of great commercial importance. Some of the best known and most extensively worked occurrences are in central and western New York; Alabaster and Grand Rapids, Michigan; Fort Dodge, Iowa; Blue Rapids, Gypsum City, and Medicine Lodge, Kansas; also various places in Oklahoma, Texas, Oregon, South Dakota, and Wyoming. Large deposits occur also at Hillsboro, Albert County, New Brunswick; and in Nova Scotia. Excellent transparent crystals are found at Ellsworth and Canfield in Trumbull County, and also in Mahoning County, Ohio; very large crystals in Wayne County, Utah. New York, Michigan, Iowa, Ohio, and Texas are the chief producers of gypsum.

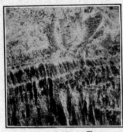

Fig. 645.—Gypsum (polished). Grand Rapids, Michigan.

Gypsum may be formed by deposition from solution or by the hydration of anhydrite; in volcanic regions by the action of sulphurous vapors upon limestone; and in metalliferous veins by the action of sulphuric acid resulting from the oxidation of metallic sulphides. The common associates are halite, celestite, sulphur, aragonite, dolomite, calcite, pyrite, and quartz.

Ground rock gypsum is used to a limited extent as a fertilizer and is called *land plaster*. It is also used as a disinfectant, flux in glass and porcelain manufacture, retarder in cement, and to weight fertilizers. Alabaster is used for statues, vases, pedestals, lamps, and bric-a-bracs. Satin spar and a small amount of selenite are used in cheap jewelry and microscopy, respectively. It is also used as an adulterant of foods, medicines, and paints. When gypsum is calcined so as to drive off $1\frac{1}{2}$ molecules of water, it forms *plaster of Paris*, which has the property of *setting* or becoming hard after being mixed with water. Plaster of Paris is used in very large quantities in patent wall plasters, stucco, white wash, dentistry, crayons, casts, and in many other ways. See also page 409.

Epsomite (*Epsom Salt*), $MgSO_4.7H_2O$.

Orthorhombic, bisphenoidal class. Occasionally in nearly square prismatic crystals (Fig. 646). Commonly as granular, fibrous, or earthy masses, or in crusts.

Perfect brachypinacoidal cleavage. Hardness, 2 to 2.5. Specific gravity, 1.7 to 1.8. Colorless or white. Transparent to translucent. Bitter salty taste. α 1.433, β 1.455, γ 1.461, $(-)$; $2V = 52°$; $r < v$.

$MgSO_4.7H_2O$. Soluble in water. Nonhygroscopic.

Epsomite is a common constituent of ocean, salt lake, and spring waters. Thus, it occurs in the springs at Epsom, England; Saidschitz and elsewhere, Bohemia; Ofen, Hungary. As an alteration product of kieserite, it is found in the salt deposits of Stassfurt, Germany. It may be the result of the action of sulphuric acid from decomposing sulphides on serpentine, talc, magnesite, or other magnesium rocks. At Montmartre, Paris, it occurs with gypsum. It is also found in limestone caves in Kentucky, Tennessee, and Indiana, and in crusts on the alkali plains of Utah, Nevada, and California. It occurs with mirabilite in Albany County, Wyoming.

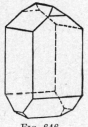

Fig. 646.

Epsomite is used in medicine, as a fertilizer in place of gypsum, and as a coating for cotton cloth.

Melanterite (*Copperas*), $FeSO_4.7H_2O$.

Monoclinic, prismatic class. Crystals are very rare. Usually as earthy, fibrous or capillary crusts or efflorescences.

Conchoidal to earthy fracture. Hardness, 2. Specific gravity, 1.8 to 1.9. Various shades of green in color, often yellowish after exposure. Vitreous to dull luster. α 1.471, β 1.478, γ 1.486, $(+)$; $2V = 86°$; $r > v$. Transparent to translucent. Sweet, astringent taste, somewhat metallic.

$FeSO_4.7H_2O$. Sometimes contains manganese, magnesium, copper, or zinc. Easily soluble in water. Loses water on exposure and crumbles to powder.

Decomposition product of iron sulphide minerals, especially pyrite, marcasite, chalcopyrite, and pyrrhotite. Some localities are the Harz Mountains, Germany; Bodenmais, Bavaria; Falun, Sweden; Rio Tinto, Spain. In the United States, it is generally found as an efflorescence with the sulphides of iron.

Melanterite does not occur abundantly enough in nature to be of commercial importance. The artificial compound is used in large quantities as a mordant in dyeing, as a disinfectant, and in the manufacture of inks, bluing, and pigments.

Chalcanthite (*Blue Vitriol, Blue Stone*), **$CuSO_4.5H_2O$.**

Triclinic, pinacoidal class. Rarely as small, flat crystals. Generally in crusts with reniform, stalactitic, or fibrous structure.

Crystals possess imperfect basal and prismatic cleavages. Conchoidal fracture. Hardness, 2.5. Specific gravity, 2.1 to 2.3. Vitreous to dull luster. α 1.516, β 1.539, γ 1.546, $(-)$; $2V = 56°$; $r < v$. Deep blue, sky blue, or greenish blue in color. White to light-blue streak. Translucent. Disagreeable metallic taste.

$CuSO_4.5H_2O$. May contain iron. Readily soluble in water, yielding a blue solution, especially when ammoniacal.

Chalcanthite is an alteration product of copper minerals, such as chalcopyrite, chalcocite, and bornite. Occurs in the mines of the Harz Mountains, Germany; also in Czechoslovakia; Falun, Sweden; Rio Tinto, Spain; Chessy, France; Cornwall, England; Wicklow, Ireland. It was formerly found in considerable quantities in the Bluestone Mine, near Reno, Nevada, and at Copiapo, Chile. Found also in the water of the copper mines of Arizona and Montana. The copper in such mine water is recovered by precipitation with scrap iron.

Only rarely does it occur in sufficient quantities to be of commercial importance. The artificial compound is used in copper plating, in batteries, as a mordant and preservative of timber, and for spraying plants.

VII. ALUMINATES, FERRITES, AND BORATES

Of the six minerals described in this division, five have analogous chemical compositions and are considered as forming the spinel group.

SPINEL GROUP

SPINEL	$Mg(AlO_2)_2$	Cubic
MAGNETITE	$Fe(FeO_2)_2$	Cubic
FRANKLINITE	$(Fe,Mn,Zn)(FeO_2)_2$	Cubic
CHROMITE	$(Fe,Cr)[(Cr,Fe)O_2]_2$	Cubic
Chrysoberyl	$Be(AlO_2)_2$	Orthorhombic
Colemanite	$Ca_2B_6O_{11}.5H_2O$	Monoclinic

Colemanite and kernite (see page 324) are the only borates occurring in nature in sufficient quantities to be of any commercial importance.

Spinel Group

Several members of this group rank among the very important minerals. All these minerals are hard, 5.5 to 8.5; those with metallic luster are the softer, varying from 5.5 to 6.5.

SPINEL, $Mg(AlO_2)_2$.

Cubic, hexoctahedral class. Octahedral crystals (Fig. 647), frequently in combination with the rhombic dodecahedron (Fig. 648).

FIG. 647.—Spinel (octahedron). Labelle County, Quebec, Canada.

FIG. 648.—Spinel (octahedron and rhombic dodecahedron) in calcite. Franklin Furnace, New Jersey.

Contact twins are common, twinned parallel to a face of the octahedron (spinel law). Generally in disseminated or loose crystals or in rounded grains.

Imperfect octahedral cleavage. Hardness, 7.5 to 8. Specific gravity, 3.5 to 4.5. Vitreous to nearly dull in luster. $n = 1.72$. All colors, but chiefly red, blue, green, brown, and black. Transparent to opaque. May become luminescent.

$Mg(AlO_2)_2$. Magnesium may be replaced by iron, zinc, or manganese; the aluminum by ferric iron and chromium. Infusible.

There are several important varieties:

1. *Ruby Spinel.*—Deep red in color, transparent.
2. *Rubicelle.*—Yellow or orange red in color.
3. *Blue Spinel.*—Light blue in color.
4. *Almandine.*—Bluish red or violet in color.
5. *Pleonaste.*—An iron-magnesium spinel. Dark green, brown, or black. Usually opaque or nearly so.
6. *Picotite.*—Contains chromium. Black, yellow, or greenish brown. Translucent to nearly opaque.
7. *Gahnite.*—Contains zinc. Commonly in fairly large crystals. Various shades of green, also brown or black. Translucent to opaque.

Spinel is a common metamorphic mineral occurring usually in granular limestones, gneiss, and serpentine. It is also an accessory constituent of basic igneous rocks. Gem spinels are frequently found in placer deposits, especially in Ceylon, Burma, and Siam. The common associates are calcite, chondrodite, corundum, graphite, and olivine. Important localities are Åker, Sweden; Orange and St. Lawrence counties, New York; Franklin Furnace, New Jersey; Bolton, Massachusetts; Macon County, North Carolina.

Synthetic spinel is an important refractory. Transparent and colored spinels (natural and synthetic) are used as gems (see page 401).

MAGNETITE (*Magnetic Iron Ore, Lodestone*), **$Fe(FeO_2)_2$.**

Cubic, hexoctahedral class. Octahedral and rhombic dodecahedral crystals are very common, often very perfect and with bright surfaces.

Fig. 649.—Magnetite crystals—octahedron, rhombic dodecahedron, tetragonal trisoctahedron, striated.

Striated faces are, however, not infrequently observed. Twinned according to the spinel law, yielding contact and polysynthetic twins. Crystals are sometimes highly modified and may be greatly distorted (Fig. 649). Usually occurs in coarse- to fine-grained masses, in lamellar to compact aggregates, as disseminated grains, or as loose grains or sand; more rarely dendritic, especially in mica.

Octahedral parting. Conchoidal to uneven fracture. Hardness, 5.5 to 6.5. Specific gravity, 4.9 to 5.2. Metallic, submetallic to dull luster. Iron-black color. Black streak. Opaque. Strongly magnetic (Fig. 650).

Fe(FeO$_2$)$_2$. Commonly written Fe$_3$O$_4$. May contain magnesium, nickel, manganese, phosphorus, or titanium. Fuses with difficulty. Alters to limonite and hematite (martite). Magnetite occurs as a pseudomorph after pyrite, hematite, and siderite.

Magnetite occurs rather widespread, being found principally as (1) a primary constituent of basic igneous rocks, such as diabase, gabbro, nepheline syenite, and basalt; (2) as a metamorphic mineral; and (3)

FIG. 650.—Magnetite: variety, lodestone. Magnet Cove, Arkansas.

FIG. 651.—Magnetite (octahedron) in chloritic schist. Zillerthal, Tirol.

as a constituent of certain river, lake, and sea sands, called *black sands*. The common associates are chlorite (Fig. 651), hornblende, pyroxene, feldspar, quartz, pyrite, chalcopyrite, epidote, chromite, garnet, and ilmenite. Large deposits are found in Norway and Sweden; the Ural Mountains; Brazil; Mineville, New York; Cornwall, Pennsylvania; Oxford, New Jersey. Black sands are rather widespread in Alaska, California, Idaho, Montana, Colorado, Oregon, and Washington. They sometimes carry small amounts of platinum. Magnetite from Magnet Cove, Arkansas, is usually very strongly magnetic and is termed *lodestone*.

Magnetite is an important iron ore. Also see page 417.

FIG. 652.—Franklinite (octahedron and rhombic dodecahedron) with calcite. Franklin Furnace, New Jersey.

FRANKLINITE (Fe, Mn, Zn)(FeO$_2$)$_2$.

Cubic, hexoctahedral class. The octahedron is rather common, sometimes with the rhombic dodecahedron (Fig. 652) and with rounded edges. Occurs usually in compact and granular masses or as rounded grains.

Imperfect octahedral cleavage. Conchoidal fracture. Hardness, 5.5 to 6.5. Specific gravity, 5 to 5.2. Metallic or dull luster. Iron black in color. Brown, reddish, or black streak. Often slightly magnetic. Opaque.

$(Fe,Mn,Zn)(FeO_2)_2$. The composition varies greatly, ZnO from 17 to 25 per cent., MnO from 10 to 12 per cent., and Fe_2O_3 about 60 per cent. When heated becomes strongly magnetic. Infusible.

Franklinite occurs extensively in the metamorphic area about Franklin Furnace and Sterling Hill, Sussex County, New Jersey, where it is associated with willemite, zincite, rhodonite, and calcite. Also found in cubical crystals at Eibach, Hessen-Nassau, Germany.

Franklinite is a source of zinc which, by heating the mineral, is easily obtained either as spelter or zinc oxide. The residue contains about 12 per cent. of manganese and 40 per cent. of iron and is used as spiegeleisen in the manufacture of steel. See pages 423 and 436.

CHROMITE (*Chrome Iron, Chromic Iron Ore*), $(Fe,Cr)[(Cr,Fe)O_2]_2$.

Cubic, hexoctahedral class. Rarely in octahedral crystals. Usually in fine granular, compact masses, or as disseminated grains.

Indistinct, octahedral cleavage. Uneven to conchoidal fracture. Hardness, 5.5. Specific gravity, 4.3 to 4.6. Pitchy submetallic to metallic luster. Iron black to brownish black in color. Dark brown to grayish streak. Opaque. Sometimes slightly magnetic.

$(Fe,Cr)[(Cr,Fe)O_2]_2$. May contain magnesium and aluminum.

Chromite occurs usually in veins and irregular masses in basic magnesium rocks, especially serpentine. It is often the result of magmatic segregation. The common associates are serpentine, talc, chrome garnet, zaratite, and corundum. It occurs at Franckenstein, Silesia; New Zealand; Rhodesia; New Caledonia; Greece; Asia Minor; India; Cuba; Texas; Lancaster County, and elsewhere in Pennsylvania; Baltimore County, Maryland; Shasta and other counties in California; also in North Carolina, Oregon, Washington, and Wyoming. Also found in platinum placers and in black sands.

Chromite is used in the manufacture of refractory chrome bricks and furnace linings; for making special grades of steels, such as ferrochrome used for cutting-tools, projectiles, and armor plate; for stainless steel and rustless iron; also for the production of pigments, dyes, and mordants, and in tanning. See also page 413.

Chrysoberyl, $Be(AlO_2)_2$.

Orthorhombic, bipyramidal class. Crystals are tabular, also heart-shaped and pseudohexagonal twins; frequently striated (Figs. 653, 654, and 655). Also as crystal fragments and loose or rounded grains.

Distinct brachypinacoidal cleavage. Conchoidal fracture. Hardness, 8.5. Specific gravity, 3.5 to 3.8. Vitreous to greasy luster. α 1.747, β 1.748, γ 1.757, $(+)$; $2V = 45°$; $r > v$. Greenish white, greenish yellow, and asparagus to emerald green in color; often red in transmitted light. Transparent to translucent. Some varieties have a bluish opalescence or chatoyancy.

$Be(AlO_2)_2$. May contain some iron and chromium. Infusible. Insoluble in acids.

There are three varieties:

1. *Ordinary Chrysoberyl.*—Usually green or pale green in color.

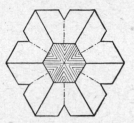

FIG. 653. FIG. 654.—Chrysoberyl (twin). Haddam, Connecticut. FIG. 655.

2. *Alexandrite.*—Emerald green in color, but red in transmitted gas or lamp light; with tungsten light, intermediate between red and green. Artificial-gem corundum exhibiting these properties is often sold as alexandrite. See page 400.

3. *Cat's-eye or Cymophane.*—An opalescent, yellow-green variety.

Chrysoberyl is usually found in gneiss, mica schist, or granite. Common associates are beryl, tourmaline, garnet, apatite, and sillimanite. It occurs in the Ural Mountains; Haddam, Connecticut; Norway and Stoneham, Maine; Greenfield, New York; as rounded pebbles in the gem placers of Ceylon, Tasmania, and Brazil.

Transparent varieties are highly prized as gems.

FIG. 656.—Colemanite (geode). San Bernardino County, California.

Colemanite, $Ca_2B_6O_{11}.5H_2O$.

Monoclinic, prismatic class. Crystals are usually short prismatic and resemble datolite (Fig. 656); often highly modified. Also in compact, granular, and cleavable masses, which look like chalk or porcelain.

Highly perfect, clinopinacoidal cleavage. Uneven to subconchoidal fracture. Hardness, 3.5 to 4.5. Specific gravity, 2.4. Vitreous to dull luster. α 1.586, β 1.592, γ 1.614, (+); $2V = 56°$; $r < v$. Colorless to white. Transparent to opaque.

$Ca_2B_6O_{11}.5H_2O$. Easily soluble in hot hydrochloric acid. Boracic acid separates on cooling. Insoluble in water. Treated with sodium carbonate or sulphate it yields borax ($Na_2B_4O_7.10H_2O$).

Commonly associated with halite, thenardite, trona, gypsum, celestite, and quartz. As a lake deposit it occurs extensively in San Bernardino, Inyo, Los Angeles, Kern, and Ventura counties, California, and Clark, Esmeralda, and Mineral counties, Nevada.

Until recently, colemanite was the chief source of borax, which is used extensively in the manufacture of soap, enamels, glass, washing powders, ointments, and lotions; also in welding, soldering, assaying, and blowpiping, and as an antiseptic, and as a preservative for meat and fish. See page 407.

Kernite (rasorite) ($Na_2B_4O_7.4H_2O$) occurs in large deposits in Kern County, California. In appearance it resembles cleavable gypsum. Monoclinic. Hardness, 2.5 to 3. Specific gravity, 1.91. Easily soluble in water, the solution yielding borax on evaporation. Occurs in clay beds associated with borax, ulexite, and colemanite. Kernite furnishes a large percentage of the annual supply of borax. See also page 407.

VIII. PHOSPHATES, COLUMBATES, AND VANADATES

A large number of minerals belonging to this division have been recorded in the literature, but only eight are of sufficient importance to warrant description.

Monazite	$(Ce,La,Di)PO_4$	Monoclinic
COLUMBITE	$(Fe,Mn)[(Cb,Ta)O_3]_2$	Orthorhombic

APATITE GROUP

APATITE	$Ca_5F(PO_4)_3$	Hexagonal
PYROMORPHITE	$Pb_5Cl(PO_4)_3$	Hexagonal
Vanadinite	$Pb_5Cl(VO_4)_3$	Hexagonal

Wavellite	$(AlOH)_3(PO_4)_2.5H_2O$	Orthorhombic
Turquois	$H_5[Al(OH)_2]_6Cu(OH)(PO_4)_4$	Triclinic
Carnotite	$K_2O.2UO_3.V_2O_5.3H_2O$	Orthorhombic

Columbite is a salt of metatantalic acid (H_2TaO_3). The phosphates can be referred to the orthophosphoric acid (H_3PO_4), while vanadinite is a derivative of a corresponding acid, H_3VO_4.

Monazite, $(Ce,La,Di)PO_4$.

Monoclinic, prismatic class. Crystals are thick tabular or square prismatic, usually small and not common. Generally found as angular disseminated masses and as rolled grains in sand.

Perfect basal cleavage. Conchoidal fracture. Hardness, 5 to 5.5. Specific gravity, 4.9 to 5.3. Brownish gray, yellow, or reddish in color. White streak. Resinous luster. α 1.786, β 1.788, γ 1.837, $(+)$; $2V = 14°$; $r < v$. Translucent to opaque.

$(Ce,La,Di)PO_4$. May contain from 0.5 to 20 per cent. of ThO_2; commercial monazite sand contains usually from 2.5 to 5 per cent.

Occurs disseminated in granites and gneisses; thus, at Arendal, Norway; Miask, Ural Mountains; Binnenthal, Switzerland; Amelia Court House, Virginia. The most important occurrence of monazite is as sand, extensive deposits of which are found in the western part of North and South Carolina and Georgia; in the provinces of Bahia, Minas Geraes, Rio de Janeiro, and São Paulo, Brazil; Travancore, India; also in the Ural Mountains. Common associates are magnetite, zircon, garnet, ilmenite, thorite, gold, chromite, and sometimes the diamond.

Monazite is the chief source of thorium dioxide which is used in the manufacture of incandescent mantles. It is also a source of cerium oxide. Most of the world's supply is obtained from Brazil and India. See page 413.

COLUMBITE, (Fe,Mn)[(Cb,Ta)O$_3$]$_2$.

Orthorhombic, bipyramidal class. Short prismatic or thick tabular crystals, often resembling those of wolframite. Also massive and disseminated.

Brachypinacoidal cleavage. Conchoidal to uneven fracture, often with iridescent tarnish. Hardness, 6. Specific gravity, 5.4 to 6.4. Brown to iron black in color. Brownish, reddish, or black streak. Greasy, submetallic to dull luster.

(Fe,Mn)[(Cb,Ta)O$_3$]$_2$. Composition varies greatly. Frequently containing tin and tungsten. When tantalum predominates, it is called *tantalite*. Infusible. Not attacked by acids.

Columbite occurs in granite pegmatites, associated with beryl, tourmaline, spodumene, lepidolite, cryolite, quartz, feldspar, wolframite, and cassiterite. It occurs at Ivigtut, southern Greenland; Bodenmais, Bavaria; Miask, Ural Mountains; Western Australia; Standish, Maine; Branchville, Connecticut; Mitchell County, North Carolina; the Black Hills, South Dakota; Amelia County, Virginia.

An important source of columbium and tantalum. Filaments of tantalum have been used in electric incandescent lamps. See also page 414.

Apatite Group

This group contains the calcium and lead salts of orthophosphoric and orthovanadic acids. These minerals form an interesting isomorphous series.

APATITE, Ca$_5$F(PO$_4$)$_3$.

Hexagonal, hexagonal bipyramidal class. Prismatic and thick tabular crystals are common, often well developed and highly modified. Sometimes large. The edges may be rounded and have a fused appearance. At times forms of the third order are to be observed (Fig. 657). Also in compact, fibrous, nodular, reniform, oölitic, or earthy masses.

Imperfect basal cleavage. Conchoidal fracture. Hardness, 5. Specific gravity, 3.1 to 3.2. Sometimes colorless and transparent but usually translucent to opaque and variously colored, brown, green, gray, yellow, red, blue, purple, or white. Sometimes unevenly colored. Vitreous to greasy luster. ω 1.634, ϵ 1.631, ($-$). May become luminescent.

Apatite is essentially an orthophosphate of calcium containing fluorine, chlorine, or hydroxyl in varying amounts. Hence, the following formulas have been assigned to it: Ca$_5$F(PO$_4$)$_3$, Ca$_5$Cl(PO$_4$)$_3$, and Ca$_5$(Cl,F,OH)(PO$_4$)$_3$. Fluorine usually predominates, *fluorapatite* being more common than *chloroapatite*. Magnesium, manganese, and iron may also be present. Fuses with difficulty. Easily soluble in acids. May phosphoresce when heated.

There are three important varieties:

1. *Ordinary Apatite.*—This includes crystallized, cleavable, and granular varieties.

2. *Phosphate Rock.*—An impure amorphous variety, containing 15 to 40 per cent. of P_2O_5. Color is gray, white, brown, or black. The hardness varies from 2 to 5. It occurs in beds, or as nodules and concretions. *Collophanite*, approximately $Ca_3(PO_4)_2.H_2O$ is an important constituent of phosphate rock.

3. *Guano.*—Animal excrement, chiefly of birds, rich in phosphoric acid. Gray to brown in color, and porous, granular, or compact in structure.

Apatite is a common accessory constituent of many igneous rocks. It is an associate of metalliferous ore deposits, especially those of magnet-

FIG. 657.—Apatite crystals—prismatic, fused edges and corners, tabular.

FIG. 658.—Apatite in calcite. Franklin Furnace, New Jersey.

ite and cassiterite. It occurs also in granular limestones (Fig. 658) and, in fact, is present in small quantities in nearly all types of rocks. Common associates are calcite, cassiterite, quartz, fluorite, wolframite, and magnetite. Some important localities are Ehrenfriedersdorf, Saxony; Schlaggenwald, Bohemia; Saint Gotthard, Switzerland; Knappenwand, Tirol; Japan; Renfrew County, Ontario; Ottawa County, Quebec; Norwich and Bolton, Massachusetts; St. Lawrence and Jefferson Counties, New York; Chester County, Pennsylvania; Franklin Furnace, New Jersey; Auburn, Maine.

Phosphate rock occurs in extensive deposits in Florida, South Carolina, Tennessee, Pennsylvania, Arkansas, Wyoming, Idaho, Utah, and Montana.

Phosphate rock is used in enormous quantities in the manufacture of fertilizers, its phosphoric acid content being rendered available by treating with sulphuric acid. Apatite is also used to some extent as a source of phosphorus and of phosphoric acid (H_3PO_4). Also see page 426.

PYROMORPHITE, $Pb_5Cl(PO_4)_3$.

Hexagonal, hexagonal bipyramidal class. Crystals are usually small, rounded, or barrel shaped (Fig. 659). Often hollow and skeletal or in parallel groups. Sometimes they resemble those of apatite. Occurs also in botryoidal and reniform aggregates, disseminated, and in crusts.

Conchoidal to uneven fracture. Hardness, 3.5 to 4. Specific gravity, 6.9 to 7.1. Usually some shade of green, but may be yellow, gray, brown, orange, or white. White to pale yellow streak. Greasy to adamantine luster. ω 2.050, ϵ 2.042, $(-)$. Translucent to opaque.

$Pb_5Cl(PO_4)_3$. May contain calcium, fluorine, or arsenic. Occurs as a pseudomorph after galena and cerussite.

FIG. 659.—Pyromorphite. Ems, Hessen-Nassau, Germany.

Pyromorphite is generally a secondary mineral formed from the decomposition of lead ores. Common associates are galena, cerussite, barite, and limonite. It occurs in the Freiberg district, Saxony; Clausthal, Harz Mountains; Ems, Hessen-Nassau, Germany; Cornwall and Cumberland, England; Phoenixville, Pennsylvania; Lubec and Lenox, Maine; Leadhills, Scotland; Coeur d'Alene, Idaho.

A minor source of lead.

Vanadinite, $Pb_5Cl(VO_4)_3$.

Hexagonal, hexagonal bipyramidal class. Crystals are usually prismatic, often skeletal and resembling those of pyromorphite. Occurs also compact, fibrous, globular, and in crusts.

Uneven to conchoidal fracture. Hardness, 3. Specific gravity, 6.7 to 7.2. Yellow, brown, or red in color. White to pale-yellow streak. Translucent to opaque. Resinous luster. ω 2.354, ϵ 2.299, $(-)$.

$Pb_5Cl(VO_4)_3$. May contain phosphorus or arsenic. *Endlichite* is a light-yellow variety containing arsenic. ω 2.25, ϵ 2.20, $(-)$. Fuses easily. Readily soluble in nitric acid.

Occurs associated with lead minerals but never in large quantities. Some localities are Zimapan, Mexico; the Ural Mountains; various places in Yuma, Maricopa, Pinal, and Yavapai counties, Arizona; Kelley, New Mexico.

It is a source of vanadium and its compounds. See page 435.

Wavellite, $(AlOH)_3(PO_4)_2.5H_2O$.

Orthorhombic, bipyramidal class. Good crystals are very rare. Usually in crystalline crusts, or hemispherical or globular masses made up of concentric layers and possessing a radial fibrous structure (Fig. 660).

Conchoidal to uneven fracture.   Hardness, 3.5 to 4.   Specific gravity, 2.3 to 2.4.   May be colorless but is usually gray, yellow, green, blue, or black.   Vitreous luster. α 1.525, β 1.534, γ 1.552,   (+); $2V = 72°$; $r > v$.   Translucent.

$(AlOH)_3(PO_4)_2.5H_2O$.   The water of crystallization may vary. Some varieties contain fluorine.   Infusible.   Soluble in hydrochloric acid.

Wavellite is a secondary mineral formed by the action of circulating waters, containing phosphoric acid, upon rocks and minerals rich in aluminum.   It is, hence, found on the surfaces of such rocks, or lining the cracks and cavities in the same.   Some localities are Devonshire and Cornwall, England; Cerhovic, Bohemia; Chester and York counties, Pennsylvania; Montgomery and Garland counties, Arkansas; Silver Hill, South Carolina.

Fig. 660.—Wavellite. Arkansas.

Fig. 661.—Turquois. Los Cerrillos, New Mexico.

Turquois, $H_5[Al(OH)_2]_6Cu(OH)(PO_4)_4$.

Triclinic.   Crystals are tabular but very rare.   Usually apparently amorphous, in reniform, botryoidal, or stalactitic masses and in veins; also as crusts, coatings (Fig. 661), and disseminated grains, or rolled and rounded pebbles.

Conchoidal fracture.   Hardness, 6.   Specific gravity, 2.6 to 2.8. Various shades of blue or green.   Darker blue in artificial light.   Translucent to opaque.   Waxy to dull luster. α 1.61, β 1.62, γ 1.65, (+); $2V = 40°$; $r < v$.   White or slightly greenish streak.

$H_5[Al(OH)_2]_6Cu(OH)(PO_4)_4$.   Infusible.   Soluble   in   acids   after ignition.

Turquois is a secondary mineral and is often associated with limonite, quartz, feldspar, or kaolin.   It occurs in trachyte near Nishapur in the Province of Khorassan, Persia; Los Cerrillos and elsewhere, New Mexico; Turquois Mountain, Arizona; San Bernardino County, California; Nye County, Nevada; Colorado.

Used as a gem mineral.   Color fades in time and is destroyed by heat.

Carnotite, $K_2O.2UO_3.V_2O_5.3H_2O$.

Orthorhombic. Crystals are small, tabular, and with a rhombic outline. Usually observed in scaly aggregates, incrustations, or as a crystalline powder.

Perfect basal cleavage. Earthy fracture. Hardness, 1 to 2. Canary to lemon yellow in color. Resinous to dull luster. α 1.750, β 1.925, γ 1.950, $(-)$; $2V$ varies from 39° to 44°; $r < v$. Transparent to translucent.

A vanadate of potassium and uranium, containing small amounts of radium.

Occurs as a powdery incrustation in loosely cohering masses or as an impregnation in sand or sandstone. Common associates are malachite, azurite, biotite, and magnetite. Occurs in San Miguel and Montrose counties, Colorado; San Juan County, Utah; Maricopa County, Arizona; Mauch Chunk, Pennsylvania; Radium Hill, South Australia.

An important source of radium. See page 435.

IX. SILICATES

This division contains a very large number of minerals, some of which are exceedingly common. For example, the members of the groups known as the feldspars, pyroxenes, amphiboles, and micas are very abundant and important as rock minerals. The feldspars alone make up 60 per cent. of the igneous rocks.

For the most part, the chemical composition of these minerals is rather complex. In contrast to such groups as the carbonates or sulphates in which the acid radical has the definite composition CO_3 or SO_4, the silicate radical may vary greatly. Thus, in the list of silicate minerals on pages 335 and 336, there will be found SiO_3, SiO_4, SiO_5, Si_2O_9, Si_3O_8, and so forth. Until recently the silicates have been interpreted as salts of various hypothetical silicic acids, all of which were derived from orthosilicic acid (H_4SiO_4). By the loss of a molecule of water, metasilicic acid (H_2SiO_3) was assumed to be formed. By the loss of water from several molecules of these acids, more complex acids were derived as follows:

Orthosilicic acid	H_4SiO_4	
Metasilicic acid	H_2SiO_3	$(H_4SiO_4 - H_2O)$
Diorthosilicic acid	$H_6Si_2O_7$	$(2H_4SiO_4 - H_2O)$
Trisilicic acid	$H_4Si_3O_8$	$(3H_4SiO_4 - 4H_2O)$
Dimetasilicic acid	$H_2Si_2O_5$	$(2H_2SiO_3 - H_2O)$

The polysilicic acids are still more complex.

In this manner, acids with the proper ratios of silicon to oxygen could be derived that would correspond to the chemical compositions of the various silicates. This method of interpreting the composition of the silicates is no longer considered adequate, although such terms as orthosilicate and metasilicate are still used. A more acceptable interpretation has been made possible through a knowledge of the crystal structures of the minerals of this group.

Structures of the Silicates.—In recent years the structures of a large number of silicates have been investigated by X-ray methods. The results have shown that invariably the silicon atom is surrounded by four oxygen atoms. These oxygen atoms may be arranged symmetrically at equal distances, occurring at the corners of a regular tetrahedron, or at unequal distances, forming a distorted tetrahedron. The Si–O distance never departs more than a few per cent. from a value of 1.62 Å. This SiO_4 tetrahedron apparently is the fundamental unit of all silicates. It may occur either singly, or in groups formed by the sharing of one or more of the oxygen atoms by adjacent tetrahedrons.

The orthosilicates have independent SiO_4 groups (Figs. 662 and 663), joined together through the positive metal atoms or ions. Among the minerals with this type of structure are olivine, zircon, garnet, and topaz.

In Fig. 662 the relative sizes of the silicon and oxygen atoms are ignored, and the symbols ● and ○, respectively, merely indicate the centers of the atoms. Actually the oxygen atoms are about five times as large as

FIG. 662.   FIG. 663.

those of silicon, and the single silicon atom occupies the space at the center of four oxygen atoms arranged tetrahedrally. This is shown in Fig. 663, where only the four oxygen atoms are visible, the silicon atom being hidden at the center.

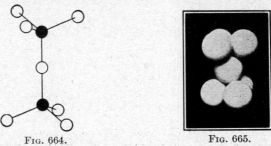

FIG. 664.   FIG. 665.

Two SiO_4 tetrahedrons may be linked together, with one oxygen atom held in common, resulting in a Si_2O_7 group (Figs. 664 and 665).

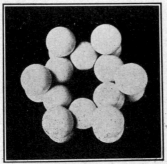

FIG. 666.

Independent groups of this kind have been found in the rare mineral thortveitite and in the melilite group. Three SiO_4 groups may be joined by shared oxygen atoms to form a triangular ring, with the composition Si_3O_9; and six may form a hexagonal ring, with the composition Si_6O_{18} (Fig. 666). Such groups have been reported for the minerals benitoite and beryl, respectively.

The two very important mineral groups, the pyroxenes and the amphiboles, have structures in which the SiO_4 tetrahedrons are linked into endless chains. In the pyroxenes the chain is single (Fig. 667), and the silicon and oxygen are present in the ratio of 1:3, giving the formula SiO_3. In the amphiboles the chain is double, corresponding to a single chain reflected across a plane of symmetry (Fig. 668). The composition of the double chain is Si_4O_{11}.

Some of the silicates, such as talc and the chlorites and micas, possess marked basal cleavages. These minerals have structures in which the SiO_4 tetrahedrons are linked together to form continuous sheets. Three oxygen atoms of each tetrahedron are held in common, resulting in the composition of Si_2O_5. This composition may be varied by the partial substitution of aluminum for silicon, giving $(Si,Al)_2O_5$.

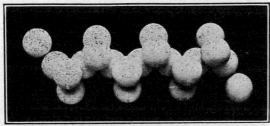

FIG. 667.

A further possibility is a structure in which all four oxygen atoms of the SiO_4 tetrahedrons are held in common. This results in a three-dimensional framework of tetrahedrons, in which the $Si:O$ ratio is $1:2$. The various forms of silicon dioxide (SiO_2) have this arrangement. The tetravalent silicon is balanced by the two divalent oxygen atoms, and no additional positive metallic ions are present. In silicates with this type of structure, the silicon is partly replaced by aluminum so that the

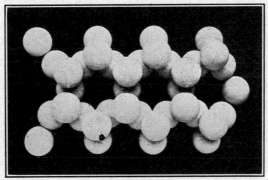

FIG. 668.

composition is $(Si,Al)O_2$. The substitution of Al^{+3} for Si^{+4} requires additional metallic ions in order to balance the valences. The feldspars and the zeolites are characterized by this type of structure. In these compounds silicon and aluminum are present in such amounts that the ratio of these elements to oxygen is $1:2$. This is readily seen in the following formulas:

Feldspars	Orthoclase	$KAlSi_3O_8$
	Anorthite	$CaAl_2Si_2O_8$
Zeolite	Analcite	$NaAlSi_2O_6 \cdot H_2O$

The various silicate structures are summarized in the following table:

	(Si,Al):O
Single SiO₄ groups.....................................	1:4
Multiple groups.......................................	2:7 3:9 6:18
Single chains...	1:3
Double chains...	4:11
Sheets...	2:5
Three-dimensional frameworks..........................	1:2

Composition of the Silicates.—The silicates show wide variation in composition because of the different $Si:O$ ratios which are possible. They also may have variable compositions because of extensive isomorphous replacement. This replacement may consist of a substitution of one element by another of the same valence, as Fe^{+2} for Mg, or Fe^{+3} for Al; or there may be a change in valence, as Ca^{+2} for Na^+, or Al^{+3} for Si^{+4}. In the latter case the valence balance must be maintained by some additional replacement. This is shown by the plagioclase feldspars, albite and anorthite, in which the substitution of Ca^{+2} for Na^+ is accompanied simultaneously by the change from $(AlSi_3)^{+15}$ to $(Al_2Si_2)^{+14}$, the formulas being $NaAlSi_3O_8$ and $CaAl_2Si_2O_8$, respectively.

Silicate Formulas.—Various methods are used for expressing the chemical composition of the silicates. Molecular structural formulas, similar to those of the organic chemist, are unsatisfactory, because in silicates the molecule does not form the structural unit. Empirical formulas, giving the total number of atoms present, are frequently used. Another common method of expressing the composition is one in which the constituents are given as a series of oxides. Thus the formula of the mineral staurolite may be written either $H_2FeAl_4Si_2O_{12}$ or $FeO.2Al_2O_3.-2SiO_2.H_2O$. Neither of these two methods gives any indication of the structural arrangement. Since the structure of staurolite has been interpreted as consisting of alternate layers of $Fe(OH)_2$ and $2Al_2SiO_5$, the formula may also be written $Fe(OH)_2.2Al_2SiO_5$.

In many cases the empirical formula does not reveal the $Si:O$ ratio, according to which the silicate structures are classified. Thus the members of the trimorphous series, andalusite, sillimanite, and cyanite, all have independent SiO_4 groups, although the formula is usually written Al_2SiO_5. The fifth oxygen atom is linked to aluminum instead of silicon, so the composition might properly be expressed as $Al_2O.SiO_4$. Moreover, many of the silicates contain chemically combined water, and in the empirical formula the oxygen of this water is grouped with the remaining oxygen, hence the characteristic $Si:O$ ratio is not revealed.

Silicate Minerals.—The following minerals include the most abundant and important silicates:

STAUROLITE	$H_2FeAl_4Si_2O_{12}$	Orthorhombic
HEMIMORPHITE	$H_2Zn_2SiO_5$	Orthorhombic

ANDALUSITE GROUP

ANDALUSITE	Al_2SiO_5	Orthorhombic
Sillimanite	Al_2SiO_5	Orthorhombic
CYANITE	Al_2SiO_5	Triclinic

TOPAZ	$Al_2(F,OH)_2SiO_4$	Orthorhombic
Datolite	$Ca(BOH)SiO_4$	Monoclinic
TOURMALINE	$M'_{20}B_2Si_4O_{21}$	Hexagonal
Chondrodite	$[Mg(F,OH)]_2Mg_3(SiO_4)_2$	Monoclinic

EPIDOTE GROUP

EPIDOTE	$Ca_2(Al,Fe)_2(AlOH)(SiO_4)_3$	Monoclinic
Orthite	$Ca_2(Al,Ce,Fe)_2(AlOH)(SiO_4)_3$	Monoclinic

VESUVIANITE	$Ca_6[Al(OH,F)]Al_2(SiO_4)_5$	Tetragonal
OLIVINE	$(Mg,Fe)_9SiO_4$	Orthorhombic
Willemite	Zn_2SiO_4	Hexagonal

ZIRCON	$ZrSiO_4$	Tetragonal
GARNETS	$M''_3M'''_2(SiO_4)_3$	Cubic

BERYL	$Be_3Al_2Si_6O_{18}$	Hexagonal
CHRYSOCOLLA	CuO, SiO_2, H_2O	Amorphous?

MICA GROUP

MUSCOVITE	$KAl_2(OH)_2AlSi_3O_{10}$	Monoclinic
PHLOGOPITE	$KMg_3(OH)_2AlSi_3O_{10}$	Monoclinic
BIOTITE	$K(Mg,Fe)_3(OH)_2AlSi_3O_{10}$	Monoclinic
Lepidolite	$K_2Li_3Al_3(OH,F)_4(AlSi_3O_{10})_2$	Monoclinic

CHLORITE	$H_8Mg_5Al_2Si_3O_{18}$	Monoclinic
TALC	$H_2Mg_3Si_4O_{12}$	Monoclinic
KAOLINITE	$H_4Al_2Si_2O_9$	Monoclinic
SERPENTINE	$H_4Mg_3Si_2O_9$	Monoclinic
Sepiolite	$H_8Mg_2Si_3O_{12}$	Monoclinic
Garnierite	$H_2(Ni,Mg)SiO_4$	Amorphous?

PYROXENE GROUP

ENSTATITE	$(Mg,Fe)_2(SiO_3)_2$	Orthorhombic
DIOPSIDE	$CaMg(SiO_3)_2$	Monoclinic
AUGITE	$\begin{cases} Ca(Mg,Fe)(Si_2O_6) \\ (Ca,Mg,Fe)(Al,Fe)(AlSiO_6) \end{cases}$	Monoclinic
SPODUMENE	$LiAl(SiO_3)_2$	Monoclinic

Wollastonite	$Ca_2(SiO_3)_2$	Triclinic
Pectolite	$HNaCa_2(SiO_3)_3$	Triclinic
RHODONITE	$Mn_2(SiO_3)_2$	Triclinic

Amphibole Group

Tremolite	$Ca_2Mg_5(OH)_2(Si_4O_{11})_2$	Monoclinic
Actinolite	$Ca_2(Mg,Fe)_5(OH)_2(Si_4O_{11})_2$	Monoclinic
HORNBLENDE	$\begin{cases} Ca_2(Mg,Fe)_4Al(OH)_2(AlSi_7O_{22}) \\ Ca_2Na(Mg,Fe)_4Al(OH)_2(Al_2Si_6O_{22}) \end{cases}$	Monoclinic

Feldspar Group

ORTHOCLASE	$KAlSi_3O_8$	Monoclinic
MICROCLINE	$KAlSi_3O_8$	Triclinic
ALBITE	$NaAlSi_3O_8(Ab)$	Triclinic
LABRADORITE	$Ab_{50}An_{50}$ to $Ab_{30}An_{70}$	Triclinic
Anorthite	$CaAl_2Si_2O_8(An)$	Triclinic

Feldspathoid Group

NEPHELITE	$(Na,K)_8Al_8Si_9O_{34}$	Hexagonal
Cancrinite	$3NaAlSiO_4.CaCO_3$	Hexagonal
Sodalite	$3NaAlSiO_4.NaCl$	Cubic
Lazurite	$3NaAlSiO_4.Na_2S$	Cubic
LEUCITE	$KAl(SiO_3)_2$	Pseudocubic

SCAPOLITE	$\begin{cases} nNa_4Al_3Si_9O_{24}Cl \\ mCa_4Al_6Si_6O_{24}CO_3 \end{cases}$	Tetragonal
TITANITE	$CaTiSiO_5$	Monoclinic
APOPHYLLITE	$KFCa_4(Si_2O_5)_4.8H_2O$	Tetragonal

Zeolite Group

Natrolite	$Na_2Al_2Si_3O_{10}.2H_2O$	Orthorhombic
ANALCITE	$NaAlSi_2O_6.H_2O$	Cubic
STILBITE	$(Ca,Na_2)Al_2Si_6O_{16}.6H_2O$	Monoclinic
CHABAZITE	$CaAl_2Si_6O_{16}.8H_2O$	Hexagonal

Most of these silicate minerals are easily distinguished by their hardness, transparency, nonmetallic luster, lack of characterizing colors, and uncolored streak.

STAUROLITE, $H_2FeAl_4Si_2O_{12}$.

Orthorhombic, bipyramidal class. Generally in well-developed prismatic crystals, consisting of the unit prism, basal and brachypinacoids, and a macrodome. Penetration twins according to two laws are common, yielding *cross-* or *plus-shape* and *x-shape twins* (Fig. 669).

Fig. 669.—Staurolite crystals—simple, and plus- and x-shape twins.

Brachypinacoidal cleavage. Conchoidal to uneven fracture. Hardness, 7 to 7.5. Specific gravity, 3.4 to 3.8. Usually reddish brown in color; also brownish black, yellowish brown, or gray when altered. Colorless streak when fresh. Vitreous to dull luster. α 1.736, β 1.741, γ 1.746, $(+)$; $2V = 88°$; $r > v$. Commonly translucent to opaque, rarely transparent.

$H_2FeAl_4Si_2O_{12}$. Composition varies greatly. May contain magnesium, manganese, and zinc. Often quite impure. Infusible. Insoluble in acids.

Occurs generally in metamorphic rocks, especially gneiss, mica schists, and slates (Fig. 670). The common associates are cyanite, garnet, tourmaline, and sillimanite. In the Saint Gotthard district, Switzer-

FIG. 670.—Staurolite in schist. Little Falls, Minnesota.

FIG. 671.—Staurolite (dark) in paragonite schist. Tessin, Switzerland.

land, it occurs with cyanite in paragonite (soda mica) schist (Fig. 671); also in Tirol; France; Brazil; Fannin and Cherokee counties, Georgia; Henry and Patrick counties, Virginia; Ducktown, Tennessee; Grantham, New Hampshire; Windham, Maine; Chesterfield, Massachusetts; Litchfield, Connecticut.

Clear and transparent crystals and plus-shape twins are sometimes used for gem purposes.

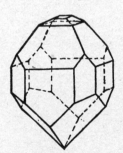

FIG. 672.

FIG. 673.—Hemimorphite. Chihuahua, New Mexico.

HEMIMORPHITE (*Calamine*), $H_2Zn_2SiO_5$.

Orthorhombic, pyramidal class. Crystals are usually thin tabular or pyramidal in habit, sometimes showing a pronounced hemimorphic development (Fig. 672). Often arranged in sheaflike or crested groups (Fig. 673). More commonly in fibrous, globular, granular, or porous and earthy masses.

Prismatic cleavage. Uneven to conchoidal fracture. Hardness, 4.5 to 5. Specific gravity, 3.3 to 3.6. Colorless, white, brown, green, or bluish. Transparent to opaque. Vitreous to dull luster. α 1.614, β 1.617, γ 1.636, (+); $2V = 46°$; $r > v$.

$H_2Zn_2SiO_5$. May also be written $Zn_4(OH)_2Si_2O_7.H_2O$. Fuses with difficulty. Gelatinizes easily with acids. Occurs as a pseudomorph after calcite, galena, dolomite, fluorite, and pyromorphite.

Hemimorphite is a secondary mineral, formed by the action of silica-bearing water upon other zinc ores, and is usually found in limestones associated with smithsonite, sphalerite, galena, cerussite, and anglesite. It is often intimately mixed with smithsonite. Some localities are Aachen, Germany; Raibel and Bleiberg, Carinthia, Austria; Silesia; Cumberland and Derbyshire, England; Sardinia; Sussex County, New Jersey; Phoenixville and Friedensville, Pennsylvania; Granby and else-where, Missouri; Pulaski and Wythe counties, Virginia; Colorado; Utah; Tennessee; Arkansas.

Hemimorphite is an important ore of zinc. See page 436.

Andalusite Group

The compound Al_2SiO_5 is trimorphous and occurs in nature as the three minerals andalusite, sillimanite, and cyanite. The first two minerals crystallize in the orthorhombic system, while the third is triclinic. Upon heating, the composition of these minerals is changed to $3Al_2O_3.2SiO_2$ (mullite) with liberation of silica. Cyanite alters at the lowest temperature (1350 to 1370°C.), sillimanite at the highest (about 1545°C.), while the change in andalusite takes place at about 1390°C.

ANDALUSITE, Al_2SiO_5.

Orthorhombic, bipyramidal class. Occurs usually in large, rough, and nearly square prismatic crystals (Figs. 674 and 675). *Chiastolite*

FIG. 674.

FIG. 675.—Andalusite. Andalusia, Spain.

is a variety with a regular internal arrangement of dark organic matter, best seen in polished cross sections (Fig. 676). Found also in fibrous, columnar, and granular masses, and in rounded pebbles.

Prismatic cleavage. Uneven fracture. Hardness, 7 to 7.5; due to alteration may be softer on the surface. Specific gravity, 3.1 to 3.2.

Gray, greenish, reddish, or bluish in color. Transparent to opaque. Vitreous to dull luster. α 1.632, β 1.638, γ 1.643, $(-)$; $2V = 85°$. Sometimes strongly pleochroic.

Al_2SiO_5. Often impure. Infusible. Insoluble in acids. Alters to cyanite, mica, kaolinite, or dense talcose-like minerals resembling steatite.

Occurs in metamorphic rocks, especially in schists and slates. Commonly associated with cyanite, sillimanite, mica, garnet, and tourmaline. Some localities are Andalusia, Spain; Tirol; in transparent crystals in Minas Geraes, Brazil; Ceylon; Westford, Lancaster, and Sterling, Massa-

Fig. 676.—Andalusite: variety, chiastolite.   Lancaster, Massachusetts.

chusetts; Litchfield and Washington, Connecticut; Standish, Maine; in large quantities in Mono County, California.

Used in the manufacture of spark-plug and chemical porcelain, and refractories; transparent varieties are sometimes used for gem purposes. See also page 403.

Sillimanite (*Fibrolite*), **Al_2SiO_5.**

Orthorhombic. Usually in long, thin, needle-like crystals; or in radiating fibrous or columnar masses. Crystals are often bent, striated, interlaced, poorly terminated, and without sharp edges.

Macropinacoidal cleavage. Uneven fracture. Hardness, 6 to 7. Specific gravity, 3.2 to 3.3.   Gray, brown, yellowish, or greenish in color. Vitreous or silky luster. α 1.659, β 1.660, γ 1.680, $(+)$; $2V = 20°$; $r > v$. Transparent to translucent.

Al_2SiO_5.   Chemical composition and behavior are the same as for andalusite.

Occurs as an accessory constituent of gneisses, quartzites, mica schists, and other metamorphic rocks.   It is sometimes associated with andalusite, zircon, or corundum.   Found at Bodenmais, Bavaria; Freiberg, Saxony; Minas Geraes, Brazil; Worcester, Massachusetts; Norwich and Willimantic, Connecticut; Westchester and Monroe counties, New York; Chester, Pennsylvania.

CYANITE (*Kyanite, Disthene*), **Al_2SiO_5.**

Triclinic, pinacoidal class.   Generally in long, broad crystals without distinct terminations; or in coarse bladed, columnar, or fibrous masses (Fig. 677).   Crystals are sometimes curved and arranged radially.

Macro- and brachypinacoidal cleavages. Hardness varies greatly with direction, 4 to 5 parallel to the long direction of the blades, 6 to 7 across them. Specific gravity, 3.5 to 3.7. Generally some shade of blue in color; also grayish, white, green, brownish, or colorless. The edges are usually lighter in color than the central portions of the blades, that is, the color is distributed in streaks or spots. Vitreous luster.

α 1.712, β 1.720, γ 1.728, $(-)$; $2V = 82°$; $r > v$. Transparent to translucent. May become luminescent.

Al_2SiO_5. Chemical composition and behavior similar to that of andalusite and sillimanite. Cyanite is, however, more resistive to the action of acids.

Cyanite is a metamorphic mineral and is commonly found in gneisses and mica schists, especially paragonite schist. Usual associates are staurolite, garnet, corundum, rutile, and lazulite. Some localities are the Saint Gotthard district, Switzerland; various places in Tirol; Sweden; Brazil; Chesterfield, Massachusetts; Litchfield and Washington, Connecticut; Chester and Delaware counties, Pennsylvania; Gaston, Rutherford, and Yancey counties, North Carolina.

Fig. 677.—Cyanite (bladed). Litchfield, Connecticut.

Used in ceramics and sometimes for gem purposes.

TOPAZ, $Al_2(F,OH)_2SiO_4$.

Orthorhombic, bipyramidal class. Generally in highly modified, prismatic crystals, which are usually developed on one end only (Figs.

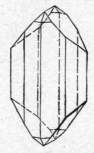
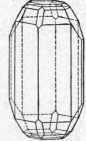

Fig. 678.   Fig. 679.   Fig. 680.

678, 679 and 680). Often vertically striated. Occurs also in granular to compact masses and in rolled fragments.

Very perfect basal cleavage. Conchoidal to uneven fracture. Hardness, 8. Specific gravity, 3.4 to 3.6. Colorless, wine yellow, grayish, violet, reddish, or bluish in color. Some colored varieties fade on exposure to sunlight. Transparent to opaque. Vitreous luster. α 1.619, β 1.620, γ 1.627, $(+)$; $2V$ varies from 49° to 66°; $r > v$.

$Al_2(F,OH)_2SiO_4$. The percentages of fluorine and hydroxyl vary greatly. Infusible. Slightly acted upon by sulphuric acid. Sometimes alters to muscovite and kaolinite.

Topaz is a characteristic mineral of the pneumatolytic process of formation and is hence generally associated with cassiterite, tourmaline, quartz, fluorite, apatite, beryl, mica, scheelite, wolframite, and zircon. It occurs in crevices, cavities, and pegmatite dikes in highly acid igneous rocks such as granites and rhyolites; also in gneisses and schists. Excellent crystals are found at Schneckenstein and elsewhere in Saxony; the Ural Mountains; Sweden; Japan; Australia; Mexico; Thomas Range, Utah; Nathrop, Colorado; San Diego County, California; and various places in Connecticut, New Hampshire, and Maine. Frequently found in the sands and gravel of the streams of Ceylon, Brazil, and the Ural Mountains.

Clear and transparent crystals are used for gem purposes. The yellow variety from Brazil is often called *precious topaz.* Much yellow quartz (citrine), colored naturally or artificially, is called topaz, especially in the jewelry trade.

Datolite, Ca(BOH)SiO₄.

Monoclinic, prismatic class. Usually prismatic, pyramidal, or tabular crystals, often highly modified (Figs. 681 and 682). Also in compact,

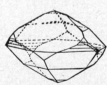

FIG. 681.

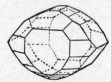

FIG. 682.

FIG. 683.—Datolite. Lake Superior copper district.

dull, or granular masses resembling Wedgwood ware or unglazed porcelain (Fig. 683).

Conchoidal to uneven fracture. Hardness, 5 to 5.5. Specific gravity, 2.9 to 3. Colorless, white, or greenish but often with yellowish, reddish, or brownish streaks and spots. Transparent to translucent, rarely opaque. Vitreous to dull luster. α 1.625, β 1.653, γ 1.669, $(-)$; $2V = 74°$; $r > v$.

$Ca(BOH)SiO_4$. Crystals are usually very pure. Gelatinizes with hydrochloric acid.

Datolite is a secondary mineral and is generally found in cracks and cavities in basic igneous rocks, such as diorite, diabase, melaphyre, gabbro, and serpentine. The common associates are native copper, calcite, epidote, magnetite, and the zeolites. Some localities are the Kilpatrick Hills, Scotland; Arendal, Norway; the Harz Mountains, Germany; Tirol; Bergen Hill, New Jersey; Westfield and elsewhere, Massachusetts; Hartford, Connecticut; in the Lake Superior copper district excellent crystals and compact porcelain-like masses.

The massive varieties are sometimes used for gem purposes.

TOURMALINE, $M'_{20}B_2Si_4O_{21}$.

Hexagonal, ditrigonal pyramidal class. Commonly in short to long prismatic crystals with vertical striations. Well-developed crystals

  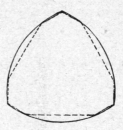

FIG. 684.　　　　FIG. 685.　　　　FIG. 686.

have rhombohedral-like terminations and possess pronounced hemimorphism (Figs. 684 and 685). Crystals show a characteristic spherical triangular outline in cross section (Figs. 686 and 687). Occurs also in compact and disseminated masses and in radially divergent aggregates, called *tourmaline suns;* also in loose crystals in secondary deposits.

Conchoidal to uneven fracture. Hardness, 7 to 7.5. Specific gravity, 2.9 to 3.2. Usually pitch black or brown in color; also gray, yellow, green, or red, and, more rarely, colorless or white. The reddish varieties are frequently called *rubellite;* the black, *schorl.* Zonal distribution of color is often very marked, especially in crystals of the lighter colors (Fig. 687). Vitreous to resinous luster. ω 1.687, ϵ 1.641, ($-$). Transparent to opaque. Strongly dichroic. May often be pyroelectric and piezoelectric. May become luminescent.

$M'_{20}B_2Si_4O_{21}$. A very complex silicate with varying amounts of iron, aluminum, magnesium, manganese, calcium, lithium, sodium, potassium, hydroxyl, and fluorine. The formula is often written $M'_9Al_3(BOH)_2$-Si_4O_{19}. Sometimes classified according to composition as lithium, iron, and magnesium tourmalines. Fusibility varies greatly. Insoluble in acids but gelatinizes after fusion or strong ignition. Alters to muscovite, biotite, or chlorite.

Tourmaline is a very characteristic mineral of pegmatite dikes associated with intrusions of granite. It is the result of pneumatolytic action, as is evidenced by the presence of fluorine, hydroxyl, and boron. It is also rather common in metamorphic rocks, such as gneisses, schists,

FIG. 687.—Tourmaline showing zonal distribution of color and spherical triangular outline. San Diego County, California.

FIG. 688.—Tourmaline in quartz. Auburn, Maine.

FIG. 689.—Tourmaline in albite. Mesa Grande, California.

and in crystalline limestones and dolomites. Some of the common associates are quartz (Fig. 688), feldspar (Fig. 689), beryl, topaz, fluorite, lepidolite (Fig. 690), apatite, and muscovite. Excellent crystals occur on the Island of Elba; in the Ural Mountains; Burma; Ceylon; Madagascar; Minas Geraes, Brazil; Paris, Auburn, and Rumford, Maine; Haddam Neck, Connecticut; Gouverneur and elsewhere in Saint Lawrence County,

FIG. 690.—Tourmaline: variety, rubellite, in lepidolite. San Diego County, California.

New York; Mesa Grande, Pala, and elsewhere in San Diego County, California.

Stones of good colors are used for gem purposes. On account of its strong absorption of light, it has been used in the making of tourmaline tongs, a simple instrument for the production of polarized light. Properly oriented sections of tourmaline are used for frequency control in short-wave radio apparatus.

Chondrodite [Mg(F,OH)]$_2$Mg$_3$(SiO$_4$)$_2$.

Monoclinic, prismatic class. Occurs in small, highly modified, pseudo-orthorhombic crystals, also in grains or lumps and in granular aggregates.

Basal cleavage. Uneven to conchoidal cleavage. Hardness, 6 to 6.5. Specific gravity, 3.1 to 3.3. Brown, yellow, or red in color. Vitreous to resinous luster. α 1.607, β 1.619, γ 1.639, $(+)$; $2V = 80°$; $r > v$. Translucent to opaque.

$[Mg(F,OH)]_2Mg_3(SiO_4)_2$. Some of the magnesium may be replaced by bivalent iron. Infusible. Gelatinizes with hydrochloric acid. Alters to serpentine and brucite.

Chondrodite is a typical contact metamorphic mineral. It occurs commonly in crystalline limestones and dolomites, associated with spinel, vesuvianite, magnetite, pyroxenes, and phlogopite. Some important localities are Pargas, Finland; Mount Vesuvius; Burma; Sparta, New Jersey; Tilly Foster Mine, near Brewster, and in Orange County, New York.

Epidote Group

Under this heading two rather complex but isomorphous silicates of calcium and aluminum will be described.

EPIDOTE, $Ca_2(Al,Fe)_2(AlOH)(SiO_4)_3$.

Monoclinic, prismatic class. Excellent prismatic and highly modified crystals are rather common; usually elongated and deeply striated parallel

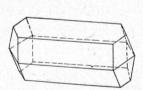

FIG. 691.

FIG. 692.—Epidote. Untersulzbachthal, Tirol.

to the b axis and terminated at one end only (Figs. 691 and 692). Occurs also in divergent or parallel fibrous and columnar aggregates, coarse- to fine-granular masses, or in rounded or angular grains.

Basal cleavage. Uneven fracture. Hardness, 6 to 7. Specific gravity, 3.3 to 3.5. Yellowish to blackish green in color; more rarely red or colorless. Crystals are usually darker in color than massive varieties. Vitreous to resinous luster. α 1.729, β 1.754; γ 1.768, $(-)$; $2V$ is large; $r > v$. Transparent to opaque. Strongly pleochroic.

$Ca_2(Al,Fe)_2(AlOH)(SiO_4)_3$. The percentages of the oxides of calcium, iron, aluminum, and silicon vary considerably. *Clinozoisite* contains little or no iron. *Zoisite* is an orthorhombic modification. Loses water when strongly ignited and gelatinizes with hydrochloric acid after ignition. Occurs as a pseudomorph after scapolite, garnet, augite, and hornblende.

Epidote is a typical metamorphic mineral. It is found in such rocks as gneiss and in schists of various kinds; often occurs very extensively, forming epidote rocks, called *epidosite*. It is commonly associated with garnet, vesuvianite, hornblende, hematite, native copper, magnetite, and the zeolites. It is also a common alteration product of minerals high in calcium and aluminum, such as feldspar, pyroxene, amphibole, scapolite, and biotite. Important localities are Zillerthal and Untersulzbachthal, Tirol; Traversella, Piedmont; the Island of Elba; Dauphiné, France; Arendal, Norway; the Ural Mountains; Haddam, Connecticut; various places in New York, New Jersey, and Colorado; with native copper in the Lake Superior copper district.

The clear and transparent dark-green crystals are sometimes used for gem purposes.

Orthite (*Allanite*), $Ca_2(Al,Ce,Fe)_2(AlOH)(SiO_4)_3$.

Monoclinic, prismatic class. Crystals are tabular or prismatic but rare. Usually in massive, granular, or bladed aggregates; also as disseminated grains.

Uneven to conchoidal fracture. Hardness, 5.5 to 6. Specific gravity, 3 to 4. Pitch black in color, sometimes brownish or grayish; often coated with a yellowish or brownish alteration product. Greenish gray to brown streak. Pitchy submetallic luster. Opaque.

$Ca_2(Al,Ce,Fe)_2(AlOH)(SiO_4)_3$. Composition varies greatly. Didymium, lanthanum, yttrium, magnesium, and water may be present. Fuses easily with intumescence to a black magnetic glass. Gelatinizes with hydrochloric acid but not if previously ignited.

Orthite occurs in small quantities in igneous rocks, such as granites and pegmatites; also in gneiss, mica and amphibolite schists, and crystalline limestones. Commonly associated with epidote, magnetite, quartz, and feldspar. Occurs in Greenland; Falun, Sweden; Miask, Ural Mountains; Edenville, New York; Haddam, Connecticut; Franklin, New Jersey; Madison and Iredell counties, North Carolina; Barringer Hill, Texas; Amherst County, Virginia. See page 413.

VESUVIANITE (*Idocrase*), $Ca_6[Al(OH,F)]Al_2(SiO_4)_5$.

Tetragonal, ditetragonal bipyramidal class. Crystals are generally short prismatic (Figs. 693, and 694), rarely pyramidal or acicular. Occurs also in compact and granular masses and in aggregates with parallel (Fig. 695) or divergent striations or furrows.

Uneven fracture. Hardness, 6.5. Specific gravity, 3.3 to 3.5. Occurs in many shades of yellow, green, and brown; more rarely blue, red, or nearly black. *Californite* is a compact green variety with colorless or white streaks, resembling jade. Vitreous greasy luster. ω 1.716, ϵ 1.721, (+); sometimes abnormally biaxial. Commonly translucent.

$Ca_6[Al(OH,F)]Al_2(SiO_4)_5$. The composition is complex and variable. May contain titanium, boron, iron, magnesium, manganese, sodium, potassium, and lithium. Fuses with intumescence to a greenish or brownish glass. After ignition, it decomposes easily with acids.

Vesuvianite is a typical contact metamorphic mineral. It is found commonly in crystalline limestones, gneisses, and schists, associated with garnet, tourmaline, chondrodite, wollastonite, epidote, and the pyroxenes. Important localities are Monzoni, Tirol; Ala Valley, Piedmont; Mount

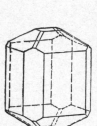

FIG. 693.　　FIG. 694.—Vesuvianite.　(a) Wilui River,　FIG. 695.—Vesuvianite.
Siberia; (b) Achmatovsk, Russia.　Egg, Norway.

Vesuvius; Morelos, Mexico; Eger, Bohemia; Egg, Norway; Wilui River, Siberia; Rumford, Maine; Amity, New York; various places in California, Ontario, and Quebec.

Clear and transparent brown and green varieties are used for gem purposes.

OLIVINE (*Chrysolite, Peridot*), $(Mg,Fe)_2SiO_4$.

Orthorhombic, bipyramidal class. Crystals are prismatic (Fig. 696) or thick tabular. Occurs generally in rounded, disseminated, glassy grains (Fig. 697), granular aggregates, or in rounded loose pebbles.

Pinacoidal cleavages. Conchoidal fracture. Hardness, 6.5 to 7. Specific gravity, 3.2 to 3.6. Vitreous luster. α 1.662, β 1.680, γ 1.699, (+); $2V$ is large; $r < v$. Commonly various shades of green, also yellowish, brown, reddish, grayish, or colorless. Transparent to translucent.

$(Mg,Fe)_2SiO_4$. The composition varies between that of *forsterite*, Mg_2SiO_4, and *fayalite*, Fe_2SiO_4. Titanium, nickel, and calcium may be present in small amounts. Infusible. Easily decomposed and gelatinizes with acids. Alters to serpentine, limonite, magnesite, opal, and garnierite.

Olivine is a constituent of many basic igneous rocks, such as basalt, gabbro, and peridotite. Found also in crystalline limestones. The common associates are augite, enstatite, spinel, plagioclase, chromite, pyrope, corundum, talc, and magnetite. Occurs in northern Egypt; on Mount

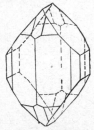

Fig. 696.

Fig. 697.—Olivine (green glassy grains).
Near Balsam, North Carolina.

Vesuvius; in Upper Burma; Snarum, Norway; Arizona; Vermont; New Hampshire; Virginia; Pennsylvania; Oregon; New Mexico; Canada; Brazil.

Peridot is a transparent green variety used for gem purposes.

Willemite, Zn_2SiO_4.

Hexagonal, trigonal rhombohedral class. Crystals are either slender or thick prismatic in habit but generally quite small. *Troostite*, a

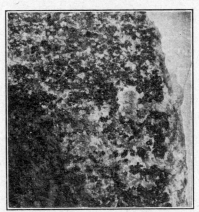

Fig. 698.—Willemite (light) with franklinite. Franklin Furnace, New Jersey.

variety containing manganese, is commonly found in larger crystals. Occurs also in compact or granular masses, and in disseminated grains (Fig. 698).

Basal cleavage. Uneven fracture. Hardness, 5 to 6. Specific gravity, 3.9 to 4.3. Greasy vitreous luster. ω 1.694, ϵ 1.723, (+). Commonly yellow, green, brown, or reddish; more rarely blue, black, white, or colorless. Transparent to opaque. Often shows luminescence.

Zn_2SiO_4. Manganese and iron may be present. Fuses with difficulty. Gelatinizes with hydrochloric acid. Sometimes pseudomorphous after hemimorphite.

The usual associates are franklinite, zincite, rhodonite, and calcite. The most important locality is Franklin Furnace and vicinity, Sussex County, New Jersey, where it occurs in large quantities. Found also at Altenberg, near Aachen, Germany; Musartut, Greenland; Merritt Mine, Socorro County, New Mexico; and Clifton, Arizona.

Willemite is an important ore of zinc. See page 436.

ZIRCON (*Hyacinth, Jargon*), $ZrSiO_4$.

Tetragonal, ditetragonal bipyramidal class. Usually in simple, well-developed crystals, consisting of the prism and bipyramid of the first order (Fig. 699); more complex crystals sometimes observed (Fig. 700). Also as rounded or angular lumps or grains in sands and gravels.

FIG. 699.   FIG. 700.   FIG. 701.—Zircon in syenite.
Miask, Ural Mountains.

Hardness, 7.5. Specific gravity, 4.4 to 4.8. Adamantine luster. High indices of refraction, ω 1.923, ϵ 1.968, ($+$). Transparent to opaque. Commonly, brown or grayish; also red, yellow, blue, and colorless. Streak uncolored. Reddish and brownish varieties are often called *hyacinth* or *jacinth;* when colorless and smoky, *jargon.* The color of some zircon crystals can be changed by heat treatment. The blue zircons from Chantabon, Siam, sometimes called *starlite,* and some of the colorless *matura diamonds* are the result of such treatment. Cut zircons possess good brilliancy and fire. May show luminescence.

$ZrSiO_4$. Often interpreted as an oxide of zirconium and silicon. Usually contains a small amount of iron.

Occurs disseminated in the more acid igneous rocks, especially granites and syenites; also found in gneiss, schist, and crystalline limestone. Occurs in nepheline syenite in southeastern Norway; Miask, Ural Mountains (Fig. 701); Wichita Mountains, Oklahoma; Litchfield, Maine. Common in the sands and gravels of Ceylon, also in Henderson, Iredell, and Buncombe counties, North Carolina, and at Pablo Beach, Florida.

Zircon is a source of ZrO_2, which, under the name *zirkite*, is used in ferro-alloys and as a refractory for lining and patching high-temperature furnaces. The varieties known as *hyacinth, jacinth, starlite,* and *jargon* are cut as gems. The colorless zircon from Matura, Ceylon, is often called *matura diamond*. Also see page 437.

Garnet Group

This group embraces minerals possessing the general formula $M''_3M'''_2(SiO_4)_3$, in which M'' may be calcium, magnesium, manganese, or ferrous iron and M''' aluminum, ferric iron, or chromium. Sometimes titanium may replace a portion of the silicon. Six varieties depending upon composition have been distinguished:

Grossularite	$Ca_3Al_2(SiO_4)_3$
Pyrope	$Mg_3Al_2(SiO_4)_3$
Spessartite	$Mn_3Al_2(SiO_4)_3$
Almandite	$Fe_3Al_2(SiO_4)_3$
Uvarovite	$Ca_3Cr_2(SiO_4)_3$
Andradite	$Ca_3Fe_2(SiO_4)_3$

These varieties grade over into one another, the composition of a given specimen being usually rather complex.

Fig. 702.—Garnet (rhombic dodecahedron). Salida, Colorado.

Fig. 703.

Fig. 704.

Cubic, hexoctahedral class. Crystals are usually rhombic dodecahedrons or tetragonal trisoctahedrons, often in combination (Figs. 702 to 706). The hexoctahedron (*s*) is quite frequently observed (Fig. 704). Other forms are rare. Generally well crystallized but occurs also as rounded disseminated glassy grains and in compact granular aggregates.

Indistinct dodecahedral cleavage. Conchoidal to uneven fracture. Hardness, 6.5 to 7.5. Specific gravity, 3.4 to 4.3; varying with the composition. Commonly red, brown, yellow, green, or black; less frequently white or colorless. Light-colored garnets are generally transparent to translucent, dark-colored varieties translucent to opaque. Vitreous to resinous luster. The index of refraction varies from 1.70 to 1.9, and the dispersion from 0.024 to 0.028. *Demantoid* has an unusually high dispersion of 0.057.

$M''_3M'''_2(SiO_4)_3$. Composition varies greatly as indicated above. The chemical properties of the six varieties differ materially. They generally fuse easily to a brownish or black glass, which is sometimes magnetic. With the exception of uvarovite, all varieties gelatinize with acids after fusion. Garnets alter readily; epidote, mica, chlorite, serpentine, hornblende, scapolite, orthoclase, calcite, and limonite have been observed occurring as pseudomorphs after garnet. Large chlorite pseudomorphs after garnet occur at Spurr Mountain Mine, Lake Superior region.

Garnet is a very common mineral. It occurs in crystalline schists, as a contact metamorphic mineral, as a constituent of many eruptive rocks, with various ores, and in secondary deposits.

Fig. 705.

Fig. 706.—Garnet (tetragonal trisoctahedrons) in mica schist. Sunday River, Maine.

Grossularite (*Hessonite, Cinnamon Stone*).—Calcium-aluminum garnet. Calcium may be partially replaced by ferrous iron, and aluminum by ferric iron. Specific gravity varies from 3.4 to 3.7. White, various shades of yellow, cinnamon brown, rose red; also green and colorless. The index of refraction varies from 1.735 to 1.763. It occurs in crystalline limestones and dolomites with wollastonite, vesuvianite, diopside, and scapolite. Some localities are Ceylon; Mussa Alp, Piedmont; Wilui River, Siberia; Morelos, Mexico; Monzoni, Tirol; Rumford, Maine; Warren, New Hampshire. Green, massive grossularite, often mottled with white, from Buffelsfontein, Transvaal, is called *South African* or *Transvaal jade*. Yellow, green, and orange grossularites are used for gem purposes.

Pyrope.—Magnesium-aluminum garnet. Calcium and ferrous iron may partially replace magnesium. Specific gravity, 3.7. Deep red to almost black. The index of refraction varies from 1.705 to 1.742. When clear and transparent is often called *precious garnet* and used as a gem. Commonly known as *Cape ruby* or *Arizona ruby*. Found usually in basic igneous rocks, such as peridotite or serpentine. Frequently considered an important associate of the diamond. Rarely found in good crystals, usually in irregular particles or rounded grains. Important localities are Teplitz, Aussig, and Bilin, Bohemia; Kimberley and other diamondiferous localities in South Africa; various places in southern Utah, Arizona, New Mexico, Madagascar, Ceylon, and Brazil.

Spessartite.—Manganese-aluminum garnet. May contain ferrous and ferric iron. Specific gravity, 4 to 4.3. Brownish to hyacinth red. $n = 1.80$. Occurs in granitic rocks with topaz, tourmaline, quartz, and orthoclase. Occurs in Tirol; Piedmont; Ceylon; Haddam, Connecticut; Amelia Court House, Virginia; Bethel, Maine; Salem, North Carolina.

Almandite (*Carbuncle*).—Iron-aluminum garnet. May contain magnesium and ferric iron. Specific gravity, 3.9 to 4.2. Deep red to brownish red or black in color. The index of refraction varies from 1.778 to 1.83. Transparent red varieties are known as precious garnets and used as gems; translucent varieties are called *common garnets*. Commonly found in mica and other schists, associated with staurolite, cyanite, andalusite, and tourmaline. Excellent specimens are obtained in India; Ceylon; Minas Novas, Brazil; Bodö, Norway; Tirol; Uruguay; Australia; Salida, Colorado; Fort Wrangel, Alaska; Charlemont, Massachusetts. *Rhodolite* is a pale-violet variety, $n = 1.76$, between pyrope and almandite, occurring in Macon and Jackson counties, North Carolina.

Uvarovite.—Calcium-chromium garnet. Emerald green in color. $n = 1.838$. Crystals are usually small. Not a common variety. Found with chromite in serpentine or in crystalline limestones and gneiss. Some localities are the Ural Mountains; western Transvaal, South Africa; Oxford, Canada; New Idria, California.

Andradite.—Calcium-iron garnet. The composition varies greatly. The color may be brownish red, brown, grayish black, black, also various shades of yellow or green. The index of refraction varies from 1.865 to 1.94. *Topazolite* is yellowish or greenish and often resembles topaz. *Demantoid* is a grass-green variety. *Melanite* is black; $n = 1.94$. These garnets occur in syenite, serpentine, chloritic schists, and crystalline limestones. Common associates are feldspar, nephelite, leucite, epidote, and magnetite. Found at Dobschau, Czechoslovakia; Tirol; the Island of Elba; Arendal, Norway; the Ural Mountains; Franklin, New Jersey; Magnet Cove, Arkansas; Henderson, North Carolina.

Pyrope and almandite furnish most of the garnets used as gems. Almandite and andradite are often called common garnets. Small garnets are sometimes used as jewels in watches of a cheaper grade; also in meters and scientific apparatus. Garnet is an important abrasive. Garnet paper and cloth are used extensively for smoothing wood surfaces and for finishing leather and rubber articles.

BERYL, $Be_3Al_2Si_6O_{18}$.

Hexagonal, dihexagonal bipyramidal class. Crystals are usually long prismatic and very simple (Figs. 707 and 708). Rarely tabular. Sometimes highly modified, showing prisms and bipyramids of the first and second orders and other forms. Crystals are frequently striated vertically and may be very large. Occurs also in columnar, granular, and compact masses and in rounded grains.

Indistinct basal cleavage. Conchoidal to uneven fracture. Hardness, 7.5 to 8; is sometimes substituted for topaz in the scale of hardness. Specific gravity, 2.6 to 2.8. Various shades of green, blue, yellow, and reddish in color; sometimes mottled. Vitreous luster. Transparent to translucent. May become luminescent. Indices of refraction vary from

Fig. 707.—Beryl. Auburn, Maine.   Fig. 708.

ω 1.568, ϵ 1.564, (−), for varieties low in alkalies to ω 1.598, ϵ 1.590, (−), for those high in alkalies.

There are five important varieties of beryl:

1. *Emerald.*—Emerald green in color. Transparent. Highly prized as a precious stone.

2. *Aquamarine.*—Usually blue to sea green in color. Transparent. Used as a gem, but not so valuable as the emerald.

3. *Yellow or Golden Beryl.* Beautiful golden yellow in color. Transparent. An attractive gem stone.

4. *Morganite.*—Pale pink to rose red in color. Transparent. Used as a gem.

5. *Common Beryl.*—Generally green, yellowish, or grayish white in color. Often mottled. Crystals are sometimes extremely large, being measured in feet and weighing several tons; thus, at Grafton, New Hampshire, and Keystone, South Dakota.

$Be_3Al_2Si_6O_{18}$. Beryllium may be partially replaced by varying amounts of calcium, iron, potassium, sodium, and cæsium. A small amount of water is present. Fuses with great difficulty, turning white and cloudy. Insoluble in acids. Alters to mica and kaolin.

Commonly found in pegmatite veins; also in gneiss, mica schist, clay slate, limestone, or in secondary deposits. The common associates are quartz (Fig. 709), feldspar, mica, topaz, tourmaline, cassiterite, chryso-beryl, garnet, zircon, and corundum. Emeralds of good quality occur in limestone at Muzo, near Bogotá, Colombia (Fig. 710); in altered dolo-mitic marble near Bom Jesus dos Meiras, Bahia, Brazil; in the district of Ekaterinburg, Ural Mountains; Tirol; Upper Egypt; Poona, Western Australia; Alexander County, North Carolina; Chaffee County, Colorado. Morganite is found on the Island of Madagascar and in San Diego County, California. Aquamarine and other gem beryls occur on the Island of Elba; Ireland; Mursinka, Ural Mountains; Mitchell County, North Carolina; in secondary deposits in Brazil, Ceylon, and India. Common beryl occurs in very large crystals as Grafton and Acworth,

Fig. 709.—Beryl in quartz. Acworth, New Hampshire.

Fig. 710.—Beryl: variety, emerald. Muzo, near Bogotá, Colombia.

New Hampshire; Royalston, Massachusetts; Paris and Stoneham, Maine; Haddam and Litchfield, Connecticut; Pennsylvania; the Black Hills, South Dakota.

Used for gem purposes and as a source of beryllium and its compounds. See also page 406.

CHRYSOCOLLA, CuO, SiO$_2$, H$_2$O.

Usually apparently amorphous. Crystals are small, acicular, and very rare. Occurs in compact, reniform, or earthy masses; also as incrus-tations and stains, and in veins. May have an enamel-like appearance and resemble opal.

Conchoidal fracture. Hardness, 2 to 4. Specific gravity, 2 to 2.2. Usually various shades of green or blue; when impure, brown to black. Translucent to opaque. Vitreous, greasy, or dull luster. The index of refraction varies from 1.575 to 1.635.

The chemical composition of chrysocolla is uncertain. It contains CuO, SiO$_2$, and H$_2$O in varying proportions. Infusible. Decomposed by acids but does not gelatinize. Forms pseudomorphs after atacamite, azurite, and cerussite.

Chrysocolla is a secondary mineral, formed by the alteration of various copper ores, such as chalcopyrite, cuprite, and tetrahedrite. Generally found in the zone of oxidation of copper ore deposits. It is commonly associated with malachite, native copper, azurite, and limonite. Some localities are Cornwall, England; the Ural Mountains; the Clifton and Bisbee copper districts, Arizona; Wyoming; Nevada; New Mexico; Lake Superior copper district; in fact, all important copper localities.

It is an ore of copper. It is sometimes cut and polished for gem purposes. At times, it is substituted for turquois.

Mica Group

Although the members of the mica group vary greatly from the chemical standpoint, they have, nevertheless, many characteristics in common. Crystals are apparently hexagonal or orthorhombic in development, but they all belong to the monoclinic system. The prism angle usually approximates 120°. Twins are not uncommon. The micas possess an excellent basal cleavage, which is sometimes considered the most perfect cleavage observed on minerals. Cleavage laminæ are elastic. As stated on page 333, the micas have structures based on sheets of linked $(Si,Al)O_4$ tetrahedrons. This structure accounts for the characteristic basal cleavage.

The micas are silicates of varying compositions of aluminum and potassium, containing hydrogen, magnesium, iron, sodium, lithium, and fluorine. The silica content varies between 33 and 55 per cent. All of the micas yield water when heated in a closed tube. They fuse with difficulty. They are important rock-forming minerals, being essential constituents of many igneous and metamorphic rocks. Some sedimentary rocks often contain considerable quantities of mica.

The compositions of the micas are often very complex, and accordingly difficult to interpret. The formulas for muscovite and phlogopite are well established, both on the basis of chemical and X-ray data, but those of biotite and lepidolite are uncertain.

Muscovite	$KAl_2(OH)_2AlSi_3O_{10}$
Phlogopite	$KMg_3(OH)_2AlSi_3O_{10}$
Biotite	$K(Mg,Fe)_3(OH)_2AlSi_3O_{10}$
Lepidolite	$K_2Li_3Al_3(OH,F)_4(AlSi_3O_{10})_2$

The minerals of the chlorite group, as well as talc and kaolinite, are closely related to the micas, both in chemical and physical properties. Like the micas, their structures are based on sheets of linked tetrahedrons, with the composition $(Al,Si)_4O_{10}$. As the result of X-ray studies it has been suggested that the chlorites have a structure with alternate layers resembling mica and brucite $(Mg(OH)_2)$, respectively, while kaolinite has composite layers corresponding to mica and hydrargyllite $(Al(OH)_3)$. These relationships are shown in the following table:

Phlogopite...................... $KMg_3(OH)_2(AlSi_3O_{10})$
Talc............................ $Mg_3(OH)_2(Si_4O_{10})$
Chlorite........................ $Mg_3(OH)_2(AlSi_3O_{10}), Mg_2Al(OH)_6$
Muscovite...................... $KAl_2(OH)_2(AlSi_3O_{10})$
Kaolinite...................... $\begin{cases} Al_2(OH)_2 \\ Al_2(OH)_6 \end{cases}(Si_4O_{10})$

In the text, the more compact formulas $H_8Mg_5Al_2Si_3O_{18}$ and $H_4Al_2Si_2O_9$ will be used for chlorite and kaolinite, respectively.

MUSCOVITE (*White Mica, Potash Mica, Isinglass*), $KAl_2(OH)_2AlSi_3O_{10}$.

Monoclinic, prismatic class. Crystals are usually tabular and possess a rhombic or hexagonal outline (Figs. 711 and 712). Tapering pyramidal habits are also observed. Crystals are often large and rough,

Fig. 711.—Muscovite (rhombic outline). Buckfield, Maine.

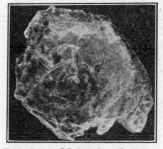

Fig. 712.—Muscovite (hexagonal outline) bordered with lepidolite. Auburn, Maine.

measuring at times several feet in diameter. Large crystals may show distinct partings perpendicular to the cleavage and are then called *ruled, ribbon,* or *A mica.* The term *wedge mica* is applied to crystals which are thicker at one end than at the other. Usually occurs in scaly, foliated, and plumose aggregates.

Highly perfect basal cleavage, permitting very thin, transparent, and elastic leaves to be split. Hardness, 2 to 3. Specific gravity, 2.8 to 3.1. Colorless, yellowish, brownish, or reddish. Transparent to translucent. Pearly to vitreous luster. α 1.561, β 1.590, γ 1.594, $(-)$; $2V$ is about 40°; $r > v$.

$KAl_2(OH)_2AlSi_3O_{10}$. Frequently contains small amounts of calcium, magnesium, iron, sodium, and fluorine. *Fuchsite* contains small amounts of chromium, while *roscoelite* has considerable vanadium replacing the aluminum (see page 435). Fuses with difficulty to a grayish or yellowish glass. Not attacked by common acids. *Sericite* is a variety consisting of fine scaly aggregates with a silky luster. It often results from the alteration of feldspars.

Muscovite is generally considered the most common mica. It occurs in granites and syenites and especially in pegmatite veins where pneumatolytic action has been effective. It is also common in metamorphic rocks, such as gneisses and schists, and in some limestones and fragmental rocks. The usual associates are feldspar, quartz, tourmaline, beryl, spodumene, garnet, apatite, and fluorite. Deposits of muscovite of commercial value occur in North Carolina, New Hampshire, South Dakota, Idaho, New Mexico, Colorado, Virginia, South Carolina, Georgia, and Alabama. Some of the principal producing localities are in Mitchell, Yancey, Macon, Jackson, Haywood, and Ashe counties, North Carolina; Custer County, South Dakota; Grafton and Cheshire counties, New Hampshire. Deposits of excellent muscovite also occur in Ottawa and Berthier counties, Quebec.

FIG. 713.—Phlogopite. Lanark County, Ontario.

Sheet mica is used principally in the manufacture of electrical apparatus and machinery such as dynamos, motors, high-voltage induction apparatus, switchboards, lamp sockets, and for flexible mica-covered insulating cloth and tape. Clear and transparent sheets are used for windows in coal, gas, and oil stoves, gas-lamp chimneys, and lamp shades. Scrap mica, that is, material too small to be cut into sheets, is ground in large quantities and used in the manufacture of wall paper, lubricants, fancy paints, rubber goods, electrical insulators, coverings for steam pipes, and roofing papers.

Micanite is prepared by cementing with shellac successive layers of small, thin sheets of mica and subjecting the mass to heat and pressure.

The United States consumes about 75 per cent. of the world's production of mica; 60 to 70 per cent. is of domestic origin, the remainder being imported from Canada and India.

PHLOGOPITE (*Magnesium Mica, Amber Mica, Bronze Mica*), $KMg_3(OH)_2AlSi_3O_{10}$.

Monoclinic, prismatic class. Crystals usually resemble those of biotite in form and habit and are sometimes large and coarse (Fig. 713). They may be hexagonal or rhombic in outline. Commonly found in disseminated scales, plates, or aggregates.

Highly perfect basal cleavage. Thin laminæ are tough and elastic. Specific gravity, 2.8 to 3. Pearly to submetallic luster. α 1.562, β 1.606, γ 1.606, $(-)$; $2V$ varies from 0° to 35°; $r < v$. Color may be silvery gray, yellow, brown, green, copper or bronze red. Thin leaves are transparent. Often shows asterism.

$KMg_3(OH)_2AlSi_3O_{10}$. Usually contains small amounts of iron, sodium, and fluorine. Whitens and fuses on thin edges. Slightly acted upon by hydrochloric acid but readily decomposed by hot concentrated sulphuric acid.

Phlogopite occurs in crystalline limestones, dolomites, schists, and in serpentine. Important localities are Pargas, Finland; Åker, Sweden; Fassathal, Tirol; St. Lawrence and Jefferson counties, New York; Morris and Warren counties, New Jersey; Sydenham and Burgess, Ontario, where crystals measuring 7 feet across the cleavage plane have been found; various localities in Quebec.

It is used chiefly as an insulator in electrical apparatus. For use on commutators, phlogopite is preferred to muscovite, as it has more nearly the same hardness as the copper of the commutator segments.

BIOTITE (*Magnesium-iron Mica, Black Mica*), $K(Mg,Fe)_3(OH)_2-AlSi_3O_{10}$.

Monoclinic, prismatic class. Crystals are usually tabular with an hexagonal (Fig. 714) or rhombic habit; sometimes striated horizontally. Crystals are rare. Generally found in plates, lamellar masses, or disseminated scales.

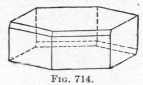

Highly perfect basal cleavage. Hardness, 2.5 to 3. Specific gravity, 2.7 to 3.2. Dark brown or black in color; more rarely, light brown, or greenish. The indices of refraction vary gener-

Fig. 714.

ally from 1.541 to 1.638; $2V$ varies from 0° to 50°; $r < v$. White to greenish streak. Transparent to opaque. Sometimes shows asterism.

$K(Mg,Fe)_3(OH)_2AlSi_3O_{10}$. The composition varies greatly. May contain titanium, sodium, and fluorine. *Lepidomelane* contains large amounts of the oxides of iron and but little MgO. Fuses with difficulty. Only slightly attacked by hydrochloric acid; completely decomposed by hot concentrated sulphuric acid. Alters to chlorite, or to epidote, quartz, and iron oxide.

Biotite is an extremely common mica, being an important constituent of many igneous and metamorphic rocks, such as granite, syenite, diorite, porphyry, gneiss, and mica schist. It is often associated with muscovite.

Biotite is of little use commercially.

Lepidolite (*Lithium Mica*), $K_2Li_3Al_3(OH,F)_4(AlSi_3O_{10})_2$.

Monoclinic, prismatic class. Crystals are short prismatic but very rare. Usually in scaly, granular masses, often resembling granular limestone, and in tabular, cleavable plates.

Perfect basal cleavage. Hardness, 2 to 4. Specific gravity, 2.8 to 2.9. Rose red or lilac in color, also white, gray, greenish, or brown. Pearly luster. α 1.560, β 1.598, γ 1.605, $(-)$; $2V$ is about 40°; $r > v$. Translucent.

$K_2Li_3Al_3(OH,F)_4(AlSi_3O_{10})_2$. Some varieties contain rubidium and cæsium. Colors the flame red and fuses to a white glass. After fusion easily acted upon by acids.

Occurs commonly in pegmatite veins, also in granites and gneisses. It is usually the result of pneumatolytic action. The common associates are tourmaline (especially rubellite) (Fig. 690, page 343), spodumene, cassiterite, muscovite, albite, and topaz. Some localities are Rozena, Moravia; the Island of Elba; Paris, Hebron, Auburn, and Rumford, Maine; Chesterfield, Massachusetts; San Diego County, California.

An important source of lithium compounds.

CHLORITE (*Prochlorite, Clinochlorite*), $H_8Mg_5Al_2Si_3O_{18}$.

The general term *chlorite* is applied to a number of minerals which are closely related to the micas.

Monoclinic, prismatic class. Crystals are tabular and six sided, resembling those of mica. Commonly in foliated, scaly, granular, or earthy masses. Often as a scaly or dusty coating on, or disseminated through, quartz, titanite, pericline, and adularia.

Perfect basal cleavage. Laminæ are flexible but inelastic. Slightly soapy feel. Hardness, 1 to 2.5. Specific gravity, 2.6 to 3. Grass green, brownish green, or blackish green in color. The indices of refraction vary from 1.576 to 1.596, ($\pm$); $2V$ varies from $0°$ to $90°$; $r < v$. Translucent to opaque, very thin laminæ may be transparent. Streak, greenish.

$H_8Mg_5Al_2Si_3O_{18}$. May also be written $Mg_5Al_2(OH)_8Si_3O_{10}$. The minerals included in this description are silicates of aluminum or trivalent iron with magnesium, bivalent iron, or manganese. They are more basic than the micas and are free from the alkalies. The composition varies greatly. They yield water when heated in a closed tube.

These minerals are of secondary origin and are usually the result of the decomposition of pyroxenes, amphiboles, garnet, biotite and vesuvianite. Very common in schists and serpentine. Often associated with garnet, diopside, magnesite, magnetite, and apatite. Very widespread. Some principal localities are the Ural Mountains; various places in Tirol; Zermatt, Switzerland; Saxony; Chester and Unionville, Pennsylvania; Brewster, New York.

TALC, $H_2Mg_3Si_4O_{12}$.

Monoclinic. Crystals are tabular or scaly but indistinctly developed. Occurs usually as foliated or compact masses and globular or stellate groups; also fibrous or granular.

Perfect basal cleavage. Laminæ are flexible but inelastic. Compact varieties have an uneven fracture. Hardness, 1 to 2.5. Specific gravity, 2.6 to 2.8. Commonly green, white, or gray in color; also yellowish, reddish, and brown. Pearly to greasy luster. α 1.539, β 1.589, γ 1.589, ($-$); $2V$ varies from $6°$ to $30°$; $r > v$. Greasy or soapy feel. Opaque to transparent.

There are several varieties of talc:

1. *Foliated Talc.*—Consists of easily separable but inelastic scales or plates. Soapy or greasy feel. Hardness 1; easily impressed by the finger nail. Light green to white in color.

2. *Steatite or Soapstone.*—Massive, often impure. Coarse to fine granular, also schistose. Gray to greenish in color. Hardness, 1.5 to 2.5. Occurs in large deposits.

3. *French Chalk.*—Soft, compact, whitish masses. Marks cloth easily. $H_2Mg_3Si_4O_{12}$. May also be written $Mg_3(OH)_2Si_4O_{10}$. May contain iron, aluminum, and nickel. Fuses with great difficulty. Yields water when strongly ignited. Unattacked by acids. Occurs as a pseudomorph after pyroxenes, hornblende, tremolite, enstatite, spinel, quartz, dolomite, and many other minerals.

Talc is usually considered an alteration product of nonaluminous magnesium minerals, such as the pyroxenes, amphiboles, and olivine. Commonly found in metamorphic rocks, especially chlorite schists; also with serpentine and magnesite. Occurs frequently as talc or talcose schist containing doubly terminated crystals of magnetite, dolomite, apatite, tourmaline, pyrite, and actinolite. Foliated talc is found at Greiner, Tirol; various places in Switzerland, Italy, France, and Germany; Grafton and elsewhere, New Hampshire; St. Lawrence County, New York. The most important producing locality in the United States for talc is in St. Lawrence County, New York, where it occurs with limestone and has been derived from tremolite and enstatite. Vermont is also an important producer of talc. Albemarle and Nelson counties, Virginia; Montgomery and Northampton counties, Pennsylvania; and Phillipsburg, New Jersey, also produce large quantities. Other important localities are in North Carolina; Georgia; Maryland; Rhode Island; Massachusetts; and California.

Talc and soapstone, cut into slabs or other shapes, are used for wash tubs, sanitary appliances, laboratory tables and tanks, electrical switchboards, mantels, hearthstones, firebricks, foot warmers, slate pencils, and as crayon for marking iron, glass, and fabrics. Ground talc is used in toilet powders and soaps, for dressing skins and leather, in waterproof cement, as a lubricant, nonconductor of heat, and as "mineral pulp" for filler in paint, paper, and roofing material. Over 40 industries use talc or soapstone in some form. See page 422.

KAOLINITE (*Kaolin, China Clay*), $H_4Al_2Si_2O_9$.

Monoclinic, prismatic class. Rarely in small scales with an hexagonal or rhombic outline. Generally in compact, friable, mealy, or clay-like masses.

Scales possess a basal cleavage. Earthy fracture. Hardness, 1 to 2.5. Specific gravity, 2.2 to 2.6. Compact masses are dull. scales pearly,

α 1.561, β 1.565, γ 1.567, $(-)$; $2V = 68°$; $r > v$.   White, yellowish, reddish, bluish, greenish, or brownish in color.   Greasy feel.   White to yellowish streak.   Opaque to translucent.   Usually adheres to the tongue and becomes plastic when moistened.   Argillaceous odor when breathed upon.

$H_4Al_2Si_2O_9$.   May also be written $Al_2(OH)_4Si_2O_5$.   May contain some iron.   Yields water on ignition.   Infusible.   Partially decomposed by hydrochloric acid.   Occurs as a pseudomorph after many minerals.

Optical and X-ray data indicate that there are three distinct minerals possessing the composition $Al_2(OH)_4Si_2O_5$, namely, kaolinite, dickite, and nacrite.   In physical characteristics they resemble one another very closely.   Kaolinite is the most common.

Kaolinite, dickite, and nacrite are always secondary minerals resulting from the action of postvolcanic, pneumatolytic, and hydrothermal processes upon rocks containing feldspar, nephelite, topaz, beryl, augite, scapolite, and other aluminous minerals.   Kaolinite may also result from ordinary weathering.   Occurs in irregular deposits in kaolinized pegmatites, granites, porphyries, and gneisses.   Also in secondary deposits, the result of transportation and deposition under water.   These occurrences are often very pure.   It is an important constituent of clay and soil.   Common associates are feldspar, quartz, corundum, and diaspore.   Some localities are Saint Yrieix, near Limoges, France; Cornwall and Devonshire, England; Meissen, Saxony.   In the United States, kaolin is mined at Newcastle and Wilmington, Delaware; also in Florida, North Carolina, Pennsylvania, Vermont, California, and Maryland.

Kaolinite is used in large quantities in the manufacture of chinaware, porcelain, tiles, and other refractory materials.

SERPENTINE, $H_4Mg_3Si_2O_9$.

Monoclinic, optically.   Never in crystals except pseudomorphs. Usually compact, columnar, fibrous, or lamellar.   Massive varieties often have a microscopically fine fibrous or foliated structure.

Conchoidal to splintery fracture.   Hardness, 2.5 to 4.   Specific gravity, 2.5 to 2.8.   Various shades of green; also yellowish, grayish, reddish, brownish, or black.   Often spotted, clouded, or multicolored. Dull resinous, greasy, or waxy luster.   The indices of refraction vary from 1.49 to 1.57; $2V$ is variable, sometimes large.   Smooth to greasy feel.

There are several varieties:

1. *Common Serpentine.*—Compact, massive.   Generally dark in color, often multicolored.   Sometimes impure.   Very abundant.

2. *Precious Serpentine.*—Massive, more or less homogeneous.   Various shades of green in color, sometimes yellowish.   Translucent.

3. *Chrysotile, Fibrous Serpentine, Asbestos.*—Consists of delicate, fine, parallel fibers, which can be easily separated (Fig. 715).   Fibers are

flexible and adapted for spinning. Silky to silky-metallic luster. Various shades of green in color; also white, yellowish or brownish. Usually found in veins with the fibers perpendicular to the walls of the veins (Fig. 716). Sometimes called *short-fibered asbestos*.

Fig. 715.—Serpentine: variety, asbestos. Near Globe, Arizona.

Fig. 716.—Serpentine: variety, asbestos (light). Thetford-Black Lake district, Canada.

4. *Verd Antique.*—Massive greenish serpentine mixed irregularly with calcite, dolomite, magnesite, or talc. Has a mottled or veined appearance (Fig. 717). Takes an excellent polish and is used extensively for ornamental purposes. It is sometimes called *serpentine marble.*

$H_4Mg_3Si_2O_9$. May also be written $Mg_6(OH)_6Si_4O_{11}.H_2O$. X-ray data indicate that in serpentine there are double chains of linked SiO_4 tetrahedrons, with the composition (Si_4O_{11}) similar to those in the amphiboles (page 332). This would explain the marked tendency to occur in fibers. Serpentine may contain iron and nickel. Yields water when ignited. Splinters fuse with difficulty. Decomposed by acids with a separation of silica. May alter to brucite, magnesite, and hydromagnesite. Serpentine is a secondary mineral resulting from the alteration of magnesium minerals and rocks,

Fig. 717.—Serpentine: variety, verd antique. Roxbury, Vermont.

such as olivine, enstatite, hornblende, tremolite, augite, chondrodite, and peridotite. Olivine is the most common source of serpentine. Common associates are magnesite, calcite, chromite, garnierite, pyrope, platinum, and talc.

Serpentine occurs in many localities, some of which are Sweden; Silesia; Chester County and Easton, Pennsylvania, where it is mined:

Milford, Connecticut; Hoboken and Montville, New Jersey; Syracuse, New York; Vermont; northern New York; Washington. Asbestos is not found in large quantities in the United States. Most of the asbestos of commerce is obtained from the mines in the Thetford-Black Lake district, Quebec; next in importance are Rhodesia, the Union of South Africa, and the Island of Cyprus.

Polished massive serpentine and verd antique are used for ornamental and interior decorative purposes. Translucent yellowish serpentine is sometimes cut and polished for gem purposes. Asbestos is used extensively in the manufacture of nonconductors of heat and in noncombustible materials such as cloth, boards, felt, rope, paper, paint, cement, and theater curtains.

Sepiolite (*Meerschaum*), $H_8Mg_2Si_3O_{12}$.

Monoclinic. Occurs only in compact nodular, earthy, or clayey masses.

Conchoidal to uneven fracture. Hardness, 2 to 2.5. Impressed by the finger nail. Specific gravity, 1 to 2. On account of its porosity it may float on water. Adheres to the tongue. Usually white, yellowish, or grayish in color. Dull luster. α 1.519, β 1.52, γ 1.529, ($-$).

$H_8Mg_2Si_3O_{12}$. Yields water when strongly ignited. Fuses with difficulty on thin edges to a white glass; some varieties first turn black. Gelatinizes with hydrochloric acid.

An alteration product of serpentine, magnesite, or impure opal containing considerable magnesium. It is found principally in nodular masses in serpentine or in secondary deposits on the plains of Eskischehr, Asia Minor. Occurs in smaller quantities in Spain; the Grecian Archipelago; Morocco; Moravia; Utah; California; New Mexico.

Meerschaum is easily carved and worked on the lathe, takes an excellent polish, and is used extensively for pipe bowls and cigar tips.

Garnierite, $H_2(Ni,Mg)SiO_4$.

Never found in crystals. Occurs commonly as rounded, pea-shaped masses with varnish-like surfaces; also compact, reniform, or earthy; apparently amorphous.

Conchoidal or earthy fracture. Hardness, 2 to 3. Specific gravity, 2.3 to 2.8. Pale, apple, or emerald green in color. Dull to greasy luster. $n = 1.59$. Greasy feel. Frequently adheres to the tongue. Streak white to greenish.

$H_2(Ni,Mg)SiO_4$. Composition varies greatly. Infusible, decrepitates, and becomes magnetic. Yields water on ignition. Attacked by acids.

An alteration of olivine and serpentine rocks. Usually associated with olivine, serpentine, chromite, and talc. Occurs in serpentine at

Nouméa, New Caledonia; also found at Franckenstein, Silesia; Webster, North Carolina; Riddle, Douglas County, Oregon.

A valuable source of nickel. See page 424.

Pyroxene Group

The members of the pyroxene group are important rock minerals. They consist of silicates of calcium, magnesium, iron, aluminum, sodium, and lithium, corresponding to the general formulas $M''_2(SiO_3)_2$ and $M'M'''(SiO_3)_2$. Although these minerals crystallize in both the orthorhombic and monoclinic systems, they are characterized by prism angles and cleavages of about 87 and 93°. The orthorhombic pyroxenes generally contain no calcium and little or no aluminum. The monoclinic members usually have considerable calcium and may, or may not, contain aluminum and the alkalies.

As stated on page 332 the pyroxenes have structures containing chains of linked SiO_4 tetrahedrons (Fig. 667). The pyroxenes are rather closely related, chemically and crystallographically, to the minerals of the amphibole group. This relationship is discussed on page 369.

The following important pyroxenes will be described:

Enstatite, Bronzite, Hypersthene	$(Mg,Fe)_2(SiO_3)_2$	Orthorhombic
Diopside	$CaMg(SiO_3)_2$	Monoclinic
Augite	$\begin{cases} Ca(Mg,Fe)(Si_2O_6) \\ (Ca,Mg,Fe)(Al,Fe)(AlSiO_6) \end{cases}$	Monoclinic
Spodumene	$LiAl(SiO_3)_2$	Monoclinic

In addition to the above, the following minerals have usually been classified as pyroxenes:

Wollastonite	$Ca_2(SiO_3)_2$	Triclinic
Pectolite	$HNaCa_2(SiO_3)_3$	Triclinic
Rhodonite	$Mn_2(SiO_3)_2$	Triclinic

These minerals differ from the pyroxenes in optical and crystallographic properties and probably also in structure.

ENSTATITE (*Bronzite, Hypersthene*), $(Mg,Fe)_2(SiO_3)_2$.

Orthorhombic, bipyramidal class. Rarely found in distinct crystals, usually in fibrous, lamellar, columnar, or compact masses. Hypersthene occurs frequently in cleavable aggregates.

Prismatic and pinacoidal cleavages. Hardness, 5 to 6. Specific gravity, 3.1 to 3.5. Translucent to opaque.

Enstatite.—Grayish white, greenish, or brownish in color. Vitreous to pearly luster. α 1.650, β 1.653, γ 1.658, $(+)$; $2V = 31°$; $r > v$. Contains little or no ferrous oxide.

Bronzite.—Darker in color than enstatite, usually brown, yellowish, or green. Pronounced pinacoidal parting, producing fibrous or irregular wavy surfaces with a chatoyant bronzy luster. Mean index of refraction

1.685, (+); $2V$ is very large.   Contains from 5 to 16 per cent. of ferrous oxide.

Hypersthene.—Black, brownish black, or green in color.   Pearly to metalloidal luster. α 1.692, β 1.702, γ 1.705, (−); $2V = 72°$; $r > v$. Often shows a copper-red iridescence on the macropinacoid.   Contains more iron than magnesium.

These minerals occur commonly in basic igneous rocks such as pyroxenite, peridotite, norite, and gabbro.   The most frequent associates are olivine, spinel, serpentine, talc, labradorite, hornblende, pyrrhotite, and magnetite.   Some localities are Norway; Styria, Austria; Bavaria; Kimberley, South Africa; St. Paul's Island, off the coast of Labrador; Laacher See, Rhenish Prussia; Greenland; Scotland; along the Hudson River and in the Adirondack Mountains, New York.

Hypersthene showing an iridescence and metalloidal luster is sometimes used in jewelry.

DIOPSIDE, $CaMg(SiO_3)_2$.

Monoclinic, prismatic class.   Crystals are generally short and thick and nearly square or octagonal in cross section, the faces of the unit

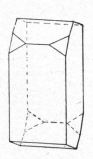

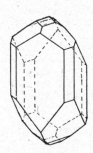

FIG. 718.   FIG. 719.   FIG. 720.—Diopside with zonal distribution of color.   Ala, Italy.

prism intersecting at angles of 87 and 93°.   Striations parallel to the basal pinacoid are frequently observed on the faces of the vertical zone. Common forms are the three pinacoids, unit prism, positive and negative hemipyramids, and the positive hemiorthodome (Figs. 718, 719, and 720).   Occurs also in compact, broad columnar, granular, lamellar, or fibrous masses.

Prismatic cleavage and basal parting are conspicuous.   Hardness, 5 to 6.   Specific gravity, 3.2 to 3.3.   Uneven to conchoidal fracture. Vitreous, resinous, or dull luster; sometimes inclining to pearly on the basal parting. α 1.673, β 1.680, γ 1.702, (+); $2V = 59°$; $r > v$.   Generally light to dark green in color; also colorless, gray, yellow, and, rarely, blue. Zonal distribution of color not uncommon (Fig. 720). White to greenish streak. Transparent to opaque. May become luminescent.

$CaMg(SiO_3)_2$. Usually contains up to 5 per cent. of FeO. *Diallage* is a thin-foliated, or lamellar variety, containing from 8 to 16 per cent. of iron oxide, and greenish or brownish in color. Aluminum and manganese may also be present. More or less fusible to a dark-colored or green glass. Not acted upon by the common acids. Alters to serpentine, talc, chlorite, and limonite.

Occurs in diorite, gabbro, basalt, pyroxenite, and peridotite; also in crystalline schists and as a contact mineral in limestone and dolomite. Common associates are vesuvianite, tremolite, garnet, scapolite, spinel, apatite, titanite, phlogopite, the amphiboles, tourmaline, and the feldspars. Found at various places in Tirol; Zermatt, Switzerland; Pargas, Finland; Sweden; Lanark and Hastings counties, Ontario; Lewis and St. Lawrence counties, New York.

Clear and transparent varieties are sometimes used for gem purposes.

AUGITE.

Monoclinic, prismatic class. Crystals are short, prismatic, or thick columnar with a prism angle of 87°, often yielding a pseudotetragonal

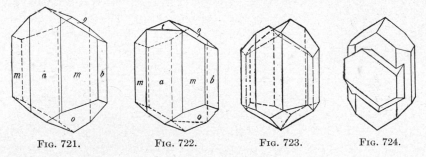

FIG. 721.   FIG. 722.   FIG. 723.   FIG. 724.

outline. The most usual combination consists of the ortho- (*a*) and clinopinacoids (*b*), unit prism (*m*), positive unit hemipyramid (*o*), and negative hemiorthodome (*t*) (Figs. 721 and 722). Sometimes occurs as contact twins, twinned parallel to the orthopinacoid (Fig. 723), or as penetration twins in which the clinohemipyramid is the twinning plane (Fig. 724). It is also observed in compact and disseminated grains and granular aggregates; rarely fibrous.

Prismatic cleavage. Conchoidal to uneven fracture. Hardness, 5 to 6. Specific gravity, 3.2 to 3.6; varying with the composition. Commonly black or greenish black in color, also leek green. Grayish green streak. Usually opaque but may be translucent. Vitreous to dull. α 1.698, β 1.704, γ 1.723, (+); $2V = 60°$; $r > v$.

Chemically, augite may be considered a mixture of $Ca(Mg,Fe)(Si_2O_6)$ and $(Ca,Mg,Fe)(Al,Fe)(AlSiO_6)$. Sodium and titanium are sometimes present. Fuses, and often forms a magnetic glass. Slightly acted upon by acids. Alters to a fibrous hornblende having the form of augite, termed *uralite*, and also to serpentine.

Augite is a common rock mineral and often occurs in disseminated crystals as an essential or accessory constituent of basalt, diabase, gabbro, tuff, and volcanic sand and ashes. Also occurs in crystalline schists and limestones and is commonly the result of contact metamorphism. Some notable localities are Fassathal, Tirol; Mount Vesuvius; Mount Etna; Kaiserstuhl, Baden; Teplitz, Bohemia; Norway; Finland; Thetford, Vermont; Amherst County, Virginia.

SPODUMENE (*Hiddenite, Kunzite*), LiAl(SiO₃)₂.

Monoclinic, prismatic class. Long, columnar crystals with the unit prism predominating; also tabular, and frequently with vertical striations

and furrows (Fig. 725). Often very large, several crystals from the Etta Mine, near Keystone, South Dakota, having measured 36, 40, 42, and 47 feet in length and from $2\frac{1}{2}$ to 6 feet in width; each weighed over 30 tons. Occurs more commonly in cleavable masses and broad columnar aggregates.

Perfect prismatic cleavage; also very easy parting parallel to the orthopinacoid. Uneven to splintery fracture. Hardness, 6 to 7. Specific gravity, 3.1 to 3.2. White, grayish, green, pink, and purple. Vitreous to pearly luster. α 1.660, β 1.666, γ 1.676, $(+)$; $2V$ is about $58°$; $r > v$. Transparent to opaque.

Fig. 725.—Spodumene. Norwich, Massachusetts.

Hiddenite is a clear-yellow to emerald-green variety from Stony Point, Alexander County, North Carolina. A transparent lilac-pink variety from Pala, San Diego County, California, is called *kunzite*. This variety phosphoresces with an orange-pink light when exposed to electric discharges, X rays, ultraviolet light, or to radium emanations.

LiAl(SiO₃)₂. Usually contains some sodium; iron, and calcium. Fuses easily, turns white, intumesces, and colors the flame purple red. Insoluble in acids. Alters to albite, muscovite, and quartz.

Occurs in pegmatite veins with tourmaline, beryl, garnet, lepidolite, feldspar, mica, and quartz as the principal associates. Some localities are Sweden; Tirol; Ireland; Windham, Maine; Sterling, Chester, and Goshen, Massachusetts; Branchville, Connecticut; Alexander and Cleveland counties, North Carolina; Etta Mine, Pennington County, South Dakota; Pala, San Diego County, California.

Hiddenite and kunzite are used for gem purposes. The output of the Etta Mine, near Keystone, South Dakota, furnishes an important source of lithium compounds, some of which are used in the manufacture of red fire and for medicinal purposes. See pages 402 and 419.

Wollastonite (*Tabular Spar*), $Ca_2(SiO_3)_2$.

Triclinic, pinacoidal class. Crystals are usually elongated parallel to the *b* axis and tabular in habit. Most commonly observed in cleavable (Fig. 726), fibrous, granular, and compact masses. The fibers may have a parallel or divergent structure.

Basal and macropinacoidal cleavages. Uneven fracture. Hardness, 4 to 5. Specific gravity, 2.8 to 2.9. Usually white, colorless, or gray; also yellowish, reddish, or brownish. Vitreous to silky luster. α 1.616, β 1.629, γ 1.631, $(-)$; $2V = 39°$; $r > v$. Transparent to translucent.

$Ca_2(SiO_3)_2$. Generally mixed with calcite and hence effervesces with acid. Fusible on the thin edges. Decomposes with hydrochloric acid with separation of silica.

Wollastonite is a typical contact metamorphic mineral and is generally associated with garnet, diopside, vesuvianite, tremolite, graphite, epidote, and calcite. It is found in granular limestone near granite contacts. Some localities are the Island of Elba; Norway; Mount Vesuvius; Rumania; Grenville, Quebec; North Burgess and elsewhere, Ontario; Lewis and Warren counties, New York; California.

Fig. 726.—Wollastonite. Harrisville, Lewis County, New York.

Pectolite $HNaCa_2(SiO_3)_3$.

Triclinic, pinacoidal class. Generally consists of aggregates of divergent fibers or acicular crystals, sometimes of considerable length and with sharp ends (Fig. 727).

Fig. 727.—Pectolite. Paterson, New Jersey.

Basal and macropinacoidal cleavages. Uneven fracture. Hardness, 4 to 5. Specific gravity, 2.7 to 2.8. Colorless, white, or grayish white. Translucent to opaque. Vitreous pearly to silky luster. α 1.595, β 1.606, γ 1.634, $(+)$; $2V = 60°$; $r > v$.

$HNaCa_2(SiO_3)_3$. Usually contains about 10 per cent. of sodium oxide. Manganese is sometimes present. Yields water in a closed tube. Decomposed by hydrochloric acid with the separation of silica. Sometimes phosphoresces when crushed in the dark.

Occurs in fissures and cavities in basic igneous and metamorphic rocks. Commonly associated with the zeolites, datolite, and calcite. Some localities are Fassathal and Monzoni, Tirol; Scotland; Thunder Bay, Ontario; Bergen Hill, Paterson, and vicinity, New Jersey; Isle Royale, Michigan.

RHODONITE (*Fowlerite*), $Mn_2(SiO_3)_2$.

Triclinic, pinacoidal class. Crystals are usually tabular or prismatic, comparatively large and with rounded edges, but not very common (Fig. 728). Occurs generally in fine grained, cleavable, or compact masses; also in disseminated grains.

Prismatic and basal cleavages. Conchoidal to uneven fracture. Hardness, 5 to 6. Specific gravity, 3.4 to 3.7. Rose red, pink, yellowish, greenish, or brownish in color; often black externally. Vitreous to pearly luster. α 1.724, β 1.728, γ 1.737, (+); $2V$ about 70°; $r < v$. Transparent to opaque.

FIG. 728.—Rhodonite. Franklin Furnace, New Jersey.

$Mn_2(SiO_3)_2$. Commonly contains some calcium and iron. *Fowlerite* is a zinciferous variety from the Franklin Furnace district, New Jersey; α 1.726, β 1.730, γ 1.737, (+); $2V$ is large. Fuses easily to a brownish or black glass. Slightly acted upon by acids, although varieties containing an admixture of calcite will effervesce.

Occurs with calcite, rhodochrosite, tetrahedrite, franklinite, willemite, zincite, quartz, and iron ores. Some localities are the Harz Mountains, Germany; Rumania; Italy; Sweden; the Ural Mountains; Peru; Cummington, Massachusetts; Franklin Furnace, New Jersey; Butte, Montana.

Sometimes used for gem and ornamental purposes.

Amphibole Group

The members of the amphibole group are closely related to the pyroxenes, being important rock minerals and silicates of magnesium, calcium, iron, sodium, and potassium. The amphiboles and pyroxenes together make up about 17 per cent. of the igneous rocks. The amphiboles differ from the pyroxenes in having double chains or bands of linked SiO_4 tetrahedrons, with the composition Si_4O_{11} (Fig. 668, page 333). Also the amphiboles contain water. Like the pyroxenes, these minerals crystallize in the orthorhombic and monoclinic systems. Only the following monoclinic amphiboles are sufficiently important to warrant description:

Tremolite...................... $Ca_2Mg_5(OH)_2(Si_4O_{11})_2$
Actinolite..................... $Ca_2(Mg,Fe)_5(OH)_2(Si_4O_{11})_2$
Hornblende................... $\begin{cases} Ca_2(Mg,Fe)_4Al(OH)_2(AlSi_7O_{22}) \\ Ca_2Na(Mg,Fe)_4Al(OH)_2(Al_2Si_6O_{22}) \end{cases}$

The principal differences between the members of the pyroxene and amphibole groups may be tabulated as follows:

	Pyroxenes	Amphiboles
Crystals	Short prismatic, complex, commonly four or eight sided.	Long prismatic, simple, commonly six sided.
Prism angles	87 and 93°, pseudotetragonal.	56 and 124°, pseudohexagonal.
Cleavages	Prismatic, nearly 90°, bladed.	Prismatic, nearly 120°, more distinct.
Structure	Single chains (SiO_3).	Double chains (Si_4O_{11}).
Masses	Lamellar or granular.	Columnar or fibrous.
Specific gravity	Higher.	
Chemical composition	Anhydrous, alter to amphibole.	Contain water. Magnesium and the alkalies are more prominent.
Occurrence	Formed at higher temperatures. Common in more basic rocks.	Common in more acid rocks.

Tremolite, $Ca_2Mg_5(OH)_2(Si_4O_{11})_2$.

Monoclinic, prismatic class. Crystals are bladed, either long or short, but generally without terminal faces (Fig. 729). Occurs also in fibrous and asbestiform aggregates and in compact columnar or granular masses.

Fig. 729.—Tremolite. Haliburton, Ontario.

Perfect prismatic cleavage, at angles of 56 and 124°. Hardness, 5 to 6. Specific gravity, 2.9 to 3.1. Generally white, gray, greenish, or yellowish in color. *Hexagonite* is an amethystine to lavender variety, due to a small amount of manganese. Vitreous to silky luster. α 1.609, β 1.623, γ 1.635, (−); $2V$ is about 85°; $r < v$. Transparent to opaque.

$Ca_2Mg_5(OH_2)(Si_4O_{11})_2$. Contains little or no iron. Not acted upon by acids. Fuses with difficulty. Alters to talc.

Tremolite is a contact metamorphic mineral and occurs in granular limestones and dolomites, and schists. Found in the Saint Gotthard district, Switzerland; Lee, Massachusetts; Easton, Pennsylvania; Edenville, Orange County, and Edwards, St. Lawrence County, New York; Pontiac County, Quebec; Renfrew and Lanark counties, Ontario.

Asbestos.—Under this term are included fibrous varieties of tremolite, actinolite, and other nonaluminous amphiboles. The fibers are sometimes long, parallel, flexible, and easily separated by the fingers. Amphibole asbestos is commonly called *long fibered asbestos*, while serpentine asbestos (see page 361) is termed *short fibered*. The heat-resisting property of the amphibole asbestos is about the same as that of the chrysotile asbestos, but the nonconductivity of heat and strength of fiber are less. It is also not so suitable for spinning as the short-fibered asbestos. Hence, serpentine or chrysotile asbestos gives the better results. Amphibole asbestos occurs at Sall Mountain, Georgia, and in Lewis County, Idaho. For the uses of asbestos, see page 362.

Actinolite, $Ca_2(Mg,Fe)_5(OH)_2(Si_4O_{11})_2$.

Monoclinic, prismatic class. Long- or short-bladed crystals, but generally without terminal faces (Fig. 730). Occurs usually in divergent

Fig. 730.—Actinolite (dark) in talc. Greiner, Tirol.

or irregular columnar, fibrous, or asbestiform aggregates; also in compact granular masses. *Nephrite* is a compact variety and is included in the general term *jade*.[1]

Perfect prismatic cleavage, at angles of about 56 and 124°. Hardness, 5 to 6. Specific gravity, 2.9 to 3.2. Usually green in color. Vitreous to silky luster. α 1.611, β 1.627, γ 1.636, $(-)$; $2V = 78°$; $r < v$. Transparent to opaque.

$Ca_2(Mg,Fe)_5(OH)_2(Si_4O_{11})_2$. Usually contains considerable iron and small amounts of aluminum and sodium. Fuses to a gray enamel. Slightly acted upon by acids. Alters to talc, chlorite, epidote, or to an aggregate of serpentine and calcite.

Actinolite occurs in crystalline schists; sometimes in such quantities that the rock may be termed *actinolite schist*. It is often the result of contact metamorphism. Some localities are Greiner, Zillerthal, Tirol; Norway; Zöblitz, Saxony; Iyo, Japan; Brome County, Quebec; Bare Hills, Maryland; Franklin Furnace, New Jersey; Delaware and Chester counties, Pennsylvania; Lee and Chester, Massachusetts; Windham, Vermont.

[1] Jade includes certain varieties of actinolite and jadeite, a compact pyroxene with the formula $NaAl(SiO_3)_2$.

HORNBLENDE.

Monoclinic, prismatic class. Prismatic crystals with a pseudo-hexagonal outline and rhombohedral-like terminations are common. The

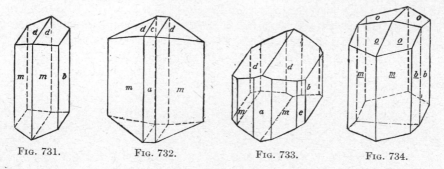

Fig. 731.   Fig. 732.   Fig. 733.   Fig. 734.

prism angles are 56 and 124°. The common forms are the unit prism (*m*), clinopinacoid (*b*), orthopinacoid (*a*), clinodome (*d*), and positive unit

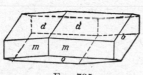

Fig. 735.

Fig. 736.—Hornblende.   Bilin, Bohemia.

hemiorthodome (*Q*) (Figs. 731, 732, 733, 735, and 736). Sometimes twinned parallel to orthopinacoid (Fig. 734). Occurs also in bladed, fibrous, columnar, granular, or compact masses.

Perfect prismatic cleavage. Hardness, 5 to 6. Specific gravity, 2.9 to 3.3. Usually dark green, brown, or black in color; grayish green to grayish brown streak. Vitreous to silky luster. May be transparent but generally only translucent to opaque. The optical constants vary; (*a*) *common hornblende*, green to black in color; α 1.661, β 1.673, γ 1.683, (−); 2V is about 84°; $r < v$; (*b*) *basaltic hornblende*, brownish black to black in color; α 1.677, β 1.695, γ 1.708, (−); 2V is large; $r < v$.

Chemically, hornblende may be considered a mixture of the two molecules $Ca_2(Mg,Fe)_4Al(OH)_2(AlSi_7O_{22})$ and $Ca_2Na(Mg,Fe)_4Al(OH)_2$-$(Al_2Si_6O_{22})$. The composition is strikingly similar to that of augite (see page 365). Some varieties contain small amounts of the alkalies and titanium. ⋅A small amount of water is present, which tends to distinguish hornblende from augite. Alters to chlorite, epidote, calcite, siderite, limonite, and quartz. *Uralite* is augite altered to hornblende with the form of the original mineral but with the cleavage of hornblende. Augite commonly alters in this way, and the process is termed *uralization*.

Hornblende is commonly associated with quartz, feldspar, pyroxenes, chlorite, and calcite. It is an essential or accessory constituent of many plutonic rocks such as granite, syenite, and diorite; also of basalt, hornblende schist, andesite, phonolite, gabbro, and crystalline limestones.

Some of the more important localities are Mount Vesuvius; Bilin, Bohemia; Pargas, Finland; Renfrew County, Ontario; Russel, Pierrepont, and DeKalb, New York; Hawley, Massachusetts; Franconia, New Hampshire; Franklin Furnace, New Jersey.

Feldspar Group

The feldspars constitute the most abundant group of minerals. They are very important rock minerals and, according to Clarke, make up about 60 per cent. of the igneous rocks. Their chemical compositions are very similar and may be expressed, in general, by the formulas $M'AlSi_3O_8$ or $M''Al_2Si_2O_8$, in which the metal may be potassium, sodium, calcium, or, more rarely, barium. The feldspars crystallize in the monoclinic and triclinic systems, but many of their physical properties are strikingly similar. The prism angles are about 120°. Hardness, 6 to 6.5. Specific gravity, 2.55 to 2.75. The color is usually white or gray but may also be reddish, yellow, or greenish. All feldspars possess good cleavages in two directions, that is, parallel to the basal and clino- or brachypinacoids. In the case of orthoclase, these cleavages make an angle of 90°, but in the case of the triclinic members they are inclined, the angles differing slightly from 90°.

The feldspars are important economic minerals. About 200,000 short tons are produced annually in the United States, most of the output being consumed in the ceramic industries. The chief producing states are North Carolina, Tennessee, Colorado, New Hampshire, Maine, New York, Virginia, and California.

The following feldspars will be described:

Orthoclase	$KAlSi_3O_8$	Monoclinic
Microcline	$KAlSi_3O_8$	Triclinic
	PLAGIOCLASES	
Albite	$NaAlSi_3O_8(Ab)$	Triclinic
Labradorite	$Ab_{50}An_{50}$ to $Ab_{30}An_{70}$	Triclinic
Anorthite	$CaAl_2Si_2O_8(An)$	Triclinic

Igneous rocks are commonly classified according to the kind of feldspar they contain.

ORTHOCLASE (*Potash Feldspar, Feldspar*), $KAlSi_3O_8$.

Monoclinic, prismatic class. Well-developed crystals are common, the habit being usually prismatic parallel to the *c* axis (Fig. 737), tabular parallel to the clinopinacoid, or square columnar and elongated parallel to the *a* axis (Fig. 738). In the latter case, the basal and clinopinacoids are about equally developed. The unit prism, positive hemiorthodomes, a clinodome, and the basal and clinopinacoids are the forms most frequently observed. Crystals are sometimes highly modified and may be quite large. Twinning is frequently observed according to three laws.

Fig. 737.—Orthoclase. Lincoln County, Nevada.

Fig. 738.—Orthoclase: variety, sanidine. Fort Bayard, New Mexico.

Figs. 739 and 740.—Orthoclase (left and right Karlsbad twins). Fort Bayard, New Mexico.

1. *Karlsbad Law.* The orthopinacoid acts as the twinning plane, or the crystallographic *c* axis may be considered the twinning axis. Irregular contact and penetration twins are common (Figs. 739 and 740).

2. *Baveno Law.*—The clinodome ($\infty a : b : 2c$) is the twinning plane. Nearly square or columnar contact twins are most common (Fig. 741).

Fig. 741.

Fig. 742.

3. *Manebach Law.*—This law yields contact twins with the basal pinacoid acting as the twinning and composition plane (Fig. 742). This law is not so common as the first two.

Aside from occurring in crystals, orthoclase is found in cleavable, compact, or granular masses and in irregular disseminated grains. Some massive orthoclase resembles jasper or flint.

Perfect basal and good clinopinacoidal cleavages, making an angle of 90° (Fig. 743). Conchoidal to uneven fracture. Hardness, 6. Specific gravity, 2.5 to 2.6. Usually colorless, white, gray, or reddish, or yellowish; more rarely greenish. Transparent to opaque. Vitreous to pearly luster. α 1.518, β 1.524, γ 1.526, (−); 2V varies from 0 to 70°. Some varieties may become luminescent.

There are three important varieties:

1. *Adularia.*—This variety occurs usually in white or colorless crystals, which may be transparent or slightly cloudy. It frequently possesses an excellent opalescence. It is then termed *moonstone* and is used for gem purposes (see page 378). Usually found in cracks and veins in gneiss and mica schist.

2. *Sanidine.*—Occurs in glassy, transparent, or translucent crystals and is sometimes called *glassy feldspar.* Generally colorless, white, or

Fig. 743.—Orthoclase showing rectangular cleavage.

Fig. 744.—Orthoclase: variety, sanidine, in trachyte. Drachenfels, Rhine Valley.

gray. Tabular and square habits and Karlsbad twins are very common. Characteristic of eruptive rocks, especially rhyolite, trachyte, and phonolite (Fig. 744). $2V$ is very small.

3. *Ordinary or Common Orthoclase.*—Generally more or less dull in color, yellowish, flesh red, dark red, or greenish. Occurs in well-developed crystals and in cleavable or compact granular masses. Very common in granite, syenite, and gneiss.

$KAlSi_3O_8$. Often contains considerable sodium. Fuses with difficulty. Insoluble in acids. Alters to kaolinite, muscovite (sericite), and epidote. Occurs as a pseudomorph after analcite and leucite.

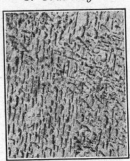

Fig. 745.—Microcline with quartz (graphic granite). Bedford, New York. (*After Bastin.*)

Orthoclase is a very common mineral. It is especially characteristic of such plutonic rocks as granite and syenite. It is also an important constituent of certain eruptive and metamorphic rocks, for example, rhyolite, trachyte, phonolite, porphyry, gneiss, and various schists. Not infrequently, it occurs in some sandstones and conglomerates. The most common associates of orthoclase are muscovite, biotite, quartz, tourmaline, the other feldspars, feldspathoids, hornblende, apatite, zircon, and beryl. It occurs widely distributed and is frequently considered the most abundant of the silicate minerals. A few localities for excellent crystals are the St. Gotthard district, Switzerland; Mount Vesuvius; Karlsbad, Bohemia; Striegau, Silesia; Norway; Ceylon; Perth, Quebec; Bedford, Ontario; Paris, Maine; Acworth, New Hampshire; Haddam, Connecticut; St. Lawrence County, New York; Mount Antero, Chaffee County, Colorado. Massive varieties are found at Bedford, Ontario; Georgetown and Brunswick, Maine; Crown Point and elsewhere, New York; Mitchell and Yancey counties, North Carolina; also in Pennsylvania, Maryland, Virginia, Minnesota, and Massachusetts.

The feldspar of commerce, which is often called orthoclase, is in reality microcline or an intergrowth of microcline and plagioclase. It is used chiefly in the manufacture of porcelain, china, or enamel ware and as a bond in the production of emery and other abrasive wheels. Small quantities are also used in opalescent glass, artificial teeth, scouring soap, and paint fillers. Moonstone and transparent yellow orthoclase are used as gems.

MICROCLINE, KAlSi₃O₈.

Triclinic, pinacoidal class. Crystals resemble very closely those of orthoclase in habit (Fig. 746), angles, crystal forms, and twinning. The angle between the basal and brachypinacoids differs slightly from 90°, being about 90° 30′. Crystals are frequently large, and, although apparently simple individuals, they are, in reality, usually polysynthetic twins according to the albite and pericline laws (see page 377), so characteristic of albite and other triclinic feldspars. Accordingly, basal sections of microcline show under the microscope a characteristic grating or gridiron structure. Also occurs in cleavable and compact granular masses.

Fig. 746.—Microcline: variety, Amazon stone. Pikes Peak, Colorado.

Basal and brachypinacoidal cleavages. Uneven fracture. Hardness, 6 to 6.5. Specific gravity, 2.54 and 2.57. Vitreous luster, inclining to pearly on the basal pinacoid. White, yellowish, gray, green, or red in color. Green varieties—often bright verdigris green—are called *amazonite* or *Amazon stone*. Transparent to translucent. α 1.522, β 1.526, γ 1.530, $(-)$; $2V = 83°$; $r > v$.

KAlSi₃O₈. Usually contains some sodium. The chemical properties are the same as for orthoclase.

The occurrence of microcline is very similar to that of orthoclase. Microcline is, however, not common in eruptive rocks, but usually is the main feldspar in pegmatites. Smoky quartz and topaz are typical associates. Intergrowths with quartz (Fig. 745) and the other feldspars are common. Some localities are Striegau, Silesia; Arendal, Norway; the Ural Mountains; Greenland; the Pikes Peak district, Colorado.

The feldspar of commerce is principally microcline. For uses see under orthoclase, page 375. Amazon stone is cut and polished for gem and ornamental purposes.

Plagioclase Feldspars

These feldspars are sometimes called the *soda-lime* feldspars. They crystallize in the triclinic system, forming an isomorphous series with albite ($NaAlSi_3O_8$) and anorthite ($CaAl_2Si_2O_8$) as the end members. The chemical compositions of the various members of the series vary within the limits indicated in the following tabulation:

$NaAlSi_3O_8(Ab)$

Ab. Per Cent.	An. Per Cent.	
100	0	Albite
90	10	
80	20	Oligoclase
70	30	
60	40	Andesine
50	50	
40	60	Labradorite
30	70	
20	80	Bytownite
10	90	
0	100	Anorthite

$CaAl_2Si_2O_8(An)$

These feldspars possess good cleavages parallel to the basal and brachypinacoids, which are inclined to each other at angles of about 86°. This inclined or oblique cleavage serves to differentiate these feldspars, the *plagioclases*, from orthoclase which possesses a rectangular cleavage.

Name	Per cent. of $NaAlSi_3O_8$	Al_2O_3	SiO_2	Na_2O	CaO	Specific gravity	Extinction angles Basal	Brachy Pinacoids	Cleavage angles
Albite............	95	20.4	67.3	11.2	1.1	2.61	$+4°$	$+17\frac{1}{2}°$	86° 26′
Oligoclase........	80	23.1	63.3	9.3	4.3	2.64	$+2°$	$+8°$	86° 18′
Andesine.........	60	26.6	58.1	6.9	8.4	2.67	$-2\frac{1}{2}°$	$-8°$	86° 10′
Labradorite.......	40	30.0	53.0	4.6	12.4	2.70	$-8\frac{1}{2}°$	$-22°$	86° 03′
Bytownite........	20	33.4	48.0	2.3	16.3	2.72	$-20°$	$-33°$	85° 56′
Anorthite.........	5	35.8	44.4	0.6	19.2	2.75	$-33°$	$-37°$	85° 48′

Twinning according to the albite law (see below) is very characteristic for this group.

The table at bottom of page 376 shows clearly the progressive changes in the physical and chemical properties of the various members of this group.

The intermediate members are important constituents of many igneous rocks and more common than either albite or anorthite. They are rarely well crystallized but can usually be recognized by the striations on the basal pinacoid, due to multiple twinning according to the albite law. Only albite, labradorite, and anorthite will be described.

ALBITE (*Soda Feldspar*), **NaAlSi$_3$O$_8$.**

Triclinic, pinacoidal class. Crystals are usually small and often similar in development to those of orthoclase (Figs. 747 and 748). They may also be tabular and elongated parallel to the *b* axis (Fig. 751). Twins are very common, single individuals being rare. There are two important laws.

| Fig. 747. | Fig. 748. | Fig. 749. | Fig. 750. |

1. *Albite Law.*—This involves the brachypinacoid acting as the twinning plane and yields simple contact and repeated twins (Figs. 749 and 750). The polysynthetic twins according to this law show striations on the basal pinacoid which extend parallel to the edge between the basal and brachypinacoids.

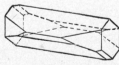 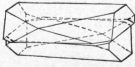

| Fig. 751. | Fig. 752. |

2. *Pericline Law.*—The *b* axis acts as the twinning axis (Fig. 752). Contact and polysynthetic twins are observed, the latter being characterized by striations on the brachypinacoid.

Albite also occurs in lamellar and granular masses, the laminæ being often curved and divergent.

Perfect basal and brachypinacoidal cleavages, *inclined* at 86° 26'. Uneven fracture. Hardness, 6 to 6.5. Specific gravity, 2.6. Usually colorless or gray; rarely colored. Transparent to translucent. α 1.525, β 1.529, γ 1.536, (+); $2V = 74°$; $r < v$. Some varieties show a bluish opalescence and are called *moonstone* (see page 374).

$NaAlSi_3O_8$. Generally contains some potassium and calcium. Fuses to a colorless or white glass. Colors the flame yellow. Not acted upon by acids.

As a rock mineral, albite is not so abundant as the other plagioclases. It occurs, nevertheless, in many gneisses and other crystalline schists, also in granite, diorite, trachyte, and other eruptive rocks; more rarely in limestone and dolomite. Frequently found in pegmatite veins but

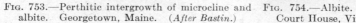

Fig. 753.—Perthitic intergrowth of microcline and   Fig. 754.—Albite.   Amelia
    albite. Georgetown, Maine. (*After Bastin.*)   Court House, Virginia.

also in cracks and crevices. Some of the associates of albite are chlorite, titanite, adularia, axinite, beryl, tourmaline, quartz, chrysoberyl, and apatite. It occurs often intergrown with orthoclase or microcline and is then known as *perthite* (Fig. 753).

Some important localities are the Saint Gotthard district, Switzerland; various places in Tirol; Rauris, Salzburg; Dauphiné, France; the Ural Mountains; Paris, Maine; Haddam and Branchville, Connecticut; Chesterfield, Massachusetts; Pikes Peak, Colorado; Amelia Court House, Virginia (Fig. 754).

LABRADORITE (*Lime-soda Feldspar*), $Ab_{50}An_{50}$ to $Ab_{30}An_{70}$.

Triclinic, pinacoidal class. Well-developed crystals are rare. In habit they are usually tabular parallel to the brachypinacoid. The twinning is the same as for albite. Generally observed in cleavable, granular, or cryptocrystalline masses.

Perfect basal and brachypinacoidal cleavages, making an angle of 86° 3'. Uneven fracture. Hardness, 6 to 6.5. Specific gravity, 2.7.

Gray, brown, or greenish in color. Often shows a beautiful play of yellowish, bluish, greenish, or reddish colors on the brachypinacoid. This *labradorescence* is due to a fine lamellar structure or to microscopic inclusions or to both. Translucent. α 1.559, β 1.563, γ 1.568, (+); $2V = 79°$; for a composition of $Ab_{40}An_{60}$.

$Ab_{50}An_{50}$ to $An_{30}An_{70}$. Fuses to a colorless or white glass. Colors the flame yellow. Decomposed with difficulty by hydrochloric acid.

Occurs in basic igneous rocks, such as gabbro, norite, basalt, diabase, and andesite. Found on Mount Etna; in Rumania; Sweden; Greenland; varieties showing an excellent play of colors are common on the coast of Labrador, also on the Isle of St. Paul; in the Adirondack Mountains, New York; the Wichita Mountains, Arkansas; and elsewhere.

Varieties showing a good play of colors are used for ornamental and decorative purposes. They are sometimes termed *Labrador spar*.

Anorthite (*Lime Feldspar*), $CaAl_2Si_2O_8$.

Triclinic, pinacoidal class. Crystals are usually prismatic parallel to the *c* axis or tabular parallel to the basal pinacoid; often very complex. Twins occur according to the laws common on albite. Also observed in cleavable, compact, and lamellar masses.

Perfect basal and brachypinacoidal cleavages, inclined at an angle of 85° 48'. Conchoidal to uneven fracture. Hardness, 6 to 6.5. Specific gravity, 2.7 to 2.8. Commonly white, colorless, or grayish; more rarely bluish, yellowish, or reddish. Vitreous luster, inclining to pearly on the cleavages. Transparent to translucent. α 1.576, β 1.584, γ 1.588, (−); $2V = 77°$; $r < v$.

$CaAl_2Si_2O_8$. Usually contains small amounts of sodium and, at times, of potassium, magnesium, and iron. Fuses with difficulty to a colorless glass. Decomposed by hydrochloric acid with a separation of gelatinous silica.

Anorthite occurs as an important constituent of basic igneous rocks, such as diorites, gabbros, and basalts; also as a contact mineral and in meteorites. Excellent crystals are found on Mount Vesuvius; the Island of Miyake, Japan; Iceland; the Monzoni district, Tirol; Rumania; the Ural Mountains; Franklin Furnace, New Jersey.

Feldspathoid Group

In this group are included several minerals which are closely related chemically to the feldspars, but which contain a lower percentage of silica, SiO_2. These minerals are called *feldspathoids*. They are important rock minerals and are formed from magmas which contain insufficient silica to produce the feldspars. The feldspathoids are never associated with primary quartz.

The most important of these minerals include the following:

Nephelite	$NaAlSiO_4$	Hexagonal
Cancrinite	$3NaAlSiO_4 \cdot CaCO_3$	Hexagonal
Sodalite	$3NaAlSiO_4 \cdot NaCl$	Cubic
Lazurite	$3NaAlSiO_4 \cdot Na_2S$	Cubic
Leucite	$KAl(SiO_3)_2$	Pseudocubic

Nephelite usually contains excess silica and some potassium, and the formula is commonly written $(Na,K)_8Al_8Si_9O_{34}$. The mineral analcite (page 387) is sometimes classified as a feldspathoid and not as a zeolite.

NEPHELITE (*Nepheline*), $(Na,K)_8Al_8Si_9O_{34}$.

Hexagonal, pyramidal class. Crystals are short prismatic or tabular. Commonly in compact masses or as disseminated grains.

Imperfect prismatic and basal cleavages. Conchoidal to uneven fracture. Hardness, 5 to 6. Specific gravity, 2.55 to 2.65. Colorless, white, yellowish, greenish, gray, or reddish. Greasy luster on cleavages, otherwise vitreous. ω 1.542, ϵ 1.538, $(-)$. Transparent to opaque.

There are two varieties:

1. *Nephelite Proper.*—This includes the light-colored, glassy occurrences showing in many instances a definite crystal outline. Common in the more recent eruptive rocks. Transparent to translucent.

2. *Elaeolite.*—This is a massive or granular variety and rarely shows a definite outline. Gray or more highly colored—green, red, brown, or blue. Cloudy or opaque. Greasy luster. Common in the older plutonic rocks, such as syenites, phonolites, and basalts.

$(Na,K)_8Al_8Si_9O_{34}$. Composition varies greatly. Formula is sometimes given as $NaAlSiO_4$, the composition of synthetic soda-nephelite. Potassium is usually present, also small amounts of calcium, lithium, and chlorine. Fuses easily to a colorless glass. Gelatinizes with hydrochloric acid, yielding on evaporation cubes of $NaCl$. Alters readily to hydronephelite, sodalite, muscovite, cancrinite, analcite, kaolinite, or garnet. Pseudomorphous after leucite.

Nephelite is commonly associated with feldspar, cancrinite, biotite, sodalite, corundum, and zircon; but not with primary quartz. Some localities are Mount Vesuvius; Katzenbuckel, Baden; Laacher See, Rhenish Prussia; southern Norway; the Ural Mountains; Brazil; Ontario, Canada; Litchfield, Maine; Cripple Creek, Colorado; Magnet Cove, Arkansas; Salem, Massachusetts.

Nephelite is used in the ceramic industry in place of feldspar.

Cancrinite, $3NaAlSiO_4 \cdot CaCO_3$.

Hexagonal, dihexagonal bipyramidal class. Crystals are columnar or prismatic, but rare. Usually in compact, lamellar, columnar, or disseminated masses.

Perfect prismatic cleavage. Uneven fracture. Hardness, 5 to 6. Specific gravity, 2.45. Generally colored; lemon to brownish yellow, reddish, green; sometimes gray, white, or colorless. Pearly luster on cleavages, elsewhere vitreous to greasy. ω 1.524, ϵ 1.496, (−). Transparent to translucent.

$3NaAlSiO_4.CaCO_3$. Composition varies; $CaCO_3$ may be replaced by $CaSO_4$, $CaCl_2$, Na_2CO_3, or $Na_2CO_3.3H_2O$. Fuses easily with intumescence to a white blebby glass. Upon ignition turns white and yields water. Effervesces with hydrochloric acid and gelatinizes on heating.

Commonly associated with sodalite, nephelite, biotite, feldspar, titanite, and apatite. May be a primary constituent of igneous rocks, although in most cases it is secondary, resulting from the alteration of nephelite. Occurs in nepheline syenites at Barkevik, Norway; Miask, Ural Mountains; Finland; Sweden; Rumania; Province of Quebec, Canada; Litchfield, Maine.

Cancrinite is of no importance commercially.

Sodalite, $3NaAlSiO_4.NaCl$.

Cubic, hextetrahedral class. Crystals are not common; when observed, usually rhombic dodecahedrons. Generally in compact, cleavage, nodular, or disseminated masses.

Distinct dodecahedral cleavage. Uneven to conchoidal fracture. Hardness, 5 to 6. Specific gravity, 2.2 to 2.4. Vitreous luster on crystal faces, greasy on cleavages. $n = 1.483$. Usually blue in color; also white, green, reddish, or gray. Transparent to opaque. Colored varieties turn white when heated.

$3NaAlSiO_4.NaCl$. Fuses with intumescence to a colorless glass. NaCl may be extracted by digesting the finely powdered mineral with water. Gelatinizes with hydrochloric acid.

Commonly associated with nephelite, cancrinite, leucite, feldspar, and zircon but not with primary quartz. Occurs at Miask, Ural Mountains; Mount Vesuvius; Norway; provinces of Quebec and Ontario, Canada; Litchfield, Maine; Montana.

Sodalite is of no importance commercially.

Lazurite (*Lapis Lazuli, Native Ultramarine*), $3NaAlSiO_4.Na_2S$.

Cubic. Crystals are rare, either dodecahedral or cubic in habit. Usually as irregular grains or in masses containing disseminated pyrite (Fig. 755).

Fig. 755.—Lazurite (lapis lazuli). Persia.

Uneven fracture. Hardness, 5 to 5.5. Specific gravity, 2.4. Vitreous to greasy luster. $n = 1.50$. Deep to azure blue in color, sometimes violet to greenish blue. Opaque to translucent.

$3NaAlSiO_4.Na_2S$, essentially. Composition varies. Fuses easily to a white blebby glass. Gelatinizes with hydrochloric acid, loses color, and evolves an odor of hydrogen sulphide.

Lazurite is a contact mineral and occurs in crystalline limestones. The principal localities are Persia; Turkestan; Afghanistan; the southern end of Lake Baikal, Siberia; Ovalle, Chile; Cascade Canyon, San Bernardino County, California.

Lazurite is highly valued for ornaments, mosaics, and vases. It was formerly used as a pigment in oil painting. Lazurite is also used for gem purposes.

LEUCITE, $KAl(SiO_3)_2$.

Dimorphous, orthorhombic and cubic. At *ordinary* temperatures, crystals are pseudocubic, in that they show what is apparently a tetragonal trisoctahedron; at times, also, the cube and rhombic dodecahedron.

Fig. 756.—Leucite (light) in basalt. Tavolato, near Rome, Italy.

Optically, the crystals consist of orthorhombic twin lamellæ, which can sometimes be recognized by the striations on the faces. Heated to a temperature of 500°C., the lamellæ disappear and the crystals become isotropic and truly cubic. Generally found in well-developed and disseminated crystals (Fig. 756); also in rounded grains.

Conchoidal fracture. Hardness, 5.5 to 6. Specific gravity, 2.5. White, gray, yellowish, or reddish in color. Vitreous to greasy luster. Translucent, rarely transparent. Usually weakly doubly refractive; the indices of refraction vary from 1.508 to 1.509.

$KAl(SiO_3)_2$. Sodium may replace some of the potassium. Infusible. Alters to analcite and kaolin.

Leucite occurs usually in eruptive rocks. The principal associates are sanidine, augite, nephelite, and olivine. Some localities are Mount

Vesuvius and the vicinity of Rome; Laacher See, Rhenish Prussia; Kaiserstuhl, Baden; Saxony; Brazil; Leucite Hills, Wyoming; Magnet Cave, Arkansas.

At present, leucite is of no importance commercially.

SCAPOLITE (*Wernerite*), $n\mathrm{Na_4Al_3Si_9O_{24}Cl} + m\mathrm{Ca_4Al_6Si_6O_{24}CO_3}$.

Tetragonal, tetragonal bipyramidal class. Commonly as thick, coarse, prismatic crystals, often large with dull and uneven faces. Crys-

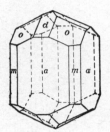

FIG. 757.

FIG. 758.—Scapolite. Ottawa County, Quebec.

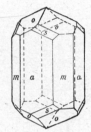

FIG. 759.

tals sometimes appear as though partially fused. The common forms are the prisms (*m* and *a*) and bipyramids (*o* and *d*) of the first and second orders; more rarely the bipyramid of the third order (*s*) is observed (Figs. 757 to 759). Occurs also in fibrous, coarse- to fine-granular, columnar, and compact masses.

Prismatic cleavage. Conchoidal fracture. Hardness, 5 to 6. Specific gravity, 2.6 to 2.8. Colorless, white, gray, greenish, bluish, or reddish. Vitreous to greasy luster. Translucent. May show luminescence. ω 1.539, ϵ 1.537, ($-$) for *marialite;* ω 1.597, ϵ 1.560, ($-$) for *meionite*.

The composition varies greatly, between *marialite*, $\mathrm{Na_4Al_3Si_9O_{24}Cl}$, and *meionite*, $\mathrm{Ca_4Al_6Si_6O_{24}CO_3}$. Some scapolites are readily decomposed by hydrochloric acid. All are quite easily fusible with intumescence. The scapolites alter to kaolin, jade, epidote, muscovite, biotite, albite, and various zeolites.

Commonly the result of metamorphism and frequently found in granular limestones near the contact with igneous rocks; also in crystalline schists and volcanic ejectamenta. Typical associates are pyroxenes, amphiboles, apatite, garnet, titanite, zircon, and biotite. Some localities are Arendal, Norway; Pargas, Finland; Laacher See, Rhenish Prussia; Mount Vesuvius; Ripon and Grenville, Quebec, and various places in Ontario, Canada; Bolton, Massachusetts; various places in northern New York; Franklin Furnace, New Jersey.

Scapolite is not important commercially. Sometimes used as a gem.

TITANITE (*Sphene*), CaTiSiO₅.

Monoclinic, prismatic class. The crystal habit varies greatly. Disseminated crystals are generally wedge or envelope shaped, while attached crystals are apt to be tabular or prismatic (Figs. 760, 761, and 762). Occurs also in compact or lamellar masses and in disseminated grains.

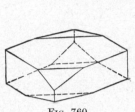

FIG. 760.   FIG. 761.   FIG. 762.—Titanite. Arendal, Norway.

Prismatic and domatic cleavages. Conchoidal fracture. Hardness, 5 to 5.5. Specific gravity, 3.4 to 3.6. Yellow, green, brown, reddish brown, red, or black in color. Vitreous luster, inclining to adamantine. Transparent to opaque. α 1.900, β 1.907, γ 2.034, (+); $2V$ is about 27°; $r > v$ marked.

CaTiSiO₅. Commonly considered as the calcium salt of the dimetasilicic acid, $H_2Si_2O_5$, in which one atom of silicon has been replaced by titanium. May also contain some iron or manganese. Fuses with intumescence on the edges to a dark-colored glass. Only partially decomposed by hydrochloric acid, completely by sulphuric and hydrofluoric acids. Alters to rutile, brookite, or ilmenite.

Titanite occurs disseminated as an important accessory constituent of many igneous rocks, especially in hornblende granite, syenite, nepheline syenite, trachyte, phonolite, and diorite; also in crystalline schists and granular limestones. It is found attached in cracks and cavities in granite, gneiss, and various schists. The common associates are the amphiboles, pyroxenes, apatite, zircon, scapolite, chlorite, feldspars, quartz, and various iron minerals. Some localities are Laacher See, Rhenish Prussia; many places in Switzerland and Tirol, especially Saint Gotthard, Tavetsch, and Zillerthal; Arendal, Norway; Ala, Piedmont; the Ural Mountains; Grenville, Quebec, and Eganville, Renfrew County, Ontario, Canada; Sanford, Maine; Bolton and Lee, Massachusetts; various places in Lewis, Orange, and other counties, New York; Franklin Furnace, New Jersey; Magnet Cove, Arkansas.

The clear, green, yellow, or brownish varieties are used for gem purposes. They are very brilliant, possess an excellent adamantine luster, but are comparatively soft.

APOPHYLLITE, KFCa₄(Si₂O₅)₄.8H₂O.

Tetragonal, ditetragonal bipyramidal class. Crystals may be (1) long and square prismatic (Fig. 764), (2) pseudocubical (Fig. 765), (3) pyramidal (Fig. 766), or (4) thin tabular (Fig. 763). The most general combination consists of the prism of the second order (*a*), unit bipyramid of the first order (*o*), and the basal pinacoid (*c*). The prism faces are often brilliant and striated vertically; those of the basal pinacoid, dull or rough, while the bipyramidal faces may be uneven. Occurs also massive and in granular and lamellar aggregates.

Perfect basal cleavage. Uneven fracture. Hardness, 4.5 to 5. Specific gravity, 2.3 to 2.4. Generally colorless or white, also green, yellow, or reddish. Vitreous to pearly luster, with *fish-eye* opalescence on basal

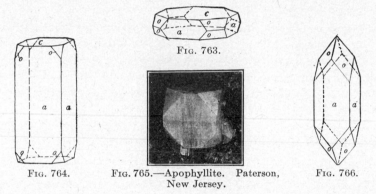

Fig. 763.

Fig. 764.   Fig. 765.—Apophyllite. Paterson,   Fig. 766.
New Jersey.

pinacoid. Usually transparent, rarely nearly opaque. Anomalous optical properties; ω 1.535 or 1.537, ε 1.537 or 1.535, (±).

KFCa₄(Si₂O₅)₄.8H₂O. The composition is somewhat variable. Potassium may be partially replaced by sodium, and fluorine by the hydroxyl (OH) group. Sometimes classified as a zeolite. Exfoliates and fuses easily to a white enamel, coloring the flame violet. Decomposed by hydrochloric acid with a separation of silica. Alters to calcite, pectolite, and kaolin.

Occurs as a secondary mineral in cracks and cavities in basic igneous rocks, also in granite and gneiss. Common associates are natrolite, analcite, datolite, prehnite, pectolite, native copper, and calcite. Found in the Harz Mountains, Germany; Freiberg, Saxony; Tirol; Sweden; Iceland; Greenland; Nova Scotia; Bergen Hill, New Jersey; Table Mountain, Colorado; the Lake Superior copper district; New Almaden, California.

Zeolite Group

The zeolites are secondary minerals, being hydrated silicates of aluminum, calcium, sodium, and potassium. The water of hydration is peculiar in that it is lost gradually and continuously upon heating, rather than at a definite temperature. The water thus lost is readily regained upon exposure to water vapor. Moreover, dehydration causes no change in the general crystalline structure, unless the water is almost completely removed. The zeolites also possess the property of base exchange. This refers to the easy substitution of various metals for the alkali element originally present. The zeolites have structures with a three-dimensional framework of linked $(Si,Al)O_4$ tetrahedrons, with (Si,Al) and O being present in the ratio of $1:2$.

The zeolites are commonly found in good crystals, have comparatively low specific gravities, 2 to 2.4, and are rather soft, the hardness varying from 3.5 to 5. Although generally colorless and transparent or translucent, they may be light colored, due to the presence of pigments. All zeolites are readily decomposed by hydrochloric acid, and on the evaporation of the acid may gelatinize. They result from the decomposition of such minerals as nephelite, leucite, sodalite, and the feldspars. They are rarely found disseminated but usually in cracks, crevices, or cavities in basic igneous rocks, such as basalt, diabase, and phonolites; less frequently in granite and mica schist. Their common associates are calcite, datolite, and pectolite.

Although the zeolite group is a large one, only the following zeolites will be discussed: natrolite, analcite, stilbite, and chabazite.

Natrolite (*Needle Zeolite*), **$Na_2Al_2Si_3O_{10}.2H_2O$.**

Orthorhombic, bipyramidal class. Crystals are slender prismatic and nearly square in cross section; also acicular and arranged in radial

FIG. 767.—Natrolite. Paterson, New Jersey.

or interlacing groups (Fig. 767). Occurs also in fibrous, granular, or compact masses.

Perfect prismatic cleavage. Hardness, 5 to 5.5. Specific gravity, 2.2 to 2.3. Colorless or white; also reddish, yellowish, or greenish. Transparent to translucent. Vitreous to silky luster. α 1.480, β 1.482, γ 1.493, (+); $2V = 63°$; $r < v$.

$Na_2Al_2Si_3O_{10}.2H_2O$. May contain some calcium and potassium. Fuses easily to colorless glass. Gelatinizes with acids. Yields water in a closed tube.

Occurs in cracks and cavities in basic igneous rocks. Common associates are chabazite, analcite, apophyllite, stilbite, calcite, and datolite.

Some notable localities are Teplitz and Aussig, Bohemia; Fassathal, Tirol; Hohentwiel and Kaiserstuhl, Baden; Nova Scotia; Bergen Hill, New Jersey; Lake Superior copper district.

ANALCITE, $NaAlSi_2O_6.H_2O$.

Cubic, hexoctahedral class. Generally in well-developed tetragonal trisoctahedrons (Fig. 768); sometimes in combination with the cube

FIG. 768.—Analcite (tetragonal trisoctahedron). Lake Superior copper district.

FIG. 769.

(Fig. 769). Crystals are usually quite small, although some measuring a foot in diameter have been observed. Occurs also in compact, granular, or earthy masses.

Uneven to conchoidal fracture. Hardness, 5 to 5.5. Specific gravity, 2.2 to 2.4. Colorless or white; also yellowish, reddish, or greenish. Vitreous luster. Transparent to nearly opaque. $n = 1.487$.

$NaAlSi_2O_6.H_2O$. Chemically it is closely related to leucite and is sometimes considered a member of the feldspathoid group (see page 379). Fuses to a colorless glass. Gelatinizes with acids.

Analcite is commonly a secondary mineral occurring with the other zeolites, calcite, datolite, native copper, magnetite, and prehnite, in basalt, diabase, granite, and gneiss. Some localities are the Cyclopean Islands, near Sicily; Tirol; Bohemia; Iceland; various places in Nova Scotia; Bergen Hill, New Jersey; the Lake Superior copper district; Table Mountain, Colorado.

STILBITE (*Desmine*), $(Ca,Na_2)Al_2Si_6O_{16}.6H_2O$.

Monoclinic, prismatic class. Simple crystals are unknown; usually as tabular penetration twins. Very commonly several twin crystals are arranged nearly parallel, forming sheaflike aggregates (Fig. 770). Occurs also in radial or globular aggregates.

Clinopinacoid cleavage. Uneven fracture. Hardness, 3 to 4. Specific gravity, 2.1 to 2.2. Vitreous to pearly luster. α 1.494, β 1.498, γ 1.500, ($-$); $2V$ is about 33°. Transparent to translucent. Colorless or white, also brown, yellow, reddish.

Fig. 770.—Stilbite. Viesch, Switzerland.

$(Ca,Na_2)Al_2Si_6O_{16}.6H_2O$. May contain some potassium. Exfoliates, swells up, and fuses to a white glass. Decomposed by hydrochloric acid with a separation of silica.

Stilbite occurs with other zeolites, datolite, and calcite, in cavities in amygdaloidal basalts and related rocks; also in granites and crystalline schists and in ore deposits. Some localities are Tirol; Sweden; Iceland; Switzerland; Kilpatrick, Scotland; Nova Scotia; Bergen Hill, New Jersey; the Lake Superior copper district; Table Mountain, Colorado.

CHABAZITE, $CaAl_2Si_6O_{16}.8H_2O$.

Hexagonal, ditrigonal scalenohedral class. Generally in cubelike rhombohedrons (Fig. 771). Sometimes crystals are complex (Fig. 773) or twinned (Fig. 772). Occurs also in compact masses.

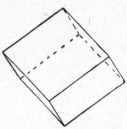

Fig. 771.

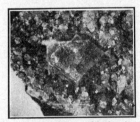

Fig. 772.—Chabazite (twinned). Paterson, New Jersey.

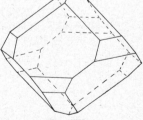

Fig. 773.

Rhombohedral cleavage. Uneven fracture. Hardness, 4 to 5. Specific gravity, 2.1 to 2.2. Colorless, white, reddish, yellowish, or brown. Vitreous luster. Transparent to translucent. Anomalous optical properties; generally uniaxial, either positive or negative with indices of refraction from 1.478 to 1.482; sometimes biaxial, positive, with $2V$ small.

$CaAl_2Si_6O_{16}.8H_2O$. Composition varies considerably. May contain potassium and sodium replacing some of the calcium. Fuses with intumescence to a nearly opaque, blebby glass. Decomposed by hydrochloric acid with a separation of silica.

Associated with the other zeolites, it generally occurs in cavities in basalts, phonolites, and related rocks. Some localities are the Giant's Causeway, Ireland; Aussig, Bohemia; Faroe Islands; Greenland; Iceland; Nova Scotia; Bergen Hill, New Jersey; Somerville, Massachusetts; Table Mountain, Colorado.

CHAPTER XVII

GEMS AND PRECIOUS STONES[1]

A considerable number of minerals occur with beautiful colors, some are transparent and exceedingly brilliant, while others possess a pleasing luster or sheen. Minerals of this character have, from the earliest times, been eagerly sought after for personal adornment and ornamentation. They constitute what we call *gems* and *precious stones*. In fact, it is well known that among primitive peoples many of these gem minerals were supposed to possess peculiar properties. Some were believed to bring good luck to the wearer, while others were thought to be useful in warding off or curing certain diseases.

Fig. 774.—M a x B a u e r (1844–1917). Professor of mineralogy and petrography in the University of Marburg (1884–1917). Distinguished authority on gems and precious stones.

Characteristics of Gems.—The outstanding qualities of a gem are (1) *splendor* or *beauty,* (2) *durability,* (3) *rarity,* (4) *fashion,* and (5) *portability.* The beauty of a gem depends upon its transparency or clarity, brilliancy, color, luster, and fire. In some cases, these qualities are seen to best advantage only when the stone is cut and polished. Red and blue diamonds, for example, embody all of these qualities to a marked extent. Sometimes the beauty of a gem does not depend upon all, but only upon several, of the above properties. Thus, the beauty of the ruby is due to its excellent color, luster, and transparency. The ruby is, however, almost totally lacking in fire. The opal is attractive principally on account of its fascinating play of colors. In the case of turquois, the beauty depends mainly upon a pleasing color. Water-white diamonds are exceptionally beautiful, but they are devoid of color, their splendor being due to their brilliancy, luster, and fire.

Many minerals may be pleasing to the eye but yet not be very serviceable as gems because of their inferior hardness. They do not wear well, that is, they lack durability. In order to serve to advantage as a gem, a mineral must be hard. It must resist abrasion. When worn on the hand, a stone is not only subject to the action of the ever-present

[1] For a more comprehensive discussion, consult Kraus and Holden, "Gems and Gem Materials," 2d ed., McGraw-Hill Book Company, Inc., New York, 1931.

dust, which consists mainly of finely divided quartz particles and, hence, is hard, but it is also subject to sudden shocks and knocks. Soft stones, even though they may take a beautiful polish and possess other necessary gem properties, become dull and worthless in a very short time. Stones of such inferior hardness serve fairly well in pins and brooches. A gem to be durable must, therefore, be hard, preferably harder than quartz. In fact, durability plays a prominent role in the classification of gems. Those which are generally classed as the distinctly *precious* stones—diamond, emerald, ruby, sapphire—all possess superior hardness, being decidedly harder than quartz. Soft gem minerals are generally regarded as *semiprecious*.

While durability is a fundamental quality of a gem, frequency of occurrence has much to do with determining the value of a mineral for gem purposes. Many minerals occur rather abundantly in nature, but only rarely are some of them found in such condition as to warrant their use as gems. Thus, the mineral beryl is fairly common. It occurs in large crystals, some of which weigh several tons, but the colors are then usually dull and the crystals are not transparent. The green transparent variety, called the emerald, is, however, seldom found and is accordingly very highly prized. There are other transparent varieties of beryl, such as golden beryl and aquamarine, but these are more frequently found and are not so valuable as the rarer emerald.

Fig. 775.—George F. Kunz (1856–1932). Author of many publications on gems and precious stones. (*Photographed by the Champlain Studios, Inc., New York City.*)

Other things being equal, the rarer the stone the greater its value, for there are many people who will always desire that which is rare and exceptional and are willing to pay enormous prices in order to obtain those gems which others cannot afford.

Fashion and style exert a definite influence upon the favor with which a gem is received. Indeed, it frequently happens that, as the result of a change in fashion or style, an excellent gem mineral—excellent with respect to the various properties referred to above—is suddenly discarded for some new and perhaps inferior stone. During the last 50 years, many stones have thus come into favor, most of which are of bright color. Hence, the number of minerals which are to be counted as gems is subject to change, the tendency being toward an extension of the list.

One of the outstanding characteristics of gems is the ease with which they can be carried from place to place, that is, their portability. This is, of course, principally due to the fact that comparatively large sums of money are generally represented by relatively small volumes of the gem mineral.

List of Gems.—The following tabulation contains the minerals, described in this text, which are used as gems. In each case, the page is indicated where the mineral has been fully described. Where special terms have been assigned to varieties of gem quality, these are also given.

Diamond, 229
Beryl, 352   (*Emerald, Aquamarine, Yellow or Golden Beryl, Morganite*)
Corundum, 275   (*Ruby, Sapphire, White Sapphire, Golden Sapphire, Oriental Emerald, Oriental Topaz, Oriental Amethyst*)
Topaz, 340   (*Precious Topaz*)
Spinel, 319   (*Ruby Spinel, Rubicelle, Blue Spinel*)
Garnet, 349 to 351
     Grossularite (*Hessonite, Cinnamon Stone*)
     Pyrope (*Cape Ruby, Arizona Ruby*)
     Spessartite
     Almandite (*Carbuncle, Rhodolite*)
     Uvarovite
     Andradite (*Topazolite, Demantoid*)
Tourmaline, 342   (*Rubellite*)
Olivine, 346   (*Peridot*)
Zircon, 348   (*Hyacinth, Jacinth, Jargon, Starlite*)
Chrysoberyl, 322   (*Alexandrite, Cat's-eye, Cymophane*)
Opal, 280   (*Precious Opal, White Opal, Black Opal, Fire Opal*)
Quartz, 267   (*Rock Crystal, Amethyst, Rose Quartz, Smoky Quartz, Cairngorm Stone, False Topaz, Spanish Topaz, Citrine, Aventurine, Rutilated Quartz, Cat's-eye, Tiger's-eye, Chalcedony, Carnelian, Sard, Chrysoprase, Heliotrope, Bloodstone, Agate, Onyx*)
Turquois, 329
Jade, 370   (*Nephrite, Jadeite*)
Feldspar, 372 to 379
     Orthoclase (*Moonstone*)
     Microcline (*Amazon Stone, Amazonite*)
     Albite (*Moonstone*)
     Labradorite (*Labrador Spar*)
Pyroxene, 363 to 368
     Hypersthene
     Diopside
     Spodumene (*Hiddenite, Kunzite*)
     Rhodonite
Titanite, 384   (*Sphene*)
Vesuvianite, 345   (*Californite*)
Lazurite, 381   (*Lapis Lazuli*)
Serpentine, 360   (*Precious Serpentine*)
Epidote, 344
Malachite and
     Azurite, 302   (*Malachite Matrix, Azurmalachite*)
Chrysocolla, 353
Cyanite, 339
Datolite, 341
Staurolite. 336

Popular Names of Gems.—Many of the names applied to gem minerals are of very ancient origin and, hence, were in use long before mineralogy was developed as a science.   Considerable ambiguity has arisen, therefore, by the simultaneous use of popular terms by jewelers and of scientific names by mineralogists.   Indeed, many of the popular terms are intentionally misleading.   Thus, yellow quartz or citrine is commonly called in the trade *Spanish, Brazilian,* or *oriental topaz.*   Popular names have frequently been based upon color, and, hence, it is not surprising to find the term *ruby* incorporated in several of the popular names given

Fig 776.—Tully total reflectometer.

to gem stones of a red color: *ruby spinel, balas ruby,* and *rubicelle* for red spinel; *cape ruby* and *Arizona ruby* for pyrope garnet; and *rubellite* for red tourmaline.   Popular names of this character suggest relations with more valuable stones which are not warranted by the facts.   Obviously, all ambiguity and misconceptions would be avoided if only the scientific names of the mineralogist were used.

Methods of Identification.—Rough and uncut gem stones can be readily determined by means of their physical properties in the same way as other minerals.   This usually involves the use of a set of mineral tables, such as are found on pages 453 to 589.   When the stones are cut and polished, the properties generally used for determination are color, index of refraction, dispersion, fracture or cleavage as revealed around the prongs of the setting, inclusions, and dichroism.   The index of refraction can be easily and quickly determined by using Tully's direct-reading total reflectometer (Figs. **776** and **777**). If it is necessary to determine the hardness of a gem, great care should be exercised not to injure a soft but otherwise perfectly good stone. Hardness pencils and the hardness wheel (Figs. 319 and 320, pages 101 and 102) are well adapted for the testing of the hardness of gems. When stones are unmounted, a determination of the specific gravity can often be made the basis of an accurate recognition of the gem under consideration.

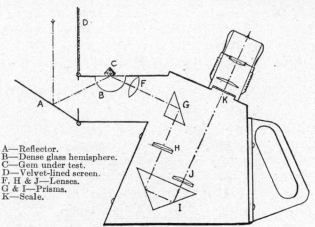

A—Reflector.
B—Dense glass hemisphere.
C—Gem under test.
D—Velvet-lined screen.
F, H & J—Lenses.
G & I—Prisms.
K—Scale.

Fɪɢ. 777.—Cross section through Tully total reflectometer.

Size and Weight of Gems.—In the sale of gem minerals four units of weight are used, namely, (1) *carat*, (2) *gram*, (3) *pennyweight*, and (4) *grain*. In addition, some gem stones are sold in terms of size, as expressed in *millimeters* or *inches*. Of these units, only the carat needs to be defined, and accordingly it will be discussed in some detail.

1. *Carat.*—The carat now in use in the principal countries of the world is 200 milligrams or two-tenths of a gram, 0.200 grams. It is often called the *metric carat.* It was adopted as the standard in the United States in 1913. The value of a gem stone, per carat, generally increases rapidly with weight.

Originally grains or leguminous seeds were used as units of weight for gems, and naturally they were not of uniform size. Consequently down to comparatively recent times the weight of the carat varied greatly in different gem centers. Thus, for many years it was taken as 0.2053 gram in London, while in Florence it was 0.1972 gram, in Madras 0.2073, Amsterdam 0.2057, and so on. In 1871 an attempt was made to establish as the standard the "international carat" of 0.205 gram. Later the metric carat was proposed, which is now the generally accepted standard.

Before the introduction of the metric carat, the weight of a gem was expressed by a series of fractions, such as 2 carats and $\frac{1}{2}$, $\frac{1}{4}$, $\frac{1}{16}$, and $\frac{1}{64}$ carat. In the metric system this weight so clumsily expressed by the older method is simplified to 2.828 carat, the sum of the fractional parts of a carat being indicated by the more convenient decimals.

The weight of a diamond is often expressed in *points*. Thus, a stone weighing 65 points actually weighs 0.65 carat. That is, a *point* is 0.01 carat.

The application of the term "carat" as a unit of weight must not be confused with its use in indicating fineness or purity of the gold in which gems are mounted. In this latter connection a carat means one twenty-fourth part. Thus, pure gold is said to be 24 carats fine. The amount of baser metal alloyed with gold is indicated by a proportional decrease in the number of carats fineness. That is, 18-carat gold is 18 twenty-fourths gold and 6 twenty-fourths base metal, while 12-carat gold is 12 twenty-fourths, or half, gold.

The carat is the unit of weight for the diamond, natural and synthetic rubies and sapphires, emerald, aquamarine, tourmaline, zircon, spinel, precious opal, superior opal doublets, and precious garnets. Pearls are sometimes sold by the carat.

2. *Gram.*—The following gem minerals are commonly sold by the gram: lapis lazuli, Spanish topaz, moonstone, amethyst, and superior grades of malachite.

3. *Pennyweight.*—In some countries the minerals listed under gram are sold by the pennyweight.

4. *Grain.*—Pearls are commonly sold by the grain (see also under carat).

5. *Millimeter* or *Inch.*—Minerals such as amazonite, garnet, most of the varieties of quartz, malachite, Swiss lapis, and the cheaper grades of opal and opal doublets are sold according to size, as expressed in millimeters or inches.

Cutting of Gems.—Although gem minerals are frequently found in nature in beautiful and well-developed crystals, they are rarely adapted for use as gems without suitable cutting and polishing. While crystals may show excellent reflections, the full optical splendor of such gem minerals is best brought out by cutting or grinding the specimen into symmetrical shapes, which will allow the stone to appear as brilliant as possible, show its best color, and exhibit the maximum amount of fire. This process of cutting involving the production of artificial faces or *facets*, as these plain surfaces are called, is of comparatively recent origin. Louis de Berquem has been generally credited with having discovered this process, about 1456, although now it is believed that the process was in common use in Italy at an earlier date.

The ancients contented themselves with simply polishing the natural crystal faces, or they ground the stone into certain rounded shapes. The *cabochon* cuts are, hence, the oldest of the various styles of cutting still in common use. The following types may be differentiated:

1. *Double or Convex Cabochon.*—This involves generally circular, elliptical, or oval forms with two convex surfaces, the upper side being more convex than the lower (Fig. 778). When the convexity is the same above and below, the cut is sometimes called *lentil shape* (Fig. 779).

FIG. 778.   FIG. 779.

2. *High Cabochon.*—This is somewhat similar to type 1, but the upper portion is very much higher and, hence, more convex than the underside (Fig. 780).

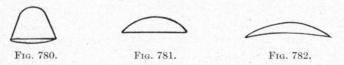

FIG. 780.   FIG. 781.   FIG. 782.

3. *Simple or Plain Cabochon.*—In this cut, the upper side is convex as in types 1 and 2, but the underside is a flat surface. Stones with this style of cutting are mounted with the plain surface down (Fig. 781).

FIG. 783.—Diamond cleaver at work.[1]

4. *Hollow or Concavo-convex Cabochon*, also called *Shell Cut.*—In this style, the upper side is convex, but the under portion is hollowed out (Fig. 782).

The cabochon cuts are used for stones exhibiting sheens, play of colors, opalescence, and asterism; thus, for tiger's-eye, opal, moonstone, and star sapphires. They are also used for many colored stones, for example, garnet, amethyst, turquois, and chrysocolla. The hollow cabochon cut is generally employed for transparent but deeply colored stones through which very little light could pass if cut in the other styles; for example, the almandite variety of garnet.

The principal style of cutting involving facets is the *brilliant cut.* Thus, in cutting the diamond, the octahedron, either natural or produced by cleavage, is made the basis, as shown in Figs. 783 and 784. The upper and lower portions are removed in such a manner

[1] Figures 783, 794, and 795 are views taken in the Diamond Cutting Works of Messrs. Stern Brothers and Company, New York.

that when the stone is cut, the portion above the edge G, which is termed the *girdle*, is generally one-half as thick as the part below the girdle. The upper portion of the cut stone is called the *crown* or *bezel*, while the lower part is the *pavilion* or *base*. The uppermost facet T is the *table*, and C is the *culet* (Figs. 785 and 786). Commonly, there are 56 facets between the table and the culet. In some cases, however, diamonds are cut in this style with as many as 66 or 74 facets, inclusive of the table and the culet. Definite relations between the height of the crown, depth of the pavilion, and width of the stone must be observed if the cut gem is to exhibit the maximum of brilliancy and fire (Fig. 787). Depending upon the character of the rough material, the outline of the cut stone varies, being either circular, quadratic, oval, elliptical, or pear shaped. While the diamond was formerly cut almost exclusively in this style, in recent years the *emerald cut* has become quite popular (Figs. 788 and 789), especially for stones of larger size. Usually stones with the emerald cut have 50 facets, including the table and culet.

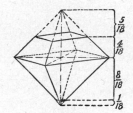

Fig. 784.

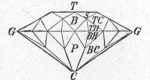

Fig. 785.

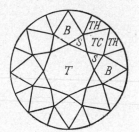

Fig. 786.

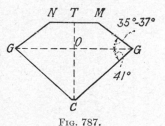

Fig. 787.

The *rose* cut has 24 triangular facets with a flat base (Figs. 790 and 791). This style of cutting is one of the earliest involving facets but it is not employed much at present. At present various fancy cuts are used, such as *baguette, cut corner triangle, epaulet, half moon, hexagon, keystone, kite, lozenge, marquise, pentagon* or *bullet, square, trapeze,* and *triangle.* Figures 792 and 793 illustrate *step, trap,* or *cushion cuts,* which are frequently used for colored stones.

Fig. 788.

Fig. 789.

Fig. 790.

Fig. 791.

In cutting gems, the stone is held in some cement or mechanical holder and placed against a rapidly revolving metallic wheel or disk containing or covered with some abrasive, such as diamond dust, carborundum, or emery. The position and inclination of the various facets are determined by the eye of the cutter, who obviously must exercise great judg-

FIG. 792.

FIG. 793.

FIG. 794.—Diamond cutters.

FIG. 795.—Diamond polisher.

ment in order to cut stones to the best advantage. These cutters become very expert, and rarely does an experienced cutter exceed the permissible limits of variation in the angles between the different facets. After the facets have been produced, they are polished in much the same manner as they were cut, except that some polishing material, such as tripolite or rouge, instead of an abrasive, is used. Diamonds are usually cut and polished by men who specialize on the diamond, while a lapidary is one who cuts and polishes all other types of gems. Amsterdam, Antwerp, Paris, London, Hanau, Idar-Oberstein, New York, and Boston are important gem-cutting centers.

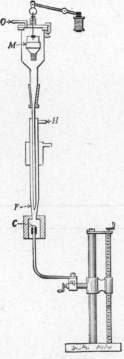

FIG. 796.

FIG. 797.—Furnaces for the manufacture of artificial rubies and sapphires. Jewel Works Company, Biel, Switzerland.

Synthetic Gems.—A synthetic gem is one prepared in the laboratory and, in its chemical and physical properties, is identical with the corresponding natural gem. For many years, scientists have endeavored to produce the diamond in the laboratory. Prominent among the many investigators who have worked on this problem are Moissan, Parsons, Noble, Crookes, and Hasslinger. These scientists believed that they had succeeded in producing small diamonds of microscopic size, but the evidence submitted by them is not incontrovertible. Hence, it is now thought that the diamond has not yet been made in the laboratory.

The most important synthetic gems are those having the composition and physical properties of the various varieties of corundum; that is, synthetic rubies and sapphires. At present, these are manufactured on a large scale, and they differ from the natural stones only in minor details. In fact, in many instances, the cut synthetics exhibit greater splendor and are usually much cleaner than natural stones.

The apparatus for producing these synthetic rubies and sapphires (Fig. 796) was devised by Verneuil. It consists of a vertical blowpipe, burning a mixture of hydrogen and oxygen, entering at H and O, respectively. By means of suitable mechanism, very finely divided particles of aluminum oxide (Al_2O_3) are introduced at M. These particles mix with the gases and fuse in the very hot flame at F, which is directed against a small fire-clay support C. These fused particles collect on this clay sup-

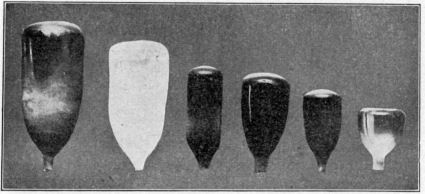

FIG. 798.—Carrot- and pear-shaped *boules* or *birnes* of different colors varying in weight from 181 to 37 carats.

port at first as a small drop, which slowly increases in size, as the process continues, until a fairly large and inverted conical, carrot- or pear-shaped, colorless drop, called the *boule* or *birne*, is formed (Figs. 797 and 798). These boules are broad on top and very narrow below where supported on the fire-clay cone and may vary in weight from 35 to 700 carats. Although the internal structure of such boules is the same as that of the natural colorless corundum or white sapphire, the only indication of crystal faces usually to be observed is a slight flattening of one of the upright sides. This flattened surface corresponds in position to the basal pinacoid in the natural gem.

By the addition to the Al_2O_3 of a small amount of chromium oxide, boules of a red color are obtained. These correspond to the ruby. The addition of the oxides of iron and titanium gives the deep-blue color of the sapphire proper. The yellow color of the beautiful golden sapphire is produced when some nickel compound and other substances, at present kept secret, are added. Green sapphire is obtained when a mixture of vanadium and cobalt oxides is added. The so-called *artificial alexandrite* is produced by the addition of small percentages of vanadium compounds to the aluminum oxide.

In chemical composition and all physical properties, such as hardness, specific gravity, and indices of refraction, these synthetic gems are identical with those occurring in nature. Due to the presence of inclusions, tension cracks, and peculiar structure lines, cut synthetic gems can, in most instances, be easily distinguished from natural stones. In some cases, however, especially if the cut stones are about ½ carat or less in size, their synthetic character may be very difficult to determine.

Synthetic spinel in beautiful colors is also produced by this process and is frequently sold as aquamarine or as the emerald.

Many attempts have been made to produce the emerald synthetically. The methods used thus far are generally complicated and involve long periods of time. They have yielded well-developed crystals up to 2 cm in length. The name *igmerald* has been suggested for some of these products. Stones sold at present as synthetic or scientific emerald or aquamarine are either synthetic sapphire or spinel, or merely glass, appropriately colored.

Cut synthetic rubies and sapphires can be obtained at varying prices up to $2 or $3 per carat, depending upon the quality of the stone. Not all of these synthetics are sold as gems. Many are used as *jewels* in the manufacture of watches and in delicate physical and electrical measuring instruments, such as balances, meters, and chronometers, where hard bearing surfaces are required.

Synthetic gems are manufactured at Locarno and Monthey, Switzerland, Annecy, and Jarrie, France, and Bitterfeld and Zwickau, Germany. The daily production of these plants is from 600,000 to 750,000 carats. while their total capacity is approximately twice as much.

CHAPTER XVIII

CLASSIFICATION OF MINERALS ACCORDING TO ELEMENTS

It is often desirable to refer to the more important minerals in which elements of economic importance occur, and the following tabulations have been prepared to meet this need. Following each table there is a discussion of some of the uses of the important commercial minerals under consideration, and whenever possible statistics of production, under normal economic conditions, are given. The minerals are given under each element in the order in which they have been described in the text. Page references to the detailed descriptions are given after the names of the minerals.

ALUMINUM

CORUNDUM, 275	Al_2O_3	Hexagonal
BAUXITE, 282	$Al_2O_3.2H_2O$	Unknown
CRYOLITE, 288	Na_3AlF_6	Monoclinic
ALUNITE, 313	$K_2(Al.2OH)_6(SO_4)_4$	Hexagonal
SPINELS, 319	$Mg(AlO_2)_2$, etc.	Cubic
Chrysoberyl, 322	$Be(AlO_2)_2$	Orthorhombic
Wavellite, 328	$(AlOH)_3(PO_4)_2.5H_2O$	Orthorhombic
Turquois, 329	$H_5[Al(OH)_2]_6Cu(OH)(PO_4)_4$	Triclinic
STAUROLITE, 336	$H_2FeAl_4Si_2O_{12}$	Orthorhombic
ANDALUSITE, 338	Al_2SiO_5	Orthorhombic
Sillimanite, 339	Al_2SiO_5	Orthorhombic
CYANITE, 339	Al_2SiO_5	Triclinic
TOPAZ, 340	$Al_2(F,OH)_2SiO_4$	Orthorhombic
TOURMALINE, 342	$M'_{20}B_2Si_4O_{21}$	Hexagonal
EPIDOTE, 344	$Ca_2(Al,Fe)_2(AlOH)(SiO_4)_3$	Monoclinic
VESUVIANITE, 345	$Ca_6[Al(OH,F)]Al_2(SiO_4)_5$	Tetragonal
GARNETS, 349	$M''_3Al_2(SiO_4)_3$	Cubic
BERYL, 352	$Be_3Al_2Si_6O_{18}$	Hexagonal
MICAS, 354	$KAl_2(OH)_2AlSi_3O_{10}$, etc.	Monoclinic
CHLORITE, 358	$H_8Mg_5Al_2Si_3O_{18}$	Monoclinic
KAOLINITE, 359	$H_4Al_2Si_2O_9$	Monoclinic
SPODUMENE, 366	$LiAl(SiO_3)_2$	Monoclinic
AMPHIBOLES, 368	Silicates of Al,Ca,Mg,Fe	Orthorhombic and monoclinic
FELDSPARS, 372	$KAlSi_3O_8$, etc.	Monoclinic and triclinic
NEPHELITE, 380	$(Na,K)_8Al_8Si_9O_{34}$	Hexagonal
Sodalite, 381	$3NaAlSiO_4.NaCl$	Cubic
LEUCITE, 382	$KAl(SiO_3)_2$	Orthorhombic and cubic
SCAPOLITE, 383	$Ca_4Al_6Si_6O_{24}CO_3$, etc.	Tetragonal
ZEOLITES, 385	Hydrated silicates	Various systems

Aluminum is the most abundant metal in nature, and the minerals in which this element is an important constituent are exceedingly numerous. Only bauxite, cryolite, andalusite, and dumortierite will be referred to in this discussion. Bauxite is used as a source of metallic aluminum and aluminum salts, and also in the manufacture of bauxite bricks and abrasives, such as *alundum, aloxite, exolon,* and *lionite.* These products, which are artificial Al_2O_3, are made by fusing bauxite in an electric furnace. The annual production of artificial abrasives made from bauxite amounts to about 70,000 short tons. Cryolite is used as a flux in the electrolytic method for the extraction of the metal from bauxite, while andalusite

Fig. 799.—Stock piles of 1232 tons of andalusite (rear) and 328 tons of dumortierite (foreground). Champion Porcelain Company, Detroit, Michigan.

and dumortierite $(8Al_2O_3.B_2O_3.6SiO_2.H_2O)$ are used in the manufacture of spark-plug and chemical porcelains and refractories (Fig. 799). Upon heating, andalusite and dumortierite break down into $3Al_2O_3.2SiO_2$ (mullite), a compound which imparts great tensile strength, high dielectric properties, and low thermal expansion to material containing it.

In the manufacture of metallic aluminum the finely powdered crude ore (bauxite) is digested with a hot caustic solution that dissolves the alumina while the impurities, mainly iron and silica, are left as a residue. From the filtrate containing sodium aluminate the aluminum is precipitated as the hydroxide. It is then filtered and ignited to the oxide. In the electrolysis, cryolite is placed in tanks lined with carbon which acts as the cathode, while suspended carbon cylinders act as the anode. The cryolite melts and readily dissolves the alumina which is added. The current decomposes the latter with the separation of metallic aluminum

which collects in the bottom of the tank.   About 2 tons of Al_2O_3 yield
1 ton of metallic aluminum.   The amount of primary metallic aluminum
produced in the United States exceeds, in normal years, 100,000 tons
annually.

Metallic aluminum finds extensive use on account of its high heat and
electrical conductivity, low density, toughness, durability, and resistance
to corrosion.   Paints in which aluminum powder is used reflect approximately 70 per cent. of the light.   Many alloys of aluminum have been
prepared.   The most important are those with copper, zinc, tin, nickel,
magnesium, manganese, silicon, and cadmium.   *Duralumin*, an important
alloy of aluminum, contains 4 per cent. copper, 0.5 per cent. magnesium,

Fig. 800.—Bauxite mining operations near Bauxite, Saline County, Arkansas.

0.6 per cent. manganese, and small amounts of iron and silicon.   When
this alloy is heated to 500°C. and quenched, after 4 days it has a strength
of about 60,000 pounds per square inch.   *Thermite*, used in welding, is a
mixture of aluminum and iron oxide, while the explosive *ammonal* consists of aluminum dust and ammonium nitrate.   Alum and aluminum
sulphate and chloride are the chief chemical salts and are employed in
water purification, dyeing, and tanning.   Bauxite bricks containing
about 77 per cent. of alumina are used in the construction of copper, iron,
and lead furnaces and of cement kilns.

Bauxite of commercial grade should contain at least 52 per cent. of
aluminum oxide, less than 3 per cent. of titanium oxide, and not more
than 15 per cent. of the combined oxides of silicon and iron.   The production of bauxite in the United States amounts to about 350,000 long tons,

of which nearly 90 per cent. is obtained from Arkansas (Fig. 800); the balance, from Georgia, Tennessee, and Alabama. About 20,000 short tons of alum and over 350,000 short tons of aluminum sulphate are produced annually. The quantity of cryolite imported from Greenland is approximately 6,000 long tons.

ANTIMONY

STIBNITE, 249	Sb_2S_3	Orthorhombic
Pyrargyrite, 263	Ag_3SbS_3	Hexagonal
Bournonite, 263	$PbCuSbS_3$	Orthorhombic
TETRAHEDRITE, 264	Cu_3SbS_3	Cubic

Of the above named antimony minerals, stibnite is the most important. Some antimony is also recovered from antimonial lead ores carrying from 12 to 20 per cent. of antimony. Except for a small amount of antimony in the form of a fine powder (*antimony black*) used for bronzing metals and plaster casts, antimony metal is used chiefly in the manufacture of alloys. These alloys include *type metal* (lead, antimony, tin, and copper), *babbitt, antifriction,* or *bearing metal* (usually antimony, tin, and copper), *britannia* or *white metal* (tin, antimony, copper, with some zinc), and so forth. Antimony imparts hardness to lead and prevents it from contracting when solidifying from a molten condition. At the present time, antimonial lead finds extensive employment in the manufacture of storage batteries. Antimony oxide is used in making opaque white enamel and other sanitary ware. The white oxide has been employed in the making of paint which is sold under the name of *timonox*. Salts of antimony are used in medicine and as a mordant in dyeing, while the sulphide of antimony is employed for vulcanizing and coloring rubber and also as paint pigments.

Under normal conditions, the United States is not a large producer of antimony ores, importing practically its entire supply from China, Bolivia, and Mexico. The annual importation reaches at times 10,000 short tons of metallic antimony while a like amount, approximately, is recovered from old alloys, scrap, and dross.

ARSENIC

Native Arsenic, 238	As	Hexagonal
REALGAR, 248	AsS	Monoclinic
ORPIMENT, 249	As_2S_3	Monoclinic
Niccolite, 253	NiAs	Hexagonal
Cobaltite, 259	CoAsS	Cubic
Smaltite, 259	$CoAs_2$	Cubic
ARSENOPYRITE, 260	FeAsS	Orthorhombic
Proustite, 262	Ag_3AsS_3	Hexagonal
TETRAHEDRITE, 264	M'_3AsS_3	Cubic
Enargite, 265	Cu_3AsS_4	Orthorhombic

Arsenopyrite is the most important arsenical mineral. The commercial uses of arsenic are very limited. Shot metal is an alloy of arsenic and lead. Arsenious oxide is used in the manufacture of insecticides, such as Paris green and the arsenates of calcium, lead, magnesium, and manganese. It is also used to counteract the iron coloration in the manufacture of glass. Arsenic compounds are also used in the preservation of wood.

The production of arsenic is recorded in the terms of *white arsenic*, arsenic trioxide (As_2O_3), very little of which is obtained directly from arsenic minerals. Large quantities are, however, available as a by-product in the smelting of copper, cobalt, gold, silver, and lead ores. The domestic production of As_2O_3 amounts to about 14,000 short tons annually.

BARIUM

WITHERITE, 300	$BaCO_3$	Orthorhombic
BARITE, 307	$BaSO_4$	Orthorhombic

Barite (barytes) is the more important of the above minerals, commercially. It is used chiefly in mixed paints. *Lithopone*, one of the chief constituents of sanitary flat wall paints, is an intimate mixture of 70 per cent. barium sulphate, 25 to 29 per cent. zinc sulphide, and 1 to 5 per cent. zinc oxide. Approximately two-thirds of the barite consumed in United States is employed in the manufacture of lithopone. *Blanc fixé*, or permanent white, is artificially prepared barium sulphate. Ground barite is used in the manufacture of rubber goods, linoleum, oil cloth, artificial ivory, and heavy glazed paper, such as playing cards, and bristol board. Barite bricks are opaque to X rays and are used in X-ray laboratories. The barium salts have a wide variety of uses: barium binoxide (BaO_2) in the preparation of hydrogen peroxide, barium chloride as a water softener, the carbonate and chloride to prevent efflorescence on bricks and as insecticides, and the carbonate, sulphate, or nitrate in the manufacture of optical glass. By the addition of a small amount of metallic barium to the electrodes of spark plugs their efficiency is increased.

Barite is obtained mainly from Missouri, Georgia, Tennessee, and California. The annual production amounts to about 250,000 short tons. Germany is also a large producer of barite.

BERYLLIUM

Chrysoberyl, 322	$Be(AlO_2)_2$	Orthorhombic
BERYL, 352	$Be_3Al_2(SiO_3)_6$	Hexagonal

Aside from the use of transparent beryllium minerals as gems, the application of beryllium alloys and compounds in industry is increasing in importance. Beryllium-copper alloys provide the chief commercial outlet for the metal. By the addition of from 1.5 to 2.5 per cent. beryllium, followed by heat treatment, the tensile strength of copper is raised from 33,000 to nearly 200,000 pounds per square inch. These alloys possess increased hardness and high fatigue resistance and are used for electrical springs, contact clips, thermostat controls and telegraph relay parts. Beryllium also forms alloys with nickel and iron. Beryllium-aluminum alloys have been suggested for pistons and in airplane construction.

Alkaline beryllium borate glasses (4.4 per cent. BeO) may replace quartz lenses for transmitting ultraviolet light. They can be sealed like ordinary glass. Beryllium oxide is used to a certain extent as a refractory because of its high melting point (2570°C.) and resistance to thermal shock.

A limited amount of beryl is obtained from the pegmatites of the Black Hills, South Dakota.

BISMUTH

Native Bismuth, 239   Bi   Hexagonal

Bismuth is extensively used in alloys with lead, tin, copper, antimony, and cadmium. The melting point of some of these alloys is as low as 64°C., and they are therefore employed as safety fuses for electrical apparatus, safety plugs for boilers, and for automatic sprinklers. Bismuth salts are used in dressing wounds. The nitrate is sometimes given internally before producing a roentgenograph, as bismuth salts are opaque to X rays. The salts are also used in calico printing and in the manufacture of high-refractive glass. No native bismuth is mined in the United States. The entire domestic production is obtained as a by-product in the electrolytic refining of lead, the bismuth being recovered from the anode slime. This source yields about 300,000 pounds of the metal annually.

BORON

Colemanite, 323	$Ca_2B_6O_{11}.5H_2O$	Monoclinic
Kernite, 324	$Na_2B_4O_7.4H_2O$	Monoclinic
Datolite, 341	$Ca(BOH)SiO_4$	Monoclinic
TOURMALINE, 342	$M'_{20}B_2Si_4O_{21}$	Hexagonal

Commercially, the most important boron compound is borax, which prior to 1927 was obtained by treating colemanite with sodium carbonate or sulphate. In 1927 large deposits of kernite (rasorite) were found in Kern County, California, and the supply of borax is now largely obtained from this mineral by solution and recrystallization. Borax is also recovered from the brines of Searles Lake, San Bernardino County, and Owens Lake, Inyo County, California. Borax is used in assaying, soldering, welding of metals, and in the manufacture of flint glass; also in making the enameled coating for cast iron used in plumbing and kitchen utensils. Because of its antiseptic and cleansing properties, it is also used in the manufacture of soap, washing powders, and ointments. Chromium borate is a green pigment employed in calico printing, and the borate of manganese is sometimes used as a drier in paints and oils.

The entire output of crude borates in United States is obtained from southern California and amounts to about 180,000 short tons.

CALCIUM

FLUORITE, 287	CaF_2	Cubic
CALCITE, 291	$CaCO_3$	Hexagonal
DOLOMITE, 294	$CaMg(CO_3)_2$	Hexagonal
ARAGONITE, 299	$CaCO_3$	Orthorhombic
ANHYDRITE, 305	$CaSO_4$	Orthorhombic
Scheelite, 310	$CaWO_4$	Tetragonal
GYPSUM, 315	$CaSO_4.2H_2O$	Monoclinic
Colemanite, 323	$Ca_2B_6O_{11}.5H_2O$	Monoclinic
APATITE, 326	$Ca_5F(PO_4)_3$	Hexagonal
Datolite, 341	$Ca(BOH)SiO_4$	Monoclinic
EPIDOTE, 344	$Ca_2(Al,Fe)_2(AlOH)(SiO_4)_3$	Monoclinic
Orthite, 345	$Ca_2(Al,Ce,Fe)_2(AlOH)(SiO_4)_3$	Monoclinic
VESUVIANITE, 345	$Ca_6[Al(OH,F)]Al_2(SiO_4)_5$	Tetragonal
GARNET, 349	$Ca_3Al_2(SiO_4)_3$, etc.	Cubic
PYROXENES, 363	$CaMg(SiO_3)_2$, etc.	Orthorhombic and monoclinic
AMPHIBOLES, 368	$Ca_2Mg_5(OH)_2(Si_4O_{11})$, etc.	Orthorhombic and monoclinic
Anorthite and PLAGIOCLASES, 376	$CaAl_2Si_2O_8$, etc.	Triclinic
SCAPOLITE, 383	$Ca_4Al_6Si_6O_{24}CO_3$, etc.	Tetragonal
TITANITE, 384	$CaTiSiO_5$	Monoclinic
ZEOLITES, 385	Hydrated silicates	Various systems

Calcium is one of the most abundant metals in nature and is an important constituent of many minerals. Of those listed above, fluorite, calcite, dolomite, scheelite, gypsum, and apatite are of prime importance commercially. The production and uses of calcite, dolomite, and gypsum only, however, will be given here.

Calcite and Dolomite.—The value of limestone, massive forms of calcite, and dolomite sold in the United States has at times amounted to about \$98,000,000 or 56 per cent. of the total value of all stone sold, while the value of marble may be placed at about \$14,000,000. The distribution of this production is shown summarized below.

	Building	Monumental	Paving, curbing, flagging	Rubble	Riprap	Crushed	Other uses
Limestone	\$16,000,000	....	\$90,000	\$500,000	\$1,500,000	\$50,000,000	\$28,000,000
Marble	\$ 9,500,000	\$3,500,000	....	....	....	....	\$ 700,000

Under other uses, in the case of limestone, are included furnace flux valued at $18,000,000, stone for alkali works and sugar factories valued at $3,000,000, and ground stone for agricultural purposes valued at $2,500,000. Furnace flux, terrazzo, and marble dust are included under other uses of marble. In addition, large quantities of limestone are employed in the manufacture of cement and lime. It is estimated that these industries use the following quantities of limestone annually:

Portland cement	40,000,000 short tons
Natural cement	300,000 short tons
Lime	9,000,000 short tons

The leading limestone-producing states are Indiana, Pennsylvania, Ohio, New York, Illinois, and Michigan.

FIG. 801.—Gypsum mine. Grand Rapids, Michigan.

Gypsum.—This mineral is used in both the uncalcined and calcined conditions. In the former state, its chief uses are (1) as a retarder in Portland cement, (2) as a pigment base for paints, especially in making cold-water paints, and (3) as a filler for paper and cloth. The use of gypsum in agriculture has, in recent years, been practically abandoned.

Calcined gypsum is used chiefly in wall plasters, wall and plaster boards, gypsum blocks and tile, molds for pottery and terra cotta, surgical casts, and for many other purposes. Gypsum tile reinforced with metal is frequently used for roof decks of laundries, foundries, and textile mills where condensation of moisture causes considerable trouble. As gypsum has a low heat conductivity, its use largely prevents this condensation or drip. *Keene's cement,* which differs from ordinary wall plasters in the time of setting and its greater hardness, is made by burning pure gypsum at a low temperature, then immersing in a solution of alum, aluminum sulphate, or borax, and recalcining at about 500°C. *Soluble anhydrite,* prepared by heating gypsum for 3 hours in an oven at about 460°F., can be used as a drying or desiccating agent.

Gypsum is produced in numerous states and in Alaska. New York is the largest producer, followed by Michigan, Iowa, and Texas. The production in the United States under normal conditions is about 5,000,000 short tons, distributed according to uses as follows:

	Short Tons
Uncalcined:	
Portland cement, paint, etc...........................	1,000,000
Calcined:	
Plaster of Paris, wall plasters, etc......................	3,000,000
As plaster and wallboards, tile, blocks, etc...............	800,000
Glass factories.......................................	20,000

CARBON

DIAMOND, 229	C	Cubic
GRAPHITE, 235	C	Hexagonal

Carbon is also an essential constituent of the carbonates (pages 290 to 304) and of such organic substances as petroleum, asphalt, and coal.

Diamond.—Africa at the present time supplies over 95 per cent. of the world's production of diamonds. Formerly the volcanic pipes furnished almost the entire output, but in recent years the production from alluvial deposits in South Africa, Southwest Africa, Angola, the Gold Coast, and British Guiana exceeds the production from the mines. About 40,000 diamonds have been recovered from Pike County, Arkansas. The largest stone found in this region weighed 40.22 carats; it is a flattened, irregular octahedron and is the largest diamond found to date on the North American continent. The value of other scattered finds in the United States rarely exceeds a few thousand dollars annually.

Aside from its use in jewelry, diamonds are extensively employed in industry. Three types are used for industrial purposes, bortz, ballas, and carbonado. These varieties are used in rock drills for prospecting operations and the determination of the character of subsurface rock formations; for truing grinding wheels, in order to retain the wheels in cylindrical shape and for restoring the cutting surface when glazed; for wire-drawing dies; for stone-cutting saws; for glass cutting; and as diamond points for drilling holes in gems, watch jewels, and glass lenses. Bearings for balances and large-capacity electric meters are sometimes composed of bortz.

The size of the core in diamond drilling varies from 1 to 4 inches, and the rate of penetration averages between 30 to 50 feet a day in granite to 100 or 200 feet in soft formations.   In drilling, six or eight diamonds are usually used, but occasionally numerous small stones are employed as this distributes the stresses over a larger number of points (see page 234). The consumption of diamonds for drilling operations alone is estimated at 5000 to 10,000 carats annually.

Fig. 802.—Premier Diamond Mine.   Near Pretoria, Transvaal.   (*Photograph by Ewing Galloway, New York City.*)

Wires drawn through diamond dies are characterized by a high polish and uniformity of size.   Wires can be drawn as fine as 0.01 mm. in diameter.   From 300 to 400 tons of copper wire can be drawn through a single die without variation in gauge.   Practically the entire production of carbonado, estimated at 23,500 carats annually, comes from Bahia in Brazil, while that of diamonds for all industrial purposes is about 2,500,000 carats.

Graphite.—The trade makes a sharp distinction between crystalline and amorphous graphite. By the former is meant *flake graphite* of sufficient size to be visible to the naked eye. The most important use of crystalline graphite is in the manufacture of crucibles used in the steel, brass, and bronze industries. For this purpose a flaky or fibrous graphite is essential, and the Ceylon lump or Madagascar flake is generally preferred, although it is sometimes mixed with American flake graphite. For crucibles, graphitic carbon should exceed 85 per cent. and, at the same time, be practically free from mica, pyrite, and iron oxide. Graphite

Fig. 803.—Mining carbonado. Paraguassu River, Bahia, Brazil. (*Photograph by Underwood and Underwood.*)

crucibles are superior to clay crucibles because of their infusibility, conductivity of heat, and ability to withstand sudden temperature changes. As graphite has but little binding strength, clay, sand, and kaolin are added in the proportion of about 3 parts of graphite, 2 parts of clay, 1 part of sand, and smaller amounts of kaolin. The increase in the number of electric furnaces, however, is decreasing the demand for crucible steel and also for graphite crucibles.

Except for the manufacture of crucibles, amorphous graphite is suitable for all purposes. For paints and for foundry facings, which consume about 70 per cent. of the graphite used, a high degree of purity is not demanded; but for lubricants, pencils, and electric purposes, high-grade material is essential. In the manufacture of self-lubricating metals, graphite is incorporated in the molten metal, and the resulting mixture contains about 60 per cent. by weight or 25 per cent. by volume of the metal.

Imported crystalline graphite is obtained chiefly from Ceylon and Madagascar, while Alabama and Texas are, under normal conditions, the principal domestic sources. The better grades of amorphous graphite are imported from Mexico and Chosen (Korea). The domestic production ordinarily amounts to about 5000 short tons, while about 17,000 short tons are imported annually.

CERIUM

Monazite, 325	$(Ce,La,Di)PO_4$	Monoclinic
Orthite, 345	$Ca_2(Al,Ce,Fe)_2(AlOH)(SiO_4)_3$	Monoclinic

When struck or scratched, alloys of cerium readily emit sparks, and this property is utilized in many forms of automatic lighters. Because of the great affinity of cerium for oxygen, it is also used as a reducing agent in the production of metallic zirconium and thorium. Cerium sulphate is employed in the manufacture of aniline black, in photography for the purpose of removing silver from overdeveloped negatives, and as a catalyst in the contact process for the manufacture of sulphuric acid. Cerium compounds have been proposed for use in color photography, arc-lamp electrodes, and in glassware. Cerium is particularly effective in absorbing ultraviolet rays and is employed, either alone or with didymium, in spectacle lenses. The oxide, ceria, is employed as a constituent of incandescent mantles.

CHROMIUM

Crocoite, 309	$PbCrO_4$	Monoclinic
CHROMITE, 322	$(Fe,Cr)[(Cr,Fe)O_2]_2$	Cubic

Chromite is the more important of these minerals. When chromium is added in small amounts (1 to 2 per cent.) to steel, it increases its hardness. In larger amounts (18 per cent. Cr and 8 per cent. Ni), it imparts corrosion resistance and is known as *stainless steel*, *enduro*, or *Allegheny metal*. Chrome steel is used in the manufacture of armor plate, armor-piercing projectiles, and for high-speed tools. Chromium is also used in plating. The coating is hard and white and somewhat resembles platinum. *Nichrome* (60 per cent. Ni, 14 per cent. Cr, 15 per cent. Fe) is used extensively in electric heating elements. *Stellite* (essentially cobalt, chromium, and tungsten or molybdenum) is used in high-speed tools and instruments of precision. A manganese-chrome-vanadium steel has been developed for automotive forgings. Chromite is an important refractory and is often employed to line copper and steel furnaces. For this purpose it has certain advantages over magnesite, as it resists corrosion, withstands sudden changes of temperature, and requires less delicate handling. Compounds of chromium are used as pigments (yellow, green, and red colors), as mordants in dyeing and printing cloth, and in tanning leather.

The chief foreign sources of chromite in recent years have been Rhodesia, New Caledonia, Greece, Turkey, and Cuba. About 250,000 long tons are imported each year. The domestic production at the present time is very small and comes from California.

COBALT

Cobaltite, 259	$CoAsS$	Cubic
Smaltite, 259	$CoAs_2$	Cubic

The metal cobalt, usually in conjunction with tungsten, is used in the manufacture of high-speed tool steels and in *stellite*, which is an alloy of cobalt, chromium, and tungsten. Cobalt increases the strength and elasticity of steel but lowers its ductility. Cobalt oxide is used as a blue pigment in the manufacture of glass and pottery. Cobalt salts are also used as driers in paints.

One of the principal sources is Canada, where the oxide is recovered as a by-product in the treatment of silver ores. The Belgian Congo is another important source for cobalt. The amount of metal and of cobalt ore and oxide imported amounts to about 1,200,000 pounds each year.

COLUMBIUM (NIOBIUM)

COLUMBITE, 326	$(Fe,Mn)[(Cb,Ta)O_3]_2$	Orthorhombic

Columbium (niobium) is of very limited economic importance at present although the carbides of columbium (and tantalum) are used in ultrahard cutting-tool materials. Tantalum, which is nearly always present in columbium minerals, is characterized by its extreme hardness, toughness, and high melting point. It is used in the manufacture of drills, watch springs, pen points, electric-lamp filaments, and chemical laboratory equipment. Many of the commercial applications of tantalum are due to its remarkable resistance to the corrosive action of all chemicals except strong alkalies and mixtures containing hydrofluoric or fuming sulphuric acid. Tantalum can be easily fabricated into bars, thin sheets, and fine wires. When heated above 350°C., it absorbs gases and therefore is used in the construction of vacuum tubes. Tantalum, used as an electrode in electrolytic solutions, acts as an electrolytic valve, passing the current in one direction only, thus automatically rectifying an alternating current. Tantalum becomes incandescent at 1700°C., more than 400° lower than the incandescent point of tungsten. A tantalum lamp is, therefore, 20 per cent. cooler than a tungsten lamp. Tantalum filaments are made by pressing a mixture of the oxide and paraffine into threads which are then reduced to the metal by the passage of an electric current in a vacuum. The use of tantalum and columbium in special steels is still under investigation.

Tantalum ore imported into United States amounts to about 35,000 pounds annually, mainly from the Pilbarra field in Western Australia.

COPPER

NATIVE COPPER, 240	Cu	Cubic
CHALCOCITE, 255	Cu_2S	Orthorhombic
CHALCOPYRITE, 261	$CuFeS_2$	Tetragonal
BORNITE, 262	Cu_5FeS_4	Cubic
Bournonite, 263	$PbCuSbS_3$	Orthorhombic
TETRAHEDRITE, 264	Cu_3SbS_3	Cubic
Enargite, 265	Cu_3AsS_4	Orthorhombic
CUPRITE, 279	Cu_2O	Cubic
MALACHITE, 302	$CuCO_3.Cu(OH)_2$	Monoclinic
AZURITE, 302	$2CuCO_3.Cu(OH)_2$	Monoclinic
Brochantite, 314	$CuSo_4.3Cu(OH)_2$	Orthorhombic
Chalcanthite, 318	$CuSO_4.5H_2O$	Triclinic
CHRYSOCOLLA, 353	CuO,SiO_2,H_2O	Amorphous

Copper is used most extensively for the transmission of electricity and in castings and alloys. *Brass* consists of copper and zinc; *German silver*

Fig. 804.—Open cut mine of the Utah Copper Company. Bingham Canyon, Utah.
(Photograph by Underwood and Underwood.)

of copper, zinc, and nickel; *bronze* and *bell metal* of copper, tin, and zinc. Other bronzes contain small amounts of nickel, manganese, silicon, or lead. A typical manganese bronze for propeller blades, valve stems, and parts requiring toughness, strength, and resistance to corrosive action of salt water contains 57 per cent. Cu, 40.5 Zn, 0.75 Sn, 1 Fe, 0.5 Al, and 0.25 per cent. Mn. *Alcumite* is an alloy of copper, aluminum, and iron. The hydrous copper sulphate, or blue vitriol, is used in calico printing.

In recent years, about 20 states and territories produced copper, with Arizona, Montana, Utah, and Michigan as the leading producers. These four states contribute about 80 per cent. of the total output. The following table shows the approximate production, in normal times, percentage of total production, copper content of the crude ore mined, and the value of gold and silver per ton recovered as by-products, in the four leading copper-producing states:

Copper-producing state	Approximate production, pounds	Per cent. of total production	Approximate per cent. in ore	Approximate value in gold and silver per ton
Arizona..............	600,000,000	40	1.44	$0.18
Montana.............	200,000,000	15	4.67	0.71
Utah.................	200,000,000	15	0.86	0.19
Michigan.............	140,000,000	10	1.65	(a)

(a) Recent figures not available.

The total annual output of this country is about 700,000 metric tons.

FLUORINE

FLUORITE, 287	CaF_2	Cubic
CRYOLITE, 288	Na_3AlF_6	Monoclinic
APATITE, 326	$Ca_5F(PO_4)_3$	Hexagonal
TOPAZ, 340	$Al_2(F,OH)_2SiO_4$	Orthorhombic
Chondrodite, 343	$[Mg(F,OH)]_2Mg_3(SiO_4)_2$	Monoclinic
VESUVIANITE, 345	$Ca_6[Al(OH,F)]Al_2(SiO_4)_5$	Tetragonal
Lepidolite, 357	$K_2Li_3Al_3(OH,F)_4(AlSi_3O_{10})_2$	Monoclinic

Fluorite.—About 80 per cent. of the domestic fluorite is consumed in the manufacture of basic open-hearth steel, as it gives fluidity to the slag and aids in the removal of phosphorus and sulphur. For this purpose, the fluorite must contain at least 80 per cent. calcium fluoride and less than 6 per cent. silica. Other uses are as a flux in blast furnaces, iron foundries, silver, copper, and lead smelters, and in the manufacture of glass and enamel ware and of hydrofluoric acid. Because of its low refractive and dispersive powers, fluorite is in demand for apochromatic lenses, used in telescopes and spectroscopes. Material suitable for this work must be glass clear and free from clouds, gas bubbles, strains, and fractures. When fluorite is fused with bauxite and soda ash, an artificial cryolite is produced.

The production, which amounts to about 120,000 short tons, is obtained principally from Illinois, Kentucky, Nevada, Colorado, and New Mexico, the first two states being the chief producers, furnishing over 85 per cent. of the total output.

GOLD

NATIVE GOLD, 244 Au Cubic

Approximately 85 per cent. of the total domestic production of gold is obtained from placers (20 per cent.) and dry or siliceous ores (65 per cent.). The remaining 15 per cent. is recovered from the refining of copper bullion and from copper, lead, and zinc ores. The six leading states, which produce about 85 per cent. of the total output, are California, South Dakota, Alaska, Colorado, Utah, and Nevada. The total production in the United States is about 3,000,000 fine ounces, valued at about \$105,000,000, based on the price of \$35 per ounce. White gold is obtained by smelting gold with a special alloy containing nickel, silver, palladium, and zinc—14 parts of gold and 10 parts of the alloy. The largest gold-producing region in the world is the Witwatersrand district of Transvaal, South Africa. The United States, including Alaska, is the third largest producer. Other important gold-producing countries are Russia and Siberia, Canada, Australasia, and Mexico.

IRON

PYRRHOTITE, 252	FeS	Hexagonal
PYRITE, 257	FeS_2	Cubic
MARCASITE, 259	FeS_2	Orthorhombic
ARSENOPYRITE, 260	$FeAsS$	Orthorhombic
CHALCOPYRITE, 261	$CuFeS_2$	Tetragonal
BORNITE, 262	Cu_5FeS_4	Cubic
HEMATITE, 276	Fe_2O_3	Hexagonal
Ilmenite, 279	$FeTiO_3$	Hexagonal
LIMONITE, 283	$Fe_2O_3.nH_2O$	?
SIDERITE, 298	$FeCO_3$	Hexagonal
WOLFRAMITE, 311	$(Fe,Mn)WO_4$	Monoclinic
Ferberite, 312	$FeWO_4$	Monoclinic
Melanterite, 317	$FeSO_4.7H_2O$	Monoclinic
SPINELS, 319	$(Fe,Mg)(AlO_2)_2$, etc.	Cubic
MAGNETITE, 320	$Fe(FeO_2)_2$	Cubic
FRANKLINITE, 321	$(Fe,Mn,Zn)(FeO_2)_2$	Cubic
CHROMITE, 322	$(Fe,Cr)[(Cr,Fe)O_2]_2$	Cubic
COLUMBITE, 326	$(Fe,Mn)[(Cb,Ta)O_3]_2$	Orthorhombic
STAUROLITE, 336	$H_2FeAl_4Si_2O_{12}$	Orthorhombic
EPIDOTE, 344	$Ca_2(Al,Fe)_2(AlOH)(SiO_4)_3$	Monoclinic
Orthite, 345	$Ca_2(Al,Ce,Fe)_2(AlOH)(SiO_4)_3$	Monoclinic
OLIVINE, 346	$(Mg,Fe)_2SiO_4$	Orthorhombic
GARNET, 349	$Fe_3Al_2(SiO_4)_3$, etc.	Cubic
BIOTITE, 357	$(K,H)_2(Mg,Fe)_2(Al,Fe)_2(SiO_4)_3$	Monoclinic
PYROXENES, 363	$(Mg,Fe)_2(SiO_3)_2$, etc.	Orthorhombic and monoclinic
AMPHIBOLES, 368	$Ca_2(Mg,Fe)_5(OH)_2(Si_4O_{11})_2$, etc.	Orthorhombic and monoclinic

The iron ores are restricted to hematite, limonite (brown ore), magnetite, and siderite, with hematite by far the most important, furnishing annually about 95 per cent. of all the iron ore mined. The uniformity in iron content in the merchantable ore produced during a recent 10-year period is remarkable. The iron content varied only from 49.91 to 50.43 per cent. This uniformity has been maintained by mixing ores from

Fig. 805.—Iron-ore steamers at docks, Duluth, Minnesota.

Fig. 806.—Iron-ore stock and ore steamer unloading. Ashtabula, Ohio.

different deposits. Most of the iron ore mined is from certain well-defined regions, such as the Lake Superior, the Birmingham, and the Adirondack districts. The Lake Superior district alone produces about 85 per cent. of the total output. The mine production of the various districts follows:

APPROXIMATE PRODUCTION IN LONG TONS (2240 pounds)

Lake Superior (Minnesota, Michigan, Wisconsin).......... 55,000,000
Birmingham (Alabama) and Chattanooga (Tennessee,
    Georgia, North Carolina).......................... 7,000,000
Adirondack (New York) and Cornwall (Pennsylvania)..... 2,000,000
Northern New Jersey................................. 200,000

The total production amounts to about 70,000,000 tons in normal times.

LEAD

GALENA, 254	PbS	Cubic
Bournonite, 263	PbCuSbS$_3$	Orthorhombic
CERUSSITE, 301	PbCO$_3$	Orthorhombic
ANGLESITE, 308	PbSO$_4$	Orthorhombic
Crocoite, 309	PbCrO$_4$	Monoclinic
Wulfenite, 310	PbMoO$_4$	Tetragonal
PYROMORPHITE, 327	Pb$_5$Cl(PO$_4$)$_3$	Hexagonal
Vanadinite, 328	Pb$_5$Cl(VO$_4$)$_3$	Hexagonal

Galena is the most important source of lead. Large quantities of metallic lead, alloys of lead, and lead pigments are consumed annually in the trade. *Solder* consists of lead and tin. *Frary metal* is an alloy of lead with small amounts of barium and calcium, and is equal in hardness to the common lead alloy with 15 per cent. of antimony. Some of the pigments obtained from lead, such as sublimed white lead (lead sulphate, 75 per cent.; lead oxide, 20 per cent.; and zinc oxide, 5 per cent.) and sublimed blue lead (lead sulphate, 45 to 53 per cent.; lead oxide, 38 to 41 per cent.; with small amounts of lead sulphide, lead sulphite, and zinc oxide), are smelted directly from the ore. Pigments chemically prepared from pig lead include white lead (basic carbonate), red lead, and litharge.

The lead ores from the Mississippi Valley and southeastern Missouri contain little or no silver, and the lead produced from them is designated as "soft" lead, in distinction from the "hard" lead obtained from many western desilverized lead antimony ores. Antimonial lead, or hard lead, is used in the manufacture of storage batteries, bearing metals, corrosion-resistant alloys, and type metal. It is estimated that about 25 per cent. of our normal annual production is used for storage batteries, while lead for cable coverings constitutes the second largest use. The refined lead produced from domestic ores is approximately 650,000 short tons each year, obtained principally from Missouri, Idaho, Utah, and Oklahoma. In addition, about 120,000 short tons of refined lead are obtained annually from foreign ores and 280,000 short tons are recovered as secondary lead mainly from scrap and alloys.

LITHIUM

TOURMALINE, 342	M'$_{20}$B$_2$Si$_4$O$_{21}$	Hexagonal
Lepidolite, 357	K$_2$Li$_3$Al$_3$(OH,F)$_4$(AlSi$_3$O$_{10}$)$_2$	Monoclinic
SPODUMENE, 366	LiAl(SiO$_3$)$_2$	Monoclinic

The bromide and iodide are used in photography and the chloride in fireworks. Synthetic coal-tar products are gradually replacing the lithium salts for medicinal purposes.

Fig. 807.—Gigantic crystal of spodumene, Etta Mine, near Keystone, South Dakota. (*Photograph by courtesy of the United States Geological Survey.*)

The production of lithium minerals in the United States is not large, amounting to about 3,000 short tons, obtained from California and South Dakota (Fig. 807).

MAGNESIUM

DOLOMITE, 294	$CaMg(CO_3)_2$	Hexagonal
MAGNESITE, 295	$MgCO_3$	Hexagonal
Epsomite, 317	$MgSO_4.7H_2O$	Orthorhombic
SPINEL, 319	$Mg(AlO_2)_2$, etc.	Cubic
TOURMALINE, 342	$M'_{20}B_2Si_4O_{21}$	Hexagonal
Chondrodite, 343	$[Mg(F,OH)]_2Mg_3(SiO_4)_2$	Monoclinic
OLIVINE, 346	$(Mg,Fe)_2SiO_4$	Orthorhombic
PYROPE, 350	$Mg_3Al_2(SiO_4)_3$	Cubic
PHLOGOPITE, 356	$KMg_3(OH)_2AlSi_3O_{10}$	Monoclinic
BIOTITE, 357	$K(Mg,Fe)_3(OH)_2AlSi_3O_{10}$	Monoclinic
CHLORITE, 358	$H_8Mg_5Al_2Si_3O_{18}$	Monoclinic
TALC, 358	$H_2Mg_3Si_4O_{12}$	Monoclinic
SERPENTINE, 360	$H_4Mg_3Si_2O_9$	Monoclinic
Sepiolite, 362	$H_8Mg_2Si_3O_{12}$	Monoclinic
Garnierite, 362	$H_2(Ni,Mg)SiO_4$	Unknown
PYROXENES, 363	$Mg_2(SiO_3)_2$, etc.	Orthorhombic and monoclinic
AMPHIBOLES, 368	$Ca_2Mg_5(OH)_2(Si_4O_{11})_2$, etc.	Orthorhombic and monoclinic

Magnesium and its compounds serve industry in five principal ways (*a*) as a refractory oxide, (*b*) as heat-resisting materials in the form of basic magnesium carbonate, (*c*) as magnesite cement, (*d*) as magnesium salts, chiefly the chloride and sulphate, and (*e*) as metallic magnesium. The uses and production of magnesite, dolomite, and talc only will be discussed.

Magnesite.—Nearly all magnesite is used in the calcined condition. Depending upon the temperature of burning, the product is either "caustic" calcined or "dead-burned" magnesite. The *caustic* magnesia results from a moderate heat treatment and retains from 3 to 8 per cent. carbon dioxide. This product is chemically active, combining readily with magnesium chloride forming an oxychloride, or *Sorel* cement. This cement solidifies into an extremely hard and strong mass and is the basis of many of the sanitary flooring and stucco preparations placed upon the market under various trade names. Fillers in this cement may be cork, talc, asbestos, clay, marble dust, sand, etc. Magnesite cement floors may be laid in large areas without cracking. They take color easily and are susceptible to polish. It is claimed that the surface does not pulverize or dust.

Dead-burned magnesite is the result of heating to incipient fusion. The product is chemically inert. This material is employed for refractory purposes, such as brick and linings in open-hearth steel and electric furnaces and in copper converters. As a refractory substance, magnesia must not only resist corrosion but, in addition, must possess sufficient bonding to retain its form in the furnace. If iron oxide is present, it acts as a binder; if absent in the crude ore, it is added in the calcining process.

Magnesite, raw or calcined, is also used in the manufacture of magnesium sulphate, employed in medicine and in the textile industries; magnesium chloride, for making Sorel cement; and magnesium bisulphite, for disintegrating wood and dissolving the noncellulose matter in the manufacture of wood-pulp paper. The basic carbonate known as *magnesia alba* is used in fire-retarding paint and as a nonconductor of heat in coverings for steam pipes. Natural brines and bitters also furnish considerable chloride and sulphate of magnesium.

The use of metallic magnesium is increasing rapidly, especially in airplane and motor construction. New uses are being constantly developed in the general fields of portable equipment and reciprocating- and rotating-machine parts. The metal makes good castings, machines well, and is about one-third lighter than aluminum and from two to four times as strong. Alloys of magnesium with zinc and aluminum can readily be prepared. The latter is known as *magnalium*. The 7-foot spherical gondola used in the Settle-Fordney stratosphere flight was constructed from a magnesium alloy, the shell being fabricated from plates ⅛ inch thick joined by welding. Metallic magnesium is also used for scavenging alloys (removing oxygen and nitrogen) and for military illumination in the form of shrapnel trailers, star bombs, and flare lights.

Almost the entire domestic consumption of primary magnesium has been supplied since 1927 by the Dow Chemical Company, by electrolysis of fused magnesium chloride derived from salt wells near Midland, Michigan.

The domestic production of magnesite is obtained mainly from California and Washington and amounts to about 175,000 short tons.

Dolomite.—The less expensive dolomite may be substituted for many of the uses given for magnesite above. This is true especially in the preparation of basic magnesium carbonate used as sheet and pipe covering and magnesium bisulphite used in paper manufacture. Likewise the quantity of dead-burned dolomite used for refractory materials exceeds the quantity of dead-burned magnesite. Dolomite is also an important source of carbon dioxide. About 1,600,000 short tons of crude dolomite are sold for these purposes annually.

Talc and Soapstone.—Talc and soapstone are, as a rule, not found together. Vermont and New York are the leading talc-producing states, furnishing nearly 80 per cent. of the total domestic output, which amounts to about 200,000 short tons annually. The bulk of this material is used as a white filler in the manufacture of paper. For this purpose, talc is replacing, to some extent, china clay and English chalk. It has been shown that 15 to 20 per cent. of talc imparts to ceramic products improved physical properties and greater resistance to thermal shock. Accordingly, it is an important ingredient of electric stove plates, gas-stove back walls, radiants, and saggers. Talc when used in the manufacture of wall tile and semivitreous bodies reduces crazing and warping. Talc is also used for foundry facing and in paints, lubricants, roofing papers, rubber goods, toilet powders, and as a water-proofing agent in concrete. Almost the entire supply of soapstone in the United States is obtained from Nelson and Albemarle counties, Virginia. This material is largely employed in the manufacture of laundry tubs, laboratory table tops, sinks, chemical hoods, firebrick, griddles, acid tanks, switchboards, insulators, furnace linings, and so forth.

MANGANESE

PYROLUSITE, 273	MnO_2	Tetragonal
MANGANITE, 282	$Mn_2O_3.H_2O$	Orthorhombic
RHODOCHROSITE, 287	$MnCO_3$	Hexagonal
Hausmannite, 303	Mn_2MnO_4	Tetragonal
Psilomelane, 303	MnO,BaO,H_2O, etc.	Unknown
Huebnerite, 311	$MnWO_4$	Monoclinic
WOLFRAMITE, 311	$(Fe,Mn)WO_4$	Monoclinic
FRANKLINITE, 321	$(Fe,Mn,Zn)(FeO_2)_2$	Cubic
COLUMBITE, 326	$(Fe,Mn)[(Cb,Ta)O_3]_2$	Orthorhombic
SPESSARTITE, 351	$Mn_3Al_2(SiO_4)_3$	Cubic
RHODONITE, 368	$Mn_2(SiO_3)_2$	Triclinic

Only the oxide and carbonate are the important ores of manganese. The economic demand for manganese is due largely to the importance of its alloys, especially *ferromanganese* and *spiegeleisen*. It is estimated that 14 pounds of manganese, in the form of an alloy, are added to every ton of steel produced. Ferromanganese contains 78 to 82 per cent. manganese and is used in making open-hearth steel, while spiegeleisen consists of from 18 to 22 per cent. manganese and finds employment in the Bessemer process. The role of manganese is to improve the rolling and forging qualities, to produce a harder steel, and to act at the same time as a deoxidizing and desulphurizing agent. Manganese is also used in special bronzes.

The oxide MnO_2 finds employment in the manufacture of chlorine and bromine. It is also used as a drier in paints and varnishes, to color glass and pottery, and in making flint glass and dry batteries. For dry batteries, the ore should contain at least 80 per cent. MnO_2, less than 1 per cent. iron, and under 0.05 per cent. of copper, nickel, or cobalt.

The four sources of manganese are (1) manganese ores, which should contain not less than 35 per cent. manganese and less than 8 per cent. silica, 6 per cent. iron, and 0.15 per cent. phosphorus; (2) manganiferous iron ores, which contain from 5 to 35 per cent. manganese; (3) manganiferous silver ores, which are used largely as a flux in smelting precious and semiprecious metals; and (4) manganiferous zinc residues, which are smelted to spiegeleisen.

The domestic production of manganese ores is by no means equal to the demand, and importations from Russia, Brazil, India, Cuba, and from the Gold Coast of West Africa are absolutely necessary. Normally, the United States uses about 50,000 long tons of manganese ore, or about one-third of the world's consumption, and depends upon foreign sources for nearly 90 per cent. of this amount.

MERCURY

CINNABAR, 256   HgS   Hexagonal

Cinnabar is the chief source of mercury. In normal times, 30 to 40 per cent. of the domestic production of mercury is used in the manufacture of mercuric fulminate for explosive caps, one flask of 76 pounds making 100 to 120 pounds of detonator. Mercury is also employed in the extraction of gold and silver by amalgamation and in scientific and electrical apparatus. The chloride (calomel) is used for medicinal purposes, and the sulphide (vermilion) and the red oxide as pigments. Antifouling paints for ship bottoms are made of the oxide of mercury, which the chlorides in the sea water convert into mercuric chloride, which serves as an effective poison.

The average content of mercury recovered from the domestic ores is only 0.5 per cent. which is less than that obtained from the ores of

Italy (0.7 per cent.) or Spain (6 per cent.).   The domestic production of mercury amounts to about 20,000 flasks of 76 pounds each, while the consumption is about 40,000 flasks.   California is the most important source in the United States, with smaller amounts coming from Nevada, Oregon, Arizona, Washington, Texas, and Arkansas.

MOLYBDENUM

Molybdenite, 250	MoS_2	Hexagonal
Wulfenite, 310	$PbMoO_4$	Tetragonal

The chief use of molybdenum is in the manufacture of special steels to increase their hardness and strength.   It is added in the form of calcium molybdate or as a ferro- or manganese-molybdenum alloy (50 to 75 per cent. molybdenum).   A nickel-molybdenum alloy is used in wire drawing.   A chrome-molybdenum steel has been used rather extensively in automobile construction.   "Alloy 548" used for steel cutting tools contains about 30 per cent. Co, 19 W, 3 Mo, 2 V, low C, and the remainder Fe.   It is given a high-temperature heat treatment at 1275°C.   Several alloys of molybdenum, titanium, and nickel carbides have been prepared for special cutting tools and the use of molybdenum boride, carbide, nitride, or silicide in percussion drills has also been proposed.   Molybdenum is likewise used for grids, plates, and reflectors in vacuum and X-ray tubes, and for windings in electric furnaces. Sodium and ammonium molybdates are employed to some extent in fireproofing fabrics and in dyeing leather, silk, and wool.   As a lubricant, molybdenite is preferable to graphite, especially for high-pressure work.

The United States is the largest producer of molybdenum concentrates in the world, the production being equivalent to about 2,500 short tons of metallic molybdenum.   The ore mined is of low grade (under 1 per cent. MoS_2); the chief deposits are in Colorado and New Mexico.

NICKEL

Niccolite, 253	NiAs	Hexagonal
Garnierite, 362	$H_2(Ni,Mg)SiO_4$	Unknown

To the above, nickeliferous pyrrhotite should be added.

The demand for nickel is due largely to the importance of its alloys. It is estimated that about 42 per cent. of the nickel consumption is used in the manufacture of ferrous alloys.   The addition of from 2 to 3.50 per cent. of nickel to steel increases both its elasticity and tensile strength.   Nickel is used, together with chromium, molybdenum, and vanadium, in many types of special steels employed for structural purposes.   *Invar*, an alloy of iron containing 36 per cent. nickel, is not affected by temperature changes and is used for scientific instruments, pendulums, and steel tapes. Other important alloys are *coinage metal* (copper and nickel); *German silver* (55 per cent. copper, 27 per cent. zinc, and 18 per cent. nickel); *nichrome* (nickel and chromium) used as a substitute for platinum in electrical resistance, crucible triangles, and as heating elements in electric appliances; and *permalloy*, used as a medium for rapidly transmitting messages by cable. It contains 80 per cent. nickel and 20 per cent. iron. *Monel* is obtained by smelting the Sudbury ores without separating the metals and consists of 67 per cent. nickel, 28 per cent. copper, and 5 per cent. other metals, mostly iron and manganese. This alloy, which accounts for 30 per cent. of the nickel consumption, has a tensile strength equal to that of nickel steel and is very resistive to corrosive agents. It is used for propellers, acid pumps, valves on high-pressure steam lines, valve stems, pickling apparatus for sheet and tin plate, and laundry and kitchen equipment. Nickel also forms alloys with aluminum and zinc.

The world's production of new or primary nickel, which amounts to about 60,000 short tons of the metal, is obtained principally from the copper and nickel ores of Sudbury, Ontario (furnishing about 90 per cent.) and from the garnierite ores of New Caledonia (furnishing about 10 per cent.). No nickel ores are mined in the United States, although an equivalent of about 300 short tons of nickel is obtained annually as a by-product in the electrolytic refining of copper. The imports each year are mainly from Canada, chiefly in the form of ore, matté, alloys, and nickel oxide, and total about 20,000 short tons.

NIOBIUM   See Columbium

NITROGEN

SODA NITER, 290 $NaNO_3$ Hexagonal

While small quantities of sodium nitrate have been found in caves and disseminated through clays in several of the western states, no deposits that can be depended upon to produce considerable amounts have been discovered in this country. Sodium nitrate is obtained almost entirely from the arid regions of northern Chile. The crude ore, containing about 25 per cent. $NaNO_3$, yields after leaching with hot water a product of 95 per cent. purity. Synthetic nitrogen compounds are, however, gradually replacing a considerable quantity of the naturally occurring soda niter.

In normal times about 800,000 short tons of niter or Chile saltpeter are imported annually. This is used principally as a fertilizer to promote stalk growth in plants, and also in the manufacture of nitric and sulphuric acids.

PHOSPHORUS

Monazite, 325	$(Ce,La,Di)PO_4$	Monoclinic
APATITE, 326	$Ca_5F(PO_4)_3$	Hexagonal
PYROMORPHITE, 328	$Pb_5Cl(PO_4)_3$	Hexagonal
Wavellite, 328	$(AlOH)_3(PO_4)_2.5H_2O$	Orthorhombic
Turquois, 329	$H_5[Al(OH)_2]_6Cu(OH)(PO_4)_4$	Triclinic

Plant life requires soluble phosphates, and an impure amorphous calcium carbonate-phosphate (collophanite), known as *phosphate rock*, a

FIG. 808.—Cars loaded with crude sodium nitrate (caliche). Maria Refinery, Nitrate Field, Chile.

variety of apatite, furnishes the raw material to supply this need. By treating the raw ground rock with approximately an equal weight of sulphuric acid, a superphosphate is formed which is readily assimilated by plants. When briquets composed of phosphate rock and pulverized coal are smelted with coke and silica gravel in a blast furnace, ferrophosphorus, elemental phosphorus, anhydrous phosphorus pentoxide, and liquid phosphoric acid are produced. Trisodium phosphate is made from the ferrophosphorus.

Under normal conditions, the United States produces annually about 4,000,000 long tons of phosphate rock. Of this amount Florida furnishes about 80 per cent. Tennessee is also a producer. Enormous deposits of phosphate rock have been located in the western states, particularly in Idaho, Utah, Wyoming, and Montana, but the production thus far from these western localities is small. In recent years, the total production of phosphate rock from the French North African countries of Tunisia,

Morocco, and Algeria has equalled or exceeded that of the United States.

PLATINUM

NATIVE PLATINUM, 239	Pt	Cubic
Sperrylite, 259	$PtAs_2$	Cubic

Of the various members of the platinum group, platinum, palladium, and iridium are the chief ones of commercial importance at present.

Some of the important uses of platinum are as a catalytic agent in the manufacture of sulphuric, acetic, and nitric acids. Because of its high fusibility and resistance to acids, platinum is in great demand in the manufacture of chemical, physical, and electrical apparatus. It is also employed in certain parts of the ignition systems of internal-combustion engines. Platinum is also used for electric furnace windings for temperatures up to 2600°F. and as pins in dental work. The jewelry trade likewise consumes large amounts, estimated at over 50 per cent. of the total platinum used in this country. As iridium imparts hardness to platinum, the so-called platinum used in electrical work and by jewelers is an alloy of platinum, iridium (10–15 per cent.), tantalum, and palladium. Palladium finds employment in dental alloys to replace gold, and as palladium leaf is silver white in color, but nontarnishable, it is used in jewelry and for decorative effects. *Palau* (80 per cent. gold and 20 per cent. palladium) is marketed as a substitute for platinum in chemical ware. Platinum with 10 per cent. rhodium is used for thermocouples. The high price of platinum has greatly stimulated research for suitable substitutes, and alloys of palladium with gold and silver, tungsten, and molybdenum have, in certain instances, replaced the more expensive metal.

The disintegration of basic magnesium rocks, such as peridotite, dunite, hornblendite, and pyroxenite, containing disseminated platinum, has frequently resulted in the concentration of the metal in platinum placers. The world's production of platinum comes largely from Canada, Colombia, Russia, and South Africa.

The United States produces a very small amount of the platinum consumed. About 300 troy ounces of platinum are recovered annually, mainly from the placers in Alaska, California, and Oregon. In addition, about 8,000 troy ounces of refined metals of the platinum group are obtained as by-products in the refining of domestic copper matte and gold bullion. A considerable amount of secondary platinum (146,000 troy ounces) is also recovered from the refining of scrap and sweeps. The imports of platinum in the United States are about 160,000 troy ounces yearly. It is estimated that the world's known workable deposits of platinum could supply an annual production of about 250,000 troy ounces of new platinum and 70,000 troy ounces of palladium.

POTASSIUM

ALUNITE, 313	$K_2(Al.2OH)_6(SO_4)_4$	Hexagonal
MICAS, 354	$KAl_2(OH)_2AlSi_3O_{10}$, etc.	Monoclinic
ORTHOCLASE, 372	$KAlSi_3O_8$	Monoclinic
MICROCLINE, 375	$KAlSi_3O_8$	Triclinic
NEPHELITE, 380	$(Na,K)_8Al_8Si_9O_{34}$	Hexagonal
LEUCITE, 382	$KAl(SiO_3)_2$	Orthorhombic
APOPHYLLITE, 385	$KFCa_4(Si_2O_5)_4.8H_2O$	Tetragonal

Potassium chloride and sulphate are used in large quantities as fertilizers. Other potassium salts are also quite essential in certain industries. Thus, caustic potash is used in the manufacture of the better grades of

Fig. 809.—Potash-salt mine.   Stassfurt, Germany.

soap; the hydrated carbonate in cut glass, optical glass, and incandescent light bulbs; the chlorate in matches; the nitrate in black powders; the bichromate in dyeing and tanning; the cyanide as a solvent in extracting gold from ores; the ferricyanide in photography. Medicinal and other chemical uses also demand varying amounts of potassium salts.

The present production in the United States, which amounts to the equivalent of about 40,000 short tons of K_2O, constitutes about 40 per cent. of the domestic requirements. The domestic sources are from natural brines in California, from flue dust of cement kilns, and from the waste from molasses distillation. Alunite and "green sand" (glauconite) are other possible sources of potash. Core drillings in western Texas and southeastern New Mexico have revealed at depths from 800 to 2000 feet beds of potash minerals—polyhalite, sylvite, langbeinite, kainite. These deposits are at present very important sources of potash.

France and Germany are, at present, the chief sources for imported potash salts, although Spain and Russia are also large potential producers. The importation annually from these countries amounts to the equivalent of about 170,000 short tons of K_2O, over 90 per cent. of which is used in agriculture.

SILICON

QUARTZ, 267	SiO_2	Hexagonal
OPAL, 280	$SiO_2.nH_2O$	Amorphous

Silicon is also an essential constituent of all silicates.

The greatest demand for quartz comes from the building trade. The value of sandstone (including quartzite) sold in the United States in normal years is about $12,000,000, which represents about 7 per cent. of the total value of all stone sold each year. The three leading states which contribute nearly 70 per cent. of the total value of sandstone are Ohio, Pennsylvania, and New York.

SILVER

NATIVE SILVER, 243	Ag	Cubic
Argentite, 255	Ag_2S	Pseudocubic
Proustite, 262	Ag_3AsS_3	Hexagonal
Pyrargyrite, 263	Ag_3SbS_3	Hexagonal
Cerargyrite, 287	$AgCl$	Cubic

About 80 per cent. of the silver is obtained as a by-product from gold, nickel, copper, lead, and zinc ores.

FIG. 810.—View of Cobalt, Ontario, with mill of Cobalt Reduction Company in the foreground.

The four most important sources of silver in the United States which furnish annually about 98 per cent. of this country's total output are dry or siliceous ores (20 per cent.), copper ores (30 per cent.), lead ores (22 per cent.), and lead-zinc ores (26 per cent.).

Siliceous ores are those consisting mainly of quartz with small amounts of gold and silver. Some of the chief deposits of this type are at Tonopah, Nevada; the Tintic district, Utah; San Juan, Leadville, and Aspen, Colorado; Granite, Jefferson, and Silver Bow counties, Montana; and California. The important silver-bearing copper ores are found at Butte, Montana; in the Bingham and Tintic districts, Utah; and at Bisbee and Jerome, Arizona. Deposits of argentiferous galena are mined in the Cœur d'Alene district, Idaho; the Park City and Tintic districts, Utah; and at Aspen and Leadville, Colorado.

Silver used as coinage contains 90 per cent. silver and 10 per cent. copper, while *sterling silver* has 92.5 per cent. silver and 7.5 per cent. copper. Silver is also used in electroplating tableware and other articles that have as a base either nickel, brass, or britannia metal (tin, antimony, copper, and zinc). Silver is likewise employed in alloys for jewelry and dental purposes. *Dental amalgam* consists of an alloy of silver and tin with small amounts of copper and zinc in a powder form. When used, the powder is mixed with mercury. Silver salts find employment in photography and in chemistry.

The normal domestic production is about 65,000,000 troy ounces. The following six states are important producers: Idaho, Utah, Montana, Arizona, Nevada, and Colorado.

SODIUM

HALITE, 285	$NaCl$	Cubic
CRYOLITE, 288	Na_3AlF_6	Monoclinic
SODA NITER, 290	$NaNO_3$	Hexagonal
Pectolite, 367	$HNaCa_2(SiO_3)_3$	Triclinic
ALBITE and PLAGIOCLASES, 376	$NaAlSi_3O_8$, etc.	Triclinic
NEPHELITE, 380	$(Na,K)_8Al_8Si_9O_{34}$	Hexagonal
Cancrinite, 380	$3NaAlSiO_4.CaCO_3$	Hexagonal
Sodalite, 381	$3NaAlSiO_4.NaCl$	Cubic
Lazurite, 381	$3NaAlSiO_4.Na_2S$	Cubic
SCAPOLITE, 383	$Ca_4Al_6Si_6O_{24}CO_3$, etc.	Tetragonal
Natrolite, 386	$Na_2Al_2Si_3O_{10}.2H_2O$	Orthorhombic
ANALCITE, 387	$NaAlSi_2O_6.H_2O$	Cubic
STILBITE, 387	$(Ca,Na_2)Al_2Si_8O_{16}.6H_2O$	Monoclinic

Halite or salt, as produced in this country, is of two types, either rock salt or brine salt. Rock salt often occurs in beds of great thickness and is mined by means of shafts. The annual output of rock salt is about 2,000,000 short tons. Brine salt may be made from natural or artificial brines. In the majority of cases, fresh water is forced through drill holes to the salt beds and the artificial brine then pumped to the surface. The salt is obtained by the evaporation of the brine by either solar or vacuum-pan processes. Other chemical products produced from the brine include salt cake, soda ash, caustic soda, sodium bicarbonate, sodium acetate, sodium chlorate, sodium phosphate, Glauber's salt, calcium chloride, bromine, potassium and sodium bromides, ethylene dibromide, iodine, chlorine, and hydrochloric acid.

The United States furnishes practically all the salt consumed in this country, and the supply seems inexhaustible. The domestic production

Fig. 811.—Mining rock salt at 1131 feet below the surface. Detroit, Michigan. The salt layer is 30 feet thick.

amounts to about 8,000,000 short tons (equivalent to 60,000,000 barrels of 280 pounds). Although 15 states report a production, the five leading producers are:

	Short Tons
Michigan	2,000,000
New York	2,000,000
Ohio	1,400,000
Kansas	800,000
Louisiana	500,000

STRONTIUM

STRONTIANITE, 300	$SrCO_3$	Orthorhombic
CELESTITE, 306	$SrSO_4$	Orthorhombic

The principal source of supply is in Great Britain, from which both the United States and continental Europe import almost the entire tonnage required. Strontium chemicals and ore imported in the United States total about 2500 tons annually. The carbonate is the more valuable ore, as it can be easily converted into the various salts, but the sulphate is more abundant. Strontium salts are used in pyrotechnics, for the recovery of sugar in beet-sugar refineries, and in medicine.

SULPHUR

NATIVE SULPHUR, 236	S	Orthorhombic
PYRITE, 257	FeS$_2$	Cubic
MARCASITE, 259	FeS$_2$	Orthorhombic

Sulphur is also an essential constituent of sulphides and sulphates.

Deposits of native sulphur in Matagorda, Fort Bend, Wharton, and Brazoria counties, Texas, and Iberia and Plaquemines parishes, Louisiana, furnish about 99 per cent. of the entire output of this country. Occurrences of minor importance are known in Wyoming, Utah, Nevada, California, Colorado, and Oregon. The annual production of sulphur is about 2,200,000 long tons. At present, the bulk of the sulphur employed in the manufacture of sulphuric acid is obtained from the

Fig. 812.—Loading sulphur.   Texas Gulf Sulphur Company, Gulf, Texas.

native element, the balance coming from pyrite and from copper- and zinc-bearing sulphides, which are burned to sulphur dioxide. The domestic production of pyrite is about 300,000 long tons, while about 400,000 tons are imported annually, mainly from Spain. In the manufacture of paper, it is estimated that ⅛ ton of sulphur is used for each ton of sulphite pulp produced.

The production of sulphuric acid calculated to a strength of 50°Bé. (62.18 per cent. H$_2$SO$_4$) is about 8,000,000 tons annually. The acid is used largely in the manufacture of fertilizers, sulphate of ammonia, and alum, in the steel industry (for pickling purposes), for the purification of petroleum, and in the manufacture of explosives, rayon and textiles, coal-tar products, paints and pigments.

TANTALUM   See Columbium

Columbite (Tantalite), 326 (Fe,Mn)[(Cb,Ta)O$_3$]$_2$ Orthorhombic

TIN

CASSITERITE, 272 SnO_2 Tetragonal

The United States is the world's leading consumer of tin, owing largely to its canning and automobile industries. While cassiterite, which is the only source of tin, is rather widely distributed, only in a few places are the occurrences of the mineral of commercial importance. The production of cassiterite in the United States is insignificant, although approximately the equivalent of 30,000 long tons of secondary tin are recovered annually from tin-plate clippings, tin-bearing alloys, and melting pot drosses. The consumption, on the other hand, in terms of the metal is approximately 80,000 tons annually, over 70 per cent. of which is used for tin plate, solder, and in babbitt and other bearing metals. Tin plate is made by coating steel sheets with pure tin. One pound of tin will make ordinarily 220 square feet of tin plate. *Terneplate* is similar to tin plate, except that an alloy of lead and tin is substituted for pure tin in the coating. *Taggers tin* is extra thin tin plate. The larger part of the tin plate and taggers tin is used for making food containers. Terneplate is used largely for roofing and for gasoline tanks on automobiles, and some is substituted for tin plate in nonfood-product containers.

Tin has the ability to strengthen and harden alloys and improves its castings. Pewter is essentially tin and lead; type metal—tin, antimony, and lead; solder—tin and lead; bronze—copper and tin; babbitt metal—tin 88.9 per cent., antimony 7.4 per cent., and copper 3.7 per cent. Deposits have been worked intermittently in Alaska, South Dakota, Texas, North Carolina, South Carolina, and California.

The world's chief sources of tin ore are the Malay States, Bolivia, Netherlands East Indies, China, Siam, Nigeria, Australia, and Cornwall, England. The world's production, if not restricted, amounts to about 190,000 tons of metallic tin.

TITANIUM

RUTILE, 272	TiO_2	Tetragonal
Ilmenite, 279	$FeTiO_3$	Hexagonal
Titanite, 384	$CaTiSiO_5$	Monoclinic

The demand for titanium is not very great. Rutile and ilmenite are both used in making *ferrotitanium* and *ferro-carbon-titanium*, which, when added to steel, serve as deoxidizing agents. They also increase the tensile strength of the steel. These alloys contain from 15 to 25 per cent. titanium. Rutile is likewise the source of titanium for *cuprotitanium* used in brass and other copper-bearing alloys. Titanium-aluminum bronze, which is extremely resistant to the action of sea water and chemical liquors, possesses physical properties equalling those of phosphor and manganese bronzes, although it is considerably lighter than either.

The oxide of titanium is used as an opacifier in enamel ware, also as a white pigment, as it is chemically inert, nontoxic, and possesses high covering power.

Paints containing titanium pigments wear down evenly without cracking or peeling. The greater part of the titanium pigment used is a composite pigment of TiO_2 (25 per cent.) and $BaSO_4$ (75 per cent.), known as *titanox*. Lithopone-titanium pigments are also on the market. Titanium oxide is likewise used for lacquer enamels and in the manufacture of rayon, rubber, glass, and certain types of light-weight paper of high opacity.

The Virginia mines and the beach deposits of Florida produce some rutile and ilmenite concentrates, which partially supply the limited demand for titanium. Imports of titanium ores are obtained from British India, Norway, and Brazil.

TUNGSTEN

Scheelite, 310	$CaWO_4$	Tetragonal
Huebnerite, 311	$MnWO_4$	Monoclinic
WOLFRAMITE, 311	$(Fe,Mn)WO_4$	Monoclinic
Ferberite, 312	$FeWO_4$	Monoclinic

While in other countries wolframite is the most important ore of tungsten, in the United States both scheelite and ferberite surpass it in importance. Over 90 per cent. of the tungsten mined is converted into ferro alloys and tungsten steels. American high-speed tool steels used for rapid cutting are capable of holding their temper at a red heat. They contain about 18 per cent. tungsten, 4.5 per cent. chromium, and 2 per cent. vanadium. In some cases, 3 to 5 per cent. of cobalt is also added. These steels are also used for armor plate and for projectiles. Tungsten alloys readily with many metals, and some of these alloys have been proposed as substitutes for platinum, particularly a tungsten-molybdenum alloy for dental work.

Metallic tungsten has an exceedingly high melting point (3370°C.) and finds employment as filaments in incandescent lights, in radio tubes, and as electrical contact points in automobile-engine timers. Manufacturers of tungsten lamp filaments usually introduce a small amount of thorium oxide into the metal. This retards crystallization and assists in preventing the filaments from becoming brittle when heated. In radio tubes the presence of some thorium is likewise necessary for the emission of electrons in the proper functioning of the tubes.

The production of tungsten ores in the United States is equivalent to about 1200 short tons of concentrates containing 60 per cent. WO_3. The domestic production is obtained mainly from Mill City, Nevada, and the Atolia district, California. Smaller amounts are obtained from Boulder County, Colorado. The world's production of concentrates is about 16,000 short tons, and about one-half of this amount comes from China.

Other important foreign producers include Burma, the Federated Malay States, Bolivia, and Portugal.

URANIUM

Uraninite, 313	UO_3,UO_2,PbO, etc.	Cubic
Carnotite, 330	$K_2O.2UO_3.V_2O_5.3H_2O$	Orthorhombic

Alloys of uranium include *ferro-uranium* and *aluminum-uranium*. *Ferro-uranium* is used to a limited extent in high-speed steel, while *aluminum-uranium* finds employment in nonferrous metals. In special steels, a small percentage of uranium may be substituted for tungsten, while in nonferrous alloys, uranium is beneficial because of its deoxidizing properties. Uranium compounds are employed to some extent in coloring glass yellow with a green reflex; in photography; in the ceramic industry to impart yellow, brown, gray, and velvety tints; and as a mordant for silk and wool. Radium is frequently recovered from uranium minerals. The amount present, however, is extremely small, about $\frac{1}{3}$ mg. of radium in 1 kg. (2.2046 pounds) of uranium. The chief uses of radium are in therapeutics (treatment of cancer and other diseases) and as an illuminant. When used as an illuminant, the radium salt is usually mixed with artificial zinc sulphide and some cementing material, such as amyl acetate. The alpha rays given off by the radium salt strike the particles of zinc sulphide and cause them to glow. Radium is also used for the detection of flaws in steel. By placing a tube containing radium on one side of the metal and a photographic plate on the opposite side, flaws are revealed on the developed plate by differences in exposure.

Carnotite from southwestern Colorado and southeastern Utah is the chief domestic source of uranium compounds, but the production is small. Rich deposits of pitchblende (uraninite) and of the numerous uranium minerals formed from its decomposition are found in Katanga, Belgian Congo. Likewise, important uraninite deposits are being worked in the Great Bear Lake region, Mackenzie district, Canada.

VANADIUM

Vanadinite, 328	$Pb_5Cl(VO_4)_3$	Hexagonal
Carnotite, 330	$K_2O.2UO_3.V_2O_5.3H_2O$	Orthorhombic
Roscoelite, 355	$H_8K_2(Mg,Fe)(Al,V)_4(SiO_3)_2$	Monoclinic

The most important use of vanadium is in the manufacture of special steels, because it removes the objectionable elements oxygen and nitrogen. The small amount of vanadium remaining in the steel increases its toughness, tensile strength, and resistance to shock. Vanadium steel is extensively used for locomotive and automobile cylinders, pistons, and bushings, and also for high-speed tools (see Tungsten), die blocks, and so forth. Because of their strength and toughness, vanadium bronzes are suitable for trolley wheels and bronze gears. Vanadium compounds are employed in ceramics to produce a golden glaze; in the preparation of indelible ink; and for fixing aniline black on silk.

Formerly the world's chief supply of vanadium was the sulphide *patronite*, which occurred only at Minasragra, Peru. The patronite has now all been mined, and the present vanadium ore is largely a mixture of hydrous calcium vanadates and the hydrous sulphate. One important domestic source of the metal and its compounds is the vanadium mica, *roscoelite*. Roscoelite occurs in the vicinity of Rifle, Placerville, and Vanadium, Colorado, where it occurs in small bands in, and disseminated throughout, a greenish sandstone. Substantial amounts of vanadium are also obtained from carnotite and vanadinite.

ZINC

SPHALERITE, 251	ZnS	Cubic
Zincite, 274	ZnO	Hexagonal
SMITHSONITE, 296	$ZnCO_3$	Hexagonal
FRANKLINITE, 321	$(Fe,Mn,Zn)(FeO_2)_2$	Cubic
HEMIMORPHITE, 337	$H_2Zn_2SiO_5$	Orthorhombic
Willemite, 347	Zn_2SiO_4	Hexagonal

The United States produces about one-third of all the zinc used in the world. In normal times, about 50 per cent. of the spelter (zinc) output is used for galvanizing, 30 per cent. in making brass, 10 per cent. is rolled into sheet zinc, 6 per cent. is used for die castings, and 4 per cent. for all other purposes. It is estimated that the average automobile contains 25 to 30 pounds of zinc in the form of die castings and rolled zinc. Zinc dust is used for precipitating gold from cyanide solutions, and some of the zinc compounds are employed as pigments. The four white pigments involving the use of zinc are zinc oxide (zinc white), leaded zinc oxide, zinc-lead oxide, and lithopone. Lithopone is a mixture obtained by chemical precipitation of zinc sulphide (28 to 30 per cent.) and barium sulphate. Zinc oxide is also used in the manufacture of a number of rubber products, such as gutta-percha, inner tubes, rubber footwear, fire hose, and conveyor belting.

The chief zinc-producing districts in the United States are:

District	Approximate Per Cent. of Total Production
Joplin (Missouri, Kansas, Oklahoma)..........	50
Franklin Furnace (New Jersey)...............	12
Butte (Montana)............................	10
Mississippi Valley (Wisconsin, Illinois).........	5
Leadville (Colorado) ⎫	
Coeur d'Alene (Idaho) ⎬.....................	15
Bingham (Utah) ⎭	
Tennessee and Virginia.....................	5

The domestic production of zinc is about 600,000 short tons annually.

ZIRCONIUM

ZIRCON, 348 $ZrSiO_4$ Tetragonal

The uses of zirconium and its compounds are very limited.   By the addition of small amounts of zirconium to steels, brass, and copper, it is claimed sound castings are secured and their strength and resistance to acids increased.   *Cooperite* is an alloy of zirconium and nickel and is very resistant to acids and alkalies.   It is also recommended for use in the manufacture of machine and cast tools.   As its heat conductivity is higher than for other high-speed metals, the cutting efficiency is increased. Cooperite is claimed to be self-hardening, and no tempering is necessary. The oxide *zirconia* glows intensely when heated and, therefore, has been used for coating the lime and magnesia pencils used in the Drummond or "lime" light.   The filaments of the Nernst lamp consisted mainly of zirconia with variable amounts of yttria, erbia, thoria, and ceria.   The oxide is used as an opacifier in enamel ware, as a permanent white pigment not affected by acids or alkalies, as a polishing powder, as an insulator for heat and electricity, and for refractory purposes.

One source is the oxide *baddeleyite* found in Minas Geraes, Brazil. The zircon in the sands along the east coast of Florida is concentrated by Wilfley tables and magnetic separators.   This is the only domestic source of zirconium.

GLOSSARY

This glossary contains all the important terms used in the descriptive and determinative portions of the book. See the Index for page references to other terms.

Acicular—needle-like.

Acute—sharply pointed.

Adamantine luster—like that of the diamond, or oiled glass.

Aggregate—mass, cluster, group.

Alkaline taste—like that of soda.

Allochromatic—having a color which is not an inherent property of the mineral, but due to pigments, inclusions, or other impurities, hence, variable.

Alluvial—relating to deposits made by flowing water.

Amorphous—devoid of crystallinity.

Amygdaloid—igneous rock containing small cavities, which are filled entirely, or in part, with minerals of secondary origin.

Arborescent—branching, tree-like.

Argillaceous—clay-like odor.

Asterism—star-like effect seen in either transmitted or reflected light.

Astringent taste—causing contraction or puckering.

Basal—parallel to the basal pinacoid.

Basalt—basic igneous rock, dark and compact.

Bipyramid—two pyramids placed base to base.

Bisphenoid—four-sided form of the tetragonal system, each face being an isosceles triangle.

Bituminous odor—due to the presence of bitumen or other organic matter.

Bladed—elongated and flattened, like a knife blade.

Botryoidal—closely united spherical masses, resembling a bunch of grapes.

Brachypinacoid—form with two faces in the orthorhombic or triclinic systems, parallel to the brachy (a) and vertical axes.

Brittle—crumbles under knife or hammer, cannot be cut into slices.

Capillary—hair- or thread-like.

Carbonatization—formation of carbonates; also termed *carbonation*.

Cellular—porous, like a sponge.

Chatoyant—having a changeable, undulating, or wavy color or luster.

Clastic—made up of fragments.

Clay—fine, soft, aluminous sediments that are plastic.

Cleavable—capable of splitting in definite directions.

Cleavage—property of many crystalline substances of breaking or splitting in definite directions, yielding more or less smooth surfaces.

Clinopinacoid—form with two faces in the monoclinic system, parallel to the clino (a) and vertical axes.

Columnar—long thick fibers, often parallelly grouped.

Compact—closely or firmly united.

Complex crystals—highly modified, having many crystal forms or faces.

Concentric—spherical layers about a common center, similar to layers of an onion.

Conchoidal—curved, shell-like.

Concretion—rounded mass formed by accumulation about a center.

439

Concretionary—formed as a concretion.

Conglomerate—sedimentary rock, composed of rounded fragments, coarse or fine.

Contact mineral—formed under the influence of an igneous intrusion.

Crested—tabular crystals arranged in ridges.

Cruciform—in the form of a cross, cross shaped.

Cryptocrystalline—finely crystalline, revealed only under the microscope.

Crystal—substance bounded, entirely or partially, by natural plane surfaces.

Crystalline—having crystal structure, with or without definite geometrical form.

Crystallization—process of solidification in the form of well-developed crystals, or in crystalline masses.

Crystallography—study of crystal forms and properties.

Cyclic—repeated twinning, yielding circular forms.

Decrepitate—to snap and break into fine powder when heated.

Dendritic—branching, fern-like.

Dichroism—property of exhibiting different colors by transmitted light when viewed in two perpendicular directions.

Dike—an igneous intrusion filling a fissure.

Disseminated—scattered through a substance.

Dodecahedral—pertaining to the rhombic dodecahedron, a form with 12 faces in the cubic system.

Domatic—relating to a dome, a horizontal prism.

Drusy—rough surface due to a large number of small, closely crowded crystals.

Ductile—capable of being drawn into wire. Ductile substances are also malleable and sectile.

Dull luster—not bright or shiny.

Earthy—without luster, dull.

Efflorescence—thin crust or coating, often powdery.

Elastic—resumes original position after bending.

Enantiomorphous—forms related to one another as is the right hand to the left; hence, not superimposable.

Eruptive rock—formed by the solidification of a surface flow of molten rock. Often used as a synonym of igneous.

Etched—corroded.

Felted—fibers closely matted.

Ferruginous—containing iron.

Fetid—emitting an offensive odor.

Fibrous—consisting of slender fibers or filaments.

Fissure—crack or crevice.

Flexible—capable of bending without breaking, and does not resume original position when the force is removed.

Fluorescence—property of emitting light during exposures to electrical discharges, or while being heated.

Folia—having the form of thin plates or leaves.

Foliated—in plates or leaves which separate easily.

Fracture—refers to surface obtained when breaking in a direction other than parallel to cleavage or parting.

Friable—easily crumbled or reduced to powder.

Furrowed—deeply striated, grooved.

Gangue—associates of more valuable minerals or ores.

Garlic—odor observed when arsenic minerals are heated.

Geode—cavity lined or completely filled with minerals, often well crystallized.

Globular—spherical or nearly so.

Gneiss—laminated or foliated metamorphic rock consisting usually of quartz, feldspar, and mica.

Granite—coarsely crystalline igneous rock, consisting usually of quartz, feldspar (orthoclase), and mica or hornblende.

Granodiorite—coarsely crystalline igneous rock, intermediate in composition between granite and quartz diorite.

Granular—consisting of closely packed grains, either coarse or fine.

Guano—excrement of sea fowl.

Habit—development or form of crystals.

Hackly—rough surface, covered with sharp points.

Hardness—resistance offered to abrasion or scratching.

Hemimorphic—having different planes about the two ends of a crystallographic axis.

Hexoctahedron—form of the cubic system having 48 faces.

Hopper shaped—cavernous and tapering, square funnel shaped.

Hydration—combining chemically with water.

Hygroscopic—property of absorbing moisture from the atmosphere.

Idiochromatic—minerals with a constant color, an inherent property.

Igneous rock—one formed by the solidification of a molten mass from within the earth.

Impregnated—finely disseminated and intimately mixed with rock.

Impressed—marked by pressure, indented.

Inclusion—foreign material enclosed within a mineral.

Incrustation—crust or coating on another substance.

Inelastic—not elastic.

Interlaced
Interwoven } interwined, confused.

Iridescence—showing play of colors, usually due to thin film or coating.

Isochromatic—lines or sections possessing the same color.

Kimberlite—altered, very basic igneous rock, consisting essentially of serpentine, olivine, augite, pyrope; sometimes diamond bearing.

Lamellæ
Laminæ } small, thin plates or layers, curved or straight.

Lamellar—consisting of lamellæ or laminæ.

Lava—molten rock, especially surface flows; also applied to the solidified product.

Lenticular—lens shaped.

Limestone—rock composed essentially of calcium carbonate, calcite.

Luster—manner in which the surface reflects light.

Macropinacoid—form with two faces in the orthorhombic or triclinic systems, parallel to the macro (*b*) and vertical axes.

Macroscopic—visible to the unaided eye, opposed to microscopic.

Malleable—capable of being flattened by hammering.

Mammillary—rounded mass, larger than that of a grape.

Marble—recrystallized limestone or dolomite; may also include other limestones susceptible to a polish, and serpentine.

Massive—without definite crystal form; either crystalline or amorphous.

Meager—rough touch.

Metallic luster—simulating a metal and exhibited by minerals which are opaque, or nearly so, and quite heavy.

Metalloidal—having the appearance of a metal.

Metamorphic rock—one that has been altered by heat, pressure, liquids, or gases, so as to render its texture either crystalline or schistose.

Meteorite—mass of stone or iron which has fallen to the earth from outer space.

Micaceous—composed of very thin plates or scales, like those of mica.

Mimicry—imitation of forms of a higher symmetry by those of lower grade of symmetry, usually the result of twinning.

Modified, highly—consisting of a large number of crystal forms or faces.

Monochromatic—homogeneous light of a definite wave length.

Mottled—spotted.

Multicolored—having many colors.

Neolithic—later stone age, that of smooth or polished stone implements.

Nodular
Nodule } rounded mass of irregular shape.

Nugget—rounded, irregular lump, especially of a metal.

Ocherous—earthy, and usually red, yellow, or brown in color.

Octahedral—pertaining to the octahedron, eight-sided form of the cubic system.

Oölitic—rounded particles the size of fish-eggs.

Opalescent—with milky or pearly reflections.

Opaque—will not transmit light even through thin layers or edges.

Ore—a mineral deposit of economic importance.

Orthopinacoid—form with two faces in the monoclinic system, parallel to the ortho (*b*) and vertical axes.

Oxidation—combining chemically with oxygen.

Paleolithic—earlier stone age, that of rough stone implements.

Parameters—linear intercepts of a crystal face on the crystallographic axes.

Parting—false cleavage, usually the result of twinning.

Pearly—similar to the luster of mother of pearl.

Peat—dark-brown to black substance, formed by the partial decomposition of vegetable tissue in marshes.

Pegmatite—very coarse grained acid igneous rock, consisting essentially of quartz, feldspar, and mica.

Peridotite—very basic igneous rock, composed largely of olivine and augite or hornblende.

Phanerocrystalline—crystals or coarsely crystalline.

Phonolite—compact extrusive rock, consisting essentially of orthoclase, nephelite, and pyroxene.

Phosphorescence—property of emitting light after exposure to electrical discharges or after being heated.

Pinacoidal—relating to forms with two planes, parallel to two or more crystallographic axes.

Pisolitic—composed of small, rounded masses, the size of peas.

Plastic—capable of being molded or shaped.

Plates—broad, relatively thin masses.

Plumose—feathery.

Pocket—cavity in a rock, often filled with minerals.

Polar—a dissimilar arrangement of forms about the ends of an axis of symmetry.

Polysynthetic—consisting of thin lamellæ due to repeated twinning.

Prismatic—elongated parallel to one of the crystallographic axes, usually the vertical axis.

Pseudo—false.

Pseudomorph
Pseudomorphous } possessing the geometrical form of another mineral.

Pungent—sharp, biting.

Pyramidal—pertaining to the pyramid, a form which usually intersects three crystallographic axes.

Pyritohedron—form of the cubic system with 12 five-sided faces.

Rectangular—intersecting at 90°.

Reduction—loss of oxygen chemically.

Refraction, double—yielding two refracted rays.

Reniform—large, rounded masses, kidney shaped.

Resinous—luster of resin.

Reticulated—fibers crossing like a net.

Rhombic—diamond shaped.

Rhombohedral—relating to the rhombohedron, a form of the hexagonal system, with six faces intersecting at angles other than 90°.

Rosette—simulating a rose.

Saline—salty.

Sandstone—sedimentary rock consisting of consolidated sand.

Scalenohedral—relating to the scalenohedron, a 12-sided form of the hexagonal system, each face being a scalene triangle.

Scaly—consisting of scales.

Schiller—peculiar bronze-like luster.

Schist—metamorphic rock with foliated or parallel structure, splitting easily along certain planes.

Seam—narrow vein.

Sectile—capable of having slices cut off.

Semiopaque—between opaque and transparent.

Shale—laminated sedimentary rock, consisting of hardened muds, silts, or clays.

Sheaf-like—resembling a sheaf of wheat.

Silky—luster of silk, due to fibrous structure.

Skeletal—pertaining to crystals with incomplete development of their faces, often with cavernous appearance.

Slate—dense, fine-grained metamorphic rock, which splits easily into broad, thin layers or sheets.

Splendent—very bright by reflected light.

Splintery—breaking into splinters.

Stalactitic—cylindrical or conical masses resembling icicles.

Stalky—consisting of long, stout fibers.

Stellate—radiating from a center producing star-like forms.

Streak—color of fine powder, usually obtained by rubbing the mineral on unglazed porcelain.

Subadamantine—imperfectly adamantine.

Subconchoidal—imperfectly conchoidal.

Sublimation—direct solidification from a vapor.

Submetallic—imperfectly metallic.

Syenite—granular igneous rock, commonly consisting of orthoclase, and hornblende or biotite.

Tabular—flat, tablet-like.

Tarnish—thin film formed on the surface when exposed to air and different in color from that of the fresh fracture.

Terminations—faces on the end of a crystal.

Tetragonal trisoctahedron—form of the cubic system with 24 trapezohedral faces.

Tetrahedral—pertaining to the tetrahedron, a four-sided form of the cubic system.

Tetrahexahedron—form of the cubic system with 24 triangular faces.

Tough—not easily broken.

Translucent—when light passes through, but objects cannot be seen distinctly.

Transparency—refers to the amount of light passing through a substance.

Transparent—when sufficient light passes through the substance so that objects may be distinctly seen.

Trap—dark, basic, fine-grained igneous rock.

Trichroism—property of exhibiting different colors by transmitted light when viewed in three perpendicular directions.

Trillings—intergrowth of three crystals in a symmetrical manner.

Twinned—crystals consisting of more than one individual, arranged in a definite manner.

Twins—symmetrical intergrowth of two crystals.

Variegated—with different colors.

Vein—crack or fissure, partially or completely filled with mineral matter.

Vitreous luster—like that of glass.

Vug—a term sometimes used for geode.

Warty—small, rounded masses resembling warts.

Waxy—luster of wax.

Zonal—in zones or layers.

TABULAR CLASSIFICATION SHOWING ELEMENTS OF SYMMETRY AND THE SIMPLE FORMS OF THE 32 CLASSES OF CRYSTALS

The use of the elements of symmetry in the classification of crystals is discussed on pages 17 to 20.

(Pages 446 to 452)

Tabular Classification Showing the Elements of Symmetry and the Simple Forms of the Thirty-Two Classes of Crystals

1. Cubic System

Class	Planes Axial	Planes Diagonal	Axes ■	Axes ▲	Axes ●	Center	a:a:a {111}	a:a:∞a {110}	a:∞a:∞a {100}	a:a:ma {hhl}	a:ma:ma {hll}	a:ma:∞a {hk0}	a:na:ma {hkl}	Representative
1. Hexoctahedral (*Holohedrism*)[1]	3	6	3	4	6	1	Octahedron (8)[2]	Rhombic Dodecahedron (12)	Hexahedron (6)	Trigonal Trisoctahedrons (24)	Tetragonal Trisoctahedrons (24)	Tetrahexahedrons (24)	Hexoctahedrons (48)	Galena PbS
2. Hextetrahedral (*Tetrahedral Hemihedrism*)	—	6	3	4 (Polar)	3	—	(±) Tetrahedrons (4)	Rhombic Dodecahedron (12)	Hexahedron (6)	(±) Tetragonal Tristetrahedrons (12)	(±) Trigonal Tristetrahedrons (12)	Tetrahexahedrons (24)	(±) Hextetrahedrons (24)	Tetrahedrite Cu₃SbS₃
3. Dyakisdodecahedral (*Pyritohedral Hemihedrism*)	3	—	—	4	3	1	Octahedron (8)	Rhombic Dodecahedron (12)	Hexahedron (6)	Trigonal Trisoctahedrons (24)	Tetragonal Trisoctahedrons (24)	(±) Pyritohedrons (12)	(±) Dyakisdodecahedrons (24)	Pyrite FeS₂
4. Pentagonal Icositetrahedral (*Plagihedral Hemihedrism*)	—	—	3	4	6	—	Octahedron (8)	Rhombic Dodecahedron (12)	Hexahedron (6)	Trigonal Trisoctahedrons (24)	Tetragonal Trisoctahedrons (24)	Tetrahexahedrons (24)	(r, l) Pentagonal Icositetrahedrons (24)	Sal Ammoniac NH₄Cl
5. Tetrahedral Pentagonal Dodecahedral (*Tetartohedrism*)	—	—	—	4 (Polar)	3	—	(±) Tetrahedrons (4)	Rhombic Dodecahedron (12)	Hexahedron (6)	(±) Tetragonal Tristetrahedrons (12)	(±) Trigonal Tristetrahedrons (12)	(±) Pyritohedrons (12)	(± r, ± l) Tetrahedral Pentagonal Dodecahedrons (12)	Sodium Bromate NaBrO₃

[1] Although the older ideas of holohedrism and hemihedrism have not been used in the development of crystallographic forms (pages 8 to 88), for the sake of completeness, however, these older terms are also given in this classification of the thirty-two classes of symmetry.

[2] The figures after the names of the forms indicate the number of faces they possess.

446

Class	Planes Horizontal Axial	Planes Vertical Axial	Planes Intermediate	Axes Vertical	Axes Horizontal	Center	$o: \infty a:a:a$ {10ī1}	$2a:2a:a:mc$ {hh2hl}	$na:pa:a:mc$ {hkil}	$a: \infty a:\infty a:\infty c$ {10ī0}	$2a:2a:a:\infty c$ {11ī0}	$na:pa:a:\infty c$ {hki0}	$\infty a:\infty a:\infty a:c$ {0001}	Representative
6. Dihexagonal Bipyramidal (*Holohedrism*)	1	3	3	1	3+3	1	Hexagonal Bipyramids First order (12)	Hexagonal Bipyramids Second order (12)	Dihexagonal Bipyramids (24)	Hexagonal Prism First order (6)	Hexagonal Prism Second order (6)	Dihexagonal Prisms (12)	Basal Pinacoid (2)	Beryl $Be_3Al_2(SiO_3)_6$
7. Dihexagonal Pyramidal (*Holohedrism with Hemimorphism*)	—	3	3	1 (*Polar*)	—	—	(u, l) Hexagonal Pyramids First order (6)	(u, l) Hexagonal Pyramids Second order (6)	(u, l) Dihexagonal Pyramids (12)	Hexagonal Prism First order (6)	Hexagonal Prism Second order (6)	Dihexagonal Prisms (12)	(u, l) Basal Pinacoids (1)	Zincite ZnO
8. Ditrigonal Bipyramidal (*Trigonal Hemihedrism*)	1	—	3	1	3 (*Polar*)	—	(±) Trigonal Bipyramids First order (6)	Hexagonal Bipyramids Second order (12)	(±) Ditrigonal Bipyramids (12)	(±) Trigonal Prisms First order (3)	Hexagonal Prism Second order (6)	(±) Ditrigonal Prisms (6)	Basal Pinacoid (2)	Benitoite $BaTiSi_3O_9$
9. Ditrigonal Scalenohedral (*Rhombohedral Hemihedrism*)	—	3	—	1	3	1	(±) Rhombohedrons First order (6)	Hexagonal Bipyramids Second order (12)	(±) Scalenohedrons (12)	Hexagonal Prism First order (6)	Hexagonal Prism Second order (6)	Dihexagonal Prisms (12)	Basal Pinacoid (2)	Calcite $CaCO_3$
10. Hexagonal Bipyramidal (*Pyramidal Hemihedrism*)	1	—	—	1	—	1	Hexagonal Bipyramids First order (12)	Hexagonal Bipyramids Second order (12)	(±) Hexagonal Bipyramids Third order (12)	Hexagonal Prism First order (6)	Hexagonal Prism Second order (6)	(±) Hexagonal Prisms Third order (6)	Basal Pinacoid (2)	Apatite $Ca_5F(PO_4)_3$
11. Hexagonal Trapezohedral (*Trapezohedral Hemihedrism*)	—	—	—	1	3+3	—	Hexagonal Bipyramids First order (12)	Hexagonal Bipyramids Second order (12)	(r, l) Hexagonal Trapezohedrons (12)	Hexagonal Prism First order (6)	Hexagonal Prism Second order (6)	Dihexagonal Prisms (12)	Basal Pinacoid (2)	β Quartz SiO_2

2. Hexagonal System (*Continued*)

Class	Planes: Horizontal Axial	Planes: Vertical Axial	Planes: Intermediate	Axes: Vertical ⬡	Axes: Vertical ▲	Axes: Horizontal ●	Center	{10\bar11} $a:\infty a:a:mc$	{hh2hl} $2a:2a:a:mc$	{hkil} $na:pa:a:mc$	{10\bar10} $a:\infty a:a:\infty c$	{11\bar20} $2a:2a:a:\infty c$	{hki0} $na:pa:a:\infty c$	{0001} $\infty a:\infty a:\infty a:c$	Representative
12. Ditrigonal Pyramidal [*Trigonal Hemihedrism with Hemimorphism*]	–	–	3	–	1 (*Polar*)	–	–	(±u, ±l) Trigonal Pyramids First order (6)	(u, l) Hexagonal Pyramids Second order (6)	(±u, ±l) Ditrigonal Pyramids (6)	(±) Trigonal Prisms First order (3)	Hexagonal Prism Second order (6)	(±) Ditrigonal Prisms (6)	(u, l) Basal Pinacoids (1)	Tourmaline $M_2B_2Si_4O_{21}$
13. Hexagonal Pyramidal [*Pyramidal Hemihedrism with Hemimorphism*]	–	–	–	1 (*Polar*)	–	–	–	(u, l) Hexagonal Pyramids First order (6)	(u, l) Hexagonal Pyramids Second order (6)	(±u, ±l) Hexagonal Pyramids Third order (6)	Hexagonal Prism First order (6)	Hexagonal Prism Second order (6)	(±) Hexagonal Prisms Third order (6)	(u, l) Basal Pinacoids (1)	Nephelite $(Na,K)_8Al_8Si_9O_{34}$
14. Trigonal Bipyramidal [*Trigonal Tetartohedrism*]	1	–	–	–	1	–	–	(±) Trigonal Bipyramids First order (6)	(±) Trigonal Bipyramids Second order (6)	(±r, ±l) Trigonal Bipyramids Third order (6)	(±) Trigonal Prisms First order (6)	(±) Trigonal Prisms Second order (3)	(±r, ±l) Trigonal Prisms Third order (3)	Basal Pinacoid (2)	Disilverortho-phosphate Ag_2HPO_4
15. Trigonal Trapezohedral [*Trapezohedral Tetartohedrism*]	–	–	–	–	1	3 (*Polar*)	–	(±) Rhombohedrons First order (6)	(±) Trigonal Bipyramids Second order (6)	(±r, ±l) Trigonal Trapezohedrons (6)	(±) Hexagonal Prism First order (6)	(±) Trigonal Prisms Second order (3)	(±) Ditrigonal Prisms (6)	Basal Pinacoid (2)	α Quartz SiO_2
16. Trigonal Rhombohedral [*Rhombohedral Tetartohedrism*]	–	–	–	–	1	–	1	(±) Rhombohedrons First order (6)	(±) Rhombohedrons Second order (6)	(±r, ±l) Rhombohedrons Third order (6)	Hexagonal Prism First order (6)	Hexagonal Prism Second order (6)	(±r, ±l) Hexagonal Prisms Third order (6)	Basal Pinacoid (2)	Dioptase H_2CuSiO_4
17. Trigonal Pyramidal (*Ogdohedrism*)	–	–	–	–	1 (*Polar*)	–	–	(±u, ±l) Trigonal Pyramids First order (3)	(±u, ±l) Trigonal Pyramids Second order (3)	[±r, u; ±l, u; ±l, u] Trigonal Pyramids Third order (3)	(±) Trigonal Prisms First order (3)	(±) Trigonal Prisms Second order (3)	(±r, ±l) Trigonal Prisms Third order (3)	(u, l) Basal Pinacoids (1)	Sodium Periodate $NaIO_4 + 3H_2O$

Class	Planes Horizontal Axial	Planes Vertical Axial	Planes Intermediate	Axes ■	Axes ●	Center	$a:a:mc$ {hkl}	$a:\infty a:mc$ {h0l}	$a:\infty a:mc$ {hkl}	$a:a:\infty c$ {110}	$a:\infty a:\infty c$ {100}	$a:\infty a:\infty c$ {hk0}	$c:\infty a:\infty a$ {001}	Representative
18. **Ditetragonal Bipyramidal** (*Holohedrism*)	1	2	2	1	2+2	1	Tetragonal Bipyramids First order (8)	Tetragonal Bipyramids Second order (8)	Ditetragonal Bipyramids (16)	Tetragonal Prism First order (4)	Tetragonal Prism Second order (4)	Ditetragonal Prisms (8)	Basal Pinacoid (2)	Cassiterite SnO_2
19. **Ditetragonal Pyramidal** [*Holohedrism with Hemimorphism*]	—	2	2	1 (Polar)	—	—	(u, l) Tetragonal Pyramids First order (4)	(u, l) Tetragonal Pyramids Second order (4)	(u, l) Ditetragonal Pyramids (8)	Tetragonal Prism First order (4)	Tetragonal Prism Second order (4)	Ditetragonal Prisms (8)	(u, l) Basal Pinacoids (1)	Silver Fluoride $AgF + H_2O$
20. **Tetragonal Scalenohedral** [*Sphenoidal Hemihedrism*]	—	—	2	—	1+2	—	(±) Tetragonal Bisphenoids First order (4)	(±) Tetragonal Bipyramids Second order (8)	(±) Tetragonal Scalenohedrons (8)	Tetragonal Prism First order (4)	Tetragonal Prism Second order (4)	Ditetragonal Prisms (8)	Basal Pinacoid (2)	Chalcopyrite $CuFeS_2$
21. **Tetragonal Bipyramidal** [*Pyramidal Hemihedrism*]	1	—	—	1	1	1	Tetragonal Bipyramids First order (8)	Tetragonal Bipyramids Second order (8)	(±) Tetragonal Bipyramids Third order (8)	Tetragonal Prism First order (4)	Tetragonal Prism Second order (4)	(±) Tetragonal Prisms Third order (4)	Basal Pinacoid (2)	Scheelite $CaWO_4$
22. **Tetragonal Trapezohedral** [*Trapezohedral Hemihedrism*]	—	—	—	1	2+2	—	Tetragonal Bipyramids First order (8)	Tetragonal Bipyramids Second order (8)	(r, l) Tetragonal Trapezohedrons (8)	Tetragonal Prism First order (4)	Tetragonal Prism Second order (4)	Ditetragonal Prisms (8)	Basal Pinacoid (2)	Nickel Sulphate $NiSO_4 + 6H_2O$
23. **Tetragonal Pyramidal** [*Pyramidal Hemihedrism with Hemimorphism*]	—	—	—	1 (Polar)	—	—	(u, l) Tetragonal Pyramids First order (4)	(u, l) Tetragonal Pyramids Second order (4)	(± u, ± l) Tetragonal Pyramids Third order (4)	Tetragonal Prism First order (4)	Tetragonal Prism Second order (4)	(±) Tetragonal Prisms Third order (4)	(u, l) Basal Pinacoids (1)	Wulfenite $PbMoO_4$
24. **Tetragonal Bisphenoidal** (*Tetartohedrism*)	—	—	—	1*	—	—	(±) Tetragonal Bisphenoids First order (4)	(±) Tetragonal Bisphenoids Second order (4)	(± r, ± l) Tetragonal Bisphenoids Third order (4)	Tetragonal Prism First order (4)	Tetragonal Prism Second order (4)	(±) Tetragonal Prisms Third order (4)	Basal Pinacoid (2)	Calcium-aluminum Silicate $Ca_2Al_2SiO_7$

* Axis of rotary reflection

Class	Symmetry			Forms							Representative
	Planes / Axial	Axes	Center	$nd:b:mc$ {hkl}	$nd:b:\infty c$ {hk0}	$\infty d:b:mc$ {0kl}	$d:\infty b:mc$ {h0l}	$\infty d:b:\infty c$ {010}	$d:\infty b:\infty c$ {100}	$\infty d:\infty b:c$ {001}	
25. Orthorhombic Bipyramidal (*Holohedrism*)	1+1+1	1+1+1 ●	1	Bipyramids (8)	Prisms (4)	Brachydomes (4)	Macrodomes (4)	Brachypinacoid (2)	Macropinacoid (2)	Basal Pinacoid (2)	Barite BaSO$_4$
26. Orthorhombic Pyramidal (*Holohedrism with Hemimorphism*)	1+1	1 (*Polar*)	–	(u, l) Pyramids (4)	Prisms (4)	(u, l) Brachydomes (2)	(u, l) Macrodomes (2)	Brachypinacoid (2)	Macropinacoid (2)	(u, l) Basal Pinacoids (1)	Calamine Zn$_2$H$_2$SiO$_5$
27. Orthorhombic Bisphenoidal (*Hemihedrism*)	–	1+1+1	–	(r, l) Bisphenoids (4)	Prisms (4)	Brachydomes (4)	Macrodomes (4)	Brachypinacoid (2)	Macropinacoid (2)	Basal Pinacoid (2)	Epsomite MgSO$_4$+7H$_2$O

5. Monoclinic System.

Class	Symmetry			Forms							Representative
	Plane	Axis	Center	$n\dot{a}:\dot{b}:m\dot{c}$ {hkl}	$n\dot{a}:\dot{b}:\infty\dot{c}$ {hk0}	$\infty\dot{a}:\dot{b}:m\dot{c}$ {0kl}	$\dot{a}:\infty\dot{b}:m\dot{c}$ {h0l}	$\infty\dot{a}:\dot{b}:\infty\dot{c}$ {010}	$\dot{a}:\infty\dot{b}:\infty\dot{c}$ {100}	$\infty\dot{a};\infty\dot{b}:\dot{c}$ {001}	
28. **Monoclinic Prismatic** (*Holohedrism*)	1	1	1	(±) **Hemi-bipyramids** (4)	Prisms (4)	Clinodomes (4)	(±) Hemi-orthodomes (2)	Clinopinacoid (2)	Orthopinacoid (2)	Basal Pinacoid (2)	Gypsum $CaSO_4 + 2H_2O$
29. **Monoclinic Domatic** (*Hemihedrism*)	1	–	–	(±u, ±l) **Tetarto-bipyramids** (2)	(f, r) Hemi-prisms (2)	(u, l) Hemi-clinodomes (2)	(±u, ±l) Tetarto-orthodomes (1)	Clinopinacoid (2)	(f, r) Orthopinacoids (1)	(u, l) Basal Pinacoids (1)	Tetrathionate of Potassium $K_2S_4O_6$
30. **Monoclinic Sphenoidal** (*Hemimorphism*)	–	1 (*Polar*)	–	(±r, ±l) **Tetarto-bipyramids** (*Sphenoids*) (2)	(r, l) Hemi-prisms (2)	(r, l) Hemi-clinodomes (2)	(±) Hemi-orthodomes (2)	(r, l) Clinopinacoids (1)	Orthopinacoid (2)	Basal Pinacoid (2)	Tartaric Acid $C_4H_6O_6$

451

6. TRICLINIC SYSTEM

Class	Symmetry			Forms							Representative
	Plane	Axis	Center	$n\dot{a}:\dot{b}:m\dot{c}$ {hkl}	$n\dot{a}:\dot{b}:\infty\dot{c}$ {hk0}	$\infty\dot{a}:\dot{b}:m\dot{c}$ {0kl}	$\dot{a}:\infty\dot{b}:m\dot{c}$ {h0l}	$\infty\dot{a}:\dot{b}:\infty\dot{c}$ {010}	$\dot{a}:\infty\dot{b}:\infty\dot{c}$ {100}	$\infty\dot{a}:\infty\dot{b}:\dot{c}$ {001}	
31. Triclinic Pinacoidal (*Holohedrism*)	–	–	1	$\left(\dfrac{u}{l}r, \dfrac{u}{l}l\right)$ Tetarto-bipyramids (2)	(r, l) Hemi-prisms (2)	(r, l) Hemi-brachydomes (2)	(u, l) Hemi-macrodomes (2)	Brachy-pinacoid (2)	Macro-pinacoid (2)	Basal Pinacoid (2)	Albite NaAlSi$_3$O$_8$
32. Triclinic Asymmetric (*Hemihedrism*)	–	–	–	$\left.\begin{array}{l}\dfrac{u}{l}r,\ f\\[2pt]\dfrac{u}{l}l,\ f\\[2pt]\dfrac{u}{l}r,\ r\\[2pt]\dfrac{u}{l}l,\ r\end{array}\right\}$ Ogdo-bipyramids (1)	$\left(\dfrac{r}{l}f, \dfrac{r}{l}r\right)$ Tetarto-prisms (1)	$\left(\dfrac{u}{l}r, \dfrac{u}{l}l\right)$ Tetarto-brachydomes (1)	$\left(\dfrac{u}{l}f, \dfrac{u}{l}r\right)$ Tetarto-macrodomes (1)	(l, r) Brachy-pinacoids (1)	(f, r) Macro-pinacoids (1)	(u, l) Basal Pinacoids (1)	Strontium bitartrate Sr(C$_4$H$_4$O$_6$H)$_2$ + 4H$_2$O

TABLES FOR THE DETERMINATION OF THE 150 MINERALS DESCRIBED IN THIS TEXT BY MEANS OF THEIR PHYSICAL PROPERTIES, OCCURRENCES, AND ASSOCIATES

(Pages 454 to 621)

DIRECTIONS FOR USING THE TABLES

These tables for the determination of minerals depend largely upon the use of those physical properties that are easily, rapidly, and accurately recognizable at sight. As luster and color can be determined at first glance, they are made the basis of the tables. Thus, the minerals are divided into two large groups depending upon whether they possess a metallic or nonmetallic luster. Minerals with metalloidal or submetallic lusters are listed in both divisions. Each of these groups is then subdivided according to color, the other property readily recognized at first glance. There are also further subgroupings according to streak, and then according to increasing hardness. Within each of the latter smaller subdivisions the minerals are listed with reference to increasing specific gravity.

To illustrate the use of the tables let us assume that we have a specimen of magnetite. As the luster is metallic and the color black, the mineral falls into group 1, page 454. The streak is then determined and is found to be black. Consequently it is placed in the second subdivision under streak. The hardness is next tested and found to be 6. Accordingly, reference should be made to page 472, where the minerals with metallic luster, black color and streak, and hardness over 3 are listed with concise descriptions. The hardness column is now followed until values of 6 or thereabouts are encountered. At this point it becomes necessary to determine the various other properties, such as crystallization, structure, transparency, cleavage, fracture, tenacity, and specific gravity, as well as the general characteristics and associates. A comparison of these observations with the descriptions of the various minerals with a hardness of approximately 6 should lead readily to an accurate determination.

Color of mineral	Streak	Hardness	Page
1. **Dark gray or black**........	White, gray, green, red, brown, or yellow	1 to 3	**456**
		3 to 6	**458**
		Over 6	**464**
	Black......................	1 to 3	**468**
		Over 3	**472**
2. **Metallic white or light metallic gray**	Metallic white or steel gray....	1 to 6	**476**
	Black......................	1 to 3	**476**
		Over 3	**478**
3. **Yellow**.................	Brown or yellow..............	1 to 6	**480**
	Black......................	Over 3	**480**
4. **Brass, bronze, or copper red**	Gray, red, or yellow...........	1 to 3	**482**
	Black......................	Over 3	**482**
5. **Red, brown, or blue**.......	White, gray, green, red, brown, or yellow	1 to 3	**486**
		3 to 6	**488**
		Over 6	**492**
	Black......................	1 to 6	**494**

B. MINERALS WITH NON-METALLIC LUSTER

Color of mineral	Streak	Hardness	Page
1. Dark gray or black........	Green, red, brown, yellow, or black	1 to 6	**496**
		Over 6	**500**
	Uncolored, white, or light gray.	1 to 3	**502**
		3 to 6	**504**
		Over 6	**506**
2. Pink, red, or red violet....	Red, brown, or yellow.........	1 to 3	**512**
		Over 3	**514**
	Uncolored, white, or light gray.	1 to 3	**518**
		3 to 6	**520**
		Over 6	**526**
3. Green, blue, or blue violet.	Blue, green, brown, or yellow...	1 to 6	**534**
	Uncolored, white, or light gray.	1 to 3	**538**
		3 to 6	**542**
		Over 6	**552**
4. Yellow or brown.........	Red, brown, or yellow.........	1 to 3	**560**
		Over 3	**562**
	Uncolored, white, or light gray.	1 to 3	**566**
		3 to 6	**572**
		Over 6	**582**
5. Colorless, white, or light gray	Uncolored, white, or light gray.	1 to 3	**590**
		3 to 6	**598**
		Over 6	**612**

Streak—White, gray, green, red, brown, or yellow

Name, Composition, and Reference	Crystallization Structure Crystals = C Massive = M	Luster Transparency	Color
CHLORITE (Prochlorite, clinochlorite) $H_8Mg_5Al_2Si_3O_{18}$	Monoclinic C—Tabular, six-sided, often bent and twisted M—Foliated, scaly, granular, earthy	Dull Submetallic Translucent to opaque	Black Greenish black
358[1]			
HEMATITE, variety *Specular iron ore* Fe_2O_3	Hexagonal C—Thin tabular, often in parallel position M—Scaly, micaceous, platy, foliated	Metallic Splendent Opaque to translucent	Iron black Dark steel gray
276			
BIOTITE (Black mica) $K(Mg,Fe)_3(OH)_2AlSi_3O_{10}$	Monoclinic C—Tabular, with hexagonal or rhombohedral habit M—Plates, disseminated scales	Submetallic Pearly Opaque to transparent	Black Brownish black Greenish black
357			
Pyrargyrite Ag_3SbS_3	Hexagonal C—Small, complex, hemimorphic, rare M—Compact, disseminated, bands, crusts	Metallic Adamantine Opaque to transparent	Dark lead gray
263			
SILVER Ag	Cubic C—Small, often distorted M—Grains, scales, plates, twisted hair- or wire-like forms	Metallic Opaque	Dark gray to black after exposure, otherwise silver white
243			

[1] Page reference for description of mineral.

Hardness 1 to 3

Hardness	Streak	Cleavage = C Fracture = F Tenacity	Specific Gravity	Characteristics and Associates
1. 2.5	Pale green	C—Basal, perfect; when foliated, conspicuous F—Scaly, earthy Tough to brittle	2.6 3.	Laminæ are flexible but inelastic, with slightly soapy feel. Common in schists and serpentine. With magnetite, garnet, diopside, magnesite. Often as a scaly or dusty coating on other minerals. Pseudomorphous after garnet.
2. 3.	Cherry red Reddish brown	C—None, but distinct parting F—Uneven Brittle to elastic	4.9 5.3	Bright, shiny scales, often loosely compact; foliated or micaceous masses. In metamorphic rocks or as sublimation p r o d u c t around volcanoes.
2.5 3.	White Grayish	C—Basal, perfect, conspicuous Tough, laminæ of fresh biotite very elastic	2.7 3.2	Easily recognized by structure, highly perfect cleavage, and elasticity. Important constituent of many igneous and metamorphic rocks—granite, syenite, gneiss.
2.5 3.	Cherry red Purplish red	C—Imperfect F—Conchoidal Brittle	5.8	Frequently as gray or dark red bands, known as *dark ruby silver ore*. With proustite; in veins with other silver minerals and galena.
2.5 3.	Silver white Light lead gray	C—None F—Hackly Malleable, ductile	10. 12.	Color and streak darken on exposure. With silver, lead, arsenic, cobalt, and nickel minerals—argentite, pyrargyrite, proustite, galena, smaltite; also fluorite, calcite, barite.

Streak—White, gray, green, red, brown, or yellow

Name, Composition, and Reference	Crystallization Structure Crystals = C Massive = M	Luster Transparency	Color
TETRAHEDRITE Cu_3SbS_3 264	Cubic C—Tetrahedral, often highly modified M—Granular, compact	Metallic Opaque	Dark steel gray Iron black
Uraninite (Pitchblende) UO_3, UO_2, PbO, etc. 313	Cubic C—Octahedral, rare M—Botryoidal, columnar, curved lamellar; granular, compact; apparently amorphous.	Pitch-like Submetallic Dull Opaque	Pitch black Brownish black Greenish black
SIDERITE $FeCO_3$ 298	Hexagonal C—Rhombohedral, curved or saddle-shaped, common M—Cleavable, granular, compact, botryoidal, rarely fibrous	Metalloidal Dull Opaque to translucent	Brownish black Black
SPHALERITE (Black Jack) ZnS 251	Cubic C—Tetrahedral, common, often very complex M—Compact, cleavable, fine or coarse granular	Submetallic Resinous Opaque to translucent	Black Yellowish black Brownish black
MANGANITE $Mn_2O_3.H_2O$ 282	Ortborhombic C—Columnar, prismatic, vertically striated; often in groups or bundles M—Columnar, granular, stalactitic	Metallic Submetallic Opaque	Iron black Dark steel gray
TITANITE (Sphene) $CaTiSiO_5$ 384	Monoclinic C—Wedge- or envelope-shaped when disseminated, tabular or prismatic when attached M—Compact, lamellar	Submetallic Vitreous Opaque to translucent	Black Brownish black

Hardness 3 to 6

Hardness	Streak	Cleavage = C Fracture = F Tenacity	Specific Gravity	Characteristics and Associates
3. 4.	Reddish brown	C—Indistinct F—Uneven Brittle	4.3 5.4	Crystals have characteristic tetrahedral habit. Sometimes coated with chalcopyrite. With sphalerite, galena, bournonite, chalcopyrite, siderite.
3. 5.5	Dark brown Olive green	F—Conchoidal, uneven Brittle	4.8 9.7	Pitch-like appearance and fracture important. Fresh material is hard and heavy. With ores of lead, silver, and bismuth; also orthite.
3.5 4.	Yellowish brown	C—Rhombohedral, perfect, conspicuous F—Conchoidal Brittle	3.7 3.9	Distinguished from sphalerite by curved crystals and rhombohedral cleavage. In ore deposits; beds and concretions in limestones and shales. With pyrite, chalcopyrite, galena, tetrahedrite, cryolite.
3.5 4.	Dark brown Yellowish brown Grayish	C—Dodecahedral, perfect, usually conspicuous F—Conchoidal Brittle	3.9 4.2	Color and streak vary with impurities. Extensively in limestone. With galena, chalcopyrite, pyrite, barite, fluorite, siderite, rhodochrosite.
3.5 4.	Reddish brown Blackish brown	C—Brachypinacoidal, perfect F—Uneven Brittle	4.2 4.4	Alters easily to pyrolusite, hence, surface may give black streak. With other manganiferous minerals; also barite, calcite, siderite.
5. 5.5	White Gray	C—Prismatic F—Conchoidal Brittle	3.4 3.6	Generally in crystals. With feldspars, pyroxenes, amphiboles, chlorite, scapolite, zircon, apatite.

Streak—White, gray, green, red, brown, or yellow

Name, Composition, and Reference	Crystallization Structure Crystals = C Massive = M	Luster Transparency	Color
LIMONITE $Fe_2O_3.nH_2O$ 283	**C**—Always pseudo-morphs, commonly after pyrite, marca-site, siderite **M**—Compact, stalactitic, botryoidal, reniform; often with internal, radial fibrous structure	Metallic Dull Opaque	Black Brownish black
Hausmannite Mn_2MnO_4 303	Tetragonal **C**—Acute pyramidal, cyclic twins not un-common **M**—Granular, compact	Metallic Greasy Opaque	Black Brownish black
Huebnerite $MnWO_4$ 311	Monoclinic **C**—Long fibrous, bladed, stalky; often diver-gent, without good terminations **M**—Compact, lamellar, granular	Submetallic Resinous Translucent to opaque	Brownish black Black
WOLFRAMITE $(Fe,Mn)WO_4$ 311	Monoclinic **C**—Thick tabular, short columnar, often large **M**—Bladed, curved lam-ellar, granular	Submetallic Metallic Opaque	Dark gray Brownish black Iron black
Ferberite $FeWO_4$ 312	Monoclinic **C**—Wedge shaped, short prismatic, tabular **M**—Fan shaped aggre-gates, bladed, granu-lar, compact	Submetallic Splendent Opaque	Iron black Brownish black

Hardness 3 to 6

Hardness	Streak	Cleavage = C Fracture = F Tenacity	Specific Gravity	Characteristics and Associates
5. 5.5	Yellowish brown	F—Conchoidal, splintery Brittle	3.6 4.	Often with black varnish-like surface, passing into the soft, yellow earthy or ocherous variety. With pyrite, hematite, magnetite, siderite. Pseudomorphs after pyrite very common.
5. 5.5	Chestnut brown	C—Basal, perfect F—Uneven Brittle	4.7 4.8	Steep, horizontally striated, octahedral-like bipyramids and complex twins. With manganese minerals—pyrolusite, psilomelane, braunite; magnetite, barite, hematite.
5. 5.5	Yellowish brown Greenish gray	C—Clinopinacoidal, perfect, conspicuous. Brittle	6.7 7.3	Structure, cleavage, and specific gravity important. Compare wolframite. In quartz veins, with fluorite, pyrite, scheelite, galena, tetrahedrite.
5. 5.5	Dark red brown	C—Clinopinacoidal, perfect, conspicuous. F—Uneven Brittle	7.1 7.5	Distinguished from huebnerite by streak. Powder may be slightly magnetic. With cassiterite, quartz, mica, fluorite, apatite, scheelite, molybdenite, huebnerite, chalcopyrite.
5. 5.5	Dark brown	C—Clinopinacoidal, perfect. F— Uneven Brittle	7.5	In granites and pegmatites. With quartz, chalcopyrite, galena, scheelite.

Streak—White, gray, green, red, brown, or yellow

Name, Composition, and Reference	Crystallization Structure Crystals = C Massive = M	Luster Transparency	Color
HORNBLENDE (Amphibole) Silicate of Ca, Mg, Fe, Al, etc. 371	Monoclinic C—Long prismatic, prism angle 124°; often with rhombohedral-like terminations M—Bladed, fibrous, granular, compact	Submetallic Vitreous Opaque to translucent	Pitch black Greenish black Brownish black
AUGITE (Pyroxene) Silicate of Ca, Mg, Fe, Al, etc. 365	Monoclinic C—Short prismatic, thick columnar, prism angle 87° M—Compact, granular, disseminated	Submetallic Vitreous Opaque to translucent	Pitch black Greenish black Brownish black
Psilomelane MnO_2, BaO, H_2O, etc. 303	Amorphous ? M—Botryoidal, reniform, stalactitic; smooth surfaces	Metallic Dull Opaque	Iron black Bluish black Dark gray
Ilmenite (Menaccanite) $FeTiO_3$ 279	Hexagonal C—Thick tabular, rhombohedral M—Thin plates, granular, compact; disseminated grains; pebbles or sand	Metallic Submetallic Opaque	Iron black Brownish black
CHROMITE $(Fe,Cr) [(Cr,Fe)O_2]_2$ 322	Cubic C—Octahedral, rare M—Compact, granular, disseminated	Submetallic Pitchy Opaque	Iron black Brownish black
Orthite (Allanite) $Ca_2(Al,Ce,Fe)_2(Al OH)(SiO_4)_3$ 345	Monoclinic C—Tabular, rare M—Compact, granular, bladed, disseminated grains	Submetallic Greasy Opaque to translucent	Black Pitch black Brownish black

Hardness 3 to 6

Hard-ness	Streak	Cleavage = C Fracture = F Tenacity	Specific Gravity	Characteristics and Associates
5. 6.	Gray Grayish green Grayish brown Yellow	C—Prismatic, perfect, conspicuous—124° Brittle	2.9 3.3	Simple, pseudohexagonal crystals and cleavages at 56° and 124° important. Very common and in nearly all types of rocks. With calcite, feldspars, quartz, pyroxenes, chlorite.
5. 6.	Grayish green Gray	C—Prismatic, perfect, conspicuous—87° Brittle	3.2 3.6	Crystals usually eight-sided, more rarely four-sided. Pseudotetragonal, with prism angles of 87° and 93°. Cleavage less distinct than on hornblende. Common in basic eruptive rocks and crystalline limestones.
5. 6.	Dark brown Blackish brown	F—Conchoidal, uneven Brittle	3.7 4.7	Often with fine sooty coating of pyrolusite. With other manganese minerals; limonite, barite.
5. 6.	Dark brown Reddish brown	C—None, partings may be noted F—Conchoidal Brittle	4.3 5.5	Often slightly magnetic. With hematite, magnetite, apatite, serpentine, titanite, rutile. Common in black sands.
5.5	Dark brown Grayish brown	C—Octahedral, indistinct F—Uneven, conchoidal Brittle	4.3 4.6	May be slightly magnetic. Pitch-like appearance. With serpentine, talc, chrome garnet; also in black sands and platinum placers.
5.5 6.	Grayish Brownish gray Pale brown	C—Pinacoidal, indistinct F—Uneven, conchoidal Brittle	3. 4.	Often coated with yellowish or brownish alteration product. Disseminated in the more acid igneous rocks; also in limestones. With magnetite, epidote, quartz, feldspars.

Streak—White, gray, green, red, brown, or yellow

Name, Composition, and Reference	Crystallization Structure Crystals = C Massive = M	Luster Transparency	Color
HEMATITE, varieties *Specular iron ore* Fe_2O_3 *Compact* *Martite* *Argillaceous*	Hexagonal C—Pyramidal, tabular, rhombohedral M—Compact, granular, micaceous, columnar, radiated reniform or botryoidal	Metallic Dull Opaque	Iron black Reddish black Dark steel gray

276

FRANKLINITE $(Fe,Mn,Zn)(FeO_2)_2$	Cubic C—Octahedrons, alone or with dodecahedron; often with rounded edges M—Compact, granular, rounded grains	Metallic Dull Opaque	Iron black

321

Streak—White, gray, green, red, brown, or yellow

Name, Composition, and Reference	Crystallization Structure Crystals = C Massive = M	Luster Transparency	Color
HEMATITE, varieties *Specular iron ore* Fe_2O_3 *Compact* *Martite* *Argillaceous*	Hexagonal C—Pyramidal, tabular, rhombohedral M—Compact, granular, micaceous, columnar, radiated reniform or botryoidal	Metallic Dull Opaque	Iron black Reddish black Dark steel gray

276

FRANKLINITE $(Fe,Mn,Zn)(FeO_2)_2$	Cubic C—Octahedrons, alone or with dodecahedron; often with rounded edges M—Compact, granular, rounded grains	Metallic Dull Opaque	Iron black

321

Hardness 3 to 6

Hardness	Streak	Cleavage = C Fracture = F Tenacity	Specific Gravity	Characteristics and Associates
5.5 **6.**	Cherry red Reddish brown	C—None, parting sometimes noted F—Uneven Brittle	4.9 5.3	*Specular iron ore,* crystals or sparkling scales and grains, often with iridescent tarnish; *compact hematite,* fibrous, columnar, reniform; *martite,* octahedral crystals, pseudomorphous after magnetite; *argillaceous hematite,* impure from sand, clay, jasper.
5.5 **6.**	Reddish brown Dark brown	C—Octahedral, indistinct F—Conchoidal Brittle	5. 5.2	Powder frequently slightly magnetic. Distinguished by associates—willemite (yellow to green), zincite (red), rhodonite (flesh red), calcite.

Hardness over 6

Hardness	Streak	Cleavage = C Fracture = F Tenacity	Specific Gravity	Characteristics and Associates
6. **6.5**	Cherry red Reddish brown	C—None, parting sometimes noted F—Uneven Brittle	4.9 5.3	*Specular iron ore,* crystals or sparkling scales and grains, often with iridescent tarnish; *compact hematite,* fibrous, columnar, reniform; *martite,* octahedral crystals, pseudomorphous after magnetite; *argillaceous hematite,* impure from sand, clay, jasper.
6. **6.5**	Reddish brown Dark brown	C—Octahedral, indistinct F—Conchoidal Brittle	5. 5.2	Powder frequently slightly magnetic. Distinguished by associates—willemite (yellow to green), zincite (red), rhodonite (flesh red), calcite.

Streak—White, gray, green, red, brown, or yellow

Name, Composition, and Reference	Crystallization Structure Crystals = C Massive = M	Luster Transparency	Color
COLUMBITE (Tantalite) $(Fe,Mn)[(Cb,Ta)O_3]_2$ 326	Orthorhombic C—Short prismatic, tabular M—Compact, disseminated	Submetallic Greasy Dull Opaque	Iron black Brownish black
RUTILE TiO_2 272	Tetragonal C—Prismatic, vertically striated; twinned, yielding knee-shaped or rosette forms M—Compact, disseminated	Metallic Adamantine Opaque to translucent	Iron black Brownish black Reddish black
CASSITERITE, varieties *Ordinary* SnO_2 *Stream tin* 272	Tetragonal C—Thick prismatic, knee-shaped twins, common M—Compact, reniform, botryoidal, rounded pebbles	Submetallic Dull Translucent to opaque	Black Brownish black
GARNET, varieties *Andradite* $M_3''M_2'''(SiO_4)_3$ *Almandite* M'' = Ca,Fe,Mg M''' = Al,Fe 349	Cubic C—Dodecahedrons, tetragonal trisoctahedrons, alone or in combination, common M—Granular, compact, lamellar, disseminated, sand	Submetallic Translucent to opaque	Velvet black Brownish black

TOURMALINE, variety
       Schorl
$M'_{20}B_2Si_4O_{21}$
M' = Na,K,Li,Mg,
  Ca,(OH),Fe,
  Al
342
	Hexagonal
	C—Prismatic, vertically striated, terminated with broken or rhombohedral-like surfaces
	M—Compact, divergent columnar, disseminated
		Submetallic
		Pitchy
		Opaque
			Pitch black
			Brownish black
			Bluish black

Hardness over 6

Hardness	Streak	Cleavage = C Fracture = F Tenacity	Specific Gravity	Characteristics and Associates
6. **6.5**	Reddish brown Blackish brown	C—Pinacoidal, not conspicuous F—Conchoidal, uneven Brittle	5.4 6.4	Fracture surface sometimes iridescent. With beryl, tourmaline, spodumene, cryolite. Tantalum predominates in *tantalite*, and specific gravity may be as high as 8.
6. **7.**	Pale yellowish brown Gray	C—Prismatic, pyramidal, n o t conspicuous F—Uneven Brittle	4.2 4.3	Not as heavy as cassiterite. Sometimes in fine hairlike inclusions. Widely distributed. With quartz, feldspar, hematite, ilmenite, chlorite, apatite.
6. **7.**	Pale brown Pale yellow White	C—Prismatic, imperfect F—Uneven Brittle	6.8 7.	Distinguished by high specific gravity and hardness. In veins cutting granite, gneiss; also in alluvial deposits, as *stream tin*. With quartz, wolframite, scheelite, arsenopyrite, molybdenite, tourmaline, fluorite, apatite.
6.5 **7.5**	White	C—Dodecahedral, indistinct F—Conchoidal, uneven Brittle	3.8 4.2	*Andradite*, commonly with magnetite, epidote, feldspars, nephelite, leucite; *almandite*, with mica, staurolite, andalusite, cyanite, tourmaline.
7. **7.5**	White Gray	C—None F—Conchoidal, uneven Brittle	2.9 3.2	Spherical triangular cross-section and hemimorphic development important. In pegmatites; metamorphic rocks; alluvial deposits. With quartz, feldspar, cassiterite, beryl, topaz, fluorite.

Streak—White, gray, green, red, brown, or yellow

Name, Composition, and Reference	Crystallization Structure Crystals = C Massive = M	Luster Transparency	Color
CORUNDUM, variety *Emery* Al_2O_3 with Fe_3O_4, Fe_2O_3, SiO_2	Hexagonal **M**—Fine to coarse granular	Metallic Dull Opaque	Dark gray Black

275

Name, Composition, and Reference	Crystallization Structure Crystals = C Massive = M	Luster Transparency	Color
SPINEL, varieties *Pleonaste* *Hercynite* $M''(M'''O_2)_2$ *Gahnite* $M'' = Mg, Fe,$ *Picotite* Zn, Mn $M''' = Al, Fe$	Cubic **C**—Octahedral, well developed, common **M**—Compact, granular, disseminated grains; sand	Submetallic Dull Nearly opaque	Black Brownish black Greenish black

319

Streak—Black

Name, Composition, and Reference	Crystallization Structure Crystals = C Massive = M	Luster Transparency	Color
Molybdenite MoS_2	Hexagonal **C**—Tabular, rare **M**—Disseminated grains, scales, foliated	Metallic Opaque	Bluish lead gray

250

Name, Composition, and Reference	Crystallization Structure Crystals = C Massive = M	Luster Transparency	Color
GRAPHITE (Plumbago, black lead) C	Hexagonal **C**—Tabular, rare **M**—Foliated, scaly, granular, earthy	Metallic Dull Opaque	Dark steel gray Iron black

235

Hardness over 6

Hard-ness	Streak	Cleavage = C Fracture = F Tenacity	Specific Gravity	Characteristics and Associates
7. 9.	Yellowish brown Blackish brown	C—Indistinct F—Uneven Brittle to tough	3.7 4.3	Corundum mixed with magnetite, h e m a t i t e, quartz. Resembles iron ore, powder may be magnetic. Properties vary with composition. With mica, amphiboles, chlorite, spinel; in crystalline limestones, schists, peridotite.
7.5 8.	Grayish Grayish green Pale-brown White	C—Octahedral, indistinct F—Conchoidal Brittle	3.6 4.4	Common contact mineral in granular limestones; in igneous rocks, especially the basic olivine-bearing types; rounded grains in placers. With calcite, chondrodite, serpentine, brucite, olivine, corundum, graphite, pyroxenes.

Hardness 1 to 3

Hard-ness	Streak	Cleavage = C Fracture = F Tenacity	Specific Gravity	Characteristics and Associates
1. 1.5	Dark lead gray; greenish on glazed porcelain (graphite, shiny black)	C—Basal, perfect Sectile, lamellæ are flexible	4.7 4.8	Marks paper. Soft and greasy like graphite, but heavier a n d l i g h t e r colored. In granite with cassiterite, wolframite; also in crystalline limestone.
1. 2.	Black, shiny Dark silver gray	C—Basal, perfect Sectile, lamellæ are flexible	1.9 2.3	Greasy feel; marks paper; darker than molybdenite and not as heavy. In crystalline limestone with garnet, spinel, pyroxenes, amphiboles; also in shale, gneiss, and mica schist.

Streak—Black

Name, Composition, and Reference	Crystallization Structure Crystals = C Massive = M	Luster Transparency	Color
PYROLUSITE MnO_2 273	Orthorhombic ? C—Often pseudomorphous after manganite M—Columnar, fibrous, acicular, often divergent; dendritic; powdery	Metallic Dull Opaque	Iron black Dark steel gray
STIBNITE Sb_2S_3 249	Orthorhombic C—Prismatic, b e n t, twisted, c o m m o n M—Fibrous, b l a d e d, columnar, granular	Metallic Opaque	Dark lead gray Black
Argentite (Silver glance) Ag_2S 255	Pseudocubic C—Octahedral, cubical, often distorted M—Compact, arborescent; coatings	Metallic Opaque	Dark lead gray Black
GALENA (Galenite) PbS 254	Cubic C—Cubes alone, or with octahedron, well developed, common M—Granular, cleavable aggregates, compact	Metallic Opaque	Dark lead gray
CHALCOCITE Cu_2S 255	Orthorhombic C—Tabular, pseudohexagonal, d e e p l y striated M—Granular, compact, disseminated	Metallic Opaque	D a r k l e a d gray, often t a r n i s h e d dull b l a c k, blue, or green
Bournonite (Cog-wheel ore) $PbCuSbS_3$ 263	Orthorhombic C—Thick tabular; cogwheel twins M—Compact, granular	Metallic Opaque	Dark steel gray Iron black

Hardness 1 to 3

Hard-ness	Streak	Cleavage = C Fracture = F Tenacity	Specific Gravity	Characteristics and Associates
1. 2.5	Black Bluish black	C—Indistinct Brittle	4.7 4.8	Often soils fingers. Darker than stibnite. With psilomelane, manganite, hematite, limonite, barite.
2. 2.5	Dark lead gray Black	C—Brachypinacoidal, perfect, conspicuous, yielding long, shiny faces Slightly sectile	4.6 4.7	Tarnishes black, sometimes iridescent. In veins with quartz, sphalerite, galena, cinnabar, barite, gold.
2. 2.5	Dark lead gray, shiny	C—Indistinct F—Hackly Perfectly sectile	7.2 7.4	Cuts and takes impression like lead, hence easily distinguished from other soft, black minerals. With silver, cobalt, nickel ores —proustite, pyrargyrite, smaltite, niccolite.
2.5	Grayish black Dark lead gray	C—Cubic, perfect, very conspicuous Brittle	7.3 7.6	Characterized by cleavage and high specific gravity. Changes to cerussite or anglesite. With sphalerite, pyrite, chalcopyrite, calcite, fluorite, barite.
2.5 3.	Dark gray, shiny Black, shiny	C—Indistinct F—Conchoidal Rather brittle	5.5 5.8	More brittle than argentite. Often coated with malachite (green), azurite (blue). With chalcopyrite, bornite, tetrahedrite, galena.
2.5 3.	Dark gray Black	C—Imperfect F—Uneven Brittle	5.7 5.9	Easily recognized by cross or cogwheel appearance. With galena, sphalerite, tetrahedrite, siderite, stibnite, chalcocite.

Streak—Black

Name, Composition, and Reference	Crystallization Structure Crystals = C Massive = M	Luster Transparency	Color
Enargite Cu₃AsS₄ **265**	Orthorhombic C—Prismatic, small, rare M—Compact, granular, columnar	Metallic Submetallic Opaque	Grayish black Iron black

Streak—Black

TETRAHEDRITE Cu₃SbS₃ **264**	Cubic C—Tetrahedral, often highly modified M—Granular, compact	Metallic Opaque	Dark steel gray Iron black
Arsenic As **238**	Hexagonal C—Rare M—Compact, scaly, fine granular, with reniform or botryoidal structure	Metallic Opaque	Dark gray to black on exposure, tin white on fresh fracture
Uraninite (Pitchblende) UO₃, UO₂, PbO, etc. **313**	Cubic C—Octahedral, rare M—Botryoidal, columnar, curved lamellar, granular, compact, apparently amorphous	Pitch-like Submetallic Dull Opaque	Pitch black Brownish black Greenish black
Ferberite FeWO₄ **312**	Monoclinic C—Wedge shaped, short prismatic, tabular M—Fan shaped aggregates, bladed, granular, compact	Submetallic Splendent Opaque	Iron black Brownish black
WOLFRAMITE (Fe, Mn)WO₄ **311**	Monoclinic C—Thick, tabular, short columnar, often large M—Bladed, curved lamellar, granular, compact	Submetallic Metallic Opaque	Dark gray Brownish black Iron black

Hardness 1 to 3

Hard-ness	Streak	Cleavage = C Fracture = F Tenacity	Specific Gravity	Characteristics and Associates
3.	Grayish black	C—Prismatic, perfect, often conspicuous F—Uneven Brittle	4.4	In artificial light usually resembles sphalerite. In veins with other copper minerals—chalcopyrite, bornite, chalcocite.

Hardness over 3

3. 4.	Dark gray Black	C—Indistinct F—Uneven Brittle	4.3 5.4	Characteristic c r y s t a l s, sometimes coated with chalcopyrite. With sphalerite, galena, bournonite, siderite, malachite.
3. 4.	Dark gray Black	C—Basal, not conspicuous F—Uneven, granular Brittle	5.6 5.8	Often breaks in concentric or onion-like l a y e r s. Color and streak darken on exposure. With silver, cobalt, n i c k e l o r e s— proustite, smaltite.
3. 5.5	Brownish black Grayish black	F—Conchoidal, uneven Brittle	4.8 9.7	Pitch-like appearance and fracture important. Fresh material is hard and heavy. With ores of lead, silver, bismuth; pyrite, orthite.
5. 5.5	Brownish black	C—Clinopinacoidal, perfect F—Uneven Brittle	7.1 7.5	In granites and pegmatites. With quartz, chalcopyrite, galena, scheelite.
5. 5.5	Brownish black Black	C—Clinopinacoidal, perfect, conspicuous F—Uneven Brittle	7.1 7.5	Structure, cleavage, and specific gravity important. Powder may be slightly magnetic. With cassiterite, quartz, mica, fluorite, apatite, scheelite, molybdenite, huebnerite.

Streak—Black

Name, Composition, and Reference	Crystallization Structure Crystals = C Massive = M	Luster Transparency	Color

Psilomelane
 	
MnO_2, BaO, H_2O, etc.
 	
303
	Amorphous?
	M—Botryoidal, r e n i-
	  f o r m, stalactitic;
	  smooth surface
		Metallic
		Dull
		Opaque
			Iron black
			Bluish black
			Dark gray

Ilmenite (Menaccanite)
 	
$FeTiO_3$
 	
279
	Hexagonal
	C—Thick tabular, rhom-
	  bohedral
	M—Thin plates, granu-
	  lar, compact, dis-
	  seminated grains,
	  pebbles, sand
		Metallic
		Submetallic
		Opaque
			Iron black
			Brownish
			  black

MAGNETITE
 	
$Fe(FeO_2)_2$
 	
320
	Cubic
	C—Octahedrons, dodeca-
	  hedrons, common
	M—Compact, granular,
	  lamellar, dissemi-
	  nated, sand
		Metallic
		Submetallic
		Dull
		Opaque
			Iron black

FRANKLINITE
 	
$(Fe,Mn,Zn)(FeO_2)_2$
 	
321
	Cubic
	C—Octahedrons, alone or
	  with dodecahedron;
	  edges often rounded
	M—Compact, granular,
	  rounded grains
		Metallic
		Dull
		Opaque
			Iron black

COLUMBITE (Tantalite)
 	
$(Fe,Mn)[(Cb,Ta)O_3]_2$
 	
326
	Orthorhombic
	C—Short prismatic, tab-
	  ular
	M—Compact, dissemi-
	  nated
		Submetallic
		Greasy
		Dull
		Opaque
			Iron black
			Brownish
			  black

Hardness over 3

Hard- ness	Streak	Cleavage = C Fracture = F Tenacity	Specific Gravity	Characteristics and Associates
5. 6.	Black Brownish black	F—Conchoidal, un- even Brittle	3.7 4.7	Often with fine, sooty coating of pyrolusite. With other manganese minerals; limonite, barite.
5. 6.	Black Brownish black	C—None, partings may be noted F—Conchoidal Brittle	4.5 5.5	Sometimes slightly mag- netic but not as strongly as magnetite. With hema- tite, magnetite, apatite, serpentine, titanite, ru- tile. Common in black sands.
5.5 6.5	Black	C—Indistinct, oc- tahedral part- ing F—Conchoidal, un- even Brittle	4.9 5.2	Very strongly magnetic. Crystals usually perfect and with bright surfaces. Independent deposits; dis- seminated; black sands. With chlorite, horn- blende, pyroxene, feld- spar, quartz, pyrite, chal- copyrite, epidote.
5.5 6.5	Black Brownish black	C—Octahedral, in- distinct F—Conchoidal Brittle	5. 5.2	Powder frequently slightly magnetic. Distinguished by associates—willemite (yellow or green), zincite (red), rhodonite (flesh red), calcite.
6. 6.5	Black Brownish black Grayish black	C—Pinacoidal, not conspicuous F—Conchoidal, un- even Brittle	5.4 6.4	Fracture surface sometimes iridescent. With beryl, tourmaline, spodumene, cryolite. Tantalum pre- dominates in *tantalite* and specific gravity may be as high as 8.

Streak—Black

Name, Composition, and Reference	Crystallization Structure Crystals = C Massive = M	Luster Transparency	Color
CORUNDUM, variety *Emery* Al_2O_3, with Fe_3O_4, Fe_2O_3, SiO_2	Hexagonal Always massive, fine to coarse granular	Metallic Dull Opaque	Dark gray Black
275			

A. MINERALS WITH METALLIC LUSTER

Streak—Metallic white or steel gray

Bismuth Bi	Hexagonal C—Rare M—Reticulated, a r b o- rescent, platy	Metallic Opaque	Silver white, with reddish tinge
239			
SILVER Ag	Cubic C—Small, often distorted M—Grains, scales, plates, twisted hair- or wire- like forms, lumps	Metallic Opaque	Silver white, tarnishing yellow, brown, or black
243			
PLATINUM Pt	Cubic C—Small, rare M—Scales, grains, nug- gets	Metallic Opaque	Tin white Steel gray
239			

Streak—Black

Molybdenite MoS_2	Hexagonal C—Tabular, rare M—Disseminated grains, scales, foliated	Metallic Opaque	Bluish lead gray
250			

Hardness over 3

Hardness	Streak	Cleavage = C Fracture = F Tenacity	Specific Gravity	Characteristics and Associates
7. 9.	Black Brownish black	C—Indistinct F—Uneven Brittle to tough	3.7 4.3	Corundum mixed with iron ore. May be magnetic. With mica, amphiboles, chlorite, spinel; in crystalline limestone, schist, peridotite.

2. METALLIC WHITE OR LIGHT METALLIC GRAY IN COLOR

Hardness 1 to 6

2. 2.5	Lead gray, shiny	C—Basal, perfect, usually conspicuous. Sectile	9.7 9.8	Often shows brassy tarnish colors. With silver, cobalt, nickel, tin ores—smaltite, niccolite, cassiterite; wolframite.
2.5 3.	Silver white, shiny Light lead gray, shiny	C—None F—Hackly Malleable, ductile	10. 12.	Color and streak darken on exposure. With silver, lead, arsenic, cobalt, nickel ores—argentite, pyrargyrite, proustite, galena, smaltite; fluorite, calcite, barite.
4. 5.	Light steel gray, shiny	C—None F—Hackly Malleable, ductile	14. 19.	Heavier than silver and does not tarnish. May be magnetic if much iron be present. With chromite, magnetite, gold.

Hardness 1 to 3

1. 1.5	Dark lead gray, greenish on glazed porcelain (graphite, shiny black)	C—Basal, perfect Sectile, lamellæ flexible	4.7 4.8	Marks paper. Soft and greasy like graphite but heavier and lighter colored. In granite with cassiterite, wolframite; in crystalline limestone.

Streak—Black

Name, Composition, and Reference	Crystallization Structure Crystals = C Massive = M	Luster Transparency	Color
STIBNITE Sb_2S_3 249	Orthorhombic C—Prismatic, bent, twisted, common M—Fibrous, bladed, columnar, granular, compact	Metallic Opaque	Light lead gray
GALENA (Galenite) PbS 254	Cubic C—Cubes, alone or with octahedron, common, well developed M—Granular, cleavable aggregates	Metallic Opaque	Lead gray

Streak—Black

Arsenic As 238	Hexagonal C—Rare M—Compact, scaly, fine grained, reniform, botryoidal	Metallic Opaque	Tin white, on fresh fracture
Cobaltite CoAsS 259	Cubic C—Cubes, pyritohedrons, small, well developed M—Granular, compact	Metallic Opaque	Silver white Steel gray, at times with reddish tinge
Smaltite $CoAs_2$ 259	Cubic C—Rare M—Granular, compact	Metallic Opaque	Tin white Light steel gray
ARSENOPYRITE FeAsS 260	Orthorhombic C—Prismatic, common M—Compact, granular, columnar, radial	Metallic Opaque	Tin white Light steel gray, tarnishes yellow

Hardness 1 to 3

Hard-ness	Streak	Cleavage = C Fracture = F Tenacity	Specific Gravity	Characteristics and Associates
2. 2.5	Dark lead gray Black	C—Brachypina-coidal, perfect, conspicuous, yielding long shiny faces Slightly sectile	4.6 4.7	Differs from galena in cleavage and specific gravity. Tarnishes black, sometimes iridescent. In veins with quartz, sphalerite, galena, cinnabar, barite, gold.
2.5	Dark lead gray Grayish black	C—Cubic, perfect, very conspicuous Brittle.	7.3 7.6	Characterized by cleavage and high specific gravity. Changes to cerussite, pyromorphite, or anglesite. With sphalerite, pyrite, chalcopyrite, calcite, fluorite, barite.

Hardness over 3

Hard-ness	Streak	Cleavage = C Fracture = F Tenacity	Specific Gravity	Characteristics and Associates
3. 4.	Lead gray Grayish black	C—Basal, not conspicuous F—Uneven, granular Brittle	5.6 5.8	Often breaks in concentric or onion-like layers. Color and streak darken on exposure. With silver, cobalt, nickel ores—proustite, smaltite.
5.5	Dark grayish black	C—Cubic, not conspicuous F—Uneven Brittle	6. 6.4	May show red tarnish Often with pink coating of erythrite (cobalt bloom). With native silver, smaltite, niccolite, pyrrhotite, chalcopyrite.
5.5	Grayish black	C—Indistinct F—Uneven Brittle	6.4 6.6	May have dull tarnish and pink coating of erythrite. With niccolite, cobaltite, native bismuth and silver, proustite, barite, fluorite, calcite.
5.5 6.	Dark grayish black	C—Prismatic, not conspicuous F—Uneven Brittle	5.9 6.2	Whiter than marcasite. More common than smaltite. With chalcopyrite, pyrite, sphalerite, cassiterite, smaltite, native gold and silver, serpentine.

Streak—Black

Name, Composition, and Reference	Crystallization Structure Crystals = C Massive = M	Luster Transparency	Color
MARCASITE (White iron pyrites) FeS$_2$ 259	Orthorhombic C—Tabular, often twinned, resembling cock's combs M—Compact, stalactitic, globular, radiated	Metallic Opaque	Steel gray Pale brass yellow, more brassy on exposure

A. MINERALS WITH METALLIC LUSTER

Streak—Brown or yellow

LIMONITE, varieties *Yellow ocher* Fe$_2$O$_3$.nH$_2$O *Bog iron ore* 283	M—Earthy, porous, clay-like	Earthy Dull Opaque	Yellow Brownish yellow
GOLD Au 244	Cubic C—Small, often distorted M—Grains, scales, nuggets, dust	Metallic Opaque	Golden yellow Brassy yellow Light yellow

Streak—Black

CHALCOPYRITE CuFeS$_2$ 261	Tetragonal C—Bisphenoids, resembling tetrahedrons, common M—Compact	Metallic Opaque	Brass yellow Golden yellow
MARCASITE (White iron pyrites) FeS$_2$ 259	Orthorhombic C—Tabular, often twinned, resembling cock's combs M—Compact, stalactitic, globular, radiated	Metallic Opaque	Pale brass yellow, more brassy on exposure

Hardness over 3

Hard-ness	Streak	Cleavage = C Fracture = F Tenacity	Specific Gravity	Characteristics and Associates
6. 6.5	Dark greenish black	C—Indistinct F—Uneven Brittle	4.6 4.8	Alters to limonite, melanterite. With other sulphides—galena, sphalerite, chalcopyrite, pyrite; calcite, dolomite.

3. YELLOW IN COLOR

Hardness 1 to 6

1. 4.	Yellowish brown	C—None F—Earthy Brittle	3.4 4.	*Yellow ocher*, earthy, may have greasy feel, when impure gritty; *bog iron ore*, porous.
2.5 3.	Golden yellow	C—None F—Hackly Malleable, ductile	15.6 19.3	Does not tarnish. Characterized by streak, specific gravity, and tenacity Frequently in quartz veins; placers. Commonly with pyrite, and other sulphides.

Hardness over 3

3.5 4.	Greenish black	C—Indistinct F—Uneven Brittle	4.1 4.3	Softer, and deeper yellow than pyrite. Frequently with iridescent tarnish. With pyrite, bornite, galena, sphalerite, tetrahedrite, chalcocite.
6. 6.5	Dark greenish black Brownish black	C—Indistinct F—Uneven Brittle	4.6 4.8	Distinguished from pyrite by crystallization and lighter color on fresh fracture. Alters m o r e readily than pyrite, forming limonite, melanterite. Occurrence same as pyrite, less abundant.

Streak—Black

Name, Composition, and Reference	Crystallization Structure Crystals = C Massive = M	Luster Transparency	Color
PYRITE (Iron pyrites, fool's gold) FeS_2 257	Cubic C—Cubes, octahedrons, pyritohedrons, common, often striated M—Compact, fine granular; botryoidal, stalactitic	Metallic Opaque	Brass yellow Golden yellow with variegated tarnish

A. MINERALS WITH METALLIC LUSTER

Streak—Gray, red, or yellow

Bismuth Bi 239	Hexagonal C—Rare M—Reticulated, arborescent, platy	Metallic Opaque	Light copper red
COPPER Cu 240	Cubic C—Cubes, octahedrons, tetrahexahedrons M—Scales, plates, lumps, arborescent aggregates	Metallic Opaque	Copper red, tarnishing readily red, blue, green, black
GOLD Au 244	Cubic C—Small, distorted, rare M—Grains, scales, dust, nuggets	Metallic Opaque	Golden yellow Brassy yellow Light yellow

Streak—Black

BORNITE Cu_5FeS_4 262	Cubic C—Rare M—Compact, granular	Metallic Opaque	Bronze brown Copper red, on fresh fracture

Hardness over 3

Hardness	Streak	Cleavage = C Fracture = F Tenacity	Specific Gravity	Characteristics and Associates
6. 6.5	Greenish black Brownish black	C—Indistinct F—Uneven Brittle	4.9 5.2	Harder than chalcopyrite Alters to limonite. Widely distributed in all types of rocks. With other sulphides—galena, sphalerite, chalcopyrite; quartz.

4. BRASS, BRONZE, OR COPPER RED IN COLOR

Hardness 1 to 3

Hardness	Streak	Cleavage = C Fracture = F Tenacity	Specific Gravity	Characteristics and Associates
2. 2.5	Lead gray, shiny	C—Basal, perfect, usually conspicuous Sectile	9.7 9.8	Often shows brassy tarnish. Frequently with silver, cobalt, nickel, tin ores; smaltite, niccolite, cassiterite, wolframite.
2.5 3.	Copper red, shiny	C—None F—Hackly Ductile, malleable	8.5 9.	Cementing material in conglomerate or filling cavities in trap rocks. With cuprite, malachite, azurite, native silver, melaconite, epidote, datolite, zeolites.
2.5 3.	Golden yellow	C—None F—Hackly Malleable, ductile	15.6 19.3	Does not tarnish. Characterized by streak, specific gravity, and tenacity. Frequently in quartz veins; placers. Commonly with pyrite and other sulphides.

Hardness over 3

Hardness	Streak	Cleavage = C Fracture = F Tenacity	Specific Gravity	Characteristics and Associates
3. 3.5	Grayish black	C—Indistinct F—Uneven Brittle	4.9 5.2	Usually with peacock tarnish colors (purple copper ore). With chalcopyrite, chalcocite, malachite, cassiterite, siderite.

Streak—Black

Name, Composition, and Reference	Crystallization Structure Crystals = C Massive = M	Luster Transparency	Color
CHALCOPYRITE $CuFeS_2$ 261	Tetragonal C—Bisphenoids, resembling tetrahedrons, common M—Compact, granular	Metallic Opaque	Brass yellow Golden yellow
PYRRHOTITE FeS 252	Hexagonal C—Tabular, rare M—Compact, granular	Metallic Opaque	Bronze yellow Bronze brown
Niccolite NiAs 253	Hexagonal C—Rare M—Compact, disseminated	Metallic Opaque	Light copper red
MARCASITE (White iron pyrites) FeS_2 259	Orthorhombic C—Tabular, often twinned resembling cock's combs M—Compact, stalactitic, globular, radiated	Metallic Opaque	Steel gray Pale brass yellow, more brassy on exposure
PYRITE (Iron pyrites, fool's gold) FeS_2 257	Cubic C—Cubes, octahedrons, pyritohedrons, very common, often striated M—Compact, fine granular; botryoidal, stalactitic	Metallic Opaque	Brass yellow Golden yellow, with variegated tarnish

Hardness over 3

Hard-ness	Streak	Cleavage = C Fracture = F Tenacity	Specific Gravity	Characteristics and Associates
3.5 4.	Greenish black	C—Indistinct F—Uneven Brittle	4.1 4.3	Softer, and deeper yellow in color than pyrite. Frequently with iridescent tarnish. With pyrite, bornite, galena, sphalerite, tetrahedrite, chalcocite.
3.5 4.5	Dark grayish black	C—Basal, not conspicuous F—Uneven Brittle	4.5 4.6	Powder frequently attracted by magnet. Subject to dark brown tarnish. In basic igneous rocks. With chalcopyrite, pyrite, galena.
5.5	Dark brownish black	C—Indistinct F—Uneven Brittle	7.3 7.7	Often with green coating of annabergite (nickel bloom). With cobalt, nickel, silver minerals—smaltite, proustite, native silver; native bismuth and arsenic; calcite.
6. 6.5	Dark greenish black	C—Indistinct F—Uneven Brittle	4.6 4.8	Distinguished from pyrite by crystallization and lighter color on fresh fracture. Alters more readily than pyrite, forming limonite, melanterite. Occurrence same as for pyrite, but not as abundant.
6. 6.5	Greenish black Brownish black	C—Indistinct F—Uneven Brittle	4.9 5.2	Alters to limonite. Widely distributed in all types of rocks. With other sulphides—galena, sphalerite, chalcopyrite; quartz.

Streak—White, gray, green, red, brown, or yellow

Name, Composition, and Reference	Crystallization Structure Crystals = C Massive = M	Luster Transparency	Color
LIMONITE, varieties *Brown ocher* $Fe_2O_3.nH_2O$ *Bog iron ore* *Brown clay* *ironstone* 283	C—Unknown M—Compact, earthy, porous, pisolitic, oölitic	Dull Earthy Opaque	Yellowish brown Dark brown
HEMATITE, varieties *Red ocher* Fe_2O_3 *Oölitic* *Fossiliferous* 276	Hexagonal M—Fine g r a n u l a r, earthy, scaly, oölitic, fossiliferous	Dull Earthy Opaque	Brownish Cherry red
CINNABAR HgS 256	Hexagonal C—Rhombohedral, thick tabular, small, rare M—Fine granular, fi- brous, disseminated, earthy coating	Adamantine Dull Transparent to opaque	Scarlet red Brownish red
Proustite Ag_3AsS_3 262	Hexagonal C—Small, complex, rare M—Disseminated, crusts, bands	Adamantine Dull Transparent to translucent	Scarlet Vermilion
Pyrargyrite Ag_3SbS_3 263	Hexagonal C—Small, complex, rare M—Disseminated, crusts, bands	Adamantine Metallic Transparent to opaque	Dark red
COPPER Cu 240	Cubic C—Cubes, octahedrons, tetrahexahedrons M—Scales, plates, lumps, arborescent a g g r e- gates	Metallic Opaque	Copper red, tarnishing readily to red, blue, green, black

Hardness 1 to 3

Hardness	Streak	Cleavage = C Fracture = F Tenacity	Specific Gravity	Characteristics and Associates
1. 3.	Yellowish brown	C—None F—Earthy Brittle	3.4 4.	*Brown ocher*, earthy, may soil fingers; *bog iron ore*, porous; *brown clay iron-stone*, massive or concretionary, impure from clay, sand.
1. 3.	Cherry red Reddish brown	C—None F—Earthy Brittle	4.9 5.3	*Red ocher*, earthy; *oölitic*, fish-egg structure; *fossiliferous*, replacement of shells.
2. 2.5	Scarlet Reddish brown	C—Prismatic, not conspicuous F—Uneven Brittle to sectile	8. 8.2	Color, streak, high specific gravity important; the latter often reduced by gangue. Disseminated in silicious rocks, with native mercury, pyrite, marcasite, realgar, stibnite.
2.5	Scarlet Aurora red	C—Indistinct F—Conchoidal Brittle	5.5 5.6	Termed light ruby silver ore. Distinguished from cinnabar by associates. With pyrargyrite, in veins with other silver minerals and galena.
2.5 3.	Cherry red Purplish red	C—Indistinct F—Conchoidal Brittle	5.8	Frequently as gray or dark red bands, dark ruby silver ore. With proustite, in veins with other silver minerals and galena.
2.5 3.	Copper red, shiny	C—None F—Hackly Ductile, malleable	8.5 9.	Cementing material in conglomerate, or filling cavities in trap rocks. With cuprite, malachite, azurite, native silver, melaconite, epidote, datolite, zeolites, quartz, calcite.

Streak—White, gray, green, red, brown, or yellow

Name, Composition, and Reference	Crystallization Structure Crystals = C Massive = M	Luster Transparency	Color
LIMONITE, varieties *Compact* $Fe_2O_3.nH_2O$ *Bog iron ore* *Brown clay* *ironstone*	C—Always p s e u d o-morphs, commonly after pyrite, marcasite, siderite M—Compact, stalactitic, botryoidal, nodular; often with internal radial fibrous structure; porous	Metallic Dull Opaque	Yellowish brown **Dark brown**
283			
Uraninite (Pitchblende) UO_3, UO_2, PbO, etc.	Cubic C—Octahedral, rare M—Botryoidal, columnar, curved lamellar, granular, compact; apparently amorphous	Submetallic Dull Opaque	Brown Blackish brown
313			
HEMATITE, varieties *Argillaceous* Fe_2O_3 *Compact*	Hexagonal M—Compact, granular, columnar, splintery, radiated, reniform and botryoidal	Submetallic Dull Opaque	Brownish red Dark red Blackish red
276			
SIDERITE $FeCO_3$	Hexagonal C—R h o m b o h e d r a l, curved or saddle-shaped, common M—Cleavable, granular, compact, botryoidal	Dull Vitreous Translucent to opaque	Dark brown Reddish brown
298			
SPHALERITE ZnS	Cubic C—Tetrahedral, common M—Cleavable, fine and coarse grained aggregates, compact	Submetallic Resinous Opaque to translucent	Brown Yellowish brown Reddish brown
251			

Hardness **3** to **6**

Hard-ness	Streak	Cleavage = C Fracture = F Tenacity	Specific Gravity	Characteristics and Associates
3. **5.5**	Yellowish brown	F—Conchoidal, un-even, earthy Brittle	3.4 4.	Often with black, varnish-like surface, passing into soft, yellow ocherous var-iety. *Compact limonite,* massive, with fibrous structure, rather pure; *brown clay ironstone* mass-ive or concretionary, im-pure from clay, sand; *bog iron ore,* porous.
3. **5.5**	Dark brown Olive green Grayish	F—Conchoidal, un-even Brittle	4.8 9.7	Structure and fracture im-portant. Fresh material is hard and heavy. With ores of lead, silver, bis-muth; also orthite.
3. **6.**	Cherry red Reddish brown	C—None, parting sometimes noted F—Uneven, splint-ery Brittle	4.9 5.3	*Argillaceous hematite,* im-pure from clay, sand, jasper; *compact hematite,* usually quite pure.
3.5 **4.**	Yellowish brown Pale yellow	C—Rhombohedral, perfect, con-spicuous F—Conchoidal Brittle	3.7 3.9	Curved crystals, cleavage, and rather high specific gravity characteristic. In ore deposits; beds and concretions in limestone and shale. With pyrite, chalcopyrite, galena, tet-rahedrite, cryolite.
3.5 **4.**	Light brown Pale yellow	C—Dodecahedral, perfect, con-spicuous F—Conchoidal Brittle	3.9 4.2	Color and streak vary with impurities. Extensively in limestone. With galena, chalcopyrite, py-rite, barite, fluorite, sider-ite, rhodochrosite.

Streak—White, gray, green, red, brown, or yellow

Name, Composition, and Reference	Crystallization Structure Crystals = C Massive = M	Luster Transparency	Color

CUPRITE
 	
Cu_2O
 	
279
	Cubic
	C—Octahedrons, dodeca-
	  hedrons, alone or in
	  combination
	M—Compact, granular,
	  earthy; slender crys-
	  tal aggregates (chal-
	  cotrichite)
		Adamantine
		Dull
		Translucent
		  to opaque
			Cochineal red
			Brick red
			Dark red

Zincite
 	
ZnO
 	
274
	Hexagonal
	C—Hemimorphic, rare
	M—Compact, granular,
	  foliated
		Subadaman-
		  tine
		Vitreous
		Translucent
		  to opaque
			Dark red
			Blood red

Huebnerite
 	
$MnWO_4$
 	
311
	Monoclinic
	C—Long, fibrous, bladed,
	  stalky, often diver-
	  gent, without good
	  terminations
	M—Compact, lamellar,
	  granular
		Submetallic
		Resinous
		Opaque to
		  translucent
			Reddish
			  brown
			Brown

WOLFRAMITE
 	
$(Fe,Mn)WO_4$
 	
311
	Monoclinic
	C—Thick, tabular, short
	  columnar, often large
	M—Bladed, curved lam-
	  ellar, granular, com-
	  pact
		Submetallic
		Opaque
			Reddish
			  brown
			Dark brown

Ferberite
 	
$FeWO_4$
 	
312
	Monoclinic
	C—Wedge shaped, short
	  prismatic, tabular
	M—Fan shaped aggre-
	  gates, bladed, granu-
	  lar, compact
		Submetallic
		Opaque
			Brown
			Blackish
			  brown

Hardness 3 to 6

Hardness	Streak	Cleavage = C Fracture = F Tenacity	Specific Gravity	Characteristics and Associates
3.5 4.	Brownish red Dirty brown	C—Indistinct F—Uneven Brittle	5.7 6.1	Characterized by associates, copper minerals— malachite (green), azurite (blue), chalcocite and melaconite (black), chalcopyrite (yellow), native copper.
4. 4.5	Reddish yellow Orange yellow	C—Basal, perfect, usually conspicuous F—Uneven Brittle	5.4 5.7	Distinguished by associates —calcite, franklinite (black), willemite (yellow to green), rhodonite (flesh red). On exposure becomes coated with the white carbonate.
4.5 5.5	Yellowish brown Greenish gray	C—Clinopinacoidal, perfect, conspicuous Brittle	6.7 7.3	Structure, cleavage, specific gravity important. In quartz veins. With fluorite, pyrite, scheelite, wolframite, galena, tetrahedrite.
5. 5.5	Dark red brown	C—Clinopinacoidal, perfect, conspicuous F—Uneven Brittle	7.1 7.5	Distinguished from huebnerite by streak. Powder may be slightly magnetic. With cassiterite, quartz, mica, fluorite, apatite, scheelite, molybdenite, huebnerite.
5. 5.5	Brown Dark brown	C—Clinopinacoidal, perfect. F—Uneven Brittle	7.5	In granites and pegmatites. With quartz, chalcopyrite, galena, scheelite.

Streak—White, gray, green, red, brown, or yellow

Name, Composition, and Reference	Crystallization Structure Crystals = C Massive = M	Luster Transparency	Color
RUTILE TiO$_2$ **272**	Tetragonal C—Prismatic, vertically striated; twinned, yielding knee-shaped or rosette forms M—Compact, disseminated	Metallic Adamantine Opaque to transparent	Reddish brown Dark red

CASSITERITE, varieties
    Ordinary
SnO$_2$ *Wood tin*
    Stream tin
 	
272
	Tetragonal
	C—Thick p r i s m a t i c, knee-shaped twins, common
	M—Compact; reniform, botryoidal, rounded pebbles, often with internal, radial fibrous structure, *wood tin*
		Adamantine
		Resinous
		Dull
		Translucent to opaque
			Reddish brown
			Yellowish brown
			Dark brown

Hardness over 6

Hard-ness	Streak	Cleavage = C Fracture = F Tenacity	Specific Gravity	Characteristics and Associates
6. 7.	Pale yellowish brown Gray	C—Prismatic, py- ramidal, n o t conspicuous F—Uneven Brittle	4.2 4.3	Not as heavy as cassiterite. Often in fine, hair-like inclusions. Widely distributed. With quartz, feldspar, ilmenite, chlorite, apatite.
6. 7.	Pale yellow Pale brown White	C—Indistinct F—Uneven Brittle	6.8 7.	Distinguished by high specific gravity. In veins cutting granite, gneiss; in alluvial deposits, as *stream tin*. With quartz, mica, wolframite, scheelite, arsenopyrite, molybdenite, tourmaline, fluorite, apatite, chlorite.

Streak—Black

Name, Composition, and Reference	Crystallization Structure Crystals = C Massive = M	Luster Transparency	Color
BORNITE (Purple copper ore) Cu_5FeS_4 262	Cubic C—Rare M—Compact, granular	Metallic Opaque	Bronze brown Copper red tarnishes readily
Uraninite (Pitchblende) UO_3, UO_2, PbO, etc. 313	Cubic C—Octahedral, rare M—Botryoidal, colum- nar, curved lamellar, granular compact, apparently amor- phous	Submetallic Dull Opaque	Brown Blackish brown
PYRRHOTITE FeS 252	Hexagonal C—Tabular, rare M—Compact, granular	Metallic Opaque	Bronze brown Bronze yellow
WOLFRAMITE • $(Fe,Mn)WO_4$ 311	Monoclinic C—Thick tabular, short columnar, often large M—Bladed, curved lam- ellar, granular	Submetallic Opaque	Grayish brown Dark brown
Niccolite NiAs 253	Hexagonal C—Rare M—Compact, dissemi- nated	Metallic Opaque	Light copper red

Hardness 1 to 6

Hard-ness	Streak	Cleavage = C Fracture = F Tenacity	Specific Gravity	Characteristics and Associates
3.	Grayish black	C—Indistinct F—Uneven Brittle	4.9 5.2	Usually with peacock tarn-ish colors—purple copper ore. With chalcopyrite, chalcocite, malachite, cas-siterite, siderite.
3. 5.5	Brownish black Grayish black	F—Conchoidal, un-even Brittle	4.8 9.7	Structure and fracture im-portant. Fresh material is hard and heavy. With ores of lead, silver, bis-muth; also pyrite, orthite.
3.5 4.5	Dark grayish black	C—Basal, not con-spicuous F—Uneven Brittle	4.5 4.6	Powder frequently at-tracted by magnet. Sub-ject to dark brown tarn-ish. In basic igneous rocks. With chalcopyrite, pyrite, galena.
5.5	Black Brownish black	C—Clinopinacoidal, perfect, con-spicuous F—Uneven Brittle	7.1 7.5	Structure, cleavage, spe-cific gravity important. Powder may be slightly magnetic. With cassiter-ite, quartz, mica, fluorite, apatite, scheelite, molyb-denite, huebnerite.
5.5	Dark brownish black	C—Indistinct F—Uneven Brittle	7.3 7.7	Often with green crust of annabergite (nickel bloom). With cobalt, nickel, silver minerals—smaltite, proustite, pyrar-gyrite; native bismuth and arsenic, calcite.

Streak—Green, red, brown, yellow, or black

Name, Composition, and Reference	Crystallization Structure Crystals = C Massive = M	Luster Transparency	Color
GRAPHITE (Plumbago, black lead) C	Hexagonal C—Tabular, rare M—Scaly, foliated, granular, earthy, sooty	Dull Opaque	Dark gray Iron black
235			
CHLORITE (Prochlorite, clinochlorite) $H_8Mg_5Al_2Si_3O_{18}$	Monoclinic C—Tabular, six-s i d e d, often bent, twisted M—Foliated, scaly, granular, earthy	Dull Submetallic Translucent to opaque	Black Greenish black
358			
Uraninite (Pitchblende) UO_3, UO_2, PbO, etc.	Cubic C—Octahedral, rare M—Botryoidal, columnar, curved lamellar, granular, compact, apparently amorphous	Pitch-like Submetallic Dull Opaque	Pitch black Brownish black Greenish black
313			
SIDERITE $FeCO_3$	Hexagonal C—Rhombohedral, curved or saddle-shaped, common M—Cleavable, granular, compact, botryoidal	Vitreous Dull Translucent to opaque	Brownish black Black
298			
SPHALERITE (Black Jack) ZnS	Cubic C—Tetrahedral, common M—Cleavable, fine and coarse grained, compact	Submetallic Resinous Opaque to translucent	Black Yellowish black Brownish black
251			

Hardness 1 to 6

Hard-ness	Streak	Cleavage = C Fracture = F Tenacity	Specific Gravity	Characteristics and Associates
1. 2.	Dark gray Iron black	C—Basal, perfect (scales) Scales flexible	1.9 2.3	Greasy feel. Marks paper. Often impure. In crystalline limestone with garnet, spinel, pyroxenes, amphiboles; also in shale, gneiss, mica schist.
1. 2.5	Pale green	C—Basal, conspicuous, when foliated F—Scaly, earthy Tough to brittle	2.6 3.	Laminæ flexible but inelastic, with slightly soapy feel. Common in schists and serpentine. With magnetite, magnesite, garnet, diopside. Often as scaly or dusty coating on other minerals. Pseudomorphous after garnet.
3. 5.5	Olive green Dark brown Brownish black Grayish black	F—Conchoidal, uneven Brittle	4.8 9.7	Pitch-like appearance and fracture characteristic. Fresh material is hard and heavy. With lead, silver, bismuth minerals; also pyrite, orthite.
3.5 4.	Yellowish brown	C—Rhombohedral, perfect, conspicuous F—Conchoidal Brittle	3.7 3.9	Curved crystals, cleavage, and rather high specific gravity characteristic. In ore deposits; beds and concretions in limestone and shale. With pyrite, chalcopyrite, galena, tetrahedrite, cryolite.
3.5 4.	Dark brown Yellowish brown Gray	C—Dodecahedral perfect, usually conspicuous F—Conchoidal Brittle	3.9 4.2	Color and streak vary with impurities. When massive distinguished from siderite by cleavage. Extensively in limestone. With galena, chalcopyrite, pyrite, barite, fluorite, siderite, rhodochrosite.

Streak—Green, red, brown, yellow, or black

Name, Composition, and Reference	Crystallization Structure Crystals = C Massive = M	Luster Transparency	Color
Huebnerite MnWO₄ 311	Monoclinic C—Long fibrous, bladed, s t a l k y; o f t e n divergent, without good terminations M—Compact, lamellar, granular	Resinous Submetallic Translucent to opaque	Brownish black Black
WOLFRAMITE (Fe,Mn)WO₄ 311	Monoclinic C—Thick tabular, short c o l u m n a r, often large M—Bladed, curved lamellar, granular	Submetallic Opaque	Dark gray Brownish black Iron black
Ferberite FeWO₄ 312	Monoclinic C—Wedge shaped, short prismatic, tabular M—Fan-shaped aggregates, bladed, granular, compact	Submetallic Splendent Opaque	Iron black Brownish black
HORNBLENDE (Amphibole) Silicate of Ca, Mg, Fe, Al, etc. 371	Monoclinic C—Long prismatic, prism angle 124°; often with rhombohedral-like terminations M—Bladed, fibrous granular, compact	Vitreous Silky Translucent to opaque	Pitch black Greenish black Brownish black
AUGITE (Pyroxene) Silicate of Ca, Mg, Fe, Al, etc. 365	Monoclinic C—Short p r i s m a t i c; thick c o l u m n a r, prism angle 87° M—Compact, granular, disseminated	Vitreous Submetallic Translucent to opaque	Pitch black Greenish black Brownish black

Hardness 1 to 6

Hard-ness	Streak	Cleavage = C Fracture = F Tenacity	Specific Gravity	Characteristics and Associates
4.5 5.5	Yellowish brown	C—Clinopinacoidal, perfect, con-spicuous Brittle	6.7 7.3	Structure, cleavage, and high specific gravity characteristic. In quartz veins. With wolframite, fluorite, pyrite, scheelite, galena, tetrahedrite.
5. 5.5	Dark reddish brown Black	C—Clinopinacoidal, perfect, con-spicuous F—Uneven Brittle	7.1 7.5	Distinguished from hueb-nerite by streak. Powder may be slightly magnetic. With cassiterite, quartz, mica, fluorite, apatite, scheelite, molybdenite, huebnerite.
5. 5.5	Dark brown Brownish black	C—Clinopinacoidal, perfect F—Uneven Brittle	7.5	In granites and pegmatites. With quartz, chalcopyrite, galena, scheelite.
5. 6.	Grayish green Grayish brown Yellow	C—Prismatic, perfect, often con-spicuous—124° Brittle	2.9 3.3	Simple, pseudohexagonal crystals, and cleavage at 124° important. Very common; in nearly all types of rocks. With calcite, quartz, feldspar, pyroxene, chlorite.
5. 6.	Pale green Grayish green	C—Prismatic, perfect, conspicu-ous—87° Brittle	3.2 3.6	Crystals usually eight-sided, more rarely four-sided; pseudotetragonal with prism angles of 87° and 93°. Cleavage less distinct than on hornblende. Common in basic eruptive rocks and crystalline limestones.

Streak—Green, red, brown, yellow, or black

Name, Composition, and Reference	Crystallization Structure Crystals = C Massive = M	Luster Transparency	Color
Psilomelane MnO_2, BaO, H_2O, etc. **303**	Amorphous? M—Botryoidal, r e n i- f o r m, stalactitic; smooth surfaces	Submetallic Dull Opaque	Iron black Bluish black Dark gray
LIMONITE $Fe_2O_3.nH_2O$ **283**	C—Pseudomorphs, after p y r i t e, marcasite, siderite M—Compact, stalactitic, botryoidal, reniform; fibrous structure	Metallic Dull Opaque	Black Brownish black
CHROMITE $(Fe,Cr)[(Cr,Fe)O_2]_2$ **322**	Cubic C—Octahedral, rare M—Compact, granular, disseminated grains	Submetallic Pitchy Opaque	Iron black Brownish black
Orthite (Allanite) $Ca_2(Al,Ce,Fe)_2(AlOH)$ $(SiO_4)_3$ **345**	Monoclinic C—Tabular, rare M—Compact, granular, bladed, disseminated grains	Submetallic Greasy Translucent to opaque	Black Pitch black Brownish black

Streak—Green, red, brown, yellow, or black

Name, Composition, and Reference	Crystallization Structure Crystals = C Massive = M	Luster Transparency	Color
RUTILE TiO_2 **272**	Tetragonal C—Prismatic, vertically striated; twinned, yielding knee-shaped or rosette forms M—Compact	Adamantine Metallic Opaque to transparent	Iron black Brownish black Reddish black
CASSITERITE SnO_2 **272**	Tetragonal C—P r i s m a t i c; knee- shaped twins com- mon M—Compact, reniform, botryoidal, pebbles, with radial fibrous structure	Submetallic Dull Translucent to opaque	Black Brownish black

Hardness 1 to 6

Hardness	Streak	Cleavage = C Fracture = F Tenacity	Specific Gravity	Characteristics and Associates
5. 6.	Black Brownish black	F—Conchoidal, uneven Brittle	3.7 4.7	Often with fine sooty coating of pyrolusite. With manganese minerals; also limonite, barite.
5. 6.	Yellowish brown	F—Conchoidal, splintery Brittle	3.6 4.	Often with black varnish-like surface, passing into the soft, yellow earthy or ocherous variety. With pyrite, hematite, magnetite, siderite.
5.5	Dark brown Grayish brown	C—Indistinct F—Uneven, conchoidal Brittle	4.3 4.6	May be slightly magnetic. Pitch-like appearance. With serpentine, talc, chrome garnet; also in black sands, platinum placers.
5.5 6.	Pale brown Grayish brown ·	C—Pinacoidal, indistinct F—Uneven, conchoidal Brittle	3. 4.	Often with yellowish or brownish coating. Disseminated through acid igneous rocks; also in limestones. With magnetite, epidote, quartz, feldspar.

Hardness over 6

Hardness	Streak	Cleavage = C Fracture = F Tenacity	Specific Gravity	Characteristics and Associates
6. 7.	Pale yellow Pale brown	C—Prismatic, pyramidal, not conspicuous F—Uneven Brittle	4.2 4.3	Not as heavy as cassiterite. Often as hair-like inclusions. Disseminated. Widely distributed. With quartz, feldspar, hematite ilmenite, chlorite.
6. 7.	Pale brown Pale yellow	C—Indistinct F—Uneven Brittle	6.8 7.	Distinguished by high specific gravity. In veins cutting granite; in alluvial deposits as *stream tin*. With wolframite, scheelite, molybdenite, tourmaline, fluorite, apatite.

Streak—Green, red, brown, yellow or black

Name, Composition, and Reference	Crystallization Structure Crystals = C Massive = M	Luster Transparency	Color
CORUNDUM, variety _Emery_ Al_2O_3, with Fe_3O_4, Fe_2O_3, SiO_2	Hexagonal M—Fine to coarse granular	Dull Submetallic Opaque	Dark gray Black
275			
SPINEL, varieties _Hercynite_ _Picotite_ $M''(M'''O_2)_2$ $M'' = Mg, Fe,$ Zn, Mn $M''' = Al, Fe$ 319	Cubic C—Octahedral, small M—Compact, granular, disseminated grains	Vitreous Dull Nearly opaque	Black Brownish black

Streak—Uncolored, white, or light gray

APATITE, variety _Phosphate rock_ Mainly calcium carbonate —phosphate (collophanite)	Amorphous M—Compact, nodular, reniform, earthy	Dull Opaque	Black
326			
BIOTITE (Black mica) $K(Mg,Fe)_3(OH)_2AlSi_3O_{10}$	Monoclinic C—Tabular, with hexagonal or rhombohedral habit M—Plates, disseminated scales	Pearly Submetallic Transparent to opaque	Black Brownish black Greenish black
357			
CALCITE, varieties $CaCO_3$ _Limestone_ _Marble_ _Stalactites, etc._ _Calcareous tufa_ _Travertine_	Hexagonal M—Cleavable, granular, fibrous, banded, stalactitic, oölitic, porous, compact, crusts, shells	Vitreous Dull Translucent to opaque	Dark gray Brownish black Black
291			

Hardness over 6

Hardness	Streak	Cleavage = C Fracture = F Tenacity	Specific Gravity	Characteristics and Associates
7. 9.	Yellowish brown Black	C—Indistinct F—Uneven Brittle to tough	3.7 4.3	Corundum mixed with iron ore. Powder may be magnetic. With mica, amphibole, chlorite, spinel; in crystalline limestones, schists, peridotites.
7.5 8.	Grayish green Pale brown	C—Octahedral, indistinct F—Conchoidal Brittle	3.9 4.1	Commonly in basic igneous rocks, especially the olivine-bearing types. With olivine, serpentine, corundum, magnetite, hornblende, garnet.

Hardness 1 to 3

Hardness	Streak	Cleavage = C Fracture = F Tenacity	Specific Gravity	Characteristics and Associates
2. 3.	White	F—Conchoidal, uneven Brittle	3.1 3.2	More or less impure masses, frequently resembling compact bituminous limestone. Independent beds, nodules, or concretions.
2.5 3.	White Grayish	C—Basal, perfect, conspicuous Tough, lamellæ of fresh biotite very elastic	2.7 3.2	Easily recognized by structure, highly perfect cleavage, and elasticity. Important constituent of many igneous and metamorphic rocks—granite, syenite, gneiss.
3.	White Gray	C—Rhombohedral, perfect F—Conchoidal Brittle	2.7	Rhombohedral cleavage generally observed. Cleavages often striated. Yields bituminous odor when struck with hammer. To distinguish varieties, see page reference.

Streak—Uncolored, white, or light gray

Name, Composition, and Reference	Crystallization Structure Crystals = C Massive = M	Luster Transparency	Color
ANHYDRITE CaSO₄ **305**	Orthorhombic C—Thick tabular, prismatic, rare M—Granular, compact, fibrous, lamellar, cleavable	Vitreous Pearly Translucent to opaque	Dark gray Blackish
SERPENTINE H₄Mg₃Si₂O₉ **360**	Monoclinic C—Unknown M—Compact, columnar, fibrous, lamellar, granular	Greasy Waxy Translucent to opaque	Greenish black Brownish black
APATITE, variety *Phosphate rock* Mainly calcium carbonate —phosphate (collophanite) **326**	Amorphous M—Compact, nodular, reniform, earthy	Dull Opaque	Black
SPHALERITE (Black Jack) ZnS **251**	Cubic C—Tetrahedral, common M—Cleavable, fine or coarse grained, compact	Submetallic Opaque to translucent	Black Brownish black Yellowish black
Huebnerite MnWO₄ **311**	Monoclinic C—Long fibrous, bladed, stalky often divergent, without good terminations M—Compact, lamellar, granular	Resinous Submetallic Translucent to opaque	Brownish black Black

Hardness 3 to 6

Hard-ness	Streak	Cleavage = C Fracture = F Tenacity	Specific Gravity	Characteristics and Associates
3. 3.5	White	C—Pinacoidal, perfect, 3 directions at 90° F—Conchoidal Brittle	2.8 3.	Color due to organic matter. Pseudocubical cleavage s o m e t i m e s noted. Granular varieties resemble marble. In limestones, shales. With halite, gypsum.
3. 4.	White	F—Conchoidal, splintery Brittle	2.5 2.8	Smooth and greasy feel. Often spotted, clouded, multi-colored. Sometimes crossed by seams of asbestos (chrysotile). With magnesite, calcite, chromite, garnierite, pyrope, platinum.
3. 5.	White	F—Conchoidal, uneven Brittle	3.1 3.2	More or less impure masses frequently resembling c o m p a c t, bituminous limestone. Independent beds, nodules, or concretions.
3.5 4.	Grayish	C—Dodecahedral perfect, usually conspicuous F—Conchoidal Brittle	3.9 4.2	Color and streak vary with impurities. Extensively in limestones with galena, chalcopyrite, pyrite, barite, fluorite, siderite, rhodochrosite.
4.5 5.5	Greenish gray	C—Clinopinacoidal, perfect, c o n-spicuous Brittle	6.7 7.3	Structure, cleavage, and specific gravity characteristic. In quartz veins. With wolframite, fluorite, pyrite, scheelite, galena, tetrahedrite.

Streak—Uncolored, white, or light gray

Name, Composition, and Reference	Crystallization Structure Crystals = C Massive = M	Luster Transparency	Color

TITANITE (Sphene)
 	
CaTiSiO₅
 	
384
	Monoclinic
	C—Wedge- or envelope-
	  shaped when dissem-
	  inated; tabular or
	  prismatic when at-
	  tached
	M—Compact, lamellar
		Vitreous
		Submetallic
		Translucent
		to opaque
			Black
			Brownish
			black

HORNBLENDE (Amphi-
bole)
Silicate of Ca, Mg, Fe, Al,
etc.
 	
371
	Monoclinic
	C—Long prismatic, prism
	  angle 124°, often
	  with rhombohedral-
	  like terminations
	M—Bladed, fibrous,
	  granular, compact
		Vitreous
		Silky
		Translucent
		to opaque
			Pitch black
			Greenish
			black
			Brownish
			black

AUGITE (Pyroxene)
 	
Silicate of Ca, Mg, Fe, Al,
etc.
 	
365
	Monoclinic
	C—Short prismatic,
	  thick columnar,
	  prism angle 87°
	M—Compact, granular,
	  disseminated
		Vitreous
		Submetallic
		Translucent
		to opaque
			Pitch
			black
			Greenish
			black
			Brownish
			black

Orthite (Allanite)
 	
Ca₂(Al,Ce,Fe)₂(AlOH)
(SiO₄)₃
 	
345
	Monoclinic
	C—Tabular, rare
	M—Compact, granular,
	  bladed, disseminated
	  grains
		Submetallic
		Greasy
		Translucent
		to opaque
			Black
			Pitch black
			Brownish
			black

Streak—Uncolored, white, or light gray

LABRADORITE (Feldspar)
 	
Silicate of Na,Ca,Al
 	
378
	Triclinic
	C—Thin tabular, often
	  with rhombic cross-
	  section
	M—Compact, cleavable,
	  granular
		Vitreous
		Pearly
		Translucent
		to nearly
		opaque
			Dark gray
			Greenish
			gray

Hardness 3 to 6

Hard- ness	Streak	Cleavage = C Fracture = F Tenacity	Specific Gravity	Characteristics and Associates
5. 5.5	White Gray	C—Prismatic, conspicuous partings often noted F—Conchoidal Brittle	3.4 3.6	With feldspars, pyroxenes, amphiboles, c h l o r i t e, scapolite, zircon.
5. 6.	Gray Greenish gray Brownish gray	C—Prismatic, perfect, often conspicuous—124° Brittle	2.9 3.3	Simple, pseudohexagonal crystals, and cleavage (124°) important. Very common. In nearly all types of rocks. With feldspars, quartz, pyroxenes, chlorite, calcite.
5. 6.	White Gray Greenish gray	C—Prismatic, perfect, conspicuous—87°, less distinct than on hornblende. Brittle	3.2 3.6	Crystals usually eight-sided, more rarely four-sided; pseudotetragonal with prism angles of 87° and 93°. In basic rocks and limestones.
5.5 6.	Gray Greenish gray Brownish gray	C—Pinacoidal, indistinct F—Uneven, c o n choidal Brittle	3. 4.	Often covered with yellowish or brownish crust. Disseminated in the more acid igneous rocks; limestones. With magnetite, epidote, quartz, feldspars.

Hardness over 6

Hard- ness	Streak	Cleavage = C Fracture = F Tenacity	Specific Gravity	Characteristics and Associates
6. 6.5	White	C—Basal, brachypinacoidal, perfect, conspicuous—86° F—Uneven, c o n choidal Brittle	2.7	Often with play of colors—yellow, green, blue, red. Inclined cleavages are striated. In basic igneous rocks. With pyroxenes, amphiboles.

Streak—Uncolored, white, or light gray

Name, Composition, and Reference	Crystallization Structure Crystals = C Massive = M	Luster Transparency	Color
EPIDOTE $Ca_2(Al,Fe)_2(AlOH)(SiO_4)_3$ **344**	Monoclinic C—Prismatic, elongated and deeply striated parallel to b axis; generally terminated on one end only M—Columnar, fibrous, parallel and divergent, granular	Vitreous Translucent to opaque	Greenish black
RUTILE TiO_2 **272**	Tetragonal C—Prismatic, vertically striated; twinned, yielding knee-shaped or rosette forms M—Compact, disseminated	Metallic Adamantine Opaque to translucent	Iron black Brownish black Reddish black
CASSITERITE SnO_2 **272**	Tetragonal C—Thick prismatic, knee-shaped twins, quite common M—Compact, reniform, botryoidal, rounded pebbles, often with internal, radial fibrous structure	Submetallic Dull Translucent to opaque	Black Brownish black
GARNET, varieties *Andradite* $M_3''M_2'''(SiO_4)_3$ *Almandite* $M'' = Ca, Fe, Mg$ $M''' = Al, Fe$ **349**	Cubic C—Dodecahedrons, tetragonal trisoctahedrons, alone or in combination M—Granular, compact, lamellar, disseminated, sand	Vitreous Translucent to opaque	Velvety black Brownish black

Hardness over 6

Hard-ness	Streak	Cleavage = C Fracture = F Tenacity	Specific Gravity	Characteristics and Associates
6. 7.	White Grayish	C—Basal, perfect F—Uneven Brittle	3.3 3.5	Crystals are often dark green or blackish green, massive aggregates lighter colored. Widely distributed. With quartz, feldspar, garnet, hornblende, pyroxene, magnetite, native copper.
6. 7.	Gray Yellowish white Brownish white	C—Prismatic, pyramidal, not conspicuous F—Uneven Brittle	4.2 4.3	Not as heavy as cassiterite. Often in hair-like inclusions. Widely distributed. With quartz, feldspar, hematite, ilmenite, chlorite.
6. 7.	White Yellowish white Brownish white	C—Indistinct F—Uneven Brittle	6.8 7.	Distinguished by high specific gravity. In veins cutting granite, gneiss; in alluvial deposits as *stream tin*. With quartz, wolframite, scheelite, molybdenite, tourmaline, fluorite, mica, chlorite.
6.5 7.5	White	C—Dodecahedral, usually indistinct F—Conchoidal, uneven Brittle	3.8 4.2	*Andradite*, commonly with magnetite, epidote, feldspars, nephelite, leucite; *almandite*, with mica, staurolite, andalusite, cyanite, tourmaline.

Streak—Uncolored, white, or light gray

Name, Composition, and Reference	Crystallization Structure Crystals = C Massive = M	Luster Transparency	Color
QUARTZ, Crystalline variety *Smoky quartz* SiO_2 269	Hexagonal C—Prismatic, horizontally striated M—Compact, granular	Vitreous Transparent to translucent	Grayish black Brownish black
Cryptocrystalline varieties *Chalcedony* *Onyx* *Flint* 270	Hexagonal Fine crystalline masses, banded, nodular, botryoidal, stalactitic	Waxy Vitreous Translucent to opaque	Grayish black Brownish black Velvet black
TOURMALINE, variety *Schorl* $M'_{20}B_2Si_4O_{21}$ $M' =$ Na,K,Li,Mg, Ca,(OH),Fe, Al 342	Hexagonal C—Prismatic, vertically striated; terminated with broken or rhombohedral-like surfaces; well developed crystals are hemimorphic M—Compact, divergent columnar	Pitchy Vitreous Translucent to opaque	Pitch black Brownish black Bluish black
STAUROLITE $H_2FeAl_4Si_2O_{12}$ 336	Orthorhombic C—Prismatic; twins plus- (+) or X-shaped, well developed, often large	Vitreous Dull Translucent to opaque	Brownish black Dark gray
SPINEL, varieties *Pleonaste* *Gahnite* $M''(M'''O_2)_2$ $M'' =$ Mg, Fe, Zn, Mn $M''' =$ Al, Fe 319	Cubic C—Octahedral, well developed, common M—Compact, granular, disseminated grains	Vitreous Dull Nearly opaque	Brownish black Grayish black Greenish black

Hardness over **6**

Hard-ness	Streak	Cleavage = C Fracture = F Tenacity	Specific Gravity	Characteristics and Associates
7.	White	C—Indistinct F—Conchoidal, conspicuous Brittle	2.6	Characteristic conchoidal fracture and glassy luster. Common in granitic rocks.
7.	White	C—Indistinct F—Conchoidal, conspicuous Brittle to tough	2.6	Conchoidal fracture characteristic. *Chalcedony*, waxy luster; *onyx*, banded; *flint*, generally with white coating; *basanite*, velvet black.
7. **7.5**	White Gray	C—None F—Conchoidal, un- even Brittle	2.9 3.2	Spherical triangular cross-section, coal black color, and lack of cleavage important. In pegmatites; metamorphic rocks; alluvial deposits. With quartz, feldspar, cassiterite, beryl, topaz, fluorite.
7. **7.5**	White Gray	C—Brachypina- coidal F—Conchoidal, un- even Brittle	3.4 3.8	Fresh crystals usually possess bright and smooth faces, when altered dull, rough, softer, and with colored streak. In metamorphic rocks—gneiss, mica schist, slate. With cyanite, garnet, tourmaline, sillimanite.
7.5 **8.**	White Grayish	C—Octahedral, in- distinct F—Conchoidal	3.6 4.4	Commonly as contact mineral in granular limestones; in more basic igneous rocks; rounded grains in placers. With calcite, chondrodite, serpentine, corundum, graphite, pyroxene, phlogopite.

Streak—Uncolored, white, or light gray

Name, Composition, and Reference	Crystallization Structure Crystals = C Massive = M	Luster Transparency	Color
CORUNDUM, varieties *Common* Al_2O_3	Hexagonal C—Prismatic, t a b u l a r, pyramidal, rhombohedral; rounded barrel-shaped M—Compact, lamellar	Vitreous Translucent to transparent	Dark gray Black
275			

DIAMOND, varieties
  Diamond proper
C *Bort*
  Carbonado
	Cubic
	C—Octahedrons, hexoctahedrons, usually with curved surfaces
	M—Rounded or irregular grains or pebbles, often with radial structure
		Adamantine
		Vitreous
		Translucent to opaque
			Black
			Dark gray

229			

B. MINERALS WITH NON-METALLIC LUSTER

Streak—Red, brown, or yellow

Name, Composition, and Reference	Crystallization Structure Crystals = C Massive = M	Luster Transparency	Color
BAUXITE $Al_2O_3.2H_2O$ **282**	Never in crystals M—Pisolitic, o ö l i t i c, rounded disseminated grains, clay-like, earthy	Dull Earthy Opaque	Red Reddish brown

HEMATITE, varieties
  Red ocher
Fe_2O_3 *Oölitic*
  Fossiliferous
276
	Hexagonal
	M—Fine g r a n u l a r, earthy, oölitic, replacement of shells
		Dull
		Opaque
			Brownish red
			Cherry red

REALGAR AsS **248**	Monoclinic C—Short prismatic, rare M—Granular, compact, incrustations	Resinous Transparent to translucent	Aurora red Orange yellow
CINNABAR HgS **256**	Hexagonal C—Rhombohedral, thick tabular, small M—Fine g r a n u l a r, fibrous, earthy coatings	Adamantine Dull Transparent to opaque	Scarlet red Brownish red

Hardness over 6

Hardness	Streak	Cleavage = C Fracture = F Tenacity	Specific Gravity	Characteristics and Associates
9.	White	C—None, nearly rectangular basal and rhombohedral partings, conspicuous; striated F—Conchoidal Brittle to tough	3.9 4.1	In limestone, granite, syenite, alluvial deposits. With magnetite, nephelite, mica, spinel, chlorite
10.	Ash gray	C—Octahedral, perfect (diamond proper) F—Conchoidal Brittle	3.1 3.5	Diamond proper, crystals and cleavage fragments; bort, translucent with radial structure; carbonado, granular to compact, opaque. In kimberlite—called blue ground, in placers. With pyrope, magnetite, chromite, zircon.

2. PINK, RED, OR RED VIOLET IN COLOR

Hardness 1 to 3

Hardness	Streak	Cleavage = C Fracture = F Tenacity	Specific Gravity	Characteristics and Associates
1. 3.	Reddish Yellowish	F—Earthy Brittle	2.5 2.6	Color and streak variable. Clay odor. With clay or kaolinite in nodules or irregular deposits in limestone or dolomite.
1. 3.	Cherry red Reddish brown	C—None F—Earthy Brittle	4.9 5.3	Red ocher, red earthy variety; oölitic hematite, fish-egg structure; fossiliferous hematite, replacement of shells.
1.5 2.	Orange yellow	C—Clinopinacoidal, basal F—Conchoidal Slightly sectile	3.4 3.6	Frequently disseminated in clay or dolomite. With orpiment, stibnite, arsenic, pyrite, barite, calcite.
2. 2.5	Scarlet Red brown	C—Prismatic, not conspicuous F—Uneven Brittle to sectile	8. 8.2	Characterized by color, streak, and high specific gravity. In siliceous rocks. With native mercury, pyrite, marcasite, realgar, stibnite.

Streak—Red, brown, or yellow

Name, Composition, and Reference	Crystallization Structure Crystals = C Massive = M	Luster Transparency	Color
Proustite Ag_3AsS_3 **262**	Hexagonal C—Small, complex, rare M—Compact, dissemi- nated, crusts, bands	Adamantine Dull Translucent to trans- parent	Scarlet Vermilion
Crocoite $PbCrO_4$ **309**	Monoclinic C—Prismatic, acicular M—Columnar, granular, crusts	Adamantine Greasy Translucent	Hyacinth red Aurora red
Pyrargyrite Ag_3SbS_3 **263**	Hexagonal C—Small, complex, rare M—Compact, dissemi- nated, crusts, bands	Adamantine Metallic Transparent to opaque	Dark red
Wulfenite $PbMoO_4$ **310**	Tetragonal C—Square, thin tabular, more rarely pyrami- dal M—Coarse, fine granular	Resinous Adamantine Transparent to trans- lucent	Orange red Bright red
Vanadinite $Pb_5Cl(VO_4)_3$ **328**	Hexagonal C—Prismatic, small, at times skeletal M—Compact, globular, fibrous, crusts	Resinous Translucent to opaque	Ruby red Brownish red Orange red

Streak—Red, brown, or yellow

HEMATITE, varieties *Argillaceous* Fe_2O_3 *Compact* **276**	Hexagonal M—Compact, granular, columnar, splintery, radiated reniform or botryoidal	Submetallic Dull Opaque	Brownish red Dark red

Hardness 1 to 3

Hardness	Streak	Cleavage = C Fracture = F Tenacity	Specific Gravity	Characteristics and Associates
2.5	Scarlet Aurora red	C—Imperfect F—Conchoidal Brittle	5.5 5.6	*Light ruby silver ore.* Distinguished from cinnabar by associates. With pyrargyrite, in veins with other silver minerals and galena. Compare pyrargyrite.
2.5	Orange yellow	C—Basal, prismatic F—Conchoidal, uneven Sectile	5.9 6.1	Resembles potassium bichromate in color. Alteration product of galena. With galena, quartz, pyrite, vanadinite, wulfenite.
2.5 3.	Cherry red Purplish red	C—Indistinct F—Conchoidal Brittle	5.8	Frequently as gray or dark red bands. Darker than proustite—*dark ruby silver ore.* With proustite, in veins with other silver minerals and galena.
3.	Lemon yellow Pale yellow	C—Pyramidal, indistinct F—Conchoidal, uneven Brittle	6.3 7.	Square plates, sometimes with forms of the third order. With lead minerals—galena, pyromorphite, vanadinite.
3.	Pale yellow Yellow	C—None F—Conchoidal, uneven Brittle	6.7 7.2	Crystal faces smooth with sharp edges. With lead minerals but never in large quantities.

Hardness over 3

Hardness	Streak	Cleavage = C Fracture = F Tenacity	Specific Gravity	Characteristics and Associates
3. 6.	Cherry red Reddish brown	C—None F—Uneven, splintery Brittle	4.9 5.3	*Argillaceous hematite,* impure from clay, sand, jasper; *compact hematite,* usually quite pure.

Streak—Red, brown, or yellow

Name, Composition, and Reference	Crystallization Structure Crystals = C Massive = M	Luster Transparency	Color
SPHALERITE ZnS **251**	Cubic C—Tetrahedral, common M—Cleavable, fine to coarse granular, compact	Resinous Submetallic Translucent to opaque	Brownish red Yellowish red
CUPRITE Cu_2O **279**	Cubic C—Octahedrons, dodeca- hedrons, alone or in combination M—Compact, granular, earthy; slender crystal aggregates (*chalcotrichite*)	Adamantine Dull Translucent to opaque	Cochineal red Brick red Dark red
Zincite ZnO **274**	Hexagonal C—Hemimorphic, rare M—Compact, granular, foliated	Adamantine Vitreous Translucent to opaque	Dark red Blood red
Huebnerite $MnWO_4$ **311**	Monoclinic C—Long, fibrous, bladed, stalky; often divergent, without good terminations M—Compact, lamellar, granular	Greasy Submetallic Translucent to opaque	Brownish red
WOLFRAMITE $(Fe,Mn)WO_4$ **311**	Monoclinic C—Thick tabular, short columnar, often large M—Bladed, curved lamellar, granular, compact	Submetallic Opaque	Brownish red

Hardness over 3

Hardness	Streak	Cleavage = C Fracture = F Tenacity	Specific Gravity	Characteristics and Associates
3.5 4.	Pale yellow Brownish yellow	C—Dodecahedral, perfect, usually conspicuous F—Conchoidal Brittle	3.9 4.2	Color and streak vary with impurities. Extensively in limestone. W i t h galena, chalcopyrite, pyrite, barite, fluorite, siderite, rhodochrosite.
3.5 4.	Brownish red Dirty brown	C—Indistinct F—Uneven Brittle	5.7 6.1	Characterized by associates, usually with copper minerals—malachite (green), azurite (blue), chalcocite and melaconite (black), chalcopyrite (yellow), native copper.
4. 4.5	Orange yellow Reddish yellow	C—Basal, s o m e-times conspicuous F—Uneven Brittle	5.4	Associates important—calcite, franklinite (black), willemite (yellow t o green), rhodonite (flesh red). On exposure becomes coated with the white carbonate.
4.5 5.5	Yellowish brown	C—Clinopinacoidal, perfect, c o n-spicuous Brittle	6.7 7.3	Structure, cleavage, and specific gravity characteristic. In quartz veins. With wolframite, fluorite, scheelite, galena, tetrahedrite.
5. 5.5	Dark reddish brown	C—Clinopinacoidal, perfect, conspicuous F—Uneven Brittle	7.1 7.5	Distinguished from huebnerite by streak. Powder may be slightly magnetic. With cassiterite, quartz, mica, scheelite, molybdenite, huebnerite.

Streak—Red, brown, or yellow

Name, Composition, and Reference	Crystallization Structure Crystals = C Massive = M	Luster Transparency	Color
RUTILE TiO_2 272	Tetragonal C—Prismatic, vertically striated; twinned, yielding knee-shaped or rosette forms M—Compact, disseminated	Adamantine Submetallic Translucent to opaque	Dark red Brownish red
CASSITERITE SnO_2 272	Tetragonal C—Thick p r i s m a t i c; knee-shaped twins quite common M—Compact, reniform, botryoidal, rounded pebbles, often with radial fibrous structure (*wood tin*)	Adamantine Dull Translucent to opaque	Brownish red Yellowish red

Streak—Uncolored, white, or light gray

GYPSUM $CaSO_4.2H_2O$ 315	Monoclinic C—Rare M—Coarse, fine granular, fibrous, cleavable, sand	Vitreous Silky Dull Transparent to opaque	Flesh red Brick red
HALITE (Rock salt) $NaCl$ 285	Cubic C—Cubes, often skeletal or hopper-shaped, rare M—Compact, cleavable, granular, fibrous, crusts, stalactitic	Vitreous Transparent to translucent	Red Reddish Purplish
Lepidolite (Lithium mica) $K_2Li_3Al_3(OH,F)_4-$ $(AlSi_3O_{10})_2$ 357	Monoclinic C—Short prismatic M—Granular, coarse or fine; scales, cleavable plates	Pearly Translucent	Pink Rose red Red violet

Hardness over 3

Hardness	Streak	Cleavage = C Fracture = F Tenacity	Specific Gravity	Characteristics and Associates
6. 6.5	Yellowish Brownish	C—Prismatic, pyramidal, not conspicuous F—Uneven Brittle	4.2 4.3	Not as heavy as cassiterite. Often in fine, hair-like inclusions. Widely distributed. With quartz, feldspars, hematite, ilmenite, chlorite.
6. 7.	Pale yellow Pale brown	C—Indistinct F—Uneven Brittle	6.8 7.	Recognized by high specific gravity. In veins cutting granite, gneiss; in alluvial deposits as *stream tin*. With quartz, wolframite, scheelite, arsenopyrite, tourmaline, fluorite, apatite, chlorite, mica.

Hardness 1 to 3

Hardness	Streak	Cleavage = C Fracture = F Tenacity	Specific Gravity	Characteristics and Associates
1.5 2.	White	C—Clinopinacoidal, perfect conspicuous; pyramidal, orthopinacoidal (crystals) F—Conchoidal Brittle, laminæ flexible	2.2 2.4	Ferruginous gypsum. In limestones, shales. With halite, celestite, sulphur, aragonite, anhydrite, ore deposits.
2. 2.5	White	C—Cubic, perfect, conspicuous F—Conchoidal Brittle	2.1 2.3	Characteristic c u b i c a l cleavage and saline taste. Color due to impurities. May absorb moisture and become damp. With shale, gypsum, anhydrite.
2. 3.	White	C—Basal, perfect F—Scaly, granular Tough	2.8 2.9	When massive may resemble granular limestone. In pegmatites, granites, gneisses. With red tourmaline (rubellite), amblygonite, spodumene, topaz.

Streak—Uncolored, white, or light gray

Name, Composition, and Reference	Crystallization Structure Crystals = C Massive = M	Luster Transparency	Color
PHLOGOPITE (Bronze mica) $KMg_3(OH)_2AlSi_3O_{10}$ 356	Monoclinic C—Tabular, prismatic, hexagonal or rhombic outline, often large and coarse M—Plates, disseminated scales	Pearly Submetallic Transparent to translucent	Copper red Bronze red Brownish red
CALCITE $CaCO_3$ 291	Hexagonal C—Scalenohedral, rhombohedral, prismatic, tabular, often highly modified, twinned M—Cleavable, granular, fibrous, compact	Vitreous Dull Transparent to nearly opaque	Pink Red Violet Amethystine
Wulfenite $PbMoO_4$ 310	Tetragonal C—Square, thin tabular, more rarely pyramidal M—Coarse to fine granular	Greasy Adamantine Transparent to translucent	Orange red Bright red
Vanadinite $Pb_5Cl(VO_4)_3$ 328	Hexagonal C—Prismatic, small, at times skeletal M—Compact, globular, fibrous, crusts	Greasy Translucent to opaque	Ruby red Orange red Brownish red

Streak—Uncolored, white, or light gray

Name, Composition, and Reference	Crystallization Structure	Luster Transparency	Color
STILBITE (Zeolite) $(Ca,Na_2)Al_2Si_6O_{16}.6H_2O$ 387	Monoclinic C—Twinned in sheaf-like, radial, or globular aggregates	Vitreous Pearly Transparent to translucent	Pale red Brick red
Lepidolite (Lithium mica) $K_2Li_3Al_3(OH,F)_4-$ $(AlSi_3O_{10})_2$ 357	Monoclinic C—Short prismatic M—Granular, coarse or fine; scales, cleavable plates	Pearly Translucent	Pink Rose red Red violet

Hardness 1 to 3

Hard-ness	Streak	Cleavage = C Fracture = F Tenacity	Specific Gravity	Characteristics and Associates
2.5 3.	White	C—Basal, perfect, conspicuous Tough, laminæ very elastic	2 8 3.	When cleavage laminæ are held close to the eye in viewing a source of light, a star-like form is some-times observed. Charac-teristic of crystalline lime-stones, dolomites, schists. With pyroxenes, amphi-boles, serpentine.
3.	White	C—Rhombohedral, perfect, very conspicuous F—Conchoidal Brittle	2.7	Rhombohedral cleavage characteristic, especially on crystals. Cleavages often show striations. Very strong double re-fraction observed when transparent.
3.	White Yellowish white	C—Pyramidal, in-distinct F—Conchoidal, un-even Brittle	6.3 7.	Square plates, sometimes with forms of the third order. With lead min-erals—galena, pyromor-phite, vanadinite.
3.	White Yellowish white	C—None F—Conchoidal, un-even Brittle	6.7 7.2	Crystal faces smooth with sharp edges. With lead minerals but never in large quantities.

Hardness 3 to 6

3. 4.	White	C—Pinacoidal F—Uneven Brittle	2 1 2.2	Radial and sheaf-like struc-ture important. In basic igneous rocks, ore depos-its. With chabazite, apo-phyllite, datolite, calcite.
3. 4.	White	C—Basal, perfect F—Scaly, granular Tough	2 8 2.9	When massive often like granular limestone. In pegmatites, granites, gneisses. With red tour-maline (rubellite), ambly-gonite, spodumene, topaz.

Streak—Uncolored, white, or light gray

Name, Composition, and Reference	Crystallization Structure Crystals = C Massive = M	Luster Transparency	Color
ALUNITE (Alum stone) $K_2(Al.2OH)_6(SO_4)_4$ 313	Hexagonal C—Rhombohedrons, resembling cubes, tabular, rare M—Compact, granular, fibrous, earthy	Vitreous Pearly Transparent to translucent	Pink Reddish white
DOLOMITE $CaMg(CO_3)_2$ 294	Hexagonal C—Rhombohedral, with curved surfaces M—Coarsely crystalline, compact, granular, friable	Vitreous Transparent to translucent	Light pink Pink Reddish
SPHALERITE ZnS 251	Cubic C—Tetrahedral, common M—Cleavable, fine or coarse granular, compact	Resinous Submetallic Translucent to opaque	Brownish red Yellowish red
RHODOCHROSITE $MnCO_3$ 297	Hexagonal C—Rhombohedral, rare M—Cleavable, granular, compact, botryoidal, crusts	Vitreous Translucent	Rose red Brownish red Pink
FLUORITE (Fluor spar) CaF_2 287	Cubic C—Cubes, alone or modified, well developed, common; penetration twins M—Cleavable, granular, fibrous	Vitreous Transparent to nearly opaque	Red violet Pink Rose red
CHABAZITE (Zeolite) $CaAl_2Si_6O_{16}.8H_2O$, etc. 388	Hexagonal C—Rhombohedral, cube-like, lenticular M—Compact	Vitreous Translucent to transparent	Flesh red Red

Hardness 3 to 6

Hardness	Streak	Cleavage = C Fracture = F Tenacity	Specific Gravity	Characteristics and Associates
3.5 4.	White	C—Basal F—Splintery, conchoidal, earthy Brittle	2.6 2.8	Hardness often greater due to admixture of quartz, feldspar, then tough. Deposits and veins in feldspathic rocks. With kaolin, pyrite, opal.
3.5 4.	White Gray	C—Rhombohedral, perfect (crystals) F—Conchoidal Brittle	2.9	Crystals generally curved or saddle-shaped. *Marble* includes some compact varieties. In fissures and cavities; with ore deposits.
3.5 4.	Gray Yellowish white	C—Dodecahedral, perfect, usually conspicuous F—Conchoidal Brittle	3.9 4.2	Color and streak vary with impurities. Extensively in limestones. With galena, chalcopyrite, pyrite, barite, fluorite, rhodochrosite.
3.5 4.5	White	C—Rhombohedral, perfect, conspicuous F—Uneven Brittle	3.3 3.6	May turn brown to black on exposure, due to MnO_2. With galena, sphalerite, pyrite, rhodonite, psilomelane, silver minerals.
4.	White	C—Octahedral, perfect, conspicuous Brittle	3. 3.2	Easily recognized by crystal form, cleavage, and hardness. Common gangue mineral of metallic ores. With galena, sphalerite, cassiterite, calcite, quartz, barite.
4. 5	White	C—Rhombohedral, not conspicuous F—Uneven Brittle	2.1 2.2	Generally in cube-like crystals. Inferior cleavage distinguishes it from fluorite and calcite. In basic igneous rocks. With analcite, stilbite.

Streak—Uncolored, white, or light gray

Name, Composition, and Reference	Crystallization Structure Crystals = C Massive = M	Luster Transparency	Color
APOPHYLLITE $KFCa_4(Si_2O_5)_4.8H_2O$ **385**	Tetragonal C—Prismatic, pyramidal, pseudocubical, tabular M—Lamellar, granular, compact	Vitreous Pearly Transparent to nearly opaque	Pale red Flesh red Rose red
APATITE $Ca_5F(PO_4)_3$ **326**	Hexagonal C—Prismatic, thick tabular, common; may be vertically striated and have fused appearance M—Granular, compact, fibrous, nodular	Greasy Vitreous Translucent to opaque	Violet red Brownish red Red
Huebnerite $MnWO_4$ **311**	Monoclinic C—Long fibrous, bladed, stalky; poorly terminated M—Compact, lamellar, granular	Resinous Submetallic Translucent to opaque	Brownish red
ANALCITE (Zeolite) $NaAlSi_2O_6.H_2O$ **387**	Cubic C—Tetragonal trisoctahedrons, cubes M—Granular, compact	Vitreous Translucent to opaque	Reddish Brick red
Datolite $Ca(BOH)SiO_4$ **341**	Monoclinic M—Compact, fibrous, granular, botryoidal	Vitreous Greasy Dull Translucent to opaque	Pink Red Red violet
TITANITE (Sphene) $CaTiSiO_5$ **384**	Monoclinic C—Wedge- or envelope-shaped when disseminated; tabular or prismatic when attached M—Compact, lamellar	Vitreous Greasy Transparent to opaque	Brownish red Red

Hardness 3 to 6

Hardness	Streak	Cleavage = C Fracture = F Tenacity	Specific Gravity	Characteristics and Associates
4.5 **5.**	White	C—Basal, perfect, conspicuous F—Uneven Brittle	2.3 2.4	Prism faces vertically striated. In fissures and cavities in basic igneous rocks. With natrolite, analcite, datolite, pectolite, native copper, calcite.
4.5 **5.**	White Reddish white	C—Basal, imperfect F—Conchoidal, uneven Brittle	3.1 3.2	Color often unevenly distributed,—mottled brown and green. In crystalline limestones, metalliferous ore deposits, igneous rocks. With quartz, cassiterite, fluorite, wolframite, magnetite.
4.5 **5.5**	Greenish gray	C—Clinopinacoidal, perfect, conspicuous Brittle	6.7 7.3	Structure, cleavage, and specific gravity characteristic. In quartz veins. With wolframite, fluorite, pyrite, scheelite, galena, tetrahedrite.
5. **5.5**	White Reddish white	C—None F—Uneven, conchoidal Brittle	2.2 2.3	Good crystals common. In basic igneous rocks with apophyllite, chabazite, natrolite, datolite, native copper, epidote.
5. **5.5**	White	C—None F—Conchoidal, uneven Brittle	2.9 3.	Compact masses often with brownish, yellowish, or whitish streaks and spots. In basic igneous rocks with calcite, epidote, native copper, zeolites.
5. **5.5**	White Gray	C—Prismatic, conspicuous parting often noted F—Conchoidal Brittle	3.4 3.6	With feldspars, pyroxenes, amphiboles, c h l o r i t e, scapolite, zircon.

Streak—Uncolored, white, or light gray

Name, Composition, and Reference	Crystallization Structure Crystals = C Massive = M	Luster Transparency	Color
Monazite $(Ce,La,Di)PO_4$ **325**	Monoclinic C—Thick tabular, square prismatic M—A n g u l a r, rolled grains	Resinous Vitreous Translucent to opaque	Hyacinth red Brownish red
SCAPOLITE (Wernerite) $\left\{ \begin{array}{l} nNa_4Al_3Si_9O_{24}Cl \\ mCa_4Al_6Si_6O_{24}CO_3 \end{array} \right.$ **383**	Tetragonal C—Prismatic M—Compact, granular, fibrous, columnar	Vitreous Greasy Translucent	Pink Red violet Brick red
RHODONITE $MnSiO_3$ **368**	Triclinic C—Tabular, prismatic, rounded edges, often large M—Compact, cleavable, granular, dissemi-nated grains	Vitreous Dull Transparent to opaque	Brownish red Flesh red Rose red

OPAL, varieties
      Fire opal
      Opal jasper
$SiO_2.nH_2O$
 	
280
	Amorphous
	M—Reniform, botryoid-al, stalactitic, com-pact
		Vitreous
		Greasy
		Transparent to opaque
			Red
			Brownish red

Streak—Uncolored, white, or light gray

ORTHOCLASE (Feldspar) $KAlSi_3O_8$ **372**	Monoclinic C—Prismatic, thick tabular, twins; often large M—Cleavable, granular, disseminated	Vitreous Pearly Translucent to opaque	Flesh red Brick red

Hardness 3 to 6

Hardness	Streak	Cleavage = C Fracture = F Tenacity	Specific Gravity	Characteristics and Associates
5. 5.5	White	C—Basal F—Conchoidal, uneven Brittle	4.9 5.3	Crystals commonly small, highly modified, or as rolled grains in sand. With magnetite, zircon, garnet, gold, chromite, diamond.
5. 6.	White	C—Prismatic, not conspicuous F—Conchoidal Brittle	2.6 2.8	Often resembles pink fluorite in color, but cleavage less distinct, and harder. In metamorphic rocks, especially granular limestones. With pyroxenes, apatite, garnet, titanite, biotite, amphiboles.
5. 6.	White Reddish white	C—Prismatic, basal F—Conchoidal, uneven Tough, when massive; crystals brittle	3.4 3.7	May be stained brown to black on exposure. *Fowlerite*, variety containing zinc. With franklinite, zincite, willemite, calcite, tetrahedrite.
5.5 6.	White	F—Conchoidal, conspicuous Brittle	1.9 2.3	Structure and fracture characteristic. *Fire opal*, transparent to translucent and red; *opal jasper*, greasy and opaque, resembling jasper. In veins, cavities, and masses of irregular outline.

Hardness over 6

Hardness	Streak	Cleavage = C Fracture = F Tenacity	Specific Gravity	Characteristics and Associates
6. 6.5	White	C—Basal, clinopinacoidal, perfect, conspicuous— 90° F—Conchoidal, uneven Brittle	⌐.5 2.6	Characterized by rectangular cleavage and absence of twinning striations. In granitic rocks. With quartz, other feldspars, mica, hornblende, zircon.

Streak—Uncolored, white, or light gray

Name, Composition, and Reference	Crystallization Structure Crystals = C Massive = M	Luster Transparency	Color
Chondrodite $[Mg(F,OH)]_2Mg_3(SiO_4)_2$ 343	Monoclinic C—Small, highly modified, rare M—Rounded, disseminated grains; compact	Vitreous Greasy Translucent to opaque	Brownish red Dark red
RUTILE TiO_2 272	Tetragonal C—Prismatic, vertically striated; twinned, yielding knee-shaped or rosette forms M—Compact, disseminated	Adamantine Submetallic Translucent to opaque	Dark red Brownish red
CASSITERITE SnO_2 272	Tetragonal C—Thick prismatic; knee-shaped twins quite common M—Compact, reniform, botryoidal, rounded pebbles, often with internal, radial fibrous structure, *wood tin*	Adamantine Resinous Dull Translucent to opaque	Brownish red Yellowish red
ANDALUSITE Al_2SiO_5 338	Orthorhombic C—Prismatic, rough, nearly square, often large and without terminations M—Columnar, fibrous, granular, disseminated	Vitreous Dull Translucent opaque	Pink Rose red Red violet

Hardness over 6

Hard-ness	Streak	Cleavage = C Fracture = F Tenacity	Specific Gravity	Characteristics and Associates
6. 6.5	White	C—Basal F—Conchoidal, un-even Brittle	3.1 3.3	Associates i m p o r t a n t. Chiefly in crystalline lime-stones and dolomites. With spinel, vesuvianite, pyroxenes, magnetite, mica.
6. 7.	Gray Yellowish white Brownish white	C—Prismatic, py-ramidal, not conspicuous F— Uneven Brittle	4.2 4.3	Not as heavy as cassiterite. Often as fine hair-like inclusions. Widely dis-tributed. With quartz, feldspar, hematite, ilmen-ite, chlorite.
6. 7.	White Yellowish white Brownish white	C—Indistinct F—Uneven Brittle	6.8 7.	Distinguished by high spe-cific gravity. In veins cutting granite, gneiss; in alluvial deposits as *stream tin*. With quartz, wolframite, s c h e e l i t e, arsenopyrite, tourmaline, fluorite, mica, chlorite.
6. 7.5	White	C—Prismatic F—Uneven Brittle	3.1 3.2	Due to alteration, surface may be covered with scales of mica and, hence, is softer. In metamorphic rocks often as rounded or knotty projections. With cyanite, sillimanite, gar-net, tourmaline.

Streak—Uncolored, white, or light gray

Name, Composition, and Reference	Crystallization Structure Crystals = C Massive = M	Luster Transparency	Color

GARNET, varieties
      Grossularite
$M_3''M_2'''$ *Pyrope*
  $(SiO_4)_3$ *Spessartite*
$M'' = Ca,$ *Almandite*
  Fe,Mg *Andradite*
$M''' = Al,Fe$
	Cubic
	C—Dodecahedrons, tetragonal trisoctahedrons, alone or in combination
	M—Granular, compact, lamellar, disseminated, sand
		Vitreous
		Transparent to opaque
			Rose red
			Ruby red
			Brownish red
			Dark red

349

| QUARTZ, Crystalline varieties
SiO₂ *Amethyst*
    Rose quartz
    Aventurine
    Ferruginous | Hexagonal
C—Prismatic, horizontally striated, common
M—Compact, granular | Vitreous
Greasy
Transparent to opaque | Red violet
Rose red
Brick red
Brownish red |

269

| Cryptocrystalline varieties
Carnelian
Agate
Sard
Jasper
Heliotrope | Hexagonal
C—Never in crystals
M—Banded, spotted, compact | Waxy
Vitreous
Translucent to opaque | Bright red
Dark red
Brownish red |

270

| Clastic varieties
Sand
Sandstone
Quartzite | Hexagonal
Loose or strongly consolidated grains or fragments | Vitreous
Dull
Translucent to opaque | Red
Brownish red
Purplish red |

271

Hardness over 6

Hard-ness	Streak	Cleavage = C Fracture = F Tenacity	Specific Gravity	Characteristics and Associates
6.5 **7.5**	White Gray	C—Dodecahedral, indistinct F—Conchoidal, un-even Brittle	3.4 4.3	*Grossularite*, in crystalline limestones and dolomites, with wollastonite, vesuvi-anite, diopside, scapolite; *pyrope*, rounded grains, in serpentine; *spessartite*, in granitic rocks, with topaz, tourmaline, quartz, ortho-clase; *almandite*, w i t h mica, staurolite, andalus-ite, cyanite; *andradite*, with magnetite, epidote, feldspar, nephelite, leu-cite.
7.	White Reddish white	C—Indistinct F—Conchoidal, conspicuous Brittle	2.6	Characteristic conchoidal fracture and glassy luster. *Amethyst*, usually in crys-tals, purple or blue violet; *rose quartz*, usually mass-ive, pink to rose red; *aventurine*, massive and glistening, due to in-cluded scales; *ferruginous quartz*, colored by iron oxide.
7.	White Reddish white	C—Indistinct F—Conchoidal, conspicuous Brittle to tough	2.6	Not as glassy as phanero-crystalline varieties. *Car-nelian*, *jasper*, uniform in color; *agate*, *sardonyx*, banded; *heliotrope*, spot-ted. To distinguish, see reference.
7.	White Reddish white	C—Indistinct F—Uneven Brittle to tough	2.6	Pigment is usually fer-ruginous matter. *Sand*, l o o s e, unconsolidated grains; *sandstone*, con-solidated sand; *quartzite*, metamorphosed s a n d-stone.

Streak—Uncolored, white, or light gray

Name, Composition, and Reference	Crystallization Structure Crystals = C Massive = M	Luster Transparency	Color
TOURMALINE, variety *Rubellite* $M'_{20}B_2Si_4O_{21}$ M' = Na,Ka,Li,Mg, Ca,(OH),Fe, Al 342	Hexagonal C—Prismatic, o f t e n vertically striated, rarely with good terminations M—Divergent, columnar, compact	Vitreous Transparent to trans- lucent	Pink Rose red Ruby red
ZIRCON $ZrSiO_4$ 348	Tetragonal C—Prismatic, pyramidal, small, well developed M—Irregular lumps, grains	Adamantine Vitreous Resinous Transparent to opaque	Brownish red Dark red
SPINEL, varieties $M''(M'''O_2)_2$ *Ruby* M'' = Mg,Fe, Mn *Rubicelle* M''' = Al,Fe *Almandine* 319	Cubic C—Octahedral, t w i n s, small M—Rounded g r a i n s, small pebbles	Vitreous Splendent Transparent to trans- lucent	Deep red Rose red Orange red Bluish red
CORUNDUM, varieties *Ruby* Al_2O_3 *Oriental amethyst Common* 275	Hexagonal C—Prismatic, tabular, pyramidal, rhombo- hedral, rough or rounded b a r r e l- shaped M—Compact, granular, lamellar	Vitreous Transparent to trans- lucent	Pink Red Red violet

Hardness over 6

Hardness	Streak	Cleavage = C Fracture = F Tenacity	Specific Gravity	Characteristics and Associates
7. 7.5	White	C—None F—Conchoidal, uneven Brittle	2.9 3.2	Spherical triangular cross-section. Often with zonal distribution of color—red, green, colorless. Frequently as long, divergent, columnar masses imbedded in lepidolite.
7.5	White	C—Indistinct F—Uneven Brittle	4.4 4.8	Often in the more acid igneous rocks—granites, syenites; alluvial deposits, with gold, spinel, corundum, garnet. *Hyacinth*, clear and transparent.
8.	White	C—Octahedral, indistinct F—Conchoidal Brittle	3.5 4.1	*Balas spinel*, rose red; *ruby spinel*, deep red; *rubicelle*, yellow to orange red; *almandine*, bluish red. Usually in precious stone placers, with zircon, garnet, magnetite; more rarely as contact mineral in crystalline limestones.
9.	White	C—None. Nearly rectangular basal and rhombohedral partings, conspicuous; often striated F—Conchoidal Brittle to tough	3.9 4.1	When massive often multicolored—blue, green, gray. *Ruby*, transparent red; *oriental amethyst*, violet. In limestones, granites; schists, peridotites, alluvial deposits. With magnetite, hematite, nephelite, mica, spinel.

Streak—Blue, green, brown, or yellow

Name, Composition, and Reference	Crystallization Structure Crystals = C Massive = M	Luster Transparency	Color
CHLORITE (Prochlorite, clinochlorite) $H_8Mg_5Al_2Si_3O_{18}$	Monoclinic C—Tabular, six-sided, often bent and twisted M—Foliated, scaly, granular, earthy	Pearly Vitreous Dull Translucent to opaque	Grass green Brownish green Blackish green
358			
CHRYSOCOLLA CuO,SiO_2,H_2O	Amorphous ? M—Compact, reniform, incrustations, seams, stains, earthy	Vitreous Greasy Dull Translucent to opaque	Green Greenish blue Blue
353			
Garnierite $H_2(Ni,Mg)SiO_4$	Amorphous ? M—Compact, reniform, earthy	Dull Greasy Opaque	Pale green Apple green Emerald green
362			
Chalcanthite (Blue vitriol) $CuSO_4.5H_2O$	Triclinic C—Tabular, small, rare, M—Crusts, reniform, stalactitic, powdery	Vitreous Dull Translucent	Deep blue Sky blue Greenish blue
318			
Brochantite $CuSO_4.3Cu(OH)_2$	Orthorhombic C—Prismatic, acicular, vertically striated M—Reniform, fibrous, drusy crusts	Vitreous Pearly Transparent to translucent	Emerald green Blackish green
314			

Hardness 1 to 6

Hardness	Streak	Cleavage = C Fracture = F Tenacity	Specific Gravity	Characteristics and Associates
1. 2.5	Pale green	C—Basal, perfect; when foliated, conspicuous F—Scaly, earthy Tough to brittle	2.6 3.	Laminæ are flexible but inelastic, with slightly soapy feel. Common in schists and serpentine. With magnetite, garnet, diopside, m a g n e s i t e. Often as a scaly or dusty coating on other minerals. Pseudomorphous a f t e r garnet.
2. 4.	Pale green Pale blue	F—Conchoidal Brittle	2: 2.2	Usually recognized by enamel-like appearance, conchoidal fracture, and n o n-fibrous structure. When impure brownish or blackish. With copper minerals—malachite, azurite, chalcopyrite.
2. 3.	Pale green	C—None F—Conchoidal, earthy Brittle	2.3 2.8	Often as rounded, pea-shaped masses with varnish-like surfaces and earthy interior. F r e-quently adheres to tongue. With olivine, serpentine, chromite, talc.
2.5	Light blue	C—Indistinct F—Conchoidal Brittle	2.1 2.3	Disagreeable metallic taste. Oxidation product of copper sulphide minerals. With chalcopyrite, bornite, melanterite, pyrite.
3.5	Light green	C—Brachypina-coidal F—Uneven Brittle	3.8 3.9	Not as common as malachite. Secondary copper mineral. With malachite, azurite, cuprite, chalcopyrite, limonite.

Streak—Blue, green, brown, or yellow

Name, Composition, and Reference	Crystallization Structure Crystals = C Massive = M	Luster Transparency	Color
AZURITE $2CuCO_3.Cu(OH)_2$ 302	Monoclinic C—Short prismatic, tab- ular, often in spher- ical aggregates M—Fibrous; botryoidal, with velvety or radial structure; earthy, crusts	Vitreous Dull Translucent to opaque	Azure blue Dark blue
MALACHITE $CuCO_3.Cu(OH)_2$ 302	Monoclinic C—Acicular, often in groups or tufts M—Fibrous; stalactitic, botryoidal, w i t h smooth surface and internal banded or radial fibrous struc- ture; velvety crusts, earthy	Silky Adamantine Dull Translucent to opaque	Emerald green Grass green Dark green
PYROMORPHITE $Pb_5Cl(PO_4)_3$ 328	Hexagonal C—Prismatic, thick tab- ular, rounded and barrel-shaped M—Globular, reniform, disseminated, crusts	Greasy Adamantine Translucent to opaque	Dark green Emerald green Yellowish green.
Lazurite (Lapis lazuli) $3NaAlSiO_4.Na_2S$ 381	Cubic C—Dodecahedrons, rare M—Compact, irregular grains	Vitreous Translucent to opaque	Azure blue Violet blue Greenish blue
HORNBLENDE (Amphi- bole) Silicate of Ca, Mg, Fe, Al, etc. 371	Monoclinic C—Long prismatic, prism angle 124°; often with rhombohedral- like terminations M—Bladed, fibrous, granular, compact	Vitreous Silky Translucent to opaque	Blackish green Dark green

Hardness 1 to 6

Hardness	Streak	Cleavage = C Fracture = F Tenacity	Specific Gravity	Characteristics and Associates
3.5 4.	Blue	C—Domatic F—Conchoidal Brittle	3.7 3.8	Common alteration product of copper minerals. With malachite, cuprite, native copper, chalcocite, chalcopyrite, b o r n i t e. Pseudomorphous a f t e r c u p r i t e, tetrahedrite. Alters to malachite.
3.5 4.	Light green	C—Basal, pina- coidal F—Conchoidal, splintery Brittle	3.7 4.1	Very common alteration product of copper minerals. With azurite, cuprite, native copper, chalcocite, chalcopyrite, bornite. Pseudomorphous after cuprite, azurite, native copper. Surface may be almost black, due to the oxide, melaconite.
3.5 4.	Yellow Greenish yellow	C—None F—Conchoidal, un- even Brittle	6.5 7.1	Alteration product of lead minerals. With galena, cerussite, barite, limonite.
5. 5.5	Pale blue	C—Dodecahedral, distinct F—Uneven Brittle	2.4	Always blue and contains disseminated p y r i t e. Occurs as contact mineral in crystalline limestone.
5. 6.	Grayish green Grayish brown Yellowish	C—Prismatic, per- fect, often con- spicuous—124° Brittle	2.9 3.3	Simple, pseudohexagonal crystals, and cleavage—124°—i m p o r t a n t. In nearly all types of igneous rocks. With quartz, feldspar, pyroxene, chlorite, calcite.

Streak—Blue, green, brown, or yellow

Name, Composition, and Reference	Crystallization Structure Crystals = C Massive = M	Luster Transparency	Color
AUGITE (Pyroxene) Silicate of Ca, Mg, Fe, Al, etc. **365**	Monoclinic C—Short, prismatic, thick columnar; prism angle 87° M—Compact, granular, disseminated	Vitreous Submetallic Translucent to opaque	Blackish green Leek green
Turquois $H_5[Al(OH)_2]_6Cu(OH)(PO_4)_4$ **329**	Triclinic C—Small, rare M—Reniform, stalactitic, disseminated, rounded pebbles	Waxy Dull Opaque to translucent	Sky blue Bluish green Apple green

Streak—Uncolored, white, or light gray

Asbestos, variety *Chrysotile* $H_4Mg_3Si_2O_9$ **360**	Monoclinic M—Fibrous, coarse or fine; felted	Silky Silky metallic Opaque	Light green Olive green
variety *Amphibole* Silicate of Ca, Mg, Fe, Al, **369** etc.	Monoclinic M—Fibrous, coarse or fine; felted	Silky Opaque	Greenish
TALC, varieties *Foliated* *Soapstone* or *steatite* $H_2Mg_3Si_4O_{12}$ **358**	Monoclinic C—Thin tabular, indistinct M—Foliated, globular, granular, compact, fibrous	Pearly Greasy Opaque to transparent	Pale green Apple green Dark green

Hardness 1 to 6

Hardness	Streak	Cleavage = C Fracture = F Tenacity	Specific Gravity	Characteristics and Associates
5. 6.	Pale green Grayish green	C—Prismatic, perfect, conspicuous—87° Brittle	3.2 3.6	Crystals, usually eight sided, more rarely four-sided; pseudotetragonal with prism angles of 87° and 93°. Cleavage less distinct than on hornblende. Common in basic eruptive rocks and crystalline limestones.
6.	Pale green	F—Conchoidal Brittle	2.6 2.8	Secondary mineral, common in thin veins, crusts, or coatings. With limonite, quartz, feldspar, kaolin.

Hardness 1 to 3

Hardness	Streak	Cleavage = C Fracture = F Tenacity	Specific Gravity	Characteristics and Associates
1. 2.5	White	F—Fibrous Flexible	1. 2.5	Delicate, fine, parallel-flexible fibers perpendicular to walls, easily separable, called *short fibered asbestos;* compare below. In veins or seams in compact serpentine.
1. 2.5	White	F—Fibrous Flexible	1. 2.5	*Long fibered asbestos,* parallel, flexible fi b e r s. Fibers parallel to walls. Compare above.
1. 2.5	White	C—Basal, conspicuous on foliated masses F—Uneven Sectile, laminæ flexible	2.6 2.8	Greasy or soapy feel. *Foliated,* easily separable, inelastic folia or plates, H = 1; *Soapstone* or *steatite,* coarse to fine granular, more or less impure, H = 1.5 − 2.5. With serpentine, dolomite, magnesite, actinolite.

Streak—Uncolored, white, or light gray

Name, Composition, and Reference	Crystallization Structure Crystals = C Massive = M	Luster Transparency	Color
CHLORITE (Prochlorite, clinochlorite) $H_8Mg_5Al_2Si_3O_{18}$	Monoclinic C—Tabular, six-s i d e d, often bent, twisted M—Foliated, scaly, granular, earthy	Pearly Vitreous Dull Translucent to opaque	Grass green Brownish green Blackish green
357			
Melanterite (Copperas) $FeSO_4.7H_2O$	Monoclinic C—Rare M—Capillary, fibrous, stalactitic, concretionary, powder	Vitreous Dull Transparent to translucent	Green Yellowish green
317			
CHRYSOCOLLA CuO,SiO_2,H_2O	Amorphous ? M—Compact, reniform, incrustations, seams, stains, earthy	Vitreous Greasy Dull Translucent to opaque	Green Greenish blue Blue
353			
Garnierite $H_2(Ni,Mg)SiO_4$	Amorphous ? M—Compact, reniform, earthy	Dull Greasy Opaque	Pale green Apple green Emerald green
362			
Actinolite (Amphibole) $Ca_2(Mg,Fe)_5(OH)_2-$ $(Si_4O_{11})_2$	Monoclinic C—Fine, acicular M—Interwoven fibrous aggregates, radiating masses	Vitreous Silky Translucent to opaque	Grass green Grayish green
370			

Hardness 1 to 3

Hard-ness	Streak	Cleavage = C Fracture = F Tenacity	Specific Gravity	Characteristics and Associates
1. **2.5**	White Greenish white	C—Basal, conspic-uous, when foliated F—Scaly, earthy Tough to brittle	2.6 3.	Laminæ flexible but in-elastic, with s l i g h t l y soapy feel. Common in schists and serpentine. With magnetite, mag-nesite, garnet, diopside. Often as scaly or dusty coating on other minerals. Pseudomorphous a f t e r garnet.
2.	White	C—Basal, not con-spicuous F—Conchoidal, earthy Brittle	1.8 1.9	On exposure loses water and crumbles to powder. Sweet, astringent taste, somewhat metallic. Oxi-dation product of iron sulphide minerals—mar-casite, pyrite, chalcopy-rite, pyrrhotite.
2. **3.**	White Greenish white Bluish white	F—Conchoidal Brittle	2. 2.2	Usually recognized by enamel-like appearance, conchoidal fracture, and n o n-fibrous structure. When impure brownish or blackish. W i t h copper m i n e r a l s—malachite, azurite, chalcopyrite; also limonite.
2. **3.**	White Greenish white	C—None F—Conchoidal, earthy Brittle	2.3 2.8	Often as rounded, pea-shaped masses, with varn-ish-like s u r f a c e s a n d earthy interior. May ad-here to tongue. With olivine, serpentine, chro-mite, talc.
2. **3.**	White Greenish white	C—Fibrous Brittle	2.9 3.2	Masses of delicate, inter-w o v e n fibers—*actinolite schist*. A pale grayish green, highly ferruginous variety (*grünerite*, $Fe_4(SiO_3)_4$) associated with quartz and magnetite is termed *magnetite-grüner-ite schist*.

Streak—Uncolored, white, or light gray

Name, Composition, and Reference	Crystallization Structure Crystals = C Massive = M	Luster Transparency	Color
Chalcanthite (Blue vitriol) $CuSO_4.5H_2O$ 318	Triclinic C—Tabular, small, rare M—Crusts, reniform, stalactitic, fibrous, powdery	Vitreous Dull Translucent	Deep blue Sky blue Greenish blue
BIOTITE (Mica) $K(Mg,Fe)_3(OH)_2AlSi_3O_{10}$ 357	Monoclinic C—Tabular, hexagonal or rhombohedral habit M—Plates, disseminated scales	Pearly Submetallic Transparent to opaque	Brownish green Blackish green
BARITE (Heavy spar) $BaSO_4$ 307	Orthorhombic C—Tabular, prismatic, crested divergent groups, common M—Compact, lamellar, fibrous, cleavable, reniform	Vitreous Pearly Transparent to opaque	Bluish Greenish
CALCITE $CaCO_3$ 291	Hexagonal M—Cleavable, granular, fibrous, compact	Vitreous Dull Transparent to nearly opaque	Sky blue Deep blue Greenish

Streak—Uncolored, white, or light gray

ANHYDRITE $CaSO_4$ 305	Orthorhombic C—Thick tabular, prismatic, rare M—Granular, compact, fibrous, lamellar, cleavable, reniform	Vitreous Pearly Translucent to opaque	Bluish Grayish blue Blue

Hardness 1 to 3

Hardness	Streak	Cleavage = C Fracture = F Tenacity	Specific Gravity	Characteristics and Associates
2.5	White Bluish white	C—Indistinct F—Conchoidal, earthy Brittle	2.1 2.3	Disagreeable m e t a l l i c taste. Oxidation product of copper sulphide minerals. With chalcopyrite, bornite, melanterite, pyrite.
2.5 3.	White Grayish	C—Basal, perfect, conspicuous Tough, laminæ of fresh biotite very elastic	2.7 3.2	Easily recognized by structure, highly perfect cleavage, and elasticity. Important constituent of many igneous and metamorphic rocks—granite, syenite, gneiss.
2.5 3.	White	C—Basal, prismatic, conspicuous F—Uneven Brittle	4.3 4.7	Characterized by rather high specific gravity and cleavages. In metalliferous veins; pockets, lenticular masses in limestone. With g a l e n a, sphalerite, chlorite, chalcopyrite; manganese and iron minerals.
3.	White	C—Rhombohedral perfect, conspicuous F—Conchoidal Brittle	2.7	Rhombohedral cleavage generally characteristic. Cleavages often s h o w striations.

Hardness 3 to 6

Hardness	Streak	Cleavage = C Fracture = F Tenacity	Specific Gravity	Characteristics and Associates
3. 3.5	White	C—Pinacoidal, perfect, 3 directions at 90° F—Conchoidal Brittle	2.8 3.	Pseudocubical cleavage, sometimes noted. Granular varieties resemble marble. Not as heavy as celestite or barite. In limestone, shale. W i t h halite, gypsum.

Streak—Uncolored, white, or light gray

Name, Composition, and Reference	Crystallization Structure Crystals = C Massive = M	Luster Transparency	Color
CELESTITE $SrSO_4$ 306	Orthorhombic C—Tabular, prismatic, common; pyramidal M—Compact, cleavable, fibrous, granular, reniform	Vitreous Pearly Transparent to translucent	Sky blue Blue Greenish
BARITE (Heavy spar) $BaSO_4$ 307	Orthorhombic C—Tabular, prismatic, crested divergent groups, common M—Compact, lamellar, fibrous, cleavable, reniform	Vitreous Pearly Transparent to translucent	Bluish Greenish
CHRYSOCOLLA CuO, SiO_2, H_2O 353	Amorphous ? M—Compact, reniform, incrustations, seams, stains, earthy	Vitreous Greasy Dull Translucent to opaque	Blue Bluish green Green
SERPENTINE $H_4Mg_3Si_2O_9$ 360	Monoclinic C—Unknown M—Compact, columnar, fibrous, lamellar, granular	Greasy Waxy Translucent to opaque	Light green Olive green Yellowish green Blackish green

Hardness 3 to 6

Hard-ness	Streak	Cleavage = C Fracture = F Tenacity	Specific Gravity	Characteristics and Associates
3. 3.5	White	C—Basal, prismatic, conspicuous F—Uneven Brittle	3.9 4.	Heavier than calcite, anhydrite; lighter than barite. In limestones, dolomites, s h a l e s. With sulphur, gypsum, aragonite, halite, galena, sphalerite.
3. 3.5	White	C—Basal, prismatic, conspicuous F—Uneven Brittle	4.3 4.7	Characterized by rather high specific gravity and cleavages. In metalliferous veins; pockets, lenticular masses in limestone. With g a l e n a, sphalerite, chalcopyrite; manganese and iron minerals.
3. 4.	White Greenish white Bluish white	F—Conchoidal Brittle	2. 2.2	Usually recognized by enamel-like appearance, conchoidal fracture, and n o n-fibrous structure. When impure brownish or blackish. With copper m i n e r a l s—malachite, azurite, chalcopyrite; also limonite.
3. 4.	White	F—Conchoidal, splintery Brittle	2.5 2.8	Smooth and greasy feel. Often spotted, clouded, and multi-colored. Sometimes crossed by seams of a s b e s t o s (chrysotile). *Verd antique*, massive, green and mixed with calcite, dolomite, or magnesite; takes an excellent polish. With magnesite, chromite, garnierite, pyrope, platinum.

Streak—Uncolored, white, or light gray

Name, Composition, and Reference	Crystallization Structure Crystals = C Massive = M	Luster Transparency	Color
Wavellite $(AlOH)_3(PO_4)_2.5H_2O$ 328	Orthorhombic C—Capillary, small M—Crusts, globular or hemispherical, with radial fibrous structure	Vitreous Translucent	Green Bluish green Blue
PYROMORPHITE $Pb_5Cl(PO_4)_3$ 328	Hexagonal C—Prismatic, thick tabular, rounded and barrel-shaped; acicular M—Globular, reniform, disseminated, crusts	Greasy Adamantine Translucent to opaque	Dark green Emerald green Yellowish green
FLUORITE (Fluor spar) CaF_2 287	Cubic C—Cubes, alone or modified, well developed, common; penetration twins M—Cleavable, granular, fibrous	Vitreous Transparent to nearly opaque	Greenish Bluish green Blue violet
CYANITE (Disthene, kyanite) Al_2SiO_5 339	Triclinic C—Long, bladed, without good terminations; sometimes curved and radially grouped M—Coarsely bladed, columnar, fibrous	Vitreous Translucent to transparent	Sky blue Greenish blue Bluish white
APATITE $Ca_5F(PO_4)_3$ 326	Hexagonal C—Prismatic, thick, tabular, common, sometimes large with rounded edges M—Granular, compact, fibrous, nodular, reniform	Greasy Vitreous Translucent to opaque	Grass green Brownish green Bluish green Blue violet

Hardness 3 to 6

Hardness	Streak	Cleavage = C Fracture = F Tenacity	Specific Gravity	Characteristics and Associates
3.5 4.	White	C—Pinacoidal, domatic F—Conchoidal, uneven, fibrous Brittle	2.3 2.4	Secondary mineral occurring on surfaces of rocks or minerals, as crystalline crusts with pronounced radial, fibrous structure.
3.5 4.	White Yellowish white	C—None F—Conchoidal, uneven Brittle	6.5 7.1	Common alteration product of lead minerals. With galena, cerussite, barite, limonite.
4.	White	C—Octahedral, perfect, conspicuous Brittle	3. 3.2	May show fluorescence. Easily recognized by crystal form, octahedral cleavage, and hardness. Common gangue of metallic ores—galena, sphalerite, cassiterite; also with calcite, barite.
4. 5.	White	C—Pinacoidal, perfect, conspicuous Brittle	3.5 3.7	Color irregularly distributed, frequently w i t h lighter longitudinal margins. Hardness varies with direction, 4–5 parallel to long direction, 6–7 at right angles thereto. In gneiss, mica schist. With staurolite, garnet, corundum.
4.5 5.	White	C—Basal, imperfect F—Conchoidal, uneven Brittle	3.1 3.2	Crystals may be vertically striated and have fused appearance. Color often unevenly distributed— brownish spots. In crystalline limestones; metalliferous ore deposits; igneous rocks.. With quartz, cassiterite, fluorite, wolframite.

Streak—Uncolored, white, or light gray

Name, Composition, and Reference	Crystallization Structure Crystals = C Massive = M	Luster Transparency	Color
SMITHSONITE $ZnCO_3$ 296	Hexagonal C—Small, usually as druses or crusts M—Botryoidal, stalactitic, granular, fibrous, compact	Vitreous Dull Translucent	Green Grayish green Greenish blue Blue
Lazurite (Lapis lazuli) $3NaAlSiO_4.Na_2S$ 381	Cubic C—Dodecahedrons, rare M—Compact, irregular grains	Vitreous Translucent to opaque	Azure blue Violet blue Greenish blue
Datolite $Ca(BOH)SiO_4$ 341	Monoclinic C—Prismatic, pyramidal, tabular, highly modified M—Compact, fibrous, granular, botryoidal	Vitreous Greasy Dull Transparent to opaque	Pale green Olive green
TITANITE (Sphene) $CaTiSiO_5$ 384	Monoclinic C—Wedge- or envelope-shaped when disseminated; tabular or prismatic when attached M—Compact, lamellar	Vitreous Greasy Transparent to translucent	Green Yellowish green
Sodalite $3NaAlSiO_4.NaCl$ 381	Cubic C—Dodecahedrons M—Compact, disseminated grains, nodular	Vitreous Greasy Transparent to translucent	Lavender blue Sky blue Dark blue Greenish
NEPHELITE (Nepheline, elaeolite) $(Na,K)_8Al_8Si_9O_{34}$ 380	Hexagonal C—Short prismatic, tabular M—Compact, disseminated grains	Greasy Vitreous Transparent to opaque	Grayish green Brownish green Grayish blue

Hardness 3 to 6

Hardness	Streak	Cleavage = C Fracture = F Tenacity	Specific Gravity	Characteristics and Associates
5.	White Gray	C—Rhombohedral, not often observed F—Uneven, splintery Brittle	4.1 4.5	With zinc minerals, especially sphalerite, hemimorphite.
5. 5.5	White Bluish white	C—Dodecahedral, imperfect F—Uneven Brittle	2.4	Always blue and contains disseminated p y r i t e. Occurs as contact mineral in crystalline limestone.
5. 5.5	White	C—None F—Conchoidal, uneven Brittle	2.9 3.	Crystals glassy and usually well developed. Compact masses often with brownish, yellowish, reddish streaks and spots. In cracks and cavities in basic igneous rocks. With calcite, native copper, magnetite, zeolites.
5. 5.5	White Grayish	C—Prismatic, conspicuous parting often noted F—Conchoidal Brittle	3.4 3.6	With feldspars, pyroxenes, amphiboles, c h l o r i t e, scapolite, zircon.
5. 6.	White	C—Dodecahedral F—Conchoidal, uneven Brittle	2.2 2.4	Commonly massive and blue in color. Recognized by associates— nephelite, cancrinite, leucite, feldspar, zircon; not with quartz.
5. 6.	White	C—Indistinct F—Conchoidal, uneven Brittle	2.6	Greasy luster and associates important. With feldspar, cancrinite, biotite, sodalite, zircon, leucite; not with quartz.

Streak—Uncolored, white, or light gray

Name, Composition, and Reference	Crystallization Structure Crystals = C Massive = M	Luster Transparency	Color
SCAPOLITE (Wernerite) $\{$ $n\mathrm{Na_4Al_3Si_9O_{24}Cl}$ $\{$ $m\mathrm{Ca_4Al_6Si_6O_{24}CO_3}$ 383	Tetragonal C—Thick prismatic, coarse, often large M—Compact, granular, fibrous, columnar	Vitreous Greasy Translucent to opaque	Grayish green Bluish

	Name, Composition, and Reference	Crystallization Structure Crystals = C Massive = M	Luster Transparency	Color
AMPHIBOLES	**Actinolite** $\mathrm{Ca_2(Mg,Fe)_5(OH)_2}$- $\mathrm{(Si_4O_{11})_2}$ 370	Monoclinic C—Bladed, without terminations M—Columnar, fibrous, often divergent; granular, compact	Vitreous Silky Transparent to opaque	Light green Grayish green Dark green
	HORNBLENDE Silicate of Ca, Mg, Fe, Al, etc. 371	Monoclinic C—Long prismatic, prism angle 124°; often with rhombohedral-like terminations M—Bladed, fibrous, granular, compact	Vitreous Silky Translucent to opaque	Blackish green Dark green
PYROXENES	**ENSTATITE** (Bronzite) $\mathrm{(Mg,Fe)_2(SiO_3)_2}$ 363	Orthorhombic C—Prismatic, rare M—Fibrous, lamellar, compact	Bronzy Silky Translucent to opaque	Grayish green Brownish green Olive green
	DIOPSIDE $\mathrm{CaMg(SiO_3)_2}$ 364	Monoclinic C—Prismatic, thick columnar, prism angle 87° M—Compact, granular, columnar, lamellar	Vitreous Dull Transparent to opaque	Pale green Bright green Dark green

(See also Augite on next page).

Hardness 3 to 6

Hard-ness	Streak	Cleavage = C Fracture = F Tenacity	Specific Gravity	Characteristics and Associates
5. 6.	White	C—Prismatic F—Conchoidal Brittle	2.6 2.8	Crystals may appear as though fused. Typical contact mineral. In meta-morphic rocks, especially granular l i m e s t o n e s. With pyroxenes, garnet, mica, amphiboles, wol-lastonite.
5. 6.	White Greenish white	C—Prismatic, often conspicuous, 124° Brittle	2.9 3.2	Often as radiating masses. In talc and chlorite schists. With serpentine, epidote, calcite. *Nephrite* and *jade* are compact massive varieties.
5. 6.	Gray Greenish gray Brownish gray	C—Prismatic, often conspicuous, 124° Brittle	2.9 3.3	Simple, pseudohexagonal crystals, and cleavage—124°—important. Com-mon in many types of rocks. With quartz, feld-spar, pyroxene, chlorite, calcite.
5. 6.	White Grayish	C—Prismatic, pina-coidal, often conspicuous F—Uneven Brittle	3.2 3.5	Cleavage surfaces often fibrous or lamellar, irregu-lar or wavy, sometimes with distinct bronzy lus-ter. In basic igneous rocks.
5. 6.	White Gray	C—Prismatic; con-spicuous basal parting F—Uneven Brittle	3.2 3.3	Crystals prismatic a n d pseudotetragonal w i t h distinct basal p a r t i n g. May have colorless and dark green zones. In crystalline limestones and schists. With vesuvian-ite, garnet, s c a p o l i t e, spinel, apatite.

Streak—Uncolored, white, or light gray

Name, Composition, and Reference	Crystallization Structure Crystals = C Massive = M	Luster Transparency	Color
AUGITE (Pyroxene) Silicate of Ca, Mg, Fe, Al, etc. 365	Monoclinic C—Short prismatic, thick columnar, prism angle 87° M—Compact, granular, disseminated	Vitreous Submetallic Translucent to opaque	Blackish green Leek green
Willemite Zn_2SiO_4 347	Hexagonal C—Prismatic M—Compact, granular, disseminated grains	Vitreous Greasy Translucent to opaque	Apple green Yellowish green
OPAL $SiO_2.nH_2O$ 280	Amorphous M—Reniform, botryoidal, compact	Vitreous Greasy Translucent to opaque	Green Bluish green Blue
Turquois $H_5[Al(OH)_2]_6Cu(OH)(PO_4)_4$ 329	Triclinic C—Small, rare M—Reniform, stalactitic, disseminated, rounded pebbles	Waxy Dull Opaque to translucent	Sky blue Bluish green Apple green

Streak—Uncolored, white, or light gray

	Name, Composition, and Reference	Crystallization Structure	Luster Transparency	Color
FELDSPARS	MICROCLINE, variety *Amazon stone* $KAlSi_3O_8$ 375	Triclinic C—Prismatic, thick tabular, twins M—Cleavable, granular, compact, disseminated	Vitreous Pearly Translucent to transparent	Bright green Bluish green
	LABRADORITE Silicate of Ca, Na, Al 378	Triclinic C—Thin tabular, often with rhombic cross-section M—Compact, cleavable, granular	Vitreous Pearly Translucent to nearly opaque	Grayish green Greenish

Hardness 3 to 6

Hardness	Streak	Cleavage = C Fracture = F Tenacity	Specific Gravity	Characteristics and Associates
5. 6.	White Gray Greenish gray	C—Prismatic, perfect, conspicuous—87°, (less distinct than on hornblende.) Brittle	3.2 3.6	Crystals usually e i g h t-sided, more rarely four-sided; pseudotetragonal with prism angles of 87° and 93°. In basic rocks and limestones.
5. 6.	White	C—Basal F—Uneven Brittle	3.9 4.3	Characterized by a s s o-ciates—f r a n k l i n i t e (black), zincite (red), rhodonite (flesh red), calcite.
5.5 6.	White	F—Conchoidal, conspicuous	1.9 2.3	Structure and fracture characteristic. *Precious opal*, play of colors. In veins, cavities, and masses of irregular outline.
6.	White Greenish white	F—Conchoidal Brittle	2.6 2.8	Secondary mineral, in thin veins, crusts, or coatings. With quartz, feldspar, kaolin, limonite.

Hardness over 6

Hardness	Streak	Cleavage = C Fracture = F Tenacity	Specific Gravity	Characteristics and Associates
6. 6.5	White	C—Basal, brachy-pinacoidal, conspicuous, 90° 30′ F—Uneven Brittle	2.5 2.6	Slightly inclined cleavages; may show twinning striations on basal pinacoid. With quartz, other feldspars, mica, hornblende, topaz.
6 6.5	White	C—Basal, brachy-pinacoidal, conspicuous, 86° F—Uneven, conchoidal Brittle	2.7	Often with play of color—yellow, green, blue, red. Inclined cleavages are striated. In basic igneous rocks. With pyroxenes, amphiboles.

Streak—Uncolored, white, or light gray

Name, Composition, and Reference	Crystallization Structure Crystals = C Massive = M	Luster Transparency	Color
EPIDOTE $Ca_2(Al,Fe)_2(AlOH)(SiO_4)_3$ 344	Monoclinic C—Prismatic, elongated and deeply striated parallel to b axis; usually terminated on one end only M—Columnar, fibrous, parallel and divergent; granular	Vitreous Transparent to opaque	Blackish green Yellowish green Brownish green Pea green
CYANITE (Disthene, kyanite) Al_2SiO_5 339	Triclinic C—Long bladed, without good terminations; sometimes curved and radially grouped M—Coarsely bladed, columnar, fibrous	Vitreous Translucent to transparent	Sky blue Greenish blue Bluish white
VESUVIANITE $Ca_6[Al(OH,F)]Al_2(SiO_4)_5$ 345	Tetragonal C—Short prismatic M—Compact, granular, aggregates with parallel or divergent striations	Vitreous Greasy Translucent to opaque	Green Brownish green Bluish
OLIVINE (Chrysolite, peridot) $(Mg,Fe)_2SiO_4$ 346	Orthorhombic C—Prismatic, thick tabular M—Rounded, disseminated glassy grains; granular aggregates	Vitreous Transparent to translucent	Grass green Olive green Yellowish green
GARNET, varieties *Grossularite* $M_2'''M_3''$ *Uvarovite* $(SiO_4)_3$ *Andradite* $M''' = Al,Fe,Cr$ $M'' = Ca,Fe,Mg$ 349	Cubic C—Dodecahedrons, tetragonal trisoctahedrons, alone or in combination M—Granular, compact, lamellar, disseminated grains, sand	Vitreous Transparent to opaque	Pale green Grass green Emerald green

Hardness over 6

Hard-ness	Streak	Cleavage = C Fracture = F Tenacity	Specific Gravity	Characteristics and Associates
6. 7.	White Grayish	C—Basal F—Uneven Brittle	3.3 3.5	Crystals are often dark or blackish green, massive aggregates lighter colored. With quartz, feldspar, garnet, hornblende, pyroxene, magnetite, native copper, zeolites.
6. 7.	White	C—Pinacoidal, per-fect, conspicu-ous Brittle	3.5 3.7	Color irregularly distrib-uted, frequently w i t h lighter longitudinal mar-gins. Hardness varies with direction, 4–5 par-allel to long direction, 6–7 at right angles thereto. In gneiss, mica schist. With staurolite, corundum.
6.5	White	C—Basal, pris-matic, in-distinct F—Uneven Brittle	3.3 3.5	In crystalline limestone, gneiss, schists. With gar-net, tourmaline, chond-rodite, wollastonite, epi-dote, pyroxene.
6.5 7.	White Yellowish white	C—Pinacoidal F—Conchoidal Brittle	3.2 3.6	In basic rocks—basalts, traps; crystalline, lime-stones. With augite, magnetite, spinel, plagio-clase, chromite, pyrope.
6.5 7.5	White	C—Dodecahedral, usually in-distinct F—Conchoidal, un-even Brittle	3.4 4.3	*Grossularite*, in crystalline limestones and dolomites, with wollastonite, vesu-vianite, diopside, scapo-lite; *uvarovite*, in ser-pentine, with chromite, or in crystalline lime-stones; *andradite*, with feldspar, nephelite, leu-cite, epidote, magnetite.

Streak—Uncolored, white, or light gray

Name, Composition, and Reference	Crystallization Structure Crystals = C Massive = M	Luster Transparency	Color
QUARTZ, Crystalline varieties SiO_2 _Cat's eye_ _Amethyst_	Hexagonal C—Prismatic, horizontally striated M—Compact, granular	Vitreous Greasy Transparent to opaque	Green Greenish blue Blue Blue violet
269			
Cryptocrystalline varieties _Chalcedony_ _Chrysoprase_ _Heliotrope_	Hexagonal C—Never in crystals M—Nodular, spotted, concretionary, stalactitic, compact	Waxy Vitreous Translucent to opaque	Light green Dark green Grayish blue Greenish blue
270			
TOURMALINE $M'_{20}B_2Si_4O_{21}$ $M' =$ Na,K,Li,Mg, Ca,(OH),Fe, Al	Hexagonal C—Prismatic, vertically striated; terminated with broken or rhombohedral-like surfaces M—Compact, columnar	Vitreous Transparent to translucent	Green Blue
342			
BERYL, varieties _Emerald_ $Be_3Al_2(SiO_3)_6$ _Aquamarine_ _Common_	Hexagonal C—Long prismatic, often vertically striated, large M—Columnar, granular, compact, rounded pebbles	Vitreous Transparent to translucent	Pale green Emerald green Bluish green Sky blue
352			

Hardness over 6

Hardness	Streak	Cleavage = C Fracture = F Tenacity	Specific Gravity	Characteristics and Associates
7.	White	C—Indistinct F—Conchoidal, conspicuous Brittle	2.6	Characteristic conchoidal fracture and glassy luster. *Chloritic quartz,* g r e e n from included chlorite; *cat's-eye,* opalescent, due to included fibers of asbestos; *amethyst,* purple or blue violet, usually in crystals.
7.	White	C—Indistinct F—Conchoidal, conspicuous Brittle to tough	2.6	Not as glassy as phanerocrystalline v a r i e t i e s. *Chalcedony, chrysoprase, prase, plasma,* uniform in color; *heliotrope,* spotted. To distinguish, see reference.
7. 7.5	White	C—None F—Conchoidal, uneven Brittle	2.9 3.2	Spherical triangular cross-section. With zonal distribution of color—green, red, colorless. In igneous and metamorphic rocks. With lepidolite, feldspar, quartz, biotite.
7.5 8.	White	C—Indistinct F—Conchoidal, uneven Brittle	2.6 2.8	Crystals usually simple—prism and base. *Emerald,* transparent and emerald green; *aquamarine,* transparent, bluish to sea green or yellowish green. In granitic rocks, m i c a schists, clay s l a t e s, placers. With q u a r t z, feldspar, mica, t o p a z, tourmaline, cassiterite, chrysoberyl, garnet.

Streak—Uncolored, white, or light gray

Name, Composition, and Reference	Crystallization Structure Crystals = C Massive = M	Luster Transparency	Color
ZIRCON ZrSiO$_4$	Tetragonal C—Prismatic, pyramidal, small, well developed M—Irregular lumps, grains	Adamantine Vitreous Resinous Transparent to opaque	Light blue Dark blue
348			
SPINEL, varieties M″(M‴O$_2$)$_2$ *Pleonaste* M″ = Mg,Fe *Gahnite* Zn,Mn *Blue spinel* M‴ = Al,Fe	Cubic C—Octahedral, usually well developed M—Compact, granular, disseminated grains	Vitreous Dull Translucent to opaque	Grass green Dark green Grayish green Light blue
319			
Chrysoberyl, varieties *Ordinary* Be(AlO$_2$)$_2$ *Alexandrite* *Cat's-eye*	Orthorhombic C—Tabular; heart-shaped, pseudohexagonal twins M—Compact; loose, rounded grains	Vitreous Greasy Transparent to translucent	Light green Yellowish green Emerald green
322			
CORUNDUM, variesties *Sapphire* Al$_2$O$_3$ *Oriental emerald* *Oriental amethyst* *Common*	Hexagonal C—Prismatic, tabular, pyramidal, rhombohedral; rough or rounded barrel-shaped M—Compact, granular, lamellar	Vitreous Transparent to opaque	Green Blue Blue violet
275			

Hardness over 6

Hard-ness	Streak	Cleavage = C Fracture = F Tenacity	Specific Gravity	Characteristics and Associates
7.5	White	C—Indistinct F—Uneven Brittle	4.4 4.8	In alluvial deposits near Bangkok, Siam. *Starlite*, clear and transparent, used as a gem.
7.5 **8.**	White Grayish	C—Octahedral, in-distinct F—Conchoidal Brittle	3.5 4.4	Commonly as contact mineral in granular limestones; in basic igneous rocks; rounded grains in placers. With calcite, chondrodite, serpentine, corundum, graphite, pyroxenes.
8.5	White	C—Brachypina-coidal F—Uneven, con-choidal Brittle	3.6 3.8	Crystals disseminated as plates with feather-like or radial striations. *Alexandrite*, red in transmitted light; *cat's eye*, opalescent. In mica schist, gneiss; granite; also in placers. With beryl, garnet, tourmaline, sillimanite.
9.	White	C—None; nearly rectangular basal and rhombohedral partings, conspicuous; often striated F—Conchoidal Brittle to tough	3.9 4.1	When massive, often multi-colored—red, gray, yellow. *Sapphire*, transparent, blue; *oriental emerald*, green, transparent; *oriental amethyst*, violet. In limestone, granite, syenite, schist, peridotite; placers. With magnetite, nephelite, mica, chlorite, spinel.

Streak—Red, brown, or yellow

Name, Composition, and Reference	Crystallization Structure Crystals = C Massive = M	Luster Transparency	Color
Carnotite $K_2O.2U_O_3.V_2O_5.3H_2O$ 330	Orthorhombic C—Tabular, small rhombic plates M—Scaly aggregates, incrustations, crystalline powder	Resinous Vitreous Dull Transparent to translucent	Canary yellow Greenish yellow
BAUXITE $Al_2O_3.2H_2O$ 282	Never in crystals M—Pisolitic, oölitic, round disseminated grains, clay-like, earthy	Dull Earthy Opaque	Yellow Yellowish brown Brown

LIMONITE, varieties
   Yellow ocher
$Fe_2O_3.nH_2O$ *Brown ocher*
   Bog iron ore
   Brown clay
    ironstone
 	
283
	M—Earthy, porous, clay-like, oölitic, pisolitic	Earthy
		Dull
		Opaque
			Yellow
			Yellowish brown
			Dark brown

ORPIMENT As_2S_3 249	Monoclinic C—Rare M—Foliated, granular, reniform, fibrous, crusts	Greasy Pearly Translucent	Lemon yellow
REALGAR AsS 248	Monoclinic C—Short prismatic, rare M—Compact, granular, iucrustations	Resinous Transparent to translucent	Reddish yellow Orange yellow
SULPHUR S 236	Orthorhombic C—Pyramidal, tabular M—Granular, fibrous, earthy, crusts, compact	Greasy Adamantine Translucent	Straw yellow Honey yellow Brownish yellow Reddish yellow

Hardness 1 to 3

Hardness	Streak	Cleavage = C Fracture = F Tenacity	Specific Gravity	Characteristics and Associates
1. 2.	Yellow	C—Basal, perfect F—Earthy Brittle		Occurs as a powder or in loosely cohering masses, intimately mixed with sand and sandstones. With malachite, azurite, biotite, magnetite.
1. 3.	Yellow Brown	F—Earthy Brittle	2.5 2.6	Color and streak variable, due to pigments. Clay odor, when b r e a t h e d upon. Commonly with pisolitic or oölitic structure. With clay or kaolinite, in nodules, grains, or irregular masses in limestone or dolomite.
1. 3.	Yellowish brown Dark brown	F—Earthy	3.4 4.	*Yellow ocher*, earthy, and yellow, when i m p u r e gritty; *brown ocher*, carthy and brown; *bog iron ore*, porous; *brown clay ironstone*, massive or concretionary, impure from c l a y, sand. Ocherous varieties may soil fingers.
1.5 2.	Lemon yellow	C—Clinopinacoidal, usually conspicuous Slightly sectile, laminæ flexible	3.4 3.5	Characteristic lemon yellow color. Frequently disseminated in clay or dolomite. With realgar, stibnite, barite, calcite.
1.5 2.	Orange yellow	C—Clinopinacoidal, basal, not conspicuous F—Conchoidal Slightly sectile	3.4 3.6	Redder in color than orpiment. Disseminated in clay or dolomite. With orpiment, stibnite, native arsenic, pyrite, barite, calcite.
1.5 2.5	Pale yellow	C—Indistinct C—Conchoidal Brittle	1.9 2.1	Independent beds in gypsum, limestone; in lava, result of volcanic exhalations. With celestite, anhydrite, aragonite, clay, metallic sulphides.

Streak—Red, brown, or yellow

Name, Composition, and Reference	Crystallization Structure Crystals = C Massive = M	Luster Transparency	Color
Wulfenite $PbMoO_4$ 310	Tetragonal C—Square, thin tabular; more rarely pyramidal M—Coarse, fine grained	Greasy Adamantine Transparent to translucent	Wax yellow Orange yellow Brown
Vanadinite $Pb_5Cl(VO_4)_3$ 328	Hexagonal C—Prismatic, small, at times skeletal M—Compact, globular, fibrous, crusts	Greasy Translucent to opaque	Straw yellow Brownish yellow Reddish brown

Streak—Red, brown, or yellow

Name, Composition, and Reference	Crystallization Structure Crystals = C Massive = M	Luster Transparency	Color

LIMONITE, varieties
    Compact
$Fe_2O_3.nH_2O$ *Bog iron ore*
    Brown clay
    ironstone
 	
283
	C—Always pseudomorphs, commonly after pyrite, marcasite, siderite
	M—Compact, stalactitic, botryoidal, nodular; often with internal, radial fibrous structure; porous, pisolitic, oölitic
		Metallic
		Dull
		Opaque
			Yellowish brown
			Dark brown

SIDERITE $FeCO_3$ 298	Hexagonal C—Rhombohedral, curved or saddle-shaped M—Cleavable, granular, compact, botryoidal, rarely fibrous	Vitreous Pearly Dull Translucent to nearly opaque	Light brown Reddish brown Dark brown
SPHALERITE ZnS	Cubic C—Tetrahedral, common M—Cleavable, fine or coarse grained, compact	Resinous Submetallic Transparent to opaque	Honey yellow Yellowish brown Reddish brown

Hardness 1 to 3

Hard-ness	Streak	Cleavage = C Fracture = F Tenacity	Specific Gravity	Characteristics and Associates
3.	Lemon yellow Pale yellow	C—Indistinct F—Conchoidal, un- even Brittle	6.3 7.	Square plates, sometimes with forms of the third order. With lead minerals—galena, pyromorphite, vanadinite.
3.	Pale yellow Yellow	C—None F—Conchoidal, un- even Brittle	6.7 7.2	Crystal faces smooth with sharp edges. With lead minerals, but never in large quantities.

Hardness over 3

Hard-ness	Streak	Cleavage = C Fracture = F Tenacity	Specific Gravity	Characteristics and Associates
3. 5.5	Yellowish brown	F—Conchoidal, splintery, earthy Brittle	3.4 4.	Often with black varnish-like surface and passing into soft, yellow ocherous variety. *Compact limonite*, massive with fibrous structure, rather pure; *bog iron ore*, porous; *brown clay ironstone*, massive or concretionary, impure from clay, sand.
3.5 4.	Pale yellow Yellowish brown	C—Rhombohedral, conspicuous F—Conchoidal Brittle	3.7 3.9	Curved crystals and rhombohedral cleavage characteristic. In ore deposits; beds and concretions in limestones and shales. With pyrite, chalcopyrite, galena, tetrahedrite, cryolite.
3.5 4.	Pale yellow Light brown	C—Dodecahedral, usually conspic- uous F—Conchoidal Brittle	3.9 4.2	Distinguished from siderite by crystallization, more greasy luster, and cleavage. Color and streak vary with impurities. Extensively in limestones. With galena, chalcopyrite, pyrite, rhodochrosite, barite, fluorite.

Streak—Red, brown, or yellow

Name, Composition, and Reference	Crystallization Structure Crystals = C Massive = M	Luster Transparency	Color
PYROMORPHITE $Pb_5Cl(PO_4)_3$ 328	Hexagonal C—Prismatic, thick tabular, rounded and barrel-shaped; acicular M—Globular, reniform, disseminated, crusts	Greasy Adamantine Translucent to opaque	Wax yellow Green yellow Yellowish brown
Zincite ZnO 274	Hexagonal C—Small, rare M—Compact, granular, foliated	Adamantine Vitreous Translucent to opaque	Orange yellow Reddish yellow
Huebnerite $MnWO_4$ 311	Monoclinic C—Long fibrous, bladed, stalky; often divergent, without good terminations M—Compact, lamellar, granular	Greasy Submetallic Translucent to opaque	Reddish brown Hair brown Pale yellow
WOLFRAMITE $(Fe,Mn)WO_4$ 311	Monoclinic C—Thick tabular, short columnar, often large M—Bladed, curved lamellar, granular, compact	Submetallic Opaque	Reddish brown Dark brown
Ferberite $FeWO_4$ 312	Monoclinic C—Wedge shaped, short prismatic, tabular M—Fan shaped aggregates, bladed, granular, compact	Submetallic Opaque	Brown Blackish brown
RUTILE TiO_2 272	Tetragonal C—Prismatic, vertically striated; twinned yielding knee-shaped or rosette forms M—Compact, disseminated	Adamantine Submetallic Translucent to opaque	Reddish brown Yellowish brown Dark brown

Hardness over 3

Hard-ness	Streak	Cleavage = C Fracture = F Tenacity	Specific Gravity	Characteristics and Associates
3.5 4.	Yellow Greenish yellow	C—None F—Conchoidal, un-even Brittle	6.5 7.1	Common alteration prod-uct of lead m i n e r a l s. With galena, cerussite, barite, limonite.
4. 4.5	Orange yellow Reddish yellow	C—Basal, some-times conspicu-ous F—Uneven Brittle	5.4 5.7	Recognized by associates. With calcite, franklinite (black), willemite (yellow to green), rhodonite (flesh red). On exposure be-comes coated with the white carbonate.
4.5 5.5	Yellowish brown	C—Clinopinacoidal, conspicuous Brittle	6.7 7.3	Structure, cleavage, and high specific gravity char-acteristic. In q u a r t z veins. With wolframite, fluorite, pyrite, scheelite. galena, tetrahedrite.
5. 5.5	Reddish brown Dark brown	C—Clinopinacoidal, conspicuous F—Uneven Brittle	7.1 7.5	Distinguished from hueb-nerite by streak. Pow-der may be slightly mag-netic. With cassiterite, quartz, mica, apatite, scheelite, molybdenite, huebnerite.
5. 5.5	Brown Dark brown	C—Clinopinacoidal, perfect F—Uneven Brittle	7.5	In granites and pegmatites. With quartz, chalcopy-rite, galena, scheelite.
6. 7.	Pale yellow Pale brown	C—Prismatic, py-ramidal, not conspicuous F—Uneven Brittle	4.2 4.3	Not as heavy as cassiterite. Often in fine hair-like in-clusions. With quartz, feldspar, hematite, ilmen-ite, chlorite, brookite.

Streak—Red, brown, or yellow

Name, Composition, and Reference	Crystallization Structure Crystals = C Massive = M	Luster Transparency	Color
CASSITERITE SnO_2 272	Tetragonal C—Thick prismatic; knee-shaped twins quite common M—Compact, reniform, botryoidal, rounded pebbles, often with internal, radial fibrous structure,— *wood tin*	Adamantine Greasy Dull Translucent to opaque	Reddish Yellowish brown Dark brown
SPINEL, variety *Picotite* $(Mg,Fe)_2(Al,Cr)_2O_4$ 319	Cubic C—Octahedral, small M—Compact, granular, disseminated grains	Vitreous Dull Nearly opaque	Yellowish brown Greenish brown Brown

Streak—Uncolored, white, or light gray

Cerargyrite (Horn silver) $AgCl$ 287	Cubic C—Rare M—Wax-like crusts and coatings; stalactitic, dendritic	Waxy Greasy Transparent to translucent	Yellowish Brownish
TRIPOLITE (Opal) $SiO_2.nH_2O$ 281	Amorphous M—Porous, earthy, chalk-like	Vitreous Dull Translucent to opaque	Yellow Yellowish brown Brown
KAOLINITE (Kaolin) $H_4Al_2Si_2O_9$ 359	Monoclinic C—Scaly, hexagonal or orthorhombic outline, rare M—Compact, friable, mealy, clay-like	Dull Pearly Earthy Opaque to translucent	Yellowish Brownish

Hardness over 3

Hard-ness	Streak	Cleavage = C Fracture = F Tenacity	Specific Gravity	Characteristics and Associates
6. 7.	Pale brown Pale yellow	C—Indistinct F—Uneven Brittle	6.8 7.2	Recognized by high specific gravity. In veins cutting granite, gneiss; in alluvial deposits as *stream tin*. With quartz, mica, wol-f r a m i t e, arsenopyrite, molybdenite, tourmaline, fluorite, chlorite.
7.5 8.	Pale brown	C—Indistinct F—Conchoidal Brittle	4.1	Commonly in basic igneous rocks, especially olivine-bearing types. With ser-pentine, olivine, corun-dum, magnetite, garnet.

Hardness 1 to 3

Hard-ness	Streak	Cleavage = C Fracture = F Tenacity	Specific Gravity	Characteristics and Associates
1. 1.5	White, shiny Gray, shiny	C—None F—Conchoidal Highly sectile	5.5 5.6	Cuts like wax, yielding shiny surfaces; on ex-posure turns v i o l e t, brown, or black. With silver minerals, especially argentite, native silver; also limonite, c a l c i t e, barite.
1. 2.5	White Gray	F—Earthy Friable	1.9 2.3	Apparently very soft, but fine particles s c r a t c h glass. Resembles kaolin-ite, but gritty and not plastic. Due to impurities may have clay odor.
1. 2.5	White Yellowish white	C—Basal,—scales F—Earthy Brittle	2.2 2.6	Not gritty like tripolite. Very strong clay odor when breathed u p o n. Usually adheres to tongue and becomes plastic when moistened. Greasy feel. With quartz, feldspar, cor-undum, topaz.

Streak—Uncolored, white, or light gray

Name, Composition, and Reference	Crystallization Structure Crystals = C Massive = M	Luster Transparency	Color
TALC, variety *Soapstone* or *steatite* $H_2Mg_3Si_4O_{12}$ **358**	Monoclinic M—Compact, globular, granular	Greasy Pearly Translucent to opaque	Yellowish Yellowish brown Brownish
Asbestos, variety *Chrysotile* $H_4Mg_3Si_2O_9$ **360**	Monoclinic M—Fibrous, coarse or fine; felted	Silky Greasy Opaque	Yellowish Brownish
variety *Amphibole* Silicate of Ca, Mg, Fe, Al, etc. **369**	Monoclinic M—Fibrous, coarse or fine; felted; compact, leather- or cork-like	Silky Dull Opaque	Yellowish Brownish
SODA NITER (Chile saltpeter) $NaNO_3$ **290**	Hexagonal C—Rare M—Granular, crusts, efflorescences	Vitreous Transparent	Yellowish Lemon yellow Reddish brown

GYPSUM, varieties
   Selenite
$CaSO_4.2H_2O$ *Satin spar*
   Ordinary
 	
315
	Monoclinic
	C—Tabular, prismatic; swallowtail twins
	M—Cleavable, coarse and fine grained, fibrous foliated, earthy
		Pearly
		Vitreous
		Silky
		Dull
		Transparent to opaque
			Yellow
			Honey yellow
			Brown

SULPHUR S **236**	Orthorhombic C—Pyramidal, tabular M—Compact, granular, fibrous, earthy, crusts	Adamantine Greasy Translucent	Straw yellow Brownish yellow Reddish yellow

Hardness 1 to 3

Hardness	Streak	Cleavage = C Fracture = F Tenacity	Specific Gravity	Characteristics and Associates
1. 2.5	White Yellowish white	F—Uneven, splintery Sectile	2.6 2.8	Greasy or soapy feel important. *Soapstone* or *steatite*, coarse to fine, granular, more or less impure. Hardness varies. With serpentine, chlorite, dolomite, magnesite, actinolite.
1. 3.	White	F—Fibrous Flexible	1. 2.5	Delicate, fine, parallel, flexible fibers, perpendicular to walls, easily separable —*short fibered asbesios*, compare below. In veins or seams in serpentine.
1. 3.	White	F—Fibrous Flexible, tough	1. 2.5	*Long fibered asbestos*, parallel, flexible fibers, parallel to walls. Compare above. *Mountain leather, mountain cork, mountain wood*, compact but light and tough.
1.5 2.	White	C—Rhombohedral F—Conchoidal Brittle	2.1 2.3	Cooling and saline taste. Absorbs moisture readily. In deposits with gypsum, sand, clay, guano.

1.5
2.
	White	C—Clinopinacoidal,
		    conspicuous;
		    pyramidal,
		    orthopinacoidal
		F—Conchoidal,
		    fibrous
		Brittle, laminæ
		flexible
			2.2
			2.4
				Selenite, crystals and cleavable plates, usually transparent; *satin spar*, fibrous with silky luster; *ordinary*, granular. In limestones and shales. With halite, celestite, sulphur, aragonite, anhydrite; ore deposits.

1.5 2.5	White Yellowish white	C—Indistinct F—Conchoidal Brittle	1.9 2.1	Independent beds in gypsum, limestone; in lava, result of volcanic exhalations. With celestite, anhydrite. aragonite, clay, metallic sulphides.

Streak—Uncolored, white, or light gray

Name, Composition, and Reference	Crystallization Structure Crystals = C Massive = M	Luster Transparency	Color
HALITE (Rock salt) NaCl **285**	Cubic **C**—Cubes, often skeletal or hopper-shaped **M**—Compact, cleavable, granular, fibrous, stalactitic, crusts	Vitreous Transparent to translucent	Yellow Yellowish brown Brownish
MUSCOVITE (Isinglass) $KAl_2(OH)_2AlSi_3O_{10}$ **355**	Monoclinic **C**—Tabular, pyramidal, with rhombic or hexagonal outline; often large and rough **M**—Scales, plates; foliated and plumose aggregates	Vitreous Pearly Transparent to translucent	Light yellow Yellowish brown Light brown
PHLOGOPITE $KMg_3(OH)_2AlSi_3O_{10}$ **356**	Monoclinic **C**—Prismatic, tabular, with hexagonal or rhombic outline; often large and coarse **M**—Plates, disseminated scales	Pearly Submetallic Transparent to translucent	Yellow Yellowish brown Brown

(MICAS — bracketing MUSCOVITE and PHLOGOPITE)

APATITE, variety *Phosphate rock* Mainly calcium carbonate—phosphate (collophanite) **326**	Amorphous **M**—Compact, nodular, reniform, earthy	Dull Opaque	Brown

Hardness 1 to 3

Hard-ness	Streak	Cleavage = C Fracture = F Tenacity	Specific Gravity	Characteristics and Associates
2. 2.5	White	C—Cubic, perfect, conspicuous F—Conchoidal Brittle	2.1 2.3	Pigment usually iron oxide. May absorb moisture and become damp. Characteristic cubical cleavage and saline taste. With shale, gypsum, anhydrite.
2. 3.	White	C—Basal, perfect, conspicuous Tough laminæ very elastic	2.8 3.1	Lighter colored than phlogopite. Structure, perfect cleavage, and elasticity important. Crystals may s h o w distinct partings perpendicular to cleavage—*ruled m i c a.* I n granitic rocks, schists, limestones. With feldspar, quartz, tourmaline, beryl, garnet.
2. 3.	White	C—Basal, perfect, conspicuous Tough, laminæ very elastic	2.8 3.1	Usually amber brown or bronze in color. When cleavage laminæ are held close to the eye in viewing a source of light a star-like form is sometimes observed. Especially c h a r a c t e r i s t i c of c r y s t a l l i n e limestones, dolomites, schists. With pyroxenes, amphiboles, serpentine.
2. 3.	White	F—Conchoidal, uneven Brittle	3.1 3.2	More or less i m p u r e masses, frequently resembling compact limestone. Independent beds, nodules, concretions.

Streak—Uncolored, white, or light gray

Name, Composition, and Reference	Crystallization Structure Crystals = C Massive = M	Luster Transparency	Color
BARITE (Heavy spar) BaSO$_4$ 307	Orthorhombic **C**—Tabular, prismatic, very common; crested divergent groups **M**—Compact, lamellar, fibrous, cleavable, reniform	Vitreous Pearly Transparent to opaque	Yellowish Brownish Dark brown

CALCITE, varieties
   Dog tooth spar
 CaCO$_3$ *Nail head spar*
   Limestone
   Marble
 	
   Calcareous tufa
   Travertine
   Stalactites, etc.
 291
	Hexagonal
	 C—Scalenohedral, rhombohedral; prismatic; tabular, acicular; may be highly modified and twinned
	 M—Cleavable, granular, fibrous, banded, stalactitic, oölitic, porous, compact, crusts, shells
		Vitreous Dull Transparent to nearly opaque	Honey yellow Yellowish brown Dark brown

Wulfenite PbMoO$_4$ 310	Tetragonal **C**—Square, thin tabular; more rarely pyramidal **M**—Coarse, fine grained	Greasy Adamantine Transparent to translucent	Wax yellow Orange yellow Brown
Vanadinite Pb$_5$Cl(VO$_4$)$_3$ 328	Hexagonal **C**—Prismatic, small, at times skeletal **M**—Compact, globular, fibrous, crusts	Greasy Translucent to opaque	Straw yellow Brownish yellow Reddish brown

Streak—Uncolored, white, or light gray

BARITE (Heavy spar) BaSO$_4$ 307	Orthorhombic **C**—Tabular, prismatic, very common; crested and divergent groups **M**—Compact, lamellar, fibrous, cleavable, reniform	Vitreous Pearly Transparent to opaque	Yellowish Brownish Dark brown

Hardness 1 to 3

Hardness	Streak	Cleavage = C Fracture = F Tenacity	Specific Gravity	Characteristics and Associates
2.5 3.	White	C—Basal, p r i s-matic, usually conspicuous F—Uneven Brittle	4.3 4.7	Characterized by rather high specific gravity and cleavages. In metalliferous veins; pockets, lenticular masses in limestones. With galena, sphalerite, fluorite, chalcopyrite; manganese and iron minerals.
3.	White	C—Rhombohedral, usually conspicuous F—Conchoidal Brittle	2.7	Often in extensive deposits. Rhombohedral cleavage characteristic especially on crystals. Cleavage surfaces often striated. Very strong double refraction easily observed when transparent. To distinguish varieties, see reference.
3.	White Yellowish white	C—Pyramidal, indistinct F—Conchoidal, uneven Brittle	6.3 7.	Square plates sometimes with forms of the third order. With lead minerals—galena, pyromorphite, vanadinite.
3.	White Yellowish white	C—None F—Conchoidal, uneven Brittle	6.7 7.2	Crystal faces smooth with sharp edges. With lead minerals, but never in large quantities.

Hardness 3 to 6

Hardness	Streak	Cleavage = C Fracture = F Tenacity	Specific Gravity	Characteristics and Associates
3. 3.5	White	C—Basal, p r i s-matic, usually conspicuous F—Uneven Brittle	4.3 4.7	Characterized by rather high specific gravity and cleavages. In metalliferous veins; pockets, lenticular masses in limestone. With galena, sphalerite, fluorite, chalcopyrite; manganese and iron minerals.

Streak—Uncolored, white or light gray

Name, Composition, and Reference	Crystallization Structure Crystals = C Massive = M	Luster Transparency	Color
CERUSSITE $PbCO_3$ 301	Orthorhombic C—Tabular, prismatic, pyramidal; pseudo-hexagonal; clusters and star-shaped groups M—Interlaced bundles, granular, stalactitic, compact	Adamantine Greasy Silky Transparent to trans-lucent	Yellow Yellowish brown
STILBITE (Zeolite) $(Ca,Na_2)Al_2Si_6O_{16}.6H_2O$ 387	Monoclinic C—Twinned, sheaf-like, radial or globular aggregates	Vitreous Pearly Transparent to trans-lucent	Yellowish Yellowish brown Brownish
SERPENTINE $H_4Mg_3Si_2O_9$ 360	Monoclinic C—Unknown M—Compact, columnar, fibrous, lamellar, granular	Greasy Waxy Translucent to opaque	Greenish brown Greenish yellow Yellowish brown
APATITE, variety *Phosphate rock* Mainly calcium carbonate —phosphate (collophanite) 326	Amorphous M—Compact, nodular, reniform	Dull Opaque	Brown
Wavellite $(AlOH)_3(PO_4)_2.5H_2O$ 328	Orthorhombic C—Capillary, small M—Crusts, globular, hemispherical aggre-gates, with radial fi-brous structure	Vitreous Translucent	Yellow Brown
DOLOMITE $CaMg(CO_3)_2$ 294	Hexagonal C—Rhombohedral, with curved surfaces M—Coarsely crystalline, compact, granular, friable	Vitreous Transparent to trans-lucent	Yellowish brown Grayish brown Dark brown

Hardness 3 to 6

Hard-ness	Streak	Cleavage = C Fracture = F Tenacity	Specific Gravity	Characteristics and Associates
3. **3.5**	White Gray	C—Indistinct F—Conchoidal Brittle	6.4 6.6	Twinning, s t r u c t u r e, luster, and specific grav-ity characteristic. With lead minerals—g a l e na, pyromorphite, anglesite; also malachite. limonite.
3. **4.**	White	C—Indistinct F—Uneven Brittle	2.1 2.2	Radial and sheaf-like struc-ture important. In basic igneous rocks and ore de-posits. With chabazite, apophyllite, d a t o l i t e, calcite.
3. **4.**	White	F—Conchoidal, splintery Brittle	2.5 2.8	Smooth and greasy feel. Often spotted, clouded, m u l t i-colored. Some-times crossed by seams of asbestos (c h r y s o t i l e). With magnesite, chro-mite, garnierite, pyrope, platinum. calcite.
3. **5.**	White	F—Conchoidal, un-even Brittle	3.1 3.2	More or less i m p u r e m a s s e s, frequently re-sembling compact, brown limestone. Independent beds, nodules, c o n c r e-tions.
3.5 **4.**	White	C—Pinacoidal, domatic F—Uneven, fibrous Brittle	2.3 2.4	Secondary mineral occur-ring on surfaces of rocks or minerals, as crystalline crusts with pronounced radial fibrous structure.
3.5 **4.**	White Gray	C—Rhombohedral, perfect (crystals) F—Conchoidal Brittle	2.9	Crystals generally curved or saddle-shaped. *Marble* includes some compact varieties. Independent beds; in fissures and cav-ities; with ore deposits.

Streak—Uncolored, white, or light gray

Name, Composition, and Reference	Crystallization Structure Crystals = C Massive = M	Luster Transparency	Color
ARAGONITE CaCO₃ 299	Orthorhombic C—Chisel- or spear-shaped; pseudohexagonal prisms; radial, columnar, acicular aggregates M—Stalactitic, reniform, crusts, oölitic	Vitreous Resinous Transparent to translucent	Wine yellow Yellowish brown
STRONTIANITE SrCO₃ 300	Orthorhombic C—Spear-shaped, columnar, acicular; often in divergent groups M—Columnar, granular, compact, botryoidal, fibrous	Vitreous Greasy Transparent to translucent	Yellow Yellowish brown Brown
SIDERITE FeCO₃ 298	Hexagonal C—Rhombohedral, curved or saddle-shaped, common M—Cleavable, granular, compact, botryoidal, rarely fibrous	Vitreous Pearly Dull Translucent to nearly opaque	Light brown Reddish brown Dark brown
SPHALERITE ZnS 251	Cubic C—Tetrahedral, common M—Cleavable, fine and coarse grained, compact	Resinous Submetallic Translucent to opaque	Honey yellow Yellowish brown Reddish brown
PYROMORPHITE Pb₅Cl(PO₄)₃ 327	Hexagonal C—Prismatic, thick tabular, rounded and barrel-shaped; acicular M—Globular, reniform, disseminated, crusts	Greasy Adamantine Translucent to opaque	Wax yellow Greenish yellow Yellowish brown

Hardness 3 to 6

Hardness	Streak	Cleavage = C Fracture = F Tenacity	Specific Gravity	Characteristics and Associates
3.5 4.	White Gray	C—Pinacoidal, prismatic F—Conchoidal Brittle	2.9 3	Twins common, often pseudohexagonal—prism and striated base. In cracks and cavities; with ore deposits; deposition from hot springs; in shells. With gypsum, celestite, sulphur, siderite, zeolites.
3.5 4.	White Gray	C—Prismatic, indistinct F—Uneven Brittle	3.6 3.8	Structure similar to aragonite. Divergent columnar masses and higher specific gravity characteristic. In ore deposits; independent beds. With galena, barite, calcite.
3.5 4.	Gray White	C—Rhombohedral, conspicuous F—Conchoidal Brittle	3.7 3.9	Distinguished from sphalerite by curved crystals and rhombohedral cleavage. In ore deposits; beds and concretions in limestones and shales. With p y r i t e, chalcopyrite, galena, tetrahedrite, cryolite.
3.5 4.	White Yellowish white	C—Dodecahedral, usually conspicuous F—Conchoidal Brittle	3.9 4.2	Resinous luster and cleavage important. Color and streak vary with impurities. Extensively in limestones. With galena, chalcopyrite, pyrite, barite, fluorite, rhodochrosite.
3.5 4.	White Yellowish white	C—None F—Conchoidal, uneven Brittle	6.5 7.1	Common alteration product of lead minerals. With galena, cerussite, barite, limonite.

Streak—Uncolored, white, or light gray

Name, Composition, and Reference	Crystallization Structure Crystals = C Massive = M	Luster Transparency	Color
FLUORITE (Fluor spar) CaF$_2$ 287	Cubic C—Cubes, alone or modified, well developed M—Cleavable, granular, fibrous	Vitreous Transparent to nearly opaque	Wine yellow Yellowish brown Brown
Scheelite CaWO$_4$ 310	Tetragonal C—Pyramidal, s m a l l, more rarely tabular M—Drusy crusts, reniform, granular, compact	Greasy Adamantine Transparent to translucent	Pale yellow Yellowish brown Grayish brown
APATITE Ca$_5$F(PO$_4$)$_3$ 326	Hexagonal C—Prismatic, thick tabular, sometimes large, with rounded edges M—Granular, compact, fibrous, nodular, reniform	Greasy Vitreous Translucent to opaque	Brown Greenish brown Reddish brown Yellow
HEMIMORPHITE (Calamine) H$_2$Zn$_2$SiO$_5$ 337	Orthorhombic C—Thin tabular, pyramidal, hemimorphic, highly modified M—Compact, globular, granular, stalactitic, cellular, earthy	Vitreous Dull Transparent to translucent	Yellow Yellowish brown Brown
Huebnerite MnWO$_4$ 311	Monoclinic C—Long fibrous, bladed, stalky; often divergent, without good terminations M—Compact, lamellar, granular	Resinous Submetallic Translucent to opaque	Reddish brown Hair brown Pale yellow

Hardness 3 to 6

Hard- ness	Streak	Cleavage = C Fracture = F Tenacity	Specific Gravity	Characteristics and Associates
4.	White	C—Octahedral, perfect, conspicuous Brittle	3. 3.2	Recognized by c r y s t a l form, octahedral cleavage, and hardness. Common gangue of metallic ores, especially galena, sphalerite, cassiterite; also with calcite, barite.
4.5	White	C—Pyramidal, not conspicuous F—Conchoidal, uneven Brittle	5.9 6.2	Small, well developed octahedral-like crystals, usually on quartz; when massive high specific gravity important. With cassiterite, wolframite, fluorite, apatite, molybdenite.
4.5 5.	White	C—Basal, imperfect F—Conchoidal, uneven Brittle	3.1 3.2	Crystals may be vertically striated and have fused appearance. Color unevenly distributed, often with greenish spots. In crystalline limestones; metalliferous deposits; igneous r o c k s. W i t h quartz, cassiterite, fluorite, wolframite.
4.5 5.	White	C—Prismatic F—Uneven, c o n-choidal Brittle	3.3 3.5	Crystals often in sheaf-like groups or druses in cavities. When m a s s i v e, often porous or cellular. In limestones. W i t h sphalerite, galena, and especially smithsonite.
4.5 5.5	Greenish gray	C—Clinopinacoidal, conspicuous Brittle	6.7 7.3	Structure, cleavage, and specific gravity characteristic. In quartz veins. With wolframite, fluorite, pyrite, scheelite, galena, tetrahedrite.

Streak—Uncolored, white, or light gray

Name, Composition, and Reference	Crystallization Structure Crystals = C Massive = M	Luster Transparency	Color
SMITHSONITE $ZnCO_3$	Hexagonal C—Small, usually as druses or crusts M—Botryoidal, stalactitic, fibrous, compact, cellular, granular	Vitreous Dull Translucent to nearly opaque	Brown Yellowish brown Orange yellow
296			
Natrolite (Zeolite) $Na_2Al_2Si_3O_{10}.2H_2O$	Orthorhombic C—Slender prismatic, nearly square, radial or interlacing groups M—Fibrous, granular, compact	Vitreous Silky Transparent to translucent	Yellowish
386			
TITANITE (Sphene) $CaTiSiO_5$	Monoclinic C—Wedge- or envelope-shaped when disseminated; tabular or prismatic when attached M—Compact, lamellar	Vitreous Greasy Transparent to opaque	Brown Reddish brown Yellow
384			
Monazite $(Ce,La,Di)PO_4$	Monoclinic C—Thick tabular, square prismatic M—Angular fragments, rolled grains	Greasy Vitreous Transparent to opaque	Reddish brown Yellowish brown Honey yellow
325			
Cancrinite $3NaAlSiO_4.CaCO_3$	Hexagonal C—Prismatic, rare M—Compact, lamellar, columnar, disseminated	Greasy Vitreous Pearly Translucent to transparent	Yellow Brownish yellow
380			
ENSTATITE (Bronzite, Pyroxene) $(Mg,Fe)_2(SiO_3)_2$	Orthorhombic C—Prismatic, rare M—Fibrous, lamellar, compact	Bronzy Silky Translucent to opaque	Bronze brown Yellowish brown
363			

Hardness 3 to 6

Hardness	Streak	Cleavage = C Fracture = F Tenacity	Specific Gravity	Characteristics and Associates
5.	White Gray	C—Rhombohedral, not often observed F—Uneven, splintery Brittle	4.1 4.5	Cellular varieties called *dry bone*. Often mixed with sand, clay, limonite, calcite. With zinc minerals, especially sphalerite, hemimorphite. Frequently pseudomorphous after calcite.
5. 5.5	White	C—Prismatic, perfect F—Uneven Brittle	2.2 2.3	Crystals have nearly square cross-section. In basalts and phonolites. With chabazite, analcite, apophyllite, stilbite, datolite.
5. 5.5	White Gray	C—Prismatic, conspicuous, parting often noted F—Conchoidal Brittle	3.4 3.6	With feldspars, pyroxenes, amphiboles, chlorite, scapolite, zircon.
5. 5.5	White	C—Basal F—Conchoidal, uneven Brittle	4.9 5.3	Crystals commonly small, highly modified; rounded grains in sand. With quartz, magnetite, zircon, garnet, gold chromite, diamond.
5. 6.	White	C—Prismatic F—Uneven Brittle	2.4 2.5	Easily recognized by associates—nephelite, sodalite, biotite, feldspar, titanite.
5. 6.	White Grayish	C—Prismatic, pinacoidal, conspicuous F—Uneven Brittle	3.2 3.5	Cleavage surfaces usually fibrous or lamellar, irregular or wavy, with distinct bronzy luster. In basic igneous rocks.

Streak—Uncolored, white, or light gray

Name, Composition, and Reference	Crystallization Structure Crystals = C Massive = M	Luster Transparency	Color
RHODONITE $MnSiO_3$ 368	Triclinic C—Tabular, prismatic rounded edges M—Cleavable, granular, dissemi- nated grains	Vitreous Dull Translucent to opaque	Yellowish Brownish
Willemite (Troostite) Zn_2SiO_4 347	Hexagonal C—Prismatic M—Compact, granular, disseminated grains	Greasy Vitreous Transparent to opaque	Yellow Greenish yellow Brown

OPAL, varieties
    Precious opal
$SiO_2.nH_2O$ *Wood opal*
    Opal jasper
    Siliceous sinter
280   *Tripolite*
	Amorphous
	M—Compact, reniform, botryoidal, porous, earthy
		Vitreous
		Greasy
		Dull
		Translucent to opaque
			Yellow
			Yellowish brown
			Brown

Streak—Uncolored, white, or light gray

ORTHOCLASE (Feldspar) $KAlSi_3O_8$ 372	Monoclinic C—Prismatic, thick tab- ular; twins; often large M—Cleavable, granular, disseminated	Vitreous Pearly Translucent to opaque	Pale yellow Brownish yellow
Chondrodite $[Mg(F,OH)]_2Mg_3(SiO_4)_2$ 343	Monoclinic C—Small, highly modi- fied, rare M—Disseminated grains, compact	Vitreous Greasy Translucent to opaque	Reddish brown Yellowish brown Honey yellow
Sillimanite (Fibrolite) Al_2SiO_5 339	Orthorhombic C—Long, thin, needle- like M—Fibrous, columnar, radiating	Vitreous Silky Transparent to trans- lucent	Hair brown Grayish brown

Hardness 3 to 6

Hard-ness	Streak	Cleavage = C Fracture = F Tenacity	Specific Gravity	Characteristics and Associates
5. 6.	White	C—Prismatic, basal F—Conchoidal, uneven Tough, crystals brittle	3.4 3.7	On exposure may be stained brown or black. *Fowlerite*, contains zinc. With franklinite, zincite, willemite, calcite, iron ores.
5. 6.	White	C—Basal, prismatic F—Uneven Brittle	3.9 4.3	Crystals of willemite small, of troostite, manganiferous variety, often large. Characterized by associates—franklinite, zincite, rhodonite, calcite.
5.5 6.	White	F—Conchoidal, conspicuous when compact; earthy Brittle	1.9 2.3	*Precious opal*, p l a y o f colors; *wood opal*, woody structure; *opal j a s p e r*, greasy, resembling jasper; *siliceous sinter*, porous; *tripolite*, earthy, gritty.

Hardness over 6

Hard-ness	Streak	Cleavage = C Fracture = F Tenacity	Specific Gravity	Characteristics and Associates
6. 6.5	White	C—Basal clinopinacoidal, c o n-spicuous—90° F—Conchoidal, uneven Brittle	2.5 2.6	Characterized by rectangular cleavages and absence of twinning striations. In granitic rocks. With quartz, other feldspars, mica, hornblende.
6. 6.5	White	C—Basal, indistinct F—Conchoidal, uneven Brittle	3.1 3.3	Associates important. In crystalline limestones and dolomites. With spinel, vesuvianite, pyroxenes, mica.
6. 7.	White	C—Macropinacoidal F—Uneven Brittle	3.2 3.3	Crystals often s l e n d e r, bent, striated, w i t h rounded edges, without good terminations, and interlaced. In metamorphic rocks—mica, schist, gneiss. With andalusite, garnet.

Streak—Uncolored, white, or light gray

Name, Composition, and Reference	Crystallization Structure Crystals = C Massive = M	Luster Transparency	Color
EPIDOTE $Ca_2[Al,Fe)_2(AlOH)(SiO_4)_3$ 344	Monoclinic C—Prismatic, elongated and deeply striated parallel to b axis; usually terminated on one end only M—Columnar; fibrous, parallel and divergent; granular	Vitreous Transparent to opaque	Greenish brown Greenish yellow Yellow
RUTILE TiO_2 272	Tetragonal C—Prismatic, vertically striated; twinned, yielding knee-shaped or rosette forms M—Compact, disseminated	Adamantine Submetallic Translucent to opaque	Reddish brown Yellowish brown Dark brown
CASSITERITE SnO_2 272	Tetragonal C—Thick prismatic; knee-shaped twins quite common M—Reniform, botryoidal, compact, rounded pebbles, often with internal radial, fibrous structure, *wood tin*	Adamantine Greasy Dull Translucent to opaque	Reddish brown Yellowish brown Dark brown
√**ESUVIANITE** $Ca_6[Al(OH,F)]Al_2(SiO_4)_5$ 345	Tetragonal C—Short prismatic M—Compact, granular; aggregates with parallel or divergent striations or furrows	Vitreous Greasy Translucent to opaque	Brown Greenish brown Sulphur yellow
GARNET, varieties *Grossularite* *Spessartite* $M_3''M_2'''$- *Almandite* $(SiO_4)_3$ *Andradite* $M'' = Ca,$- Fe,Mg,Mn $M''' = Al,Fe$ 349	Cubic C—Dodecahedrons, tetragonal trisoctahedrons, alone or in combination M—Granular, compact, lamellar, disseminated grains, sand	Vitreous Transparent to opaque	Yellow Cinnamon brown Reddish brown

Hardness over 6

Hardness	Streak	Cleavage = C Fracture = F Tenacity	Specific Gravity	Characteristics and Associates
6. 7.	White Grayish	C—Basal F—Uneven Brittle	3.3 3.5	Crystals often darker than when massive. W i t h quartz, feldspar, vesuvianite, hornblende, pyroxenes, magnetite, native copper.
6. 7.	Gray Yellowish white Brownish white	C—Prismatic, pyramidal, n o t conspicuous F—Uneven Brittle	4.2 4.3	Not as heavy as cassiterite. Often in fine hair-like inclusions. W i t h quartz, feldspar, hematite, ilmenite, chlorite.
6. 7.	White Yellowish white Brownish white	C—Indistinct F—Uneven Brittle	6.8 7.	Distinguished by high specific gravity. In veins cutting granite, gneiss; in alluvial deposits as *stream tin*. With quartz, wolframite, scheelite, molybdenite, tourmaline, fluorite, mica, chlorite.
6.5	White	C—Indistinct F—Uneven Brittle	3.3 3.5	In crystalline limestone, gneiss, schist. With garnet, tourmaline chondrodite, wollastonite, epidote, pyroxenes.
6.5 7.5	White	C—Dodecahedral, usually indistinct F—Conchoidal, uneven Brittle	3.4 4.3	*Grossularite*, in crystalline limestone, dolomite, with wollastonite, vesuvianite, diopside, scapolite; *spessartite*, in granitic rocks, with quartz, tourmaline, orthoclase; *almandite*, with mica, staurolite, andalusite, cyanite; *andradite*, with epidote, feldspar, nephelite, leucite.

Streak—Uncolored, white, or light gray

Name, Composition, and Reference	Crystallization Structure Crystals = C Massive = M	Luster Transparency	Color

QUARTZ, Crystalline varieties
   SiO₂   Smoky quartz
      False topaz
      Aventurine
      Ferruginous
      Cat's-eye
	Hexagonal
	 C—Prismatic, horizont-
	   ally striated
	 M—Compact, granular
		Vitreous
		 Greasy
		 Transparent
		 to opaque
			Yellow
			 Yellowish
			 brown
			 Smoky brown
			 Reddish
			 brown

269

Cryptocrystalline varieties
    Chalcedony
    Agate
    Jasper
    Flint
	Hexagonal
	 C—Never in crystals
	 M—Nodular, botryoidal,
	   banded, concretion-
	   ary, stalactitic, com-
	   pact
		Waxy
		 Vitreous
		 Translucent
		 to opaque
			Yellow
			 Brown
			 Blackish
			 brown

270

Clastic varieties
    Sand
    Sandstone
    Quartzite
	Hexagonal
	 M—Grains, fragments,
	   either loose or
	   strongly consoli-
	   dated
		Vitreous
		 Dull
		 Translucent
		 to opaque
			Yellow
			 Yellowish
			 brown
			 Brown

271

TOURMALINE
 	
 M′₂₀B₂Si₄O₂₁
 M′ = Na,K,Li,Mg,
      Ca,(OH),Fe,Al
	Hexagonal
	 C—Prismatic, vertically
	   striated; terminated
	   with broken or rhom-
	   bohedral-like surfaces
	 M—Compact, granular
		Vitreous
		 Translucent
		 to opaque
			Brown
			 Yellowish
			 brown
			 Yellow

342

Hardness over 6

Hardness	Streak	Cleavage = C Fracture = F Tenacity	Specific Gravity	Characteristics and Associates
7.	White Yellowish white Brownish white	C—Indistinct F—Conchoidal, conspicuous Brittle	2.6	Characteristic conchoidal fracture and glassy luster. *Smoky quartz*, smoky yellow to brownish black; *false topaz*, yellow; *aventurine*, glistening with included scales; *ferruginous*, colored by iron oxide, *cat's-eye*, opalescent, due to inclusions of fibers of asbestos.
7.	White Yellowish white Brownish white	C—Indistinct F—Conchoidal, conspicuous Brittle to tough	2.6	Not as glassy as phanerocrystalline v a r i e t i e s. *Chalcedony*, pale to dark brown, waxy luster; *agate*, banded or clouded; *jasper*, commonly yellow and uniform in color; *flint*, smoky or blackish brown, nodular, often with white coating.
7.	White Yellowish white Brownish white	C—Indistinct F—Uneven Brittle to tough	2.6	Pigment is usually ferruginous matter. *S a n d*, l o o s e, unconsolidated grains; *sandstone*, consolidated sand; *quartzite*, metamorphosed s a n dstone.
7. 7.5	White	C—None F—Conchoidal, uneven Brittle	2.9 3.2	Spherical, triangular cross-section. Commonly as contact mineral in granular limestone and dolomite. With tremolite, scapolite, vesuvianite, apatite, garnet, spinel.

Streak—Uncolored, white, or light gray

Name, Composition, and Reference	Crystallization Structure Crystals = C Massive = M	Luster Transparency	Color
STAUROLITE $H_2FeAl_4Si_2O_{12}$ **336**	Orthorhombic C—Prismatic; twins plus- (+) or X-shaped; well developed	Vitreous Dull Translucent to opaque	Reddish brown Yellowish brown Blackish brown
ZIRCON $ZrSiO_4$ **348**	Tetragonal C—Square prisms and bipyramids, small, well developed M—Irregular lumps, grains	Adamantine Vitreous Greasy Transparent to opaque	Reddish brown Dark brown Brownish yellow
BERYL $Be_3Al_2(SiO_3)_6$ **352**	Hexagonal C—Long prismatic, often vertically striated, large M—Columnar, granular, compact	Vitreous Transparent to trans- lucent	Pale yellow Honey yellow Brownish yellow
SPINEL, varieties *Pleonaste* $M''(M'''O_2)_2$ *Gahnite* $M'' = Mg,Fe,Zn$ $M''' = Al,Fe$ **319**	Cubic C—Octahedral, well de- veloped M—Compact, granular, disseminated grains	Vitreous Dull Nearly opaque	Yellow Grayish brown Brown
TOPAZ $Al_2(F,OH)_2SiO_4$ **340**	Orthorhombic C—Prismatic, vertically striated, highly modified M—Compact, granular, rolled fragments	Vitreous Transparent to opaque	Straw yellow Wine yellow Yellowish brown

Hardness over 6

Hardness	Streak	Cleavage = C Fracture = F Tenacity	Specific Gravity	Characteristics and Associates
7. 7.5	White Grayish	C—Brachypinacoidal F—Conchoidal, uneven Brittle	3.4 3.8	Fresh crystals usually possess bright, smooth faces, when altered dull, rough, softer and with colored streak. In metamorphic rocks—g n e i s s, m i c a schist, slate. With cyanite, garnet, tourmaline, sillimanite
7.5	White	C—Indistinct F—Uneven Brittle	4.4 4.8	In the more acid igneous rocks—granite, syenite; alluvial deposits, w i t h gold, spinel, corundum, garnet. *Hyacinth*, clear and transparent.
7.5 8.	White	C—Basal, indistinct F—Conchoidal, uneven Brittle	2.6 2.8	Crystals usually simple, prism and base. In granitic rocks, mica schists, clay slates. With quartz, feldspar, mica, chrysoberyl, topaz, cassiterite, garnet.
7.5 8.	White Grayish	C—Indistinct F—Conchoidal Brittle	3.6 4.4	Commonly as contact mineral in granular limestone; in more basic igneous rocks; as rounded grains in placers. With calcite, chondrodite, serpentine, brucite, graphite, pyroxenes.
8.	White	C—Basal, perfect, conspicuous F—Conchoidal, uneven Brittle	3.4 3.6	Crystals usually developed on one end only. Color may fade on exposure. Massive varieties distinguished from quartz by higher specific gravity and basal cleavage. In veins and cavities in granitic rocks, also in placers. With cassiterite, tourmaline, fluorite, a p a t i t e, beryl, wolframite.

Streak—Uncolored, white, or light gray

Name, Composition, and Reference	Crystallization Structure Crystals = C Massive = M	Luster Transparency	Color

Chrysoberyl
 	
$Be(AlO_2)_2$
 	
322
	Orthorhombic
	C—Tabular; heart-
	  shaped, pseudohex-
	  agonal twins
	M—Fragments, loose,
	  rounded grains
		Vitreous
		Greasy
		Transparent
		to trans-
		lucent
			Yellow
			Greenish
			yellow
			Brown

CORUNDUM, varieties
        Oriental
Al_2O_3 *topaz*
      Common
 	
275
	Hexagonal
	C—Prismatic, tabular,
	  pyramidal, rhombo-
	  hedral; rough or
	  rounded barrel-
	  shaped
	M—Compact, granular,
	  lamellar
		Vitreous
		Translucent
		to trans-
		parent
			Yellow
			Brown

B. MINERALS WITH NON-METALLIC LUSTER

Streak—Uncolored, white, or light gray

Cerargyrite (Horn silver)
 	
AgCl
 	
287
	Cubic
	C—Rare
	M—Wax-like crusts,
	  coatings; stalactitic,
	  dendritic
		Waxy
		Greasy
		Transparent
		to trans-
		lucent
			Pearl gray
			Grayish

Asbestos, variety
    Chrysotile
$H_4Mg_3Si_2O_9$
 	
360
	Monoclinic
	M—Coarse or fine fibrous,
	  felted
		Silky
		Silky
		metallic
		Opaque
			White
			Greenish
			white
			Yellowish
			white

variety
    Amphibole
Silicate of Ca, Mg, Fe, Al,
    etc.
 	
369
	Monoclinic
	M—Coarse or fine fibrous,
	  felted; compact,
	  leather- or cork-like
		Silky
		Dull
		Opaque
			White
			Greenish
			white
			Yellowish
			white

Hardness over 6

Hardness	Streak	Cleavage = C Fracture = F Tenacity	Specific Gravity	Characteristics and Associates
8.5	White	C—Brachypina- coidal F—Uneven, con- choidal Brittle	3.5 3.8	Crystals disseminated as plates, often with feather-like or radial striations. In granite, gneiss, placers. With beryl, garnet, tourmaline, sillimanite.
9.	White	C—None, nearly rectangular basal and rhom- bohedral part- ings, conspicu- ous; striated F—Conchoidal Brittle to tough	3.9 4.1	When massive often multi-colored—red, blue, green, gray. *Oriental topaz*, transparent, yellow. In limestone, granite, syenite, alluvial deposits. With magnetite, nephelite, mica, spinel, chlorite.

5. COLORLESS, WHITE, OR LIGHT GRAY IN COLOR

Hardness 1 to 3

Hardness	Streak	Cleavage = C Fracture = F Tenacity	Specific Gravity	Characteristics and Associates
1. 1.5	White, shiny Gray, shiny	C—None F—Conchoidal Highly sectile	5.5 5.6	Cuts like wax; on exposure turns violet, brown, or black. With silver minerals; also limonite, calcite, barite.
1. 2.5	White	F—Fibrous Flexible	1. 2.5	*Short-fibered asbestos*, delicate, fine, parallel, flexible fibers, easily separable, perpendicular to walls. Compare below. In veins or seams in serpentine.
1. 2.5	White	F—Fibrous Flexible, tough	1. 2.5	*Long-fibered asbestos*, parallel, flexible fibers, parallel to walls. *Mountain leather, mountain cork, mountain wood,* compact, but light and tough.

Streak—Uncolored, white, or light gray

Name, Composition, and Reference	Crystallization Structure Crystals = C Massive = M	Luster Transparency	Color
TRIPOLITE (Opal) $SiO_2.nH_2O$	Amorphous M—Porous, earthy, chalk-like	Dull Opaque	Gray White Yellowish white
2°1			
KAOLINITE (Kaolin, china clay) $H_4Al_2Si_2O_9$	Monoclinic C—Scaly, rare M—Compact, friable, mealy, clay-like	Dull Pearly Opaque to translucent	White Gray Colorless
359			
CALCITE, varieties Chalk $CaCO_3$ Marl	Hexagonal M—Loose or compact, earthy	Earthy Dull Opaque	White Grayish Yellowish white
293			
TALC, varieties Foliated Soapstone or steatite French chalk $H_2Mg_3Si_4O_{12}$	Monoclinic C—Thin tabular, indistinct M—Foliated, globular, fibrous, granular, compact	Pearly Greasy Transparent to opaque	White Greenish white Gray
258			
BAUXITE $Al_2O_3.2H_2O$	Never in crystals M—Pisolitic, oölitic, rounded disseminated grains; clay-like, earthy	Dull Earthy Opaque	White Grayish
282			

Hardness 1 to 3

Hard-ness	Streak	Cleavage = C Fracture = F Tenacity	Specific Gravity	Characteristics and Associates
1. 2.5	White	F—Earthy Friable	1.9 2.3	Apparently very soft, but fine particles s c r a t c h glass. Resembles chalk and kaolinite, but gritty, and not plastic when moistened. Due to impurities may have clay odor.
1. 2.5	White	C—Basal (scales) F—Earthy Brittle	2.2 2.6	Not gritty like tripolite. Very strong clay odor when breathed u p o n. Usually adheres to tongue and becomes plastic when moistened. Greasy feel. With quartz, feldspar, corundum.
1. 2.5	White	C—None F—Earthy Brittle	2.7	*Chalk*, earthy masses; *marl*, more clay-like and frequently contains organic material—leaves, twigs. In extensive deposits.
1. 2.5	White	C—Basal, conspicuous, when foliated F—Uneven, splintery Sectile, laminæ flexible	2.6 2.8	Greasy or soapy feel important. *Foliated t a l c*, easily separable, inelastic folia or plates, H = 1; *soapstone* or *steatite*, coarse to fine granular, rather impure, H = 1.5—2.5; *French chalk*, soft, compact, marks cloth distinctly. With serpentine, dolomite, chlorite, magnesite, actinolite.
1. 3.	White	F—Earthy Brittle	2.5	Clay odor when breathed upon. Usually distinguished from clay by pisolitic or oölitic structure. With clay or kaolin in nodules, grains, or irregular masses in limestone or dolomite.

Streak—Uncolored, white, or light gray

Name, Composition, and Reference	Crystallization Structure Crystals = C Massive = M	Luster Transparency	Color
SODA NITER (Chile saltpeter) $NaNO_3$ 290	Hexagonal C—Similar to those of calcite, rare M—Granular, crusts, efflorescences	Vitreous Transparent	Colorless White Grayish
GYPSUM, varieties *Selenite* $CaSO_4.2H_2O$ *Satin spar* *Alabaster* *Common* 315	Monoclinic C—Tabular, prismatic; swallow-tail twins M—Cleavable, coarse or fine grained, fibrous, foliated, earthy	Pearly Vitreous Silky Dull Transparent to opaque	Colorless White Gray
Melanterite (Copperas) $FeSO_4.7H_2O$ 317	Monoclinic C—Rare M—Capillary, fibrous, stalactitic, concretionary, powder	Vitreous Dull Transparent to translucent	White Greenish white Yellowish white
Sepiolite (Meerschaum) $H_8Mg_2Si_3O_{12}$ 362	Monoclinic M—Compact, nodular with smooth feel; earthy, clay-like	Dull Opaque	White Grayish white
Epsomite (Epsom salt) $MgSO_4.7H_2O$ 317	Orthorhombic C—Prismatic, nearly square, rare M—Granular, fibrous, earthy, crusts	Vitreous Dull Transparent to translucent	White Colorless Gray
HALITE (Rock salt) $NaCl$ 285	Cubic C—Cubes, often skeletal or hopper-shaped M—Compact, cleavable, granular, fibrous, stalactitic, crusts	Vitreous Transparent to translucent	Colorless White Grayish

Hardness 1 to 3

Hard-ness	Streak	Cleavage = C Fracture = F Tenacity	Specific Gravity	Characteristics and Associates
1.5 **2.**	White	C—Rhombohedral F—Conchoidal Brittle	2.1 2.3	Cooling and saline taste. Absorbs moisture readily. In extensive deposits. With gypsum, sand, clay, guano.
1.5 **2.**	White	C—Clinopinacoidal, conspicuous; pyramidal, orthopinacoidal F—Conchoidal, fibrous Brittle, laminæ flexible	2.2 2.4	*Selenite*, crystals and cleavage plates, usually transparent; *satin spar*, fibrous with silky luster; *alabaster*, granular. In limestones, shales. With halite, celestite, sulphur, aragonite, dolomite, ore deposits.
2.	White	C—Basal F—Conchoidal, earthy Brittle	1.8 1.9	On exposure loses water and crumbles. Sweet, astringent taste, somewhat metallic. Oxidation product of iron sulphide minerals—marcasite, pyrite, chalcopyrite, pyrrhotite.
2. **2.5**	White	C—None F—Conchoidal, uneven Brittle	1. 2.	Recognized by smooth feel, adherence to tongue, low specific gravity and lack of clay odor when breathed upon. Impressed by finger nail. With serpentine, magnesite, chlorite.
2. **2.5**	White	C—Brachypinacoidal F—Conchoidal Brittle	1.7 1.8	Non-hygroscopic. Bitter, salty taste. In limestone caves. With serpentine, talc, magnesite.
2. **2.5**	White	C—Cubic, perfect, conspicuous F—Conchoidal Brittle	2.1 2.3	May absorb moisture and become damp. Characteristic cubical cleavage and saline taste. With slate, gypsum, anhydrite.

Streak—Uncolored, white, or light gray

Name, Composition, and Reference	Crystallization Structure Crystals = C Massive = M	Luster Transparency	Color
Lepidolite $K_2Li_3Al_3(OH,F)_4-$ $(AlSi_3O_{10})_2$ 357	Monoclinic C—Short prismatic M—Coarse or fine granular, scales, cleavable plates	Pearly Translucent	White Pinkish white Lavender Gray
MUSCOVITE (Isinglass) $KAl_2(OH)_2AlSi_3O_{10}$ 355	Monoclinic C—Tabular, pyramidal, with rhombic or hexagonal outline; often large and rough M—Scales, plates; foliated and plumose aggregates.	Vitreous Pearly Transparent to translucent	Colorless Yellowish white Brownish white
APATITE, variety *Phosphate rock* Mainly calcium carbonate —phosphate (collophanite) 326	Amorphous M—Compact, nodular, reniform, earthy	Dull Opaque	White Gray
CRYOLITE Na_3AlF_6 288	Monoclinic C—Small, pseudocubical rare M—Cleavable, compact, granular	Vitreous Greasy Pearly Transparent to translucent	Snow white Gray Colorless
BARITE (Heavy spar) $BaSO_4$ 307	Orthorhombic C—Tabular, prismatic; crested divergent groups M—Compact, cleavable, lamellar, fibrous, reniform	Vitreous Pearly Transparent to translucent	Colorless White Gray

MICAS

Hardness 1 to 3

Hard-ness	Streak	Cleavage = C Fracture = F Tenacity	Specific Gravity	Characteristics and Associates
2. 3.	White	C—Basal, perfect F—Scaly granular Tough	2.8 2.9	When massive often resembles granular limestone. In pegmatites, granites, gneisses. With red tourmaline (rubellite), spodumene, cassiterite.
2. 3.	White	C—Basal, perfect, conspicuous Tough, laminæ very elastic	2.8 3.1	Structure, perfect cleavage, and elasticity important. Large crystals often show distinct partings perpendicular to cleavage, *ruled mica*. In granitic rocks, schists, limestones. With feldspar, quartz, beryl, tourmaline, garnet, spodumene.
2. 3.	White	F—Conchoidal, uneven Brittle	3.1 3.2	More or less impure masses, frequently resembling compact limestone. Independent beds, nodules, concretions.
2.5 3.	White	C—Basal, prismatic, nearly at 90°; sometimes conspicuous F—Uneven Brittle	2.9 3.	Frequently resembles snow ice. Often contains disseminated siderite, chalcopyrite, galena, pyrite, fluorite, columbite.
2.5 3.	White	C—Basal, prismatic, conspicuous F—Uneven Brittle	4.3 4.7	Characterized by rather high specific gravity and cleavages. In metalliferous veins; pockets and lenticular masses in limestones. With galena, sphalerite, fluorite, chalcopyrite; manganese and iron ores.

Streak—Uncolored, white, or light gray

Name, Composition, and Reference	Crystallization Structure Crystals = C Massive = M	Luster Transparency	Color

CALCITE, varieties
 	
CaCO₃   *Dog tooth spar*
    Nail head spar
    Iceland spar
    Satin spar
    Limestone
    Coquina
    Marble
    Calcareous tufa
    Travertine
291   *Stalactites, etc.*
	Hexagonal
	C—Scalenohedral, rhombohedral, prismatic, tabular, acicular; highly modified; twins
	M—Cleavable, granular, fibrous, banded, stalactitic, oölitic, porous, compact, crusts shells
		Vitreous
		Dull
		Transparent to nearly opaque
			White
			Grayish
			Colorless

Streak—Uncolored, white, or light gray

ANHYDRITE CaSO₄ **305**	Orthorhombic C—Thick tabular, prismatic, rare M—Granular, compact, fibrous, cleavable, lamellar, reniform	Vitreous Pearly Transparent to translucent	White Bluish white Reddish white Grayish
CELESTITE SrSO₄ **306**	Orthorhombic C—Tabular, prismatic, common; pyramidal M—Compact, cleavable, fibrous, granular, reniform	Vitreous Pearly Transparent to translucent	Colorless White Gray
BARITE (Heavy spar) BaSO₄ **307**	Orthorhombic C—Tabular, prismatic; crested divergent groups M—Compact, cleavable, lamellar, fibrous, reniform	Vitreous Pearly Transparent to translucent	Colorless White Gray

Hardness 1 to 3

Hard-ness	Streak	Cleavage = C Fracture = F Tenacity	Specific Gravity	Characteristics and Associates
3.	White	C—Rhombohedral, perfect, usually conspicuous F—Conchoidal Brittle	2.7	Rhombohedral cleavage characteristic, especially on crystals. Cleavage surfaces often striated. Very strong double refraction easily observed w h e n transparent. To distinguish varieties, see reference.

Hardness 3 to 6

Hard-ness	Streak	Cleavage = C Fracture = F Tenacity	Specific Gravity	Characteristics and Associates
3. 3.5	White	C—Pinacoidal, 3 directions at 90°, sometimes conspicuous F—Conchoidal Brittle	2.7 3.	Pseudocubical cleavage sometimes noted. Granular varieties resemble marble. Not as heavy as celestite or barite. With halite, gypsum.
3. 3.5	White	C—B a s a l, prismatic, conspicuous F—Uneven Brittle	3.9 4.	Usually with faint bluish tinge. Heavier than calcite, anhydrite; lighter than barite. Good cleavages. In limestones, dolomites, shales. With sulphur, gypsum, aragonite, halite, galena, sphalerite.
3. 3.5	White	C—B a s a l, prismatic, conspicuous F—Uneven Brittle	4.3 4.7	Characterized by rather high specific gravity and cleavages. In metalliferous veins; pockets and lenticular masses in limestones. With g a l e n a, sphalerite, fluorite, chalcopyrite; manganese and iron ores.

Streak—Uncolored, white, or light gray

Name, Composition, and Reference	Crystallization Structure Crystals = C Massive = M	Luster Transparency	Color
ANGLESITE $PbSO_4$ **308**	Orthorhombic **C**—Prismatic, tabular, pyramidal **M**—Compact, granular, nodular	Adamantine Greasy Transparent to translucent	Colorless White Gray
CERUSSITE $PbCO_3$ **301**	Orthorhombic **C**—Tabular, prismatic, pyramidal; pseudo-hexagonal; clusters and star-shaped groups **M**—Interlaced bundles, granular, stalactitic, compact	Adamantine Greasy Silky Transparent to translucent	Colorless White Gray
STILBITE (Zeolite) $(Ca,Na_2)Al_2Si_6O_{16}.6H_2O$ **387**	Monoclinic **C**—Twinned, sheaf-like, radial, or globular aggregates	Vitreous Pearly Transparent to translucent	White Yellowish white Gray
Lepidolite (Mica) $K_2Li_3Al_3(OH,F)_4$-$(AlSi_3O_{10})_2$ **357**	Monoclinic **C**—Short prismatic **M**—Granular, coarse or fine; scales, cleavable plates	Pearly Translucent	White Pinkish white Lavender Gray
PHOSPHATE ROCK (Apatite) Mainly calcium carbonate—phosphate (collophanite) **326**	Amorphous **M**—Compact, nodular, reniform, earthy	Dull Opaque	White Gray

Hardness 3 to 6

Hard-ness	Streak	Cleavage = C Fracture = F Tenacity	Specific Gravity	Characteristics and Associates
3. 3.5	White	C—B a s a l, pris-matic F—Conchoidal Brittle	6.1 6.4	Luster and very high spe-cific gravity important. Distinguished from cerus-site by absence of twins. Oxidation product of lead m i n e r a l s. Usually in cracks and cavities, with galena, cerussite.
3. 3.5	White	C—Indistinct F—Conchoidal Brittle	6.4 6.6	Twinning, structure, luster, and specific gravity char-acteristic. With l e a d minerals—galena, p y r o-morphite, anglesite; also malachite, limonite.
3. 4.	White	C—Pinacoidal F—Uneven Brittle	2.1 2.2	Radial or sheaf-like struc-ture. In basic igneous rocks; ore deposits. With chabazite, apophyllite, datolite, calcite.
3. 4.	White	C—Basal, perfect F—Scaly, granular Tough	2.8 2.9	When massive often re-sembles granular l i m e-s t o n e. In pegmatites, granites, gneisses. With red tourmaline (rubellite), spodumene, topaz.
3. 5.	White	F—Conchoidal, un-even Brittle	3.1 3.2	More or less i m p u r e masses, frequently re-sembling compact lime-stone. Independent beds, nodules, concretions.

Streak—Uncolored, white, or light gray

Name, Composition, and Reference	Crystallization Structure Crystals = C Massive = M	Luster Transparency	Color
ANDALUSITE Al_2SiO_5	Orthorhombic C—Prismatic, rough, nearly square, often large without terminations M—Columnar, fibrous, granular, disseminated **338**	Vitreous Dull Transparent to opaque	White Pearl gray Reddish gray
Wavellite $(AlOH)_3(PO_4)_2.5H_4O$ **328**	Orthorhombic C—Capillary, small M—Crusts, globular or hemispherical, with radial fibrous structure	Vitreous Translucent	White Gray Colorless
ALUNITE (Alum stone) $K_2(Al.2OH)_6(SO_4)_4$ **313**	Hexagonal C—Rhombohedrons, resembling cubes; tabular, rare M—Compact, granular, fibrous, earthy	Vitreous Pearly Transparent to translucent	Colorless White Gray
DOLOMITE $CaMg(CO_3)_2$ **294**	Hexagonal C—Rhombohedral with curved surfaces (*pearl spar*) M—Coarsely crystalline, compact, granular, friable	Vitreous Pearly Transparent to translucent	White Gray Colorless
ARAGONITE $CaCO_3$ **299**	Orthorhombic C—Chisel- or spear-shaped; pseudohexagonal prisms; radial, columnar, acicular aggregates M—Branching forms (*flos ferri*), stalactitic, reniform, crusts, oölitic	Vitreous Greasy Transparent to translucent	Colorless White Gray

Hardness 3 to 6

Hard-ness	Streak	Cleavage = C Fracture = F Tenacity	Specific Gravity	Characteristics and Associates
3. **6.**	White	C—Prismatic F—Uneven Brittle	3.1 3.2	Due to alteration, surface may be covered with scales of mica, hence, soft. *Chiastolite*, regular, internal arrangement of dark, organic matter, best seen in cross section. In metamorphic rocks, often as rounded or knotty projections. With cyanite, sillimanite, garnet, tourmaline.
3.5 **4.**	White	C—Pinacoidal, domatic F—Uneven, conchoidal Brittle	2.3 2.4	Secondary mineral, occurring on surfaces of rocks or minerals as crystalline crusts with pronounced radial, fibrous structure.
3.5 **4.**	White	C—Basal F—Splintery, conchoidal, earthy Brittle	2.6 2.8	Hardness often greater due to admixture of quartz, feldspar; then tough. Deposits and veins in feldspathic rocks. With kaolin, pyrite, opal.
3.5 **4.**	White Gray	C—Rhombohedral, perfect (crystals) F—Conchoidal Brittle	2.9	Crystals generally curved or saddle-shaped with pearly luster. *Marble* includes some compact varieties. Independent beds; in fissures and cavities; with ore deposits.
3.5 **4.**	White	C—Pinacoidal, prismatic, indistinct F—Conchoidal Brittle	2.9 3.	Twins common, often pseudohexagonal—prism and striated base. In cracks and cavities; with ore deposits; deposition from hot springs; in shells. With gypsum, celestite, sulphur, siderite, serpentine.

Streak—Uncolored, white, or light gray

Name, Composition, and Reference	Crystallization Structure Crystals = C Massive = M	Luster Transparency	Color
STRONTIANITE $SrCO_3$ **300**	Orthorhombic **C**—Spear-shaped, columnar, acicular, often divergent **M**—Columnar, granular, compact, fibrous, botryoidal	Vitreous Transparent to translucent	Colorless Gray White
WITHERITE $BaCO_3$ **300**	Orthorhombic **C**—Pseudohexagonal bipyramids resembling quartz **M**—Radial fibrous, compact, globular, granular, lamellar	Vitreous Greasy Translucent to transparent	White Grayish Colorless
Colemanite $Ca_2B_6O_{11}.5H_2O$ **323**	Monoclinic **C**—Prismatic, highly modified **M**—Granular, cleavable, compact	Vitreous Dull Transparent to opaque	Colorless Milky white Yellowish white
MAGNESITE $MgCO_3$ **295**	Hexagonal **C**—Rhombohedral, rare **M**—Compact, granular, resembling unglazed porcelain on fresh fracture	Vitreous Dull Translucent to transparent	Snow white Gray Colorless
FLUORITE (Fluor spar) CaF_2 **287**	Cubic **C**—Cubes, alone or modified, well developed **M**—Cleavable, granular, fibrous	Vitreous Transparent to translucent	Colorless White Greenish white

Hardness 3 to 6

Hardness	Streak	Cleavage = C Fracture = F Tenacity	Specific Gravity	Characteristics and Associates
3.5 **4.**	White	C—Indistinct F—Uneven Brittle	3.6 3.8	Similar to aragonite. Divergent columnar structure and higher specific gravity characteristic. In ore deposits; independent masses. With g a l e n a, barite, calcite.
3.5 **4.**	White	C—Indistinct F—Uneven Brittle	4.2 4.3	Crystals, apparently hexagonal bipyramids; massive, often radial fibrous resembling strontianite, but heavier. Usually with galena.
3.5 **4.5**	White	C—Pinacoidal, perfect, conspicuous F—Uneven, c o n-choidal Brittle	2.2 2.4	Transparent crystals, resemble those of datolite, but softer; c o m p a c t masses look like chalk or porcelain. With gypsum, celestite, quartz.
3.5 **5.**	White	C—Rhombohedral, perfect (c r y s-tals) F—Conchoidal, conspicuous Tough to brittle	2.9 3.1	Conchoidal fracture generally prominent. Compact varieties are apparently very hard. Disseminated in talcose and chloritic schists, serpentine, gypsum; independent beds.
4.	White	C—Octahedral, perfect, conspicuous Brittle	3. 3.2	Recognized by c r y s t a l form, octahedral cleavage, and hardness. Common gangue of metallic ores, especially galena, sphalerite, cassiterite; also with calcite, barite.

Streak—Uncolored, white, or light gray

Name, Composition, and Reference	Crystallization Structure Crystals = C Massive = M	Luster Transparency	Color
CHABAZITE (Zeolite) $CaAl_2Si_6O_{16}.8H_2O$ 388	Hexagonal C—Rhombohedral, cube-like; lenticular M—Compact	Vitreous Translucent to trans-parent	White Colorless Gray
APOPHYLLITE $KFCa_4(Si_2O_5)_4.8H_2O$ 385	Tetragonal C—Prismatic, pyramidal, pseudocubical, tabular M—Lamellar, granular, compact	Vitreous Pearly Transparent to nearly opaque	Colorless White Yellowish white
Pectolite $HNaCa_2(SiO_3)_3$ 367	Triclinic C—Acicular, rarely ter-minated; tabular M—Compact radial fibrous aggregates	Vitreous Silky Translucent to opaque	White Grayish
CYANITE (Disthene, kyan-ite) Al_2SiO_5 339	Triclinic C—Long, bladed, with-out good termi-nations; sometimes curved and radially grouped M—Coarsely bladed, columnar, fibrous	Vitreous Translucent to trans-parent	White Grayish Colorless
Scheelite $CaWO_4$ 316	Tetragonal C—Pyramidal, s m a l l; more rarely tabular M—Drusy crusts, com-pact, reniform, gran-ular, disseminated	Adamantine Greasy Transparent to trans-lucent	Gray White Yellowish white

Hardness 3 to 6

Hard-ness	Streak	Cleavage = C Fracture = F Tenacity	Specific Gravity	Characteristics and Associates
4. 5.	White	C—Rhombohedral, not conspicuous F—Uneven Brittle	2.1 2.	Generally in cube-like crystals. Inferior cleavage distinguishes it from fluorite. In basic igneous rocks. With analcite, stilbite.
4. 5.	White	C—Basal, perfect, conspicuous F—Uneven Brittle	2.3 2.4	Fish-eye opalescence often observed on basal pinacoid. Prism faces vertically striated. In fissures and cavities in basic igneous rocks. With natrolite, analcite, datolite, native copper, calcite.
4. 5.	White Grayish	C—Basal, macro-pinacoidal F—Uneven, fibrous Brittle	2.7 2.8	Fibers usually divergent, long, and very sharp. In fissures and cavities in basic igneous and metamorphic rocks. With zeolites, datolite.
4. 5.	White	C—Pinacoidal perfect, conspicuous Brittle	3.5 3.7	Often with bluish streaks or spots irregularly distributed. Hardness varies with direction, 4–5 parallel to long direction, 6–7 at right angles thereto. In gneiss, mica schist. With staurolite, garnet, corundum.
4.5	White	C—Pyramidal, not conspicuous F—Conchoidal, uneven Brittle	5.9 6.2	Small, well developed octahedral-like crystals, usually on quartz; when massive high specific gravity important. With cassiterite, wolframite, fluorite, apatite, molybdenite.

Streak—Uncolored, white, or light gray

Name, Composition, and Reference	Crystallization Structure Crystals = C Massive = M	Luster Transparency	Color
Wollastonite (Tabular spar) $CaSiO_3$	Triclinic C—Tabular, prismatic M—Cleavable, fibrous, granular, compact	Vitreous Silky Transparent to translucent	White Gray Colorless
367			
APATITE $Ca_5F(PO_4)_3$	Hexagonal C—Prismatic, thick tabular M—Granular, compact, fibrous, nodular, reniform	Vitreous Greasy Transparent to translucent	White Gray Colorless
326			
HEMIMORPHITE (Calamine) $H_2Zn_2SiO_5$	Orthorhombic C—Thin tabular, pyramidal, hemimorphic, highly modified M—Compact, globular, stalactitic, fibrous, granular, cellular, earthy	Vitreous Dull Transparent to opaque	Colorless White Gray
337			
SMITHSONITE $ZnCO_3$	Hexagonal C—Small, usually as druses or crusts M—Botryoidal, stalactitic, granular, cellular, fibrous, compact	Vitreous Pearly Dull Transparent to nearly opaque	White Brownish white Gray Colorless
296			
ANALCITE (Zeolite) $NaAlSi_2O_6.H_2O$	Cubic C—Tetragonal trisoctahedrons, cubes M—Granular, compact	Vitreous Transparent to nearly opaque	Colorless White Grayish
387			

Hardness 3 to 6

Hardness	Streak	Cleavage = C Fracture = F Tenacity	Specific Gravity	Characteristics and Associates
4.5 5.	White	C—Basal, macro-pinacoidal F—Uneven Brittle	2.8 2.9	Fibers may be parallel or divergent. Typical contact mineral often in crystalline limestone. With garnet, diopside, vesuvianite, graphite.
4.5 5.	White	C—Basal, imperfect F—Conchoidal, uneven Brittle	3.1 3.2	Crystals may be vertically striated and highly modified. In crystalline limestone; ore deposits, igneous rocks. With quartz, cassiterite, fluorite, wolframite.
4.5 5.	White	C—Prismatic F—Uneven, conchoidal Brittle	3.3 3.5	Crystals often in sheaf-like groups or druses in cavities. When massive may be porous. In limestones. With sphalerite, galena, and especially smithsonite.
5.	White Gray	C—Rhombohedral, not often observed F—Uneven, splintery Brittle	4.1 4.5	Cellular varieties are called *dry bone*. Often mixed with sand, clay, limonite, calcite. With zinc minerals, especially sphalerite, hemimorphite. Frequently as a pseudomorph after calcite.
5. 5.5	White	C—None F—Uneven, conchoidal Brittle	2.2 2.3	Good crystals common. In fissures and cavities in basic igneous rocks. With apophyllite, chabazite, natrolite, datolite, native copper, epidote.

Streak   Uncolored, white, or light gray

Name, Composition, and Reference	Crystallization Structure Crystals = C Massive = M	Luster Transparency	Color
Natrolite (Zeolite) $Na_2Al_2Si_3O_{10}.2H_2O$ 386	Orthorhombic C—Slender prismatic, nearly square; radial or interlacing groups M—Fibrous, granular, compact	Vitreous Silky Transparent to trans-lucent	White Colorless Grayish
Datolite $Ca(BOH)SiO_4$ 341	Monoclinic C—Prismatic, pyramidal, tabular, highly modified M—Compact fibrous, granular, botryoidal	Vitreous Greasy Dull Transparent to opaque	Colorless Greenish white Gray
NEPHELITE (Nepheline, eläeolite) $(Na,K)_8Al_8Si_9O_{34}$ 380	Hexagonal C—Short prismatic, tab-ular M—Compact, dissemi-nated grains	Greasy Vitreous Transparent to opaque	White Bluish gray Greenish gray Colorless
SCAPOLITE (Wernerite) $\begin{cases} nNa_4Al_3Si_9O_{24}Cl \\ mCa_4Al_6Si_6O_{24}CO_3 \end{cases}$ 383	Tetragonal C—Thick prismatic, coarse, often large M—Compact, fibrous, columnar, granular	Vitreous Greasy Translucent	White Gray Greenish gray
Tremolite (Amphibole) $Ca_2Mg_5(OH)_2(Si_4O_{11})_2$ 369	Monoclinic C—Bladed, without ter-minations M—Compact, columnar, granular	Silky Vitreous Transparent to opaque	White Yellowish white Colorless

Hardness 3 to 6

Hardness	Streak	Cleavage = C Fracture = F Tenacity	Specific Gravity	Characteristics and Associates
5. 5.5	White	C—Prismatic F—Uneven Brittle	2.2 2.3	Needle-like crystals have nearly square cross section. With chabazite, analcite, apophyllite, stilbite, datolite.
5. 5.5	White	C—None F—Conchoidal, uneven Brittle	2.9 3.	Crystals glassy, often with greenish tinge; compact masses resemble wedgewood ware or unglazed porcelain; often with reddish, brownish, or yellowish streaks and spots. In cracks and cavities in basic igneous rocks. With native copper, calcite, zeolites.
5. 6.	White	C—Indistinct F—Conchoidal, uneven Brittle	2.6	Distinguished from orthoclase by inferior cleavage and more greasy luster. With feldspar, cancrinite, biotite, sodalite, zircon, corundum; not with quartz.
5. 6.	White	C—Prismatic F—Conchoidal Brittle	2.6 2.8	Crystals may appear as though fused. Typical contact mineral. In metamorphic rocks, especially granular limestones. With pyroxenes, amphiboles, apatite, garnet, biotite.
5. 6.	White	C—Prismatic, conspicuous—124° Brittle	2.9 3.1	Silky luster and distinct cleavage (124°) important. Common contact mineral. In limestones, dolomites, schists.

Streak—Uncolored, white, or light gray

Name, Composition, and Reference	Crystallization Structure Crystals = C Massive = M	Luster Transparency	Color
DIOPSIDE (Pyroxene) $CaMg(SiO_3)_2$ **364**	Monoclinic C—Prismatic, thick columnar, prism angle 87° M—Compact, granular, lamellar, columnar	Vitreous Dull Transparent to opaque	Gray Greenish gray Yellowish white Colorless

OPAL, varieties
     Precious opal
$SiO_2.nH_2O$ *Milk opal*
     Wood opal
     Hyalite
     Siliceous sinter
     Tripolite
 	
280
	Amorphous
	M—Reniform, botryoidal, porous, earthy, compact
		Vitreous
		Pearly
		Dull
		Transparent to opaque
			Colorless
			Gray
			Milk white
			Yellowish white

LEUCITE $KAl(SiO_3)_2$ **382**	Pseudocubic C—Tetragonal trisoctahedrons M—Rounded disseminated grains	Vitreous Greasy Translucent to opaque	Gray White Yellowish white

Streak—Uncolored, white, or light gray

	Name, Composition, and Reference	Crystallization Structure	Luster Transparency	Color

FELDSPARS	ORTHOCLASE,
	    varieties
	$KAlSi_3O_8$ *Adularia*
	    Sanidine
	    Ordinary
	
	372
		Monoclinic
		C—Prismatic, thick tabular; twins; often large
		M—Cleavable, granular, disseminated
			Vitreous
			Pearly
			Translucent to transparent
				White
				Gray
				Colorless

	MICROCLINE $KAlSi_3O_8$ **375**	Triclinic C—Prismatic, thick tabular; twins; often large M—Cleavable, granular disseminated	Vitreous Pearly Translucent to transparent	Gray White Yellowish white

(Feldspars continued on next page.)

Hardness 3 to 6

Hard-ness	Streak	Cleavage = C Fracture = F Tenacity	Specific Gravity	Characteristics and Associates
5. 6.	White Gray	C—Prismatic; con-spicuous basal parting F—Uneven Brittle	3.2 3.3	Prismatic, pseudotetrag-onal crystals, with dis-tinct basal parting. May show colorless and dark green zones. In crystal-line limestones. W i t h vesuvianite, g a r n e t, scapolite, spinel, apatite.
5.5 6.	White	F—Conchoidal, conspicuous when compact; earthy Brittle	1.9 2.3	*Precious opal*, with play of colors; *milk opal*, com-pact, milk white; *wood opal*, woody structure; *hyalite*, resembles drops of melted glass; *siliceous sinter*, porous or botry-oidal; *tripolite*, earthy and gritty.
5.5 6.	White	C—Indistinct F—Conchoidal Brittle	2.5	Well developed crystals or rounded grains, dissemi-nated in eruptive rocks. With sanidine, augite, nephelite, olivine.

Hardness over 6

Hard-ness	Streak	Cleavage = C Fracture = F Tenacity	Specific Gravity	Characteristics and Associates
6. 6.5	White	C—Basal, c l i n o-pinacoidal, con-spicuous, 90°; often step-like F—Conchoidal, un-even Brittle	2.5 2.6	Distinguished from other feldspars by rectangular cleavage and absence of twinning striations. *Adu-laria*, opalescent, trans-parent or slightly cloudy; *sanidine*, glassy, tabular or square crystals. With quartz, other feldspars, mica, hornblende, zircon.
6. 6.5	White	C—Basal, brachy-pinacoidal, con-spicuous, 90° 30′ F—Uneven Brittle	2.5 2.6	Resembles orthoclase, but w i t h slightly inclined cleavages and may show twinning striations on basal pinacoid. Occur-rence and associates same as for orthoclase.

Streak—Uncolored, white, or light gray

Name, Composition, and Reference	Crystallization Structure Crystals = C Massive = M	Luster Transparency	Color
FELDSPARS — **Plagioclases** **ALBITE** $NaAlSi_3O_8(Ab)$ 377	Triclinic C—Tabular, twins, small M—Compact, curved or divergent lamellar, granular	Vitreous Pearly Transparent to trans-lucent	White Gray Colorless
LABRADORITE $Ab_{50}An_{50}...Ab_{30}An_{70}$ 378	Triclinic C—Thin tabular, often with rhombic cross-section M—Compact, cleavable, granular	Vitreous Pearly Translucent to nearly opaque	Gray Greenish gray White
Anorthite $CaAl_2Si_2O_8(An)$ 379	Triclinic C—Prismatic, tabular complex M—Compact, cleavable, lamellar	Vitreous Pearly Transparent to trans-lucent	Colorless White Gray
SPODUMENE (Pyroxene) $LiAl(SiO_3)_2$ 366	Monoclinic C—Prismatic, tabular, vertically striated M—Cleavable, broad columnar	Vitreous Pearly Transparent to opaque	White Grayish white Greenish white
Sillimanite (Fibrolite) Al_2SiO_5 339	Orthorhombic C—Long, thin, needle-like M—Fibrous, columnar, radiating	Vitreous Silky Transparent to trans-lucent	Gray Yellowish gray Grayish white

Hardness over 6

Hardness	Streak	Cleavage = C Fracture = F Tenacity	Specific Gravity	Characteristics and Associates
6. 6.5	White	C—Basal, brachypinacoidal, conspicuous, 86° 24' F—Uneven Brittle	2.6	Inclined cleavages often show fine, parallel twinning striations. *Moonstone*, opalescent. With quartz, other feldspars, mica, chlorite, beryl, rutile.
6. 6.5	White	C—Basal, brachypinacoidal, conspicuous, 86° 4' F—Uneven Brittle	2.7	Often with play of colors—yellow, green, blue, red. Inclined cleavages a r e striated. In basic igneous rocks. With pyroxenes, amphiboles.
6. 6.5	White	C—Basal, brachypinacoidal, conspicuous, 85° 50' F—Uneven Brittle	2.7 2.8	Commonly in small, glassy, highly modified crystals. In basic igneous rocks; crystalline limestones. With olivine, pyroxenes, pyrrhotite, magnetite.
6. 7.	White	C—Prismatic; pinacoidal parting conspicuous F—Uneven, splintery Brittle	3.1 3.2	Commonly in broad plates due to distinct pinacoidal parting. Prism angle 93°. May have irregular brownish s t a i n s. In g r a n i t i c rocks. With tourmaline, lepidolite, beryl.
6. 7.	White	C—Macropinacoidal F—Uneven Brittle	3.2 3.3	Crystals often large, bent, striated, with rounded edges, without good terminations, and interlaced. In metamorphic rocks—mica schist, gneiss. With andalusite, zircon.

Streak—Uncolored, white, or light gray

Name, Composition, and Reference	Crystallization Structure Crystals = C Massive = M	Luster Transparency	Color
CYANITE (Disthene, kyanite) Al_2SiO_5 339	Triclinic C—Long, bladed, without good terminations; sometimes curved and radially grouped M—Coarsely bladed, columnar, fibrous	Vitreous Translucent to transparent	White Grayish Colorless
ANDALUSITE Al_2SiO_5 338	Orthorhombic C—Prismatic, rough, nearly square, often large, without terminations M—Columnar, fibrous, granular, disseminated	Vitreous Dull Translucent to opaque	White Pearl gray Reddish gray
GARNET, variety Grossularite $Ca_3Al_2(SiO_4)_3$ 349	Cubic C—Dodecahedrons, tetragonal trisoctahedrons, alone or in combination M—Granular, compact, lamellar, disseminated grains	Vitreous Transparent to translucent	Colorless White Greenish white Yellowish white
QUARTZ, Crystalline varieties SiO_2 Rock crystal Milky quartz Ordinary 269	Hexagonal C—Prismatic, horizontally striated columnar M—Compact, granular	Vitreous Greasy Transparent to translucent	Colorless White Gray Milky
Cryptocrystalline varieties Chalcedony Agate Onyx Hornstone 270 Chert	Hexagonal C—Never in crystals M—Nodular, botryoidal, banded, clouded, concretionary, stalactitic, compact	Waxy Vitreous Translucent to opaque	White Gray

(Quartz continued on next page.)

Hardness over 6

Hardness	Streak	Cleavage = C Fracture = F Tenacity	Specific Gravity	Characteristics and Associates
6. 7.	White	C—Pinacoidal, perfect, conspicuous Brittle	3.5 3.7	Often with bluish streaks or spots, irregularly distributed. Hardness varies with direction, 4–5 parallel to long direction, 6–7 at right angles thereto. In gneiss, mica schist. With staurolite, corundum, garnet.
6. 7.5	White	C—Prismatic F—Uneven Brittle	3.1 3.2	Due to alteration, surface may be coated with scales of mica, then softer. In metamorphic rocks, often as rounded or knotty projections. With cyanite, sillimanite, garnet.
6.5 7.5	White	C—Dodecahedral, usually indistinct F—Conchoidal, uneven Brittle	3.4 3.7	Typical contact mineral, in crystalline limestones and dolomites. With wollastonite, vesuvianite, diopside, scapolite.
7.	White	C—Indistinct F—Conchoidal, conspicuous Brittle	2.6	Characteristic conchoidal fracture, glassy luster. *Rock crystal*, colorless, or nearly so, generally crystallized; *milky quartz*, milk white and nearly opaque.
7.	White	C—Indistinct F—Conchoidal, conspicuous Brittle to tough	2.6	Not as glassy as phanerocrystalline v a r i e t i e s. *Chalcedony, h o r n s t o n e, chert,* uniform in color; *agate, onyx,* clouded or banded. To distinguish, see reference.

Streak—Uncolored, white, or light gray

Name, Composition, and Reference	Crystallization Structure Crystals = C Massive = M	Luster Transparency	Color
QUARTZ. Clastic varieties *Sand* SiO_2 *Sandstone* *Itacolumite* *Quartzite* 271	Hexagonal M—Grains, fragments, either loose or strongly consolidated	Vitreous Dull Translucent to opaque	Gray White
ZIRCON $ZrSiO_4$ 348	Tetragonal C—Square prisms with bipyramids, small, well developed M—Irregular lumps, grains	Adamantine Vitreous Pearly Transparent to opaque	Brownish gray Lavender gray Colorless
BERYL $Be_3Al_2(SiO_3)_6$ 352	Hexagonal C—Long prismatic, often vertically striated, large M—Columnar, granular, compact	Vitreous Transparent to translucent	White Yellowish white Greenish white Colorless
TOPAZ $Al_2(F,OH)_2SiO_4$ 340	Orthorhombic C—Prismatic, vertically striated, highly modified M—Compact. granular, rolled fragments	Vitreous Transparent to opaque	Colorless White Grayish
CORUNDUM Al_2O_3 275	Hexagonal C—Prismatic, tabular, pyramidal, rhombohedral; rough or rounded barrel-shaped M—Compact, granular, lamellar	Vitreous Translucent to transparent	Gray Greenish gray Bluish gray

Hardness over 6

Hard-ness	Streak	Cleavage = C Fracture = F Tenacity	Specific Gravity	Characteristics and Associates
7.	White	C—Indistinct F—Uneven Brittle to tough	2.6	*Sand*, loose, unconsolidated grains; *sandstone*, consolidated sand; *itacolumite*, flexible sandstone; *quartzite*, metamorphosed sandstone.
7.5	White	C—Indistinct F—Uneven Brittle	4.4 4.8	In acid igneous rocks—granite; syenite; alluvial deposits; with gold, spinel, corundum, garnet. *Jargon*, colorless or smoky.
7.5 8.	White	C—Indistinct F—Conchoidal, uneven Brittle	2.6 2.8	Crystals usually simple—prism and base. In granitic rocks, mica schists, clay slates. With quartz, feldspars, mica, chrysoberyl, garnet, topaz, tourmaline.
8.	White	C—Basal, perfect, conspicuous F—Conchoidal, uneven Brittle	3.4 3.6	Crystals usually developed on one end only. Massive varieties distinguished from quartz by higher specific gravity and basal cleavage. In veins and cavities in granitic rocks; alluvial deposits. With cassiterite, tourmaline, fluorite, beryl, scheelite, wolframite.
9.	White	C—None, nearly rectangular basal and rhombohedral partings conspicuous; often striated F—Conchoidal Brittle to tough	3.9 4.1	When massive often multi-colored—blue, green, red, yellow. In limestones, granites, syenites, schists, alluvial deposits. With magnetite, nephelite, mica, spinel, chlorite.

Streak—Uncolored, white, or light gray

Name, Composition, and Reference	Crystallization Structure Crystals = C Massive = M	Luster Transparency	Color
DIAMOND C **229**	Cubic C—Octahedrons, hexoctahedrons, usually with curved surfaces M—Rounded or irregular grains or pebbles, often with internal radial structure	Adamantine Greasy Transparent to translucent	Colorless Gray White

Hardness over 6

Hard-ness	Streak	Cleavage = C Fracture = F Tenacity	Specific Gravity	Characteristics and Associates
10.	Ash gray	C—Octahedral, perfect, usually conspicuous F—Conchoidal Brittle	3.5	May be tinged yellow, brown, red, blue. In serpentine rocks—kimberlite, peridotite, called *blue ground;* placers; with pyrope, magnetite, chromite, cassiterite, zircon, gold.

INDEX

Names of minerals described or referred to in the text are printed in **black-face type,** synonyms and names of varieties in *italics*, and general subjects in light-faced type. When there is more than one reference, the important one is printed in black-face type.

A

Actinolite, 370, 540, 550
  schist, 370
Adularia, **374,** 612
Agate, **270,** 398, 530, 586, 616
  banded, 270
  clouded, 270
  moss, 270
Agricola, G., 4
Ahrens prism, 125
Airy's spirals, 140
Alabandite, 257
Alabaster, **316,** 594
Albite, 14, 88, 94, 96, **377,** 392, 432, 614
  law, 94, 377
Alcumite, 415
Alexandrite, **323,** 392, 406, 558
Allanite, **345,** 462, 500, 506
Allegheny metal, 413
Allochromatic, 97
"Alloy 548," 424
Almandine, **320,** 532
Almandite, **351,** 392, 466, 508, 530, 584
Aloxite, 276, 403
Altaite, 255
Alum, 8
Aluminates, 319
Aluminum, minerals, 402
  tests for, 211
  -uranium, 435
Alum stone, **313,** 522, 602
Alundum, 276, 403
Alunite, 313, 402, 428, 522, 602
Amazonite, **375,** 392
Amazonstone, **375,** 392, 552
Amethyst, **269,** 392, 530, 556
  oriental, **275,** 392, 532, 558
Ammonal, 404
Ammonium polysulphide, 188
  reactions with, 193

Ammonium, test for, 211
Amorphous, 111
Amphibole, 368, 402, 408, 417, 420, 462, 498, 506, 536, 540, 550, 568, 610
  structure of, 333
Analcite, 28, **387,** 430, 524, 608
Analyzer, 119
Andalusite, 338, 393, 402, 528, 602, 616
Andesine, 376
Andesite, 179
Andradite, **351,** 392, 466, 508, 530, 554, 584
Angles, constancy of, 8
  measurement of, 120
Anglesite, 13, **308,** 419, 600
Anhydrite, 5, 170, **305,** 408, 504, 542, 598
Anisotropic, 117
Anorthic system, 85
Anorthite, 379, 408, 614
Antimonite, 249
Antimony, black, 405
  gray, 249
  minerals, 405
  tests for, 211
Apatite, 52, **326,** 408, 416, 426, 502, 504, 524, 546, 570, 574, 578, 596, 600, 608
  chloro, 326
  fluor, 326
Aplite, 179
Apophyllite, 68, **385,** 428, 524, 606
Aquamarine, **352,** 392, 556
Aragonite, 13, 78, 93, 95, 168, **299,** 408, 576, 602
  test for, 209, 210
Argentite, 28, **255,** 429, 470
Arizona ruby, **350,** 392, 393
Arkose, 181
Arsenic, 238, 405, 472, 478
  minerals, 405
  tests for, 212

Arsenic, white, 406
Arsenical gold ore, 249
Arsenides, 248
Arsenopyrite, 78, **260**, 405, 417, 478
Asbestos, *amphibole*, **369**, 538, 568, 590
　chrysotile, **360**, 538, 568, 590
　long fibered, **370**
　short fibered, **361**, 370
Assembly of blowpipe apparatus, 187, 189
Asterism, 99
Asymmetric system, 85
Atomic planes, 149
Augite, 84, **365**, 462, 498, 506, 538, 552
Auripigment, 249
Aventurine, **269**, 392, 530, 586
Axes, crystallographic, 10
　of symmetry, 18
　optic, 117
　　dispersion of, 138
　topical, 146
　　application of, **147**
Axial cross, 10
Axial ratio, 13
Axinite, 88
Axis, brachy, **72, 85**
　clino, 79
　intermediate, 37, 62
　lateral, 37, 62
　macro, 72, 85
　ortho, 79
　principal, 37, 62
Azurite, **302**, 392, 415, 536
Azurmalachite, **303**, 392

B

Babbitt metal, 405, 433
Baddeleyite, 437
Ballas, 234
Bar theory, 285
Barite, 78, 171, **307**, 406, 542, 544, 572, 596, 598
Barium, minerals, 406
　tests for, 212
Barytes, **307**
Basal pinacoid, 44, 55, 66, 76, 82, 86
Basalt, 179
Bauxite, **282**, 402, 403, 404, 512, 560, 592
Baveno law, 93, 373
Bauer, M., 390
Bead tests, 203
Bearing metal, 405

Becke, F. J., 121
　method, 120
Bell metal, 415
Beryl, 45, 153, 165, **352**, 392, 402, 406, 556, 588, 618
　golden, 352
　yellow, 352
Beryllium, minerals, 406
　tests for, 213
Biaxial crystals, 117, 134
　behavior in polarized light, 134
　figures, 135, 136, 137
Biotite, **357**, 417, 420, 456, 502, 542
Bipyramid, brachy, 74
　dihexagonal, 41
　ditetragonal, 64
　hemi, 80
　hexagonal, first order, 39
　　second order, 40
　　third order, 50
　macro, 74
　orthorhombic, 73
　tetarto, 85
　tetragonal, first order, 63
　　second order, 64
　trigonal, 57
Birefringence, 117
Birne, 400
Bismuth, **239**, 407, 476, 482
　flux, 187
　reactions with, **193**, 198
　minerals, 407
　tests for, 213
Bismuthinite, 250
Bisphenoids, tetragonal, 69
Blackband, 298
Black hematite, 303
　jack, **251**, 458, 496, 504
　lead, **235**, 496
　oxide of manganese, 273
　sand, 321
Blanc fixé, 406
Blende, 251
　zinc, 251
Bloodstone, **270**, 392
Blowpipe, 185, 186
　apparatus, 185, 187, 189
　methods, 185
　portable outfit, 189
　reactions, 192
　reagents, 187, 188
Blue carbonate of copper, 302
　ground, 230